Contents in Brief

Focal Points and Connections
See page T15 for key.

Volume 1

Start Smart

Chapter ❶ Describe and Compare Numbers — G1-FP2

Chapter ❷ Develop Addition Concepts — G1-FP1

Chapter ❸ Develop Subtraction Concepts — G1-FP1

Chapter ❹ Organize and Use Data — G1-FP5C

Chapter ❺ Develop Addition Strategies — G1-FP2, G1-FP6C

Chapter ❻ Develop Subtraction Strategies — G1-FP2, G1-FP6C

Chapter ❼ Measure Time — G1-FP5C

Chapter ❽ Recognize Number Patterns — G1-FP2

Volume 2

Chapter ❾ Compare Measurements — G1-FP2, G1-FP5C

Chapter ❿ Solve Addition and Subtraction Problems — G1-FP2, G1-FP6C

Chapter ⓫ Identify Coins — G1-FP4C

Chapter ⓬ Identify Geometric Figures — G1-FP3

Chapter ⓭ Understand Place Value — G1-FP2

Chapter ⓮ Describe Fractional Parts — G1-FP3

Chapter ⓯ Solve Two-Digit Addition and Subtraction Problems — G1-FP4C

Looking Ahead

Problem-Solving Projects

About the Cover

Plane figures and solid figures are featured topics in first grade. The triangle on the boat is an example of a plane figure. The shape of the lighthouse is an example of a solid figure. Ask students to identify other solid and plane figures on the cover.

Three Horizontally Aligned Programs

- Common vocabulary
- Common manipulatives
- Common technology
- Common Professional Development
- Aligned to NCTM Focal Points

Grade 1
NSF-funded, integrated performance assessment aligned with investigative instruction

Grade 1
Intensive Intervention for students two or more years below grade level (Tier 3 RTI)

The McGraw·Hill Companies

 Macmillan/McGraw-Hill

Send all inquiries to:
Macmillan/McGraw-Hill
8787 Orion Place
Columbus, OH 43240-4027

Volume 1
ISBN: 978-0-02-105737-5 *(Teacher Edition)*
MHID: 0-02-105737-0 *(Teacher Edition)*
ISBN: 978-0-02-105725-2 *(Student Edition)*
MHID: 0-02-105725-7 *(Student Edition)*

Printed in the United States of America.

5 6 7 8 9 10 WEB/LEH 16 15 14 13 12 11 10

Benefits of Student Edition Organization

Math Connects, grade 1 Student Edition, has a 4-part organization.

1. **Start Smart** gets students ready for grade 1 with a review of key math standards from kindergarten that are prerequisites for grade 1.

2. **Chapters 1–15** Each chapter has coherent groups of lessons focused on related grade 1 math standards and the NCTM Focal Points.

3. **Preparing for Standardized Tests** provides test success tips, step-by-step solutions for standards-based multiple-choice questions, and an extensive practice section to review before your state test.

4. **Looking Ahead** prepares students for success with lessons on several key math standards.

The organization and pacing of *Math Connects* helps ensure in-depth coverage of all grade 1 standards, success on your state test, and a good start for grade 2.

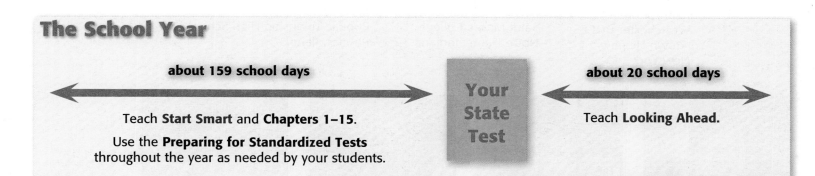

The School Year

about 159 school days ⟷

Teach **Start Smart** and **Chapters 1–15**.

Use the **Preparing for Standardized Tests** throughout the year as needed by your students.

Your State Test

about 20 school days ⟷

Teach **Looking Ahead.**

Pacing Guide Each chapter includes days for review and assessment.	
Start Smart	Optional
Chapter 1	11 days
Chapter 2	12 days
Chapter 3	12 days
Chapter 4	10 days
Chapter 5	10 days
Chapter 6	9 days
Chapter 7	9 days
Chapter 8	11 days
Chapter 9	11 days
Chapter 10	11 days
Chapter 11	11 days
Chapter 12	11 days
Chapter 13	11 days
Chapter 14	9 days
Chapter 15	11 days
Total	159 days
State Test	
Looking Ahead	20 days

Mary Behr Altieri
Putnam/Northern
   Westchester BOCES
Yorktown Heights,
   New York

Don S. Balka
Professor Emeritus
Saint Mary's College
Notre Dame, Indiana

Roger Day, Ph.D.
Mathematics Department Chair
Pontiac Township High School
Pontiac, Illinois

Philip D. Gonsalves
Mathematics Coordinator
Alameda County Office
   of Education and
   California State
   University East Bay
Hayward, California

Ellen C. Grace
Mathematics Consultant
Albuquerque,
   New Mexico

Stephen Krulik
Professor Emeritus
   Mathematics Education
Temple University
Cherry Hill, New Jersey

Carol E. Malloy, Ph.D
Associate Professor of
   Mathematics Education
University of North
   Carolina at Chapel Hill
Chapel Hill, North
   Carolina

Rhonda J. Molix-Bailey
Mathematics Consultant
Mathematics by Design
Desoto, Texas

Lois Gordon Moseley
Staff Developer
NUMBERS: Mathematics
   Professional
   Development
Houston, Texas

Brian Mowry
Independent Math Educational
   Consultant/Part-Time Pre-K
   Instructional Specialist
Austin Independent School District
Austin, Texas

Christina L. Myren
Consultant Teacher
Conejo Valley Unified
    School District
Thousand Oaks, California

Jack Price
Professor Emeritus
California State
    Polytechnic University
Pomona, California

Mary Esther Reynosa
Instructional Specialist for
    Elementary Mathematics
Northside Independent
    School District
San Antonio, Texas

Rafaela M. Santa Cruz
SDSU/CGU Doctoral
    Program in Education
San Diego State University
San Diego, California

Robyn Silbey
Math Content Coach
Montgomery County
    Public Schools
Gaithersburg, Maryland

Kathleen Vielhaber
Mathematics Consultant
St. Louis, Missouri

Contributing Authors

Donna J. Long
Mathematics Consultant
Indianapolis, Indiana

FOLDABLES Dinah Zike
Educational Consultant
Dinah-Might Activities, Inc.
San Antonio, Texas

Consultants

Macmillan/McGraw-Hill wishes to thank the following professionals for their feedback. They were instrumental in providing valuable input toward the development of this program in these specific areas.

Mathematical Content

Viken Hovsepian
Professor of Mathematics
Rio Hondo College
Whittier, California

Grant A. Fraser, Ph.D.
Professor of Mathematics
California State University, Los Angeles
Los Angeles, California

Arthur K. Wayman, Ph.D.
Professor of Mathematics Emeritus
California State University, Long Beach
Long Beach, California

Assessment

Jane D. Gawronski, Ph.D.
Director of Assessment and Outreach
San Diego State University
San Diego, California

Cognitive Guided Instruction

Susan B. Empson, Ph.D.
Associate Professor of Mathematics
  and Science Education
University of Texas at Austin
Austin, Texas

English Learners

Cheryl Avalos
Mathematics Consultant
Los Angeles County Office of Education, Retired
Hacienda Heights, California

Kathryn Heinze
Graduate School of Education
Hamline University
St. Paul, Minnesota

Family Involvement

Paul Giganti, Jr.
Mathematics Education Consultant
Albany, California

Literature

David M. Schwartz
Children's Author, Speaker, Storyteller
Oakland, California

Vertical Alignment

Berchie Holliday
National Educational Consultant
Silver Spring, Maryland

Deborah A. Hutchens, Ed.D.
Principal
Norfolk Highlands Elementary
Chesapeake, Virginia

Reviewers

Each Reviewer reviewed at least two chapters of the Student Edition, giving feedback and suggestions for improving the effectiveness of the mathematics instruction.

Ernestine D. Austin
Facilitating Teacher/
    Basic Skills Teacher
LORE School
Ewing, NJ

Susie Bellah
Kindergarten Teacher
Lakeland Elementary
Humble, Texas

Megan Bennett
Elementary Math Coordinator
Hartford Public Schools
Hartford, CT

Susan T. Blankenship
5th Grade Teacher – Math
Stanford Elementary School
Stanford, KY

Wendy Buchanan
3rd Grade Teacher
The Classical Center at Vial
Garland, Texas 75043

Sandra Signorelli Coelho
Associate Director for
    Mathematics
PIMMS at Wesleyan University
Middletown, CT

Joanne DeMizio
Asst. Supt., Math and Science
    Curriculum
Archdiocese of New York
New York, NY

Anthony Dentino
Supervisor of Mathematics
Brick Township Schools
Brick, NJ

Lorrie L. Drennon
Math Teacher
Collins Middle School
Corsicana, TX 75110

Ethel A. Edwards
Director of Curriculum and
    Instruction
Topeka Public Schools
Topeka, Kansas

Carolyn Elender
District Elementary Math
    Instructional Specialist
Pasadena ISD
Pasadena, Texas

Monica Engel
Educator Second Grade
Pioneer Elementary School
Bolingbrook, IL

Anna Dahinden Flynn
Math Teacher
Coulson Tough K–6 Elementary
The Woodlands, TX

Brenda M. Foxx
Principal
University Park Elementary
University Park, MD

Katherine A. Frontier
Elementary Teacher
Laidlaw
Western Springs, IL

Susan J. Furphy
5th Grade Teacher
Nisley Elementary
Grand Jct., CO 81503

Peter Gatz
Student Services Coordinator
Brooks Elementary
Aurora, IL

Amber Gregersen
Teacher – 2nd Grade
Nisley Elementary
Grand Junction, Colorado

Roberta Grindle
Math and Language Arts
    Academic Intervention
    Service Provider
Cumberland Head Elementary
    School
Plattsburgh, NY

Sr. Helen Lucille Habig, RSM
Assistant Superintendent/
    Mathematics
Archdiocese of Cincinnati
Cincinnati, Ohio

Holly L. Hepp
Math Facilitator
Barringer Academic Center
Charlotte, NC

Martha J. Hickman
2nd Grade Teacher
Dr. James Craik Elementary
    School
Pomfret, MD

Margie Hill
District Coordinating Teacher for
    Mathematics, K–12
Blue Valley USD 229
Overland Park, Kansas

Carol H. Joyce
5th Grade Teacher
Nathanael Greene Elementary
Liberty, NC

Stella K. Kostante
Curriculum Coach
Roosevelt Elementary
Pittsburgh, PA

Pamela Fleming Lowe
Fourth Grade eMINTS Teacher
O'Neal Elementary
Poplar Bluff, Missouri

Lauren May, NBCT
4th Grade Teacher
May Watts Elementary School
Naperville, IL

Lorraine Moore
Grade 3 Math Teacher
Cowpens Elementary School
Cowpens, SC

Shannon L. Moorhead
4th Grade Teacher
Centerville Elementary
Anderson, SC

Gina M. Musselman, M.Ed
Kindergarten Teacher
Padeo Verde Elementary
Peoria, AZ

Jen Neufeld
3rd Grade Teacher
Kendall
Naperville, IL

Cathie Osiecki
K-5 Mathematics Coordinator
Middletown Public Schools
Middletown, CT

Phyllis L. Pacilli
Elementary Education Teacher
Fullerton Elementary
Addison, IL

Cindy Pearson
4th/5th Grade Teacher
John D. Spicer Elementary
Haltom City, TX 76137

Herminio M. Planas
Mathematics Curriculum
    Specialist
Administrative Offices-Bridgeport
    Public Schools
Bridgeport, Connecticut

Jo J. Puree
Educator
Lackamas Elementary
Yelm, WA

Teresa M. Reynolds
Third Grade Teacher
Forrest View Elementary
Everett, WA

Dr. John A. Rhodes
Director of Mathematics
Indian Prairie SD #204
Aurora, IL

Amy Romm
1st Grade Teacher
Starline Elementary
Lake Havasu, AZ

Delores M. Rushing
Numeracy Coach
Dept. of Academic Services-
    Mathematics Department
Washington, DC

Daniel L. Scudder
Mathematics/Technology
    Specialist
Boone Elementary
Houston, Texas

Laura Seymour
Resource Teacher Leader –
    Elementary Math & Science,
    Retired
Dearborn Public Schools
Dearborn, MI

Petra Siprian
Teacher
Army Trail Elementary School
Addison, IL

Sandra Stein
K-5 Mathematics Consultant
St. Clair County Regional
    Educational Service Agency
Marysville, MI

Barb Stoflet
Curriculum Specialist
Roseville Area Schools
Roseville, MN

Kim Summers
Principal
Dynard Elementary
Chaptico, MD

Ann C. Teater
4th Grade Teacher
Lancaster Elementary
Lancaster, KY

Anne E. Tunney
Teacher
City of Erie School District
Erie, PA

Joylien Weathers
1st Grade Teacher
Mesa View Elementary
Grand Junction, CO 81503

Christine F. Weiss
Third Grade Teacher
Robert C. Hill Elementary School
Romeoville, IL

Teacher Handbook

Mathematics Teacher Handbook

Table of Contents
PreK–12 Mathematics: Focus on Grade 1

✔ Vertical Alignment

Welcome to Math Connects T10
An overview of the vertical alignment of Macmillan/McGraw-Hill's and Glencoe's PreK–12 mathematics programs

The Research Base T12
*The research and process used to develop **Math Connects***

NCTM Focal Points T14
*Complete listing of NCTM Focal Points for grade 1 and correlation to **Math Connects***

Program Philosophy T16
Balanced approach of concepts, skills, and problem solving

✔ Assessment

Comprehensive Assessment System T20
Diagnostic, Formative, and Summative assessments linked to Data-Driven Decision Making

✔ Differentiated Instruction

Differentiated Instruction T24
How to meet the diverse needs of your students

Blending Your Instruction T26
*Blended from the beginning for effective integration of **Math Connects, IMPACT Mathematics,** and **Math Triumphs** in your daily classroom*

✔ Teacher Convenience

Planning for Success T28
Make planning easy with all of the components – print, technology, online, manipulatives – you need

PreK–12 Data-Driven Professional Development T32
Extensive options for purposeful, point-of-use, and consistent PreK–12 professional development

Welcome to
Math Connects

Concepts • Skills • Problem Solving

The only true vertically aligned PreK–12 Mathematics Curriculum

Math Connects offers three dimensions of vertical alignment.

❶ Content Design

Vertical content alignment is a process that ensures you and your students experience an articulated, coherent sequence of content from grade level to grade level. This provides you with the assurance that content is introduced, reinforced, and assessed at appropriate times in the series, eliminating gaps and unnecessary duplication. You are able to target your instruction to student needs because you are not teaching content intended to be covered later or that students have previously mastered.

❷ Instructional Design

Our strong vertical alignment in instructional approach from PreKindergarten through Algebra 2 provides a smooth transition for students from elementary to middle school to high school. Our common vocabulary, technology, manipulatives, lesson planning, and Data-Driven Decision Making reduces the confusion students often encounter when transitioning between grade levels without this built-in articulation.

❸ Visual Design

The student pages of *Math Connects* have a consistent visual design from grade to grade. This aids students' transition from elementary school to middle school and from middle school to Algebra 1. Students are more likely to succeed when they are already familiar with how to navigate student pages.

PreK-2

3–5

5 Keys to Success

1 Backmapping

According to College Board research, about 80% of students who successfully complete Algebra 1 and Geometry by 10th grade attend and succeed in college. (Changing the Odds: Factors Increasing Access to College, 1990) *Math Connects* was conceived and developed by backmapping with the final result in mind—student success in Algebra 1 and beyond.

2 Balanced, In-Depth Content

Math Connects was developed to specifically target the skills and topics that give students the most difficulty, such as Problem Solving, in each grade span.

Grades K–2	Grades 3–5
1. Problem Solving 2. Money 3. Time 4. Measurement 5. Fractions 6. Computation	1. Problem Solving 2. Fractions 3. Measurement 4. Decimals 5. Time 6. Algebra

Grades 6–8	Grades 9–12
1. Fractions 2. Problem Solving 3. Measurement 4. Algebra 5. Computation	1. Problem Solving 2. Fractions 3. Algebra 4. Geometry 5. Computation 6. Probability

– *K–12 Math Market Analysis Survey*, Open Book Publishing, 2006

3 Ongoing Assessment

Math Connects includes diagnostic, formative, and summative assessment; data-driven instruction; intervention options; and performance tracking, as well as remediation, acceleration, and enrichment tools throughout the program.

4 Intervention and Differentiated Instruction

A three-tiered Response To Intervention (RTI) is provided.

TIER 1 **Daily Intervention** Reteach masters and Alternative Strategy suggestions address concepts from a different modality or learning style.

TIER 2 **Strategic Intervention** Teachers can use the myriad of intervention tips and ancillary materials, such as the Strategic Intervention Guide (1–5) and Study Guide and Intervention (6–8).

TIER 3 **Intensive Intervention** For students who are two or more years below grade level, *Math Triumphs* provides step-by-step instruction, vocabulary support, and data-driven decision making to help students succeed.

5 Professional Development

Math Connects includes many opportunities for teacher professional development. Additional learning opportunities in various formats—video, online, and on-site instruction—are fully aligned and articulated from Kindergarten through Algebra 2.

6–8   Pre-Algebra and Algebra 1   Geometry and Algebra 2

The Research Base

Continuous research with teachers, students, academician, and leading experts helps to build a solid foundation for **Math Connects.**

1 Program Development Research

- Evaluating state and local standards
- Qualitative market research
- Academic content research

For more detailed information about our classroom research results, please consult the **Math Connects** *Program Efficacy Research Report.*

The Research Base for

Math Connects

Program Efficacy Research

Glencoe   Macmillan McGraw-Hill

for *Math Connects*

② Formative Research

- Pedagogical research base
- Classroom field tests
- Teacher advisory boards
- Academic consultants and reviewers

Student Data from 2006–2007 Classroom Field Tests

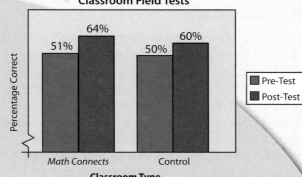

Percentage Correct

| Math Connects | Control |

Classroom Type

- Pre-Test
- Post-Test

Students using a field test of the *Math Connects* program (**experimental group**) had *higher* pre-test to post-test gains than students using other textbook programs (**control group**).

③ Summative Research

- Evidence of increased test scores
- Quasi-experimental program efficacy research
- Longitudinal studies
- Qualitative program evaluations

Access all *Math Connects* research at macmillanmh.com.

NCTM Focal Points

The NCTM Focal Points

In 2006, the National Council of Teachers of Mathematics (NCTM) released the Curriculum Focal Points for Pre-Kindergarten through Grade 8 Mathematics. These Curriculum Focal Points focus on the most important mathematical topics for each grade level. The concepts are vertically-aligned and expect a level of depth, complexity, and rigor at each level. They comprise related ideas, concepts, skills, and procedures that form the foundation for understanding and lasting learning. The Focal Points emphasize depth versus breadth. The Focal Points will be addressed and highlighted throughout our PreK-8 and Pre-Algebra series.

What is the benefit to you in your classroom?

These Focal Points identify content for each grade level that should be mastered in order for your students to have true mathematical understanding—being able to not only calculate the answer, but to explain the answer and how to apply the calculation. The NCTM Focal Points were used as the basis in the development of *Math Connects.* The authors have incorporated the Focal Points into the content to assist you in building depth of understanding.

NCTM Focal Points for Grade 1	Supporting Chapters in *Math Connects*
Number and Operations and *Algebra*	Chapters 2, 3, 5, 6, 10, 11
Number and Operations	Chapters 1, 5, 6, 8, 9, 10, 11, 13
Geometry	Chapters 12, 14
Connections to the Focal Points	
Number and Operations and *Algebra*	Chapters 8, 11, 13, 15
Measurement and Data Analysis	Chapters 4, 7, 9
Algebra	Chapters 1, 2, 3, 5, 6, 8, 10

The Curriculum Focal Points identify key mathematical ideas for this grade. They are not discrete topics or a checklist to be mastered; rather, they provide a framework for the majority of instruction at a particular grade level and the foundation for future mathematics study. The complete document may be viewed at www.nctm.org/focalpoints.

KEY

G1-FP1
Grade 1 Focal Point 1

G1-FP2
Grade 1 Focal Point 2

G1-FP3
Grade 1 Focal Point 3

G1-FP4C
Grade 1 Focal Point 4
Connection

G1-FP5C
Grade 1 Focal Point 5
Connection

G1-FP6C
Grade 1 Focal Point 6
Connection

G1-FP1 *Number and Operations* and *Algebra:* **Developing understandings of addition and subtraction and strategies for basic addition facts and related subtraction facts**

Children develop strategies for adding and subtracting whole numbers on the basis of their earlier work with small numbers. They use a variety of models, including discrete objects, length-based models (e.g., lengths of connecting cubes), and number lines, to model "part-whole," "adding to," "taking away from," and "comparing" situations to develop an understanding of the meanings of addition and subtraction and strategies to solve such arithmetic problems. Children understand the connections between counting and the operations of addition and subtraction (e.g., adding two is the same as "counting on" two). They use properties of addition (commutativity and associativity) to add whole numbers, and they create and use increasingly sophisticated strategies based on these properties (e.g., "making tens") to solve addition and subtraction problems involving basic facts. By comparing a variety of solution strategies, children relate addition and subtraction as inverse operations.

G1-FP2 *Number and Operations:* **Developing an understanding of whole number relationships, including grouping in tens and ones**

Children compare and order whole numbers (at least to 100) to develop an understanding of and solve problems involving the relative sizes of these numbers. They think of whole numbers between 10 and 100 in terms of groups of tens and ones (especially recognizing the numbers 11 to 19 as 1 group of ten and particular numbers of ones). They understand the sequential order of the counting numbers and their relative magnitudes and represent numbers on a number line.

G1-FP3 *Geometry:* **Composing and decomposing geometric shapes**

Children compose and decompose plane and solid figures (e.g., by putting two congruent isosceles triangles together to make a rhombus), thus building an understanding of part-whole relationships as well as the properties of the original and composite shapes. As they combine figures, they recognize them from different perspectives and orientations, describe their geometric attributes and properties, and determine how they are alike and different, in the process developing a background for measurement and initial understandings of such properties as congruence and symmetry.

Connections to the Focal Points

G1-FP4C *Number and Operations* **and** *Algebra:* Children use mathematical reasoning, including ideas such as commutativity and associativity and beginning ideas of tens and ones, to solve two-digit addition and subtraction problems with strategies that they understand and can explain. They solve both routine and nonroutine problems.

G1-FP5C *Measurement* **and** *Data Analysis:* Children strengthen their sense of number by solving problems involving measurements and data. Measuring by laying multiple copies of a unit end to end and then counting the units by using groups of tens and ones supports children's understanding of number lines and number relationships. Representing measurements and discrete data in picture and bar graphs involves counting and comparisons that provide another meaningful connection to number relationships.

G1-FP6C *Algebra:* Through identifying, describing, and applying number patterns and properties in developing strategies for basic facts, children learn about other properties of numbers and operations, such as odd and even (e.g., "Even numbers of objects can be paired, with none left over"), and 0 as the identity element for addition.

 # Program Philosophy

Balanced Instruction, Vertically-Aligned from Grades PreK through Algebra 1

The vertical alignment of *Math Connects* PreK-8 and *Algebra 1* incorporates a balance of instruction throughout. These programs provide students a balanced approach to mathematics by:

- investigating concepts and building conceptual understanding.
- developing, reinforcing, and mastering computational and procedural skills.
- applying mathematics to problem-solving situations.

This sequence of Student Edition pages illustrates the vertically-aligned development of the conceptual understanding and corresponding computational and procedural skills for an important algebra topic.

Primary Students use two-color counters to model addition sentences. This activity forms a basis for future understanding of and success in solving algebraic equations.

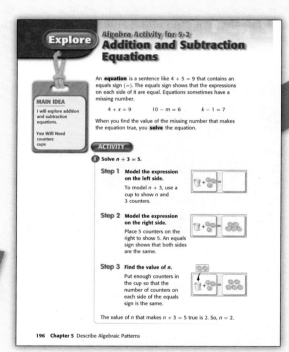

Math Connects, Grade 4, Student Edition, page 196

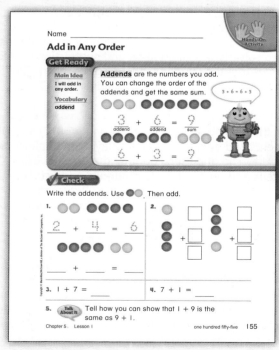

Math Connects, Grade 1, Student Edition, page 155

Intermediate Students build on their experience with counters to using cups and counters to model and solve addition and subtraction equations. The exercises are designed to help students bridge the gap from using cups and counters to solving equations symbolically.

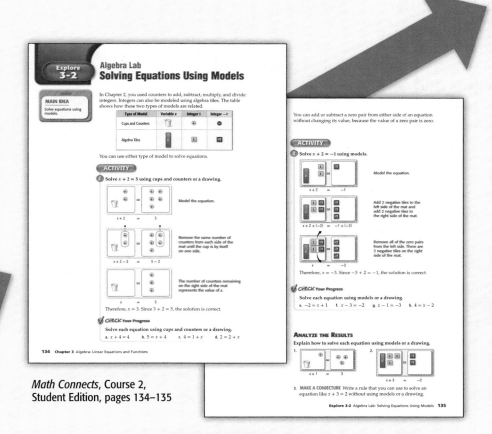

Glencoe Algebra 1,
Student Edition, page 91

Algebra 1 Students continue the use of algebra tiles to investigate solving multi-step equations. In the next lesson, students apply the procedure developed in the Algebra Lab to a symbolic approach.

Math Connects, Course 2,
Student Edition, pages 134–135

Middle School Students represent the variable *x* as a cup, as a counter, or as a written *x*. In this Algebra Lab, students make the transition from cups and counters to the more abstract algebra tiles. In the next lesson, students solve simple equations symbolically.

Continuity of Instruction The instructional sequence described demonstrates the power of backward mapping from the desired result, success in Algebra 1. This process of development avoids gaps and overlaps between grade levels and ensures that at each grade level the concepts and skills are built on the strong foundation developed in previous grades. The same approach was used across all strands throughout the entire PreK-12 series.

Program Philosophy Balance of Instruction

Relevant Problem Solving

Math Connects provides students with the appropriate development of problem-solving strategies, skills, and applications from PreK through grade 5. In grades 6–8, students continue to learn and apply problem-solving skills and strategies. Students are provided with ongoing opportunities to apply their math skills and solve problems using visual thinking, logical reasoning, number sense, and algebra.

Problem-Solving Strategies and Skills

Problem-Solving Strategy or **Skill** lessons introduce students to multiples methods for solving problems all using the *four-step* plan.

- **U**nderstand
- **P**lan
- **S**olve
- **C**heck

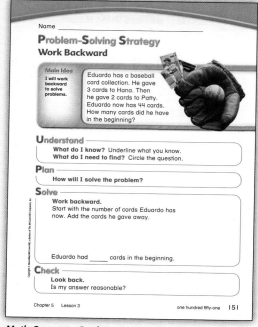

Math Connects, Grade 2
Student Edition, page 151

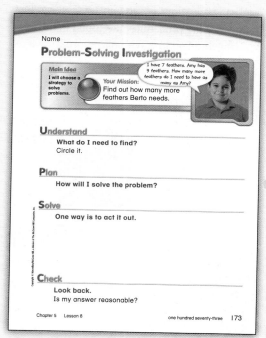

Math Connects, Grade 1
Student Edition, page 173

Problem-Solving Investigations

Problem-Solving Investigation lessons help students learn to choose appropriate strategies and apply them in problem-solving situations.

Real-World Problem Solving

Each chapter has a Problem Solving lesson that makes a tie to another discipline. These lessons encourage students to see problem solving in real-world applications.

Math Connects, Kindergarten
Student Edition, pages 143–144

Real-World Problem Solving Readers

Fiction and nonfiction leveled readers extend problem-solving skills and strategies and make real-world applications. The books are provided for On Level, Sheltered English, and Spanish readers.

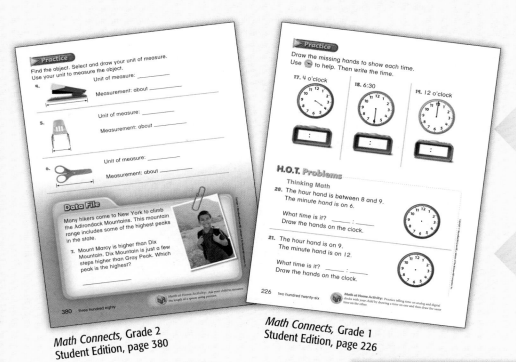

Math Connects, Grade 2
Student Edition, page 380

Math Connects, Grade 1
Student Edition, page 226

Data File Problems

The Data File features present math in real-world settings. Students are asked to use data to solve problems.

H.O.T. Problems

H.O.T. Problems require students to use **Higher Order Thinking** skills to solve problems.

Looking Ahead

Looking Ahead lessons introduce important concepts and skills that students can use.

Math Connects, Kindergarten
Student Edition, pages LA1–LA2

 # Comprehensive Assessment System

PRINT SOLUTIONS

Data-Driven Decision Making

Math Connects offers frequent and meaningful assessment of student progress within the curriculum structure and printed teacher support materials. See pages T22 and T23 for digital assessment solutions.

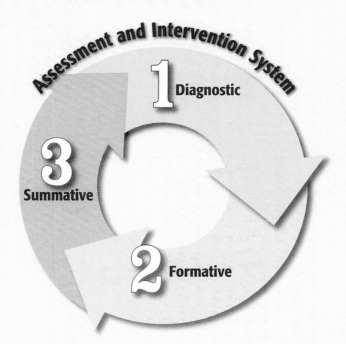

Assessment and Intervention System

1 Diagnostic

2 Formative

3 Summative

1 Diagnostic

Initial Assessment Assess students' knowledge **at the beginning of the year** with the *Diagnostic and Placement Tests*. This booklet will help you determine whether your students need additional materials and resources to meet grade-level standards.

Entry–Level Assessment Assess students' prior knowledge **at the beginning of a chapter or lesson** with one of the following options.

Student Edition
• Are You Ready?

Teacher Edition
• Intervention Options
• 5-Minute Check

Additional Resources
• Chapter Resource Masters, Chapter Diagnostic Test

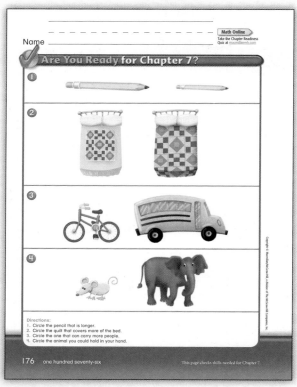

Math Connects, Kindergarten
Student Edition, page 176

Formative

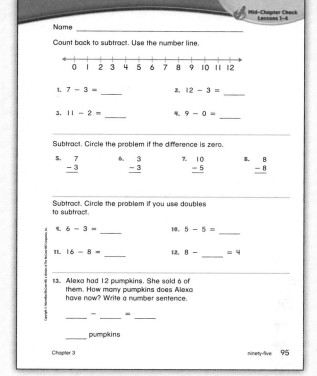

Math Connects, Grade 2
Student Edition, page 95

Progress Monitoring Determine if students are progressing adequately as you teach each lesson. Use the assessments to differentiate lesson instruction and practice.

Student Edition
- Mid-Chapter Check
- Find the Error
- Check What You Know
- Talk About It
- Writing in Math
- Study Guide and Review
- Foldables™

Teacher Edition
- Alternate Teaching Strategy
- Step 4 (Assess) of the Teaching Plan
- Quick Check
- Data-Driven Decision Making

Additional Resources
Chapter Resource Masters
- Mid-Chapter Test
- 3 Quizzes

Summative

Summative Evaluation Assess student success in learning the concepts in each chapter.

Student Edition
- Chapter Test
- Test Practice
- Foldables™

Teacher Edition
- Data-Driven Decision Making

Additional Resources
Chapter Resource Masters
- Oral Assessment
- Listening Assessment
- 4 Leveled Chapter Tests
- Cumulative Test

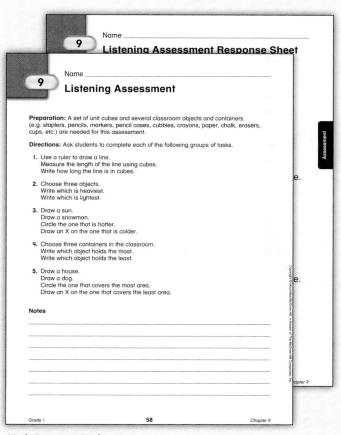

Math Connects, Grade 1
Chapter 9 Resource Masters, pages 58–59

 Comprehensive Assessment System

Data-Driven Decision Making

Math Connects provides digital assessment options to create, customize, administer, and instantly score a variety of assessments. These digital solutions offer the same quality assessments and reporting as the print resources in easy-to-use technology tools.

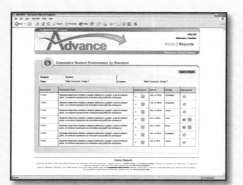

Math Connects, Grade 4

Advance Tracker helps teachers administer online tests, diagnose student achievement, and create prescriptive reports for a student or class.

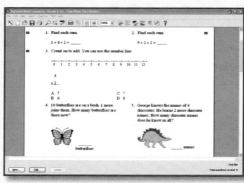

Math Connects, Grade 1

ExamView Assessment Suite allows teachers to create and customize their own assessment and assignments. Print in one or two columns to match state test.

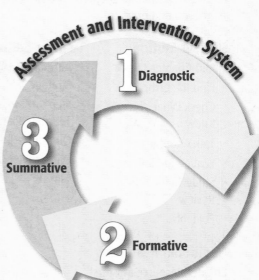

Assessment and Intervention System

1 Diagnostic

2 Formative

3 Summative

1 Diagnostic

Initial Assessment Assess students' knowledge **at the beginning of the year** with the *Diagnostic and Placement Tests.* These assessments will help you determine whether your students need additional materials and resources to meet grade-level standards.

ExamView Assessment Suite

- Diagnostic and Placement Tests

- Diagnostic and Placement Tests

Entry–Level Assessment Assess students' prior knowledge **at the beginning of a chapter or lesson.**

Math Online ▶ macmillanmh.com Students can complete online tests and the results are emailed to the teacher.

- Chapter Readiness

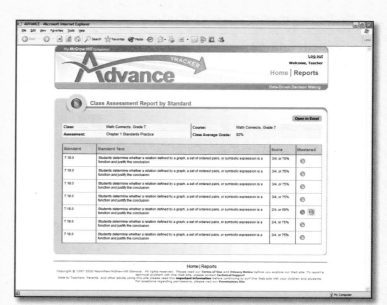

Math Connects Grade 2 Advance Tracker

Formative

Progress Monitoring Determine if students are progressing adequately as you teach each lesson. Use the assessments to differentiate lesson instruction and practice.

 ExamView® Assessment Suite

 Advance TRACKER

- Mid-Chapter Test
- Study Guide and Review

My Math Zone

Math Online macmillanmh.com

- Self-Check Quizzes

Math Connects, Kindergarten, Advance Tracker

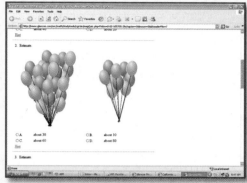

Math Connects, Grade 1, Self-Check Quiz

 Summative

Summative Evaluation Assess students' success in learning the concepts in each chapter.

 ExamView® Assessment Suite

- Chapter Tests
- Cumulative Standardized Test Practice

 Advance TRACKER

- Chapter Tests
- Cumulative Standardized Test Practice

Math Online  macmillanmh.com

- Chapter Tests

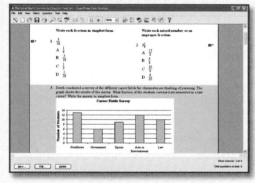

Math Connects, Grade 2, ExamView Assessment Suite

Math Connects, Grade 1, Advance Tracker

 # Differentiated Instruction

Reaching All Learners

Math Connects, provides extensive support for reaching all learners.

Every chapter and lesson includes suggestions for identifying and meeting your students' needs. Strategies include differentiation in pacing and student grouping, alternate approaches, ways to enhance instruction with manipulatives, questions to promote higher-order thinking, and language hints.

Personalize instruction for:

- **BL** Students who are below or approaching grade level
- **ELL** English language learners
- **AL** Students who are above or beyond grade level

Leveled Exercise Sets

The assignments for each lesson are leveled for students.

- **BL** Below or Approaching Grade Level
- **OL** On Grade Level
- **AL** Above or Beyond Grade Level

Leveled Resources

All of the blackline masters and transparencies that accompany the program, as well as all of the Teacher Edition pages, are available on the **TeacherWorks Plus™ CD-ROM.** Resources and assignments are leveled for students who are:

- **BL** Below or Approaching Grade Level
- **OL** On Grade Level
- **AL** Above or Beyond Grade Level
- **ELL** English Language Learners

Learning Stations

Cross-curricular learning centers offer students guided opportunities to explore chapter concepts as individuals or in small groups. Content areas include:

- Science
- Social Studies
- Reading
- Art
- Health
- Writing
- Music

Learning Station cards are English on one side and Spanish on the other.

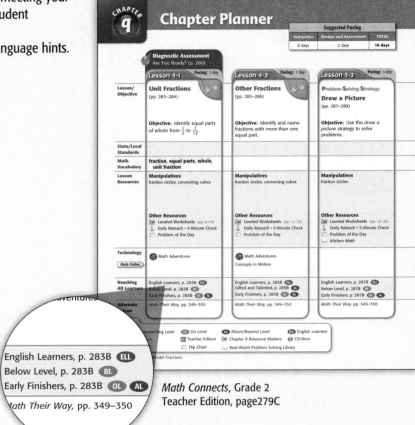

Math Connects, Grade 2
Teacher Edition, page279C

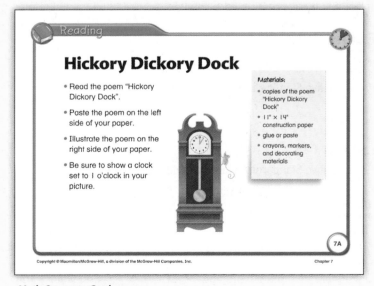

Math Connects, Grade 1
Learning Station Card 7A

Advanced Learners

Acceleration and Enrichment Resources and assignments for students who are above level may be used with advanced learners. In particular, the **Enrich Masters** provide students with valuable opportunities for extending your lessons.

ⓔⓛⓛ English Language Learners

Our authors have identified seven keys for effective instruction with English language learner students and used them throughout the program.

1. Simplify language, not concepts.
2. Activate background knowledge.
3. Teach in multiple modalities.
4. Use core vocabulary and common use verbs.
5. Express mathematical understanding in different ways.
6. Incorporate higher-level problem-solving skills.
7. Provide a mathematics-rich classroom environment.

The English Language Learners Guide provides additional support for English language learner students that can be used alone or with core instruction in the Student Edition and Teacher Edition.

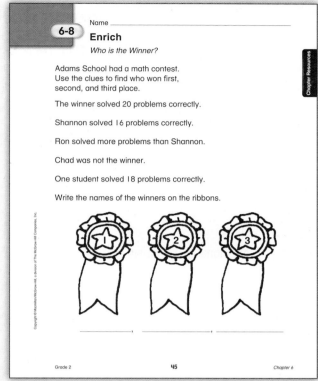

Math Connects, Grade 2,
Chapter 6 Resource Masters, page 45

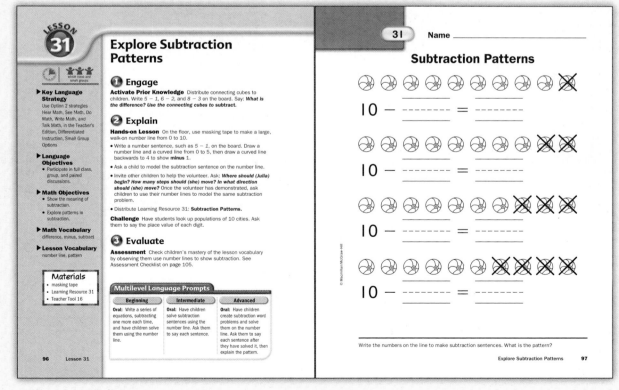

Math Connects, Kindergarten
ELL Guide, pages 96–97

 # Blending Your Instruction
Basal — NSF-Funded — Tier 3 Intervention

Math Connects, IMPACT Mathematics, and ***Math Triumphs*** provide a three-pronged approach to mathematics instruction. This unique combination provides built-in strategies to easily tip the balance of instruction to a more conceptual approach or to a more skills-based approach, depending on the needs of your students.

These programs are horizontally aligned in the following ways.

- Common vocabulary
- Common manipulatives
- Common teacher planning guides
- Common technology
- Common authors
- Common professional development

Basal Program—Focused on Comprehensive Instruction

NSF Program—Focused on Investigations

Intensive Intervention (Tier 3 RTI)—Focused on Skills

RTI (Response to Intervention)

In the *Math Connects* Teacher Editions, the Data-Driven Decision Making chart provides a comprehensive RTI (Response to Intervention) beginning with diagnostic review and continuing with prescriptions at all three RTI tiers.

- **Tier 1** – Leveled exercise sets and leveled resources
- **Tier 2** – Strategic Intervention Guide (1–5), Study Guide and Intervention (6–8)
- **Tier 3** – Intensive Intervention, *Math Triumphs*

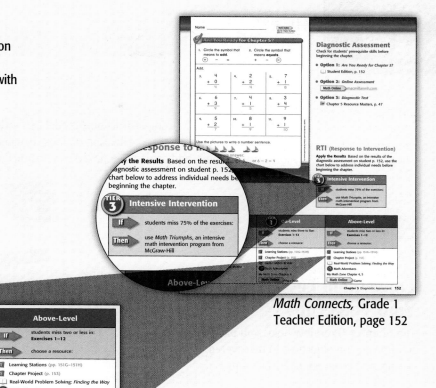

Math Connects, Grade 1
Teacher Edition, page 152

The Chapter Planner, also in the Teacher Edition of *Math Connects*, references alternative lessons found in *IMPACT Mathematics*. These lessons provide opportunities for investigative instruction with hands-on explorations.

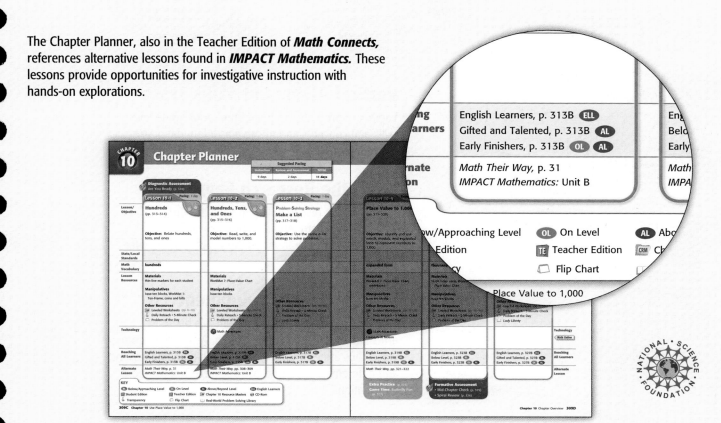

Math Connects, Grade 2
Teacher Edition, pages 309C–309D

 # Planning for Success

Ease of Use

Math Connects has a strong instructional model that includes differentiated instructional options, reteaching, reinforcement, and extension options, Teacher Tips to help address various learners, Pre-AP/Advanced items, and assessment linked with instruction.

Convenient Lesson Planning at Your Fingertips

The **Chapter Overview** helps you plan your instruction by showing the objectives to be covered, suggested pacing, and coverage of Focal Points.

TeacherWorks™ Plus

This electronic lesson planner contains multi-purpose management software including the Teacher Edition pages, program blackline masters, and daily calendars that make planning a snap.

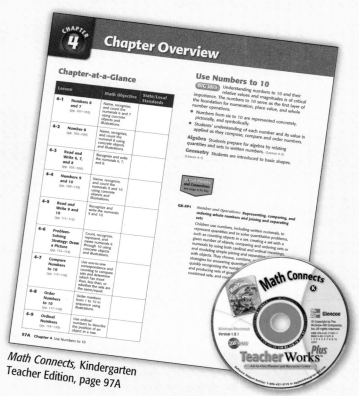

Math Connects, Kindergarten
Teacher Edition, page 97A

Math Connects, Kindergarten
Teacher Edition, page 97B

Vertical Alignment Skills Trace

Topics are presented to build upon prior grade level skills and concepts and to serve as a foundation for future topics.

What the Research Says

Citations from research help to validate *Math Connects* program. An additional Research Bibliography can be found in the **Teacher Reference Handbook.**

Professional Development

Targeted professional development has been articulated throughout the program. Actual classroom video clips are especially helpful when planning lessons and differentiating instruction. See page T32 for more information.

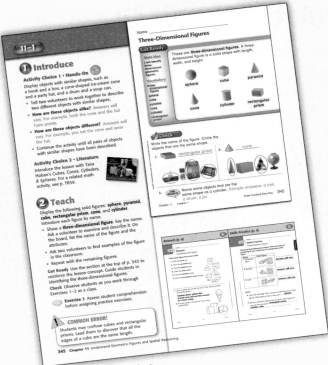

Math Connects, Grade 2
Teacher Edition, page 345

Four-Step Teaching Plan

Organizes your instruction as you **Focus** and **Teach** and help your students **Practice** and **Assess** what they've learned.

Scaffolding Questions

Each lesson contains **Scaffolding Questions** for you to use to help students investigate and understand the main ideas of the lesson.

Vertical Alignment

Vertical Alignment at the beginning of each chapter shows the objectives that lead into and follow the current lesson's content for a coherent PreK–12 scope and sequence.

Differentiated Practice

Because most classrooms include students at a wide range of ability levels, **Differentiated Practice** allows you to customize your assignments.

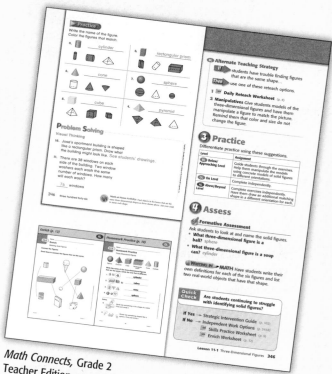

Math Connects, Grade 2
Teacher Edition, page 346

 # Planning for Success
State-of-the-Art Technology

Math Connects provides fully integrated technology resources for teachers, students, and parents.

For Teachers

 TeacherWorks™ Plus is your all-in-one planner and resource center.
- entire Teacher Edition
- all print ancillaries
- electronic lesson planner

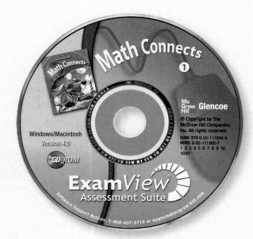

ExamView® Assessment Suite allows teachers to create and customize their own assessment and assignments.

New features:
- correlated to state standards
- online content update
- one- or two-column formatting

Advance Learner Management System helps you track progress and differentiate your instruction.
- formative assessments aligned to standards
- links to intervention help

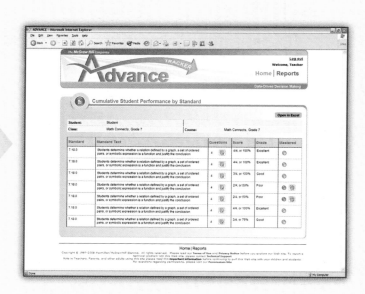

Other Technology: My Math Zone (CD-ROM)
Math Songs (English and Spanish, CD-ROM)

For Students

 StudentWorks™ Plus is your students'
backpack solution.
- entire Student Edition
- all student worksheets
- links to **Math Online**

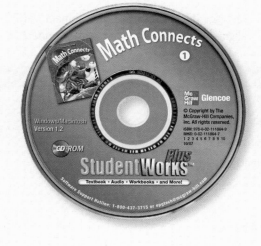

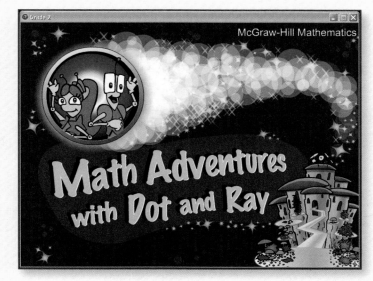

Math Online provides a wealth of resources –
convenient for students and parents!

- Self-Check Quizzes
- Personal Tutor
- Concepts in Motion
- Math Adventures with Dot and Ray
- eGlossary (14 languages)
- Math Tool Chest
- And much, much more!

Math Online *Math Connect's* **eBook** is easy
to use, easy to read, and packed with features.

- links to online study tools and resources right
  from the page
- includes audio

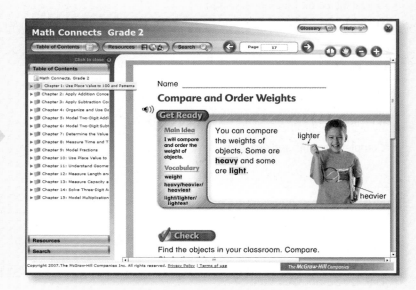

Other Technology: Math Adventures with Dot and Ray (CD-ROM)
Math Tool Chest (CD-ROM)

PreK-12 Data-Driven Professional Development

McGraw-Hill Professional Development (MHPD) provides a comprehensive plan for mathematics that is fully aligned and articulated with **Math Connects K–8** and the **Glencoe Mathematics** high school series.

Professional Development Needs	Online Courses	DVD Workshops	Video Library	Teach-Use-Succeed	Ready-Access Math
Has immediate classroom application	✔	✔	✔	✔	✔
Builds content knowledge	✔	✔			✔
Promotes best teaching practices		✔	✔		
Supports new and experienced teachers	✔	✔	✔	✔	✔
Allows customization of courses	✔	✔			✔
Can be self-paced	✔	✔		✔	✔
Adaptable for various timeframes	✔	✔	✔	✔	✔
Is grade-level specific		✔		✔	✔
Promotes a learning community	✔	✔			✔
Provides vertically-aligned content	✔	✔	✔		✔
Helps with RTI (Response to Intervention), Tiers 1–3	✔	✔	✔		✔

Use students' mathematics achievement data to help develop a targeted Professional Development Plan.

Accredited Online Courses

(available for purchase)

- Watch video clips of math classrooms
  Complete interactive exercises
  Develop electronic portfolios.
- Complete each 3- to 5-hour online module one segment at a time.
- University credit (additional tuition charge)

DVD Workshops

- Watch video clips of classroom mathematics lessons and commentaries by leading educators.
- Complete lessons and activities.

MHPD Online

- Access this online Professional Development resource for K–12 educators.
- Link to relevant Web sites.
- Download grade-level student resources.

McGraw-Hill Professional Development Portfolio

- Professional Development Web sites
- McGraw-Hill's Experienced Consultants
- Ready Access Math Training Materials
- Textbook Implementation Modules
- Mini Clip Video Library
- Video Workshops Mentor-led or Self-Study
- Accredited Online Courses

Video Library — Math Online

- Access hundreds of K–12 video clips.
- See clips that illustrate mathematics content and instructional strategies.
- Watch demonstrations or commentaries by math specialists

Teach-Use-Succeed Textbook Implementation Modules

- Watch an experienced teacher demonstrate the *Math Connects* K–8 Student Editions, Teacher Editions, and program ancillaries
- Online or DVD

Ready-Access Math, Personalized Professional Development

- Access training materials for nearly 300 mathematics professional development lessons.
- Create a customized sequence of professional development sessions.
- Deliver 45–60 minute after-school professional development sessions.

Teacher Edition

Macmillan McGraw-Hill

Math Connects

1

OUTER BARKS BEACH

Volume 1

Authors

Altieri • Balka • Day • Gonsalves • Grace • Krulik
Malloy • Molix-Bailey • Moseley • Mowry • Myren
Price • Reynosa • Santa Cruz • Silbey • Vielhaber

Macmillan/McGraw-Hill

Contents

Start Smart

1 **Problem Solving**: Goldenrods 2

2 Number and Operations: Zoo Animals 3

3 Algebra: Watermelon 5

4 Measurement: Longleaf Pines 7

5 Geometry: Sand Castles 9

6 Data Analysis: Illinois Forest 11

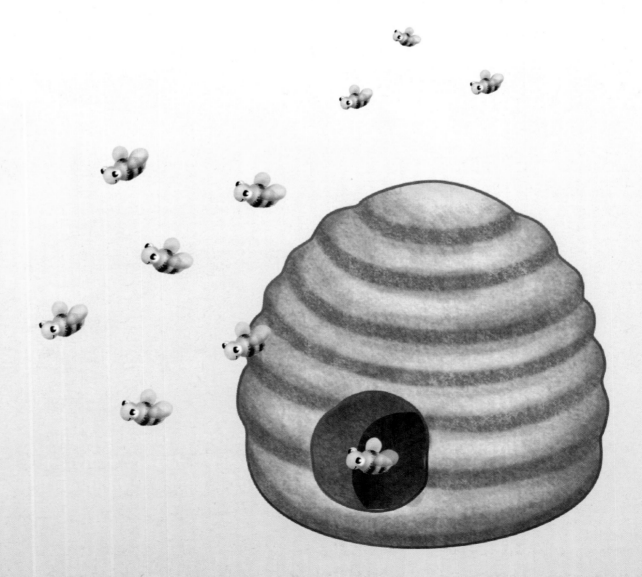

Contents

CHAPTER 1
Describe and Compare Numbers

Are You Ready for Chapter 1? 14

Family Letter. 15

1 Extend a Pattern . . . . Algebra. 17

 2 Create a Pattern . . . . Algebra. 19

3 Problem-Solving Strategy

    Look for a Pattern . . . . Algebra. 21

4 Numbers to 10. 23

5 Numbers 11 to 15. 27

6 Numbers 16 to 20 29

    Mid-Chapter Check/Spiral Review 31

7 Problem-Solving Investigation

    Choose a Strategy. . . . . Algebra. 33

 8 Compare Numbers. . . . . Algebra. 35

    Extra Practice. 37

    Game Time The Bigger the Better 38

9 Order Numbers. . . . . Algebra. 39

    Problem Solving in Science 41

    Chapter Review/Test 43

    Test Practice. 45

 = Hands-On Activity

Focal Points and Connections
See page iv for key.

G1-FP2 *Number and Operations*

H.O.T. Problems
  Higher Order Thinking 36

Problem Solving 18, 28, 30, 40

WRITING IN ►MATH 20

Contents

CHAPTER 2

Develop Addition Concepts

Are You Ready for Chapter 2?		48
Family Letter		49
1 Addition Stories		51
2 Modeling Addition		53
3 Addition Sentences	Algebra	55
Extra Practice		57
Game Time Snack Time		58
4 Adding Zero	Algebra	59
5 Problem-Solving Strategy		
Write a Number Sentence	Algebra	61
Mid-Chapter Check/Spiral Review		63
6 Ways to Make 4, 5, and 6		65
7 Ways to Make 7, 8, and 9		67
8 Ways to Make 10, 11, and 12		69
9 Problem-Solving Investigation		
Choose a Strategy		73
10 Vertical Addition		75
Problem Solving in Health		77
Chapter Review/Test		79
Test Practice		81

Focal Points and Connections
See page iv for key.

G1-FP1 *Number and Operations* and *Algebra*

H.O.T. Problems
Higher Order Thinking 54, 60, 66, 76

Problem Solving 52, 68

WRITING IN MATH 56

Contents

CHAPTER 3

Develop Subtraction Concepts

Are You Ready for Chapter 3?. **84**

Family Letter. **85**

1 Subtraction Stories. **87**

2 Modeling Subtraction **89**

3 Subtraction Sentences . . . . .Algebra. . . . **91**
   Extra Practice. **93**
   Game Time Subtracting to Swim **94**

4 Subtract Zero and All . . . . .Algebra. **95**

5 **Problem-Solving Strategy**
   Draw a Picture. **97**
   Mid-Chapter Check/Spiral Review. **99**

6 Subtract from 4, 5, and 6 . . . . **101**

7 Subtract from 7, 8, and 9 . . . . **103**

8 **Problem-Solving Investigation**
   Choose a Strategy. **105**

9 Subtract from 10, 11, and 12 . . . . **107**

10 Vertical Subtraction **111**
   Problem Solving in Social Studies. **113**
   Chapter Review/Test **115**
   Test Practice. **117**

= Hands-On Activity

= Technology Link

Focal Points and Connections
See page iv for key.

G1-FP1 *Number and Operations* and *Algebra*

H.O.T. Problems
Higher Order Thinking 92, 102, 104

Problem Solving 88, 96, 112

Writing In ►MATH 90

Contents

CHAPTER 4 Organize and Use Data

	Are You Ready for Chapter 4?	120
	Family Letter	121
1	Sort and Classify	123
2	Picture Graphs	125
3	**Problem-Solving Strategy**	
	Make a Table	127
4	Tally Charts	129
	Mid-Chapter Check/Spiral Review	131
5	Read a Bar Graph	133
	Extra Practice	135
	Game Time Animal Race	136
6	Make a Bar Graph	137
7	**Problem-Solving Investigation**	
	Choose a Strategy .... Algebra	141
8	Certain or Impossible	143
	Problem Solving in Science	145
	Chapter Review/Test	147
	Test Practice	149

Focal Points and Connections
See page iv for key.

G1-FP5C *Measurement* and *Data Analysis*

H.O.T. Problems
Higher Order Thinking 140, 144

Problem Solving 124, 126

WRITING IN ▶MATH 130

Contents

CHAPTER 5 Develop Addition Strategies

Are You Ready for Chapter 5? 152

Family Letter 153

 1 Add in Any Order . . . . Algebra 155

 2 Count On 1, 2, or 3 157

Extra Practice 159

Game Time All Mixed Up 160

3 **Problem-Solving Strategy**

Act It Out 161

4 Add 1, 2, or 3 163

5 Use a Number Line to Add 165

Mid-Chapter Check/Spiral Review 167

 6 Doubles 169

 7 Doubles Plus 1 171

8 **Problem-Solving Investigation**

Choose a Strategy 173

Problem Solving in Social Studies 175

Chapter Review/Test 177

Test Practice 179

 = Hands-On Activity

Focal Points and Connections
See page iv for key.

G1-FP2 *Number and Operations*
G1-FP6C *Algebra*

H.O.T. Problems
Higher Order Thinking 156, 170

Problem Solving 166, 172

WRITING IN ►MATH 158

Contents

CHAPTER 6

Develop Subtraction Strategies

Are You Ready for Chapter 6?. **182**

Family Letter. **183**

1 Count Back 1, 2, or 3. . . . . **185**

2 **Problem-Solving Strategy**

Write a Number Sentence . . . . Algebra **187**

3 Use a Number Line to Subtract **189**

Mid-Chapter Check/Spiral Review. **191**

4 **Problem-Solving Investigation**

Choose a Strategy. **193**

5 Use Doubles to Subtract. **195**

6 Relate Addition to Subtraction . . . . Algebra **197**

7 Fact Families . . . . Algebra **199**

Extra Practice. **201**

Game Time Related or Not? **202**

Problem Solving in Science **203**

Chapter Review/Test **205**

Test Practice **207**

Focal Points and Connections
See page iv for key.

G1-FP2 *Number* and *Operations*
G1-FP6C *Algebra*

H.O.T. Problems
 Higher Order Thinking 200

Problem Solving 186, 198

WRITING IN ►MATH 196

Contents

CHAPTER 7 Measure Time

Are You Ready for Chapter 7? 210

Family Letter 211

1 Ordering Events 213

 2 Time to the Hour 215

3 Time to the Half Hour 217

4 Problem-Solving Strategy
Make a Table 219

Mid-Chapter Check/Spiral Review 221

5 Telling Time to the Hour and Half Hour 223

6 Relate Time to Events 227

Extra Practice 229

Game Time Switch It! 230

7 Problem-Solving Investigation
Choose a Strategy 231

Problem Solving in Music 233

Chapter Review/Test 235

Test Practice 237

 = Hands-On Activity

Focal Points and Connections
See page iv for key.

G1-FP5C *Measurement* and *Data Analysis*

H.O.T. Problems
Higher Order Thinking 226

Problem Solving 214, 216

WRITING IN MATH 218

Contents

CHAPTER 8 · Recognize Number Patterns

	Are You Ready for Chapter 8?	**240**
	Family Letter	**241**
1	Counting to 20	**243**
2	Counting by Tens	**245**
3	Problem-Solving Strategy	
	Look for a Pattern	**247**
4	Hundred Chart	**249**
	Mid-Chapter Check/Spiral Review	**253**
5	Estimating With Groups of Tens	**255**
6	Problem-Solving Investigation	
	Choose a Strategy	**257**
7	Skip Counting by 2s, 5s, and 10s .... Algebra	**259**
8	Skip Counting on a Hundred Chart .... Algebra	**261**
9	Even and Odd	**263**
	Extra Practice	**265**
	Game Time Slide Through the Digits	**266**
	Problem Solving in Social Studies	**267**
	Chapter Review/Test	**269**
	Test Practice	**271**

Focal Points and Connections
See page iv for key.

G1-FP2 *Number and Operations*

H.O.T. Problems
Higher Order Thinking 244, 260

Problem Solving 246, 256, 264

WRITING IN ▶MATH 252

Contents

CHAPTER 9

Compare Measurements

Are You Ready for Chapter 9?. 274

Family Letter. 275

 1 Compare and Order Lengths. 277

2 Nonstandard Units of Length. 279

3 Problem-Solving Strategy

Guess and Check. 281

Extra Practice. 283

Game Time Busy Beavers 284

4 Compare and Order Weights 285

Mid-Chapter Check/Spiral Review. 289

5 Compare and Order Capacities 291

6 Compare and Order Temperatures 295

7 Problem-Solving Investigation

Choose a Strategy. 299

8 Compare Areas. 301

9 Order Areas. 305

Problem Solving in Science 307

Chapter Review/Test 309

Test Practice 311

 = Hands-On Activity

 Tech Link = Technology Link

Focal Points and Connections
See page iv for key.

G1-FP2 *Number and Operations*
G1-FP5C *Measurement* and *Data Analysis*

H.O.T. Problems
Higher Order Thinking 304

Problem Solving 280, 294, 298, 306

WRITING IN ►MATH 278

Contents

CHAPTER 10 Solve Addition and Subtraction Problems

Are You Ready for Chapter 10? 314

Family Letter 315

1 Doubles 317

2 Doubles Plus 1 319

Extra Practice 321

Game Time Circle Up 322

3 Make a 10 to Add . . . . Algebra 323

4 **Problem-Solving Strategy**

Draw a Picture . . . . Algebra 325

Mid-Chapter Check/Spiral Review 327

5 Use Doubles to Subtract 329

6 Relate Addition and Subtraction . . . . Algebra 331

7 **Problem-Solving Investigation**

Choose a Strategy . . . . Algebra 333

8 Fact Families . . . . Algebra 335

9 Ways to Model Numbers 339

Problem Solving in Social Studies 341

Chapter Review/Test 343

Test Practice 345

Focal Points and Connections
See page iv for key.

G1-FP2 *Number and Operations*
G1-FP6C *Algebra*

H.O.T. Problems
Higher Order Thinking 320, 324, 332

Problem Solving 318, 330

WRITING IN MATH 338

SEAL ISLAND

Contents

11 Identify Coins

Are You Ready for Chapter 11?..........................348

Family Letter...349

1 Pennies and Nickels...............................351

 2 Pennies and Dimes................................353

 3 Pennies, Nickels, and Dimes.....................355

4 Counting Money..................................357

5 **P**roblem-**S**olving **S**trategy

Act It Out..359

Mid-Chapter Check/Spiral Review..................361

6 Equal Amounts...................................363

7 Quarters...365

8 **P**roblem-**S**olving **I**nvestigation

Choose a Strategy................................369

9 Money Amounts.................................371

Extra Practice......................................373

Game Time Who Has More?.....................374

Problem **S**olving in **S**ocial **S**tudies...............375

Chapter Review/Test..............................377

Test Practice.....................................379

 = Hands-On Activity

 = Technology Link

Focal **P**oints
and Connections
See page iv for key.

G1-FP4C *Number and Operations* and *Algebra*

H.O.T. Problems
Higher Order Thinking 354

Problem **S**olving 352, 356, 358, 372

WRITING IN ▸MATH 364

Contents

CHAPTER 12 Identify Geometric Figures

Are You Ready for Chapter 12? 382

Family Letter 383

1 Three-Dimensional Figures 385

2 Faces and Corners 387

3 Problem-Solving Strategy

Look for a Pattern 389

4 Two- and Three-Dimensional Figures 391

Extra Practice 393

Game Time Corners 394

5 Two-Dimensional Figures 395

Mid-Chapter Check/Spiral Review 397

6 Problem-Solving Investigation

Choose a Strategy 399

7 Position 401

8 Make New Figures 405

9 Give and Follow Directions 407

Problem Solving in Art 409

Chapter Review/Test 411

Test Practice 413

Focal Points and Connections
See page iv for key.

G1-FP3 *Geometry*

H.O.T. Problems
Higher Order Thinking 396, 406

Problem Solving 388, 392, 404

Writing in MATH 386

Contents

CHAPTER 13

Understand Place Value

	Are You Ready for Chapter 13?		416
	Family Letter		417
1	Tens		419
2	Tens and Ones		423
	Extra Practice		425
	Game Time Lizzie the Lizard		426
3	**Problem-Solving Strategy** Guess and Check	Algebra	427
4	Numbers to 50		429
5	Numbers to 100		433
	Mid-Chapter Check/Spiral Review		437
6	Estimate Numbers		439
7	**Problem-Solving Investigation** Choose a Strategy		441
8	Compare Numbers to 100	Algebra	443
9	Order Numbers to 100	Algebra	445
	Problem Solving in Science		447
	Chapter Review/Test		449
	Test Practice		451

= Hands-On Activity

Tech Link = Technology Link

Focal Points and Connections
See page iv for key.

G1-FP2 *Number and Operations*

H.O.T. Problems
Higher Order Thinking 422

Problem Solving 436, 440, 444, 446

WRITING IN MATH 424

Contents

CHAPTER 14 Describe Fractional Parts

Are You Ready for Chapter 14? 454

Family Letter 455

1 Equal Parts 457

2 **Problem-Solving Strategy**
Draw a Picture 459

3 One Half 461

4 One Third and One Fourth 463

Extra Practice 465

Game Time The Equalizer 466

Mid-Chapter Check/Spiral Review 467

5 Non-Unit Fractions 469

6 Fractions of a Set 471

7 **Problem-Solving Investigation**
Choose a Strategy 473

Problem Solving in Science 475

Chapter Review/Test 477

Test Practice 479

Focal Points and Connections
See page iv for key.

G1-FP3 *Geometry*

H.O.T. Problems
Higher Order Thinking 464

Problem Solving 458, 462

WRITING IN MATH 470

Contents

CHAPTER 15

Solve Two-Digit Addition and Subtraction Problems

Are You Ready for Chapter 15? **482**

Family Letter **483**

1 Add and Subtract Tens **485**

2 Add with Two-Digit Numbers **487**

3 Problem-Solving Strategy
Guess and Check . . . . Algebra **489**

4 Add Two-Digit Numbers **491**

Extra Practice **493**

Game Time Adding Colors **494**

5 Estimate Sums **495**

Mid-Chapter Check/Spiral Review **497**

6 Subtract with Two-Digit Numbers **499**

7 Subtract Two-Digit Numbers **501**

8 Problem-Solving Investigation
Choose a Strategy **503**

9 Estimate Differences **505**

Problem Solving in Social Studies **507**

Chapter Review/Test **509**

Test Practice **511**

 = Hands-On Activity

Focal Points and Connections
See page iv for key.

G1-FP4C *Number and Operations* and *Algebra*

H.O.T. Problems
Higher Order Thinking 488

Problem Solving 492, 496, 500, 502

WRITING IN ►MATH 506

xvii

Contents

Looking Ahead

1 Missing Addends. **LA3**

2 Count on Tens and Ones. **LA5**

3 Hundreds, Tens, Ones. **LA7**

4 Place Value to 1,000. . . . . **LA9**

5 Measure to the Nearest Inch **LA11**

6 Measure to the Nearest Centimeter **LA13**

H.O.T. Problems
Higher Order Thinking LA10

Problem Solving LA4, LA6, LA12, LA14

WRITING IN ►MATH LA8

Contents

Problem-Solving Projects

1 I Spy Patterns!.. **P3**

2 Fruit Kabob Factory **P7**

3 Let's Go to the Zoo! **P11**

4 Toys From the Past and Present **P15**

Contents

Student Handbook

Concept and Skills Bank **CS1**

Reference

Preparing for Standardized Tests **TP1**

English-Spanish Glossary. **G1**

Facts Practice. **FP1**

Photo Credits

WorkMat 1: Ten-Frame

WorkMat 2: Ten-Frames

WorkMat 3: Part-Part-Whole

WorkMat 4: Number Lines

WorkMat 5: Number Lines

WorkMat 6: Grid

WorkMat 7: Tens and Ones Chart

WorkMat 8: Hundreds, Tens, and Ones Chart

Start Smart

Begin the year with the lessons found in the **Start Smart** section. These lessons help students get ready for the coming year by reviewing and reinforcing skills and concepts they learned in kindergarten. The Start Smart lessons also prepare for skills and concepts students will need for success in first grade.

Initial Assessment

Inventory/Placement Test At the beginning of the year, administer the Inventory/Placement Test found in the Chapter 1 Resource Masters. This two-page test assesses key concepts from kindergarten as well as those students will need during the coming year.

Use the results to help differentiate instruction for each student throughout the year as well as to identify what concepts to review before beginning Chapter 1.

CRM Chapter 1 Resource Masters
Inventory/Placement Test (p. 51)

End-of-Year Assessment

At the end of the year, use the End-of-Year Test to assess student comprehension of the skills and concepts presented in Grade 1. Each question in the End-of-Year Test provides the lesson number from Grade 1 where the concept was first presented to help you review any areas where students continue to struggle.

CRM Chapter 15 Resource Masters
End-of-Year Test (pp. 74–77)

Start Smart
Let's Review!

Problem Solving 2
Number and Operations 3
Algebra 5
Measurement 7
Geometry 9
Data Analysis 11

Statue of Liberty

Name: _____

1 Problem Solving

Did you Know?
The goldenrod is the Kentucky state flower.

A field of goldenrods

Julie found 6 goldenrod plants.
Steve found 3 goldenrod plants.
How many goldenrod plants did they find in all?
Draw a picture to solve.

_____9_____ goldenrods

2　two

Start Smart

Options for Review

Concept	Review Options
Problem Solving Strategy: Act It Out	Kindergarten, Lesson 11-9
Addition Stories	Kindergarten, Lesson 11-1 Kindergarten, Lesson 11-2

More FUN Facts
- Goldenrods can be used for making tea.
- Thomas Edison created rubber from the goldenrod.
- Sunflower seeds are crushed to make oil. Sunflower oil can be used for cooking.

Start Smart 1

Lesson Planner

Objective
Review drawing a picture in order to solve a problem.

Review Vocabulary
count, in all, add

Activate Prior Knowledge

Read and discuss the introduction and Did You Know on p. 2.
- **What color is the goldenrod?** yellow
- Have students count the objects in the classroom that are yellow. Answers will vary depending on classroom.

4-Step Problem-Solving Plan
Understand Review what the students know and what they need to find.
Plan Have students use the facts they know to draw a picture.
- **How many plants did Julie find?** 6 plants
- Ask students to draw six plants.
- **How many plants did Steve find?** 3
- Ask students to draw three plants.

Solve Guide students to use the picture to solve the problem.
- Have the students **count** the goldenrod plants they drew.
- **How many plants were found in all?** 9 plants
- Explain to the students that they drew a picture to help them **add**. Six plants plus 3 plants equals 9 plants.
- On the board, draw the plants and write the corresponding number sentence.

Check Help students check the reasonableness of their answers.
- **Does the answer make sense?**
- **Does it answer the question?**

Assess and Close

Tell the class a number story. Have them draw a picture to solve the problem. Let students share their drawings with the class.

Lesson Planner

Objective

Review counting concrete and pictorial models and comparing groups.

Review Vocabulary

count, compare

Materials: toy animals or animal stickers
Manipulatives: two-colored counters or connecting cubes

Activate Prior Knowledge

Read and discuss the introduction and Did You Know on p. 3.

- Lead a class discussion about visiting the zoo.
- **What animals can you see at the zoo?** Sample answers: monkeys, zebras, lions, penguins

Using student page 3.

- Remind students that when they want to find the total number of objects in a group, it helps to touch each object as they **count**.
- Help students count three toy zoo animals or animal stickers using one-to-one correspondence. **How many animals?** 3 animals
- Repeat counting other groups of zoo animals with students until they are able to count accurately.
- Have students count, trace the number, and write how many in Exercises 1–4.

Name: _____

Number and Operations

Did you Know

The Buffalo Zoo in New York has many different animals; including the Bighorn Sheep.

Zoo Animals

A Rocky Mountain Bighorn Sheep

Count. Then write how many.

1. _____ 4
2. _____ 7
3. _____ 6
4. _____ 2

Start Smart   three **3**

Options for Review

Concept	Review Options
Count	Kindergarten, Lesson 2-3 Kindergarten, Lesson 2-4
Compare Groups	Kindergarten, Lesson 2-7 Kindergarten, Lesson 4-8

Count. Write the number. Then circle the group that has more.

5.

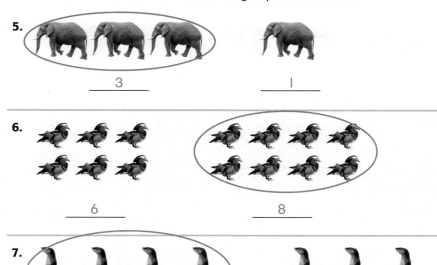

      3   I

6.

      6   8

7.

      4   3

8. Draw 8 red ladybugs. Draw 5 orange ladybugs. Circle the group that has less ladybugs.

Check students' drawings.

4   four   Start Smart

Using student page 4.

- Explain to students that when they **compare** objects, they are finding how the objects are alike or different.
- Show students a group of two toy animals and a group of four toy animals. Compare the groups.
- **Which group has more?** the group of 4
- **Which group has less?** the group of 2
- Have students count and write the number of objects in Exercises 5–7. Discuss which group students circled in each.
- Have students work in pairs to complete Exercise 8. The students can use connecting cubes or two-colored counters to model each group of ladybugs.

Assess and Close

Animal Drawings Have students work in pairs. Ask each pair to fold a sheet of construction paper in half.

- Point out that the fold makes two work spaces on the paper. Explain that each partner will draw a group of one kind of animal in their work space.
- Ask students to count and write the number of animals they drew.
- Ask students to make a train of cubes to model the number of animals they drew.
- Have partners compare their groups and draw a circle around the group that has more.
- Encourage partners to share their drawings with the class.

More FUN Facts

- Penguins can survive for more than 100 days without food or water.
- Every zebra has a unique pattern of stripes.
- Alligators and crocodiles do not chew their food. They swallow it whole.
- Frogs drink through their skin.
- Cheetahs are the fastest land animals.

Lesson Planner

Objective

Review using pictures and manipulatives to solve addition problems.

Review Vocabulary

join, plus sign

Materials: highlighter or yellow marker, pencil, paper
Manipulatives: connecting cubes

Activate Prior Knowledge

Read and discuss the introduction and *Did You Know?* on p. 5.

- Lead a discussion about experiences with watermelons.
- **When do you eat watermelon?** summer
- **How does it taste?** sweet, juicy
- **What does it look like?** green rind, pink inside, black or brown seeds
- **What do you need to plant to grow a watermelon?** Sample answers: watermelons seeds; water; soil; sun
- **Where can you find the seeds?** inside the watermelon

Using student page 5.

- Share with students that they are going to add. Explain that they will **join** two groups to add.
- Have students look at Exercise 1. **How many watermelon seeds are in the first group?** 4 Write four. **How many watermelon seeds are in the second group?** 2 Write two. **How many watermelon seeds in all?** 6 seeds.

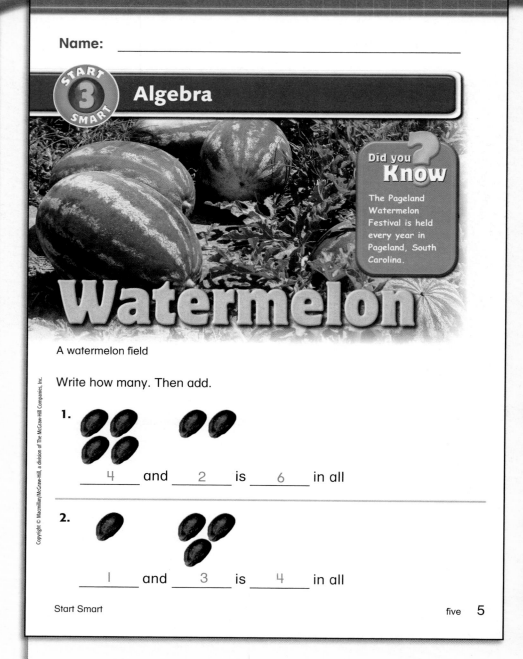

Write how many. Then add.

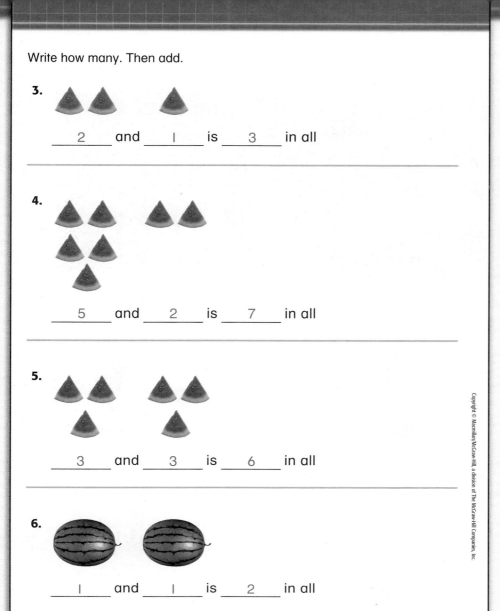

3.

___2___ and ___1___ is ___3___ in all

4.

___5___ and ___2___ is ___7___ in all

5.

___3___ and ___3___ is ___6___ in all

6.

___1___ and ___1___ is ___2___ in all

6 six

Start Smart

More **FUN** Facts

- Watermelon are mostly made up of water (92%), and early explorers used watermelons as canteens.
- Every part of the melon is edible, including the seeds and rind.
- In some cultures, it is popular to bake watermelon seeds and eat them.
- Watermelon Thump is a festival that takes place in Luling, Texas. The Guiness Book of World Record seed spitting contest is held here. The current record is a little less than 69 feet.
- In Japan, farmers have found a way to grow cube-shaped watermelons. They grow the watermelons in glass boxes, and the fruit naturally stays in the shape of a cube. Cube-shaped watermelons do not roll, so they are easier to store and cut.

Using student page 6.

Invite students to use cubes and work with a partner to model each group of watermelons in Exercises 3–6.

Assess and Close

Addition Sentences Give small groups of students an addition sentence. Ask the students to use cubes to model each number. Encourage students to share their group's number sentence and their model.

Lesson Planner

Objective

Review comparing objects according to length and weight.

Review Vocabulary

shorter, taller

Materials: crayons, pencil, paper, scissors, glue, construction paper

Activate Prior Knowledge

Read and discuss the introduction and *Did You Know?* on p. 7.

- **What object can you find in the classroom that is shorter than your desk?** Sample answers: a plant; book; ruler
- Ask students to practice putting objects in order according to length. **Which of the following is the shortest: a crayon, a desk, a pencil?** a crayon

Using student page 7.

- Have the students look at the pine trees on p. 7. **What is different about the pine trees?** They are different heights.
- Ask students to look at the pine trees in Exercise 1. **Which pine tree is taller?** the tree on the left **Which pine tree is shorter?** the tree on the right **Circle the shorter tree.**

Name: _____

Measurement

Longleaf Pines

Longleaf pine trees

Circle the tree that is shorter.

1.

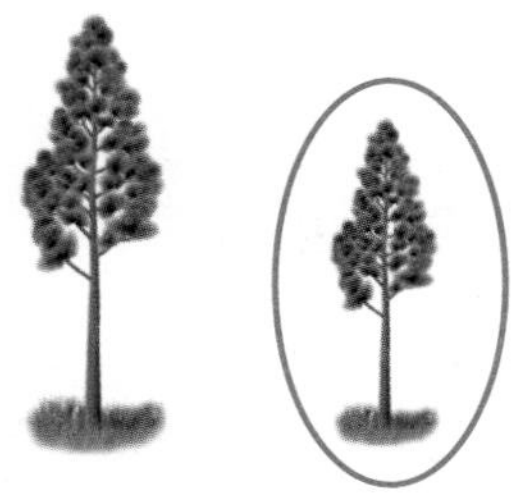

2.

3.

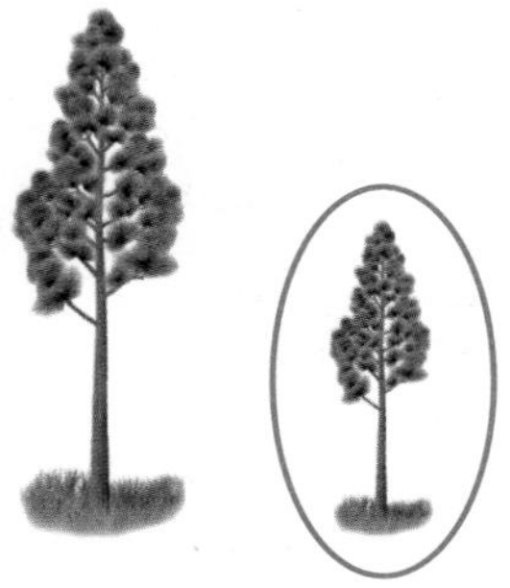

Did you Know?

North Carolina's state tree is the Longleaf Pine.

Options for Review

Concept	Review Options
Length/Height	Kindergarten, Lesson 7-1

Circle the tree that is taller.

4.

5.

6.

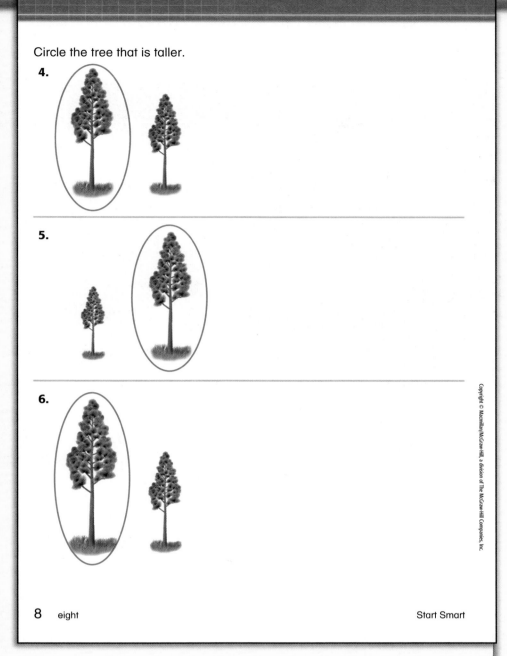

More **FUN** Facts

- Trees are the longest living organisms on earth.
- The shade from trees helps cool the Earth's temperature.
- Trees are good noise barriers. They make cities and neighborhoods quieter.
- Trees located along streets act as a glare and reflection control.
- The world's oldest known trees are Bristlecone pines. Some are over 4,600 years old!

Using student page 8.

- Remind students that the words **shorter** and **taller** are used to compare the height of objects.
- Show students a crayon and book. **Which object is taller?** book
- **Can you find an object in the classroom that is taller than you?** Sample answers: bookshelf, bulletin board
- Have students complete Exercises 4–6 and share their answers with the class.

Assess and Close

Size Order Divide students into small groups and give each group a handful of connecting cubes.

- Have each group of students use connecting cubes to make three stacks of cubes that are different heights.
- Ask groups to put the stacks in order from shortest to tallest and then tallest to shortest.
- **Which stack uses the most cubes? Why?** The tallest stack uses the most cubes because it is the biggest.
- **Which stack uses the least cubes? Why?** The shortest stack uses the least amount of cubes because it is the smallest.
- Have students turn their stacks of cubes on their sides.
- Show that the height of each stack is the same now. **What is different?** the length

WRITING IN ►MATH Direct students to complete Exercises 4–6. Let students share their answers. Have students write about shorter and taller objects that they see at home.

Lesson Planner

Objective

Review two-dimensional and three-dimensional shapes.

Review Vocabulary

two-dimensional figures
three-dimensional figures

Materials: construction paper, crayons
Manipulatives: geometric solids, pattern blocks

Activate Prior Knowledge

Read and discuss the introduction and *Did You Know?* on p. 9. Then lead a class discussion about building sandcastles.

- **Have you ever built a sandcastle? How can math help you build a sandcastle?** Sample answers: knowing about geometric figures; measuring; making patterns

- **Which two-dimensional figures and three-dimensional figures could you use when building a sandcastle?** Sample answers: squares, rectangles, cones, circles, cylinders, cubes

Using student page 9.

- Display pattern blocks and geometric solids to introduce these shapes and their names with students.

- **What geometric figures do you see in the classroom?** Sample answers: The tissue box is a rectangular prism; the paper towel roll is a cylinder.

- Have students circle the geometric figures they see in the sand castle in Exercise 1.

Name: _____

5 Geometry

Sand Castles

Did you Know?
There are thousands of miles of beaches in Michigan.

A sand castle on the beach

1. Look at the sandcastle. Circle the shapes you see. See students' work.

Options for Review

Concept	Review Options
Geometric Figures	Kindergarten, Chapter 10

2. Look at the sand castle. Color the different shapes.

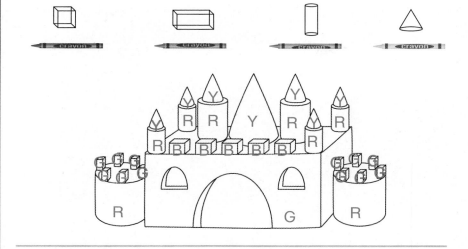

3. Draw a sand castle. Use these shapes. Check students' drawings.

Using student page 10.

- Have students use blue, green, yellow, and red crayons to color the different geometric figures that make the sandcastle in Exercise 2.
- Monitor to make sure students are coloring each shape the correct color.

Assess and Close

Shape Pictures Provide students with a handful of pattern blocks to use to create an illustration.

- Have students trace pattern blocks with a pencil to create an illustration of an activity they enjoy or a scene of their neighborhood.
- Ask students to color their illustrations with crayons and write a sentence about the shapes that make up their picture.
- Encourage students to share the sandcastles they drew in Exercise 3.

More **FUN** Facts

- A person who studies fish for a living is called an ichthyologist [ik-thee-ah-low-jist].
- Goldfish have longer life spans than both cats and dogs. They can live to be over 20 years old. That is the same life span of a lobster.
- Young seahorses are called fry.
- The world's smallest fish is the stout infant fish. It is about a quarter-of-an-inch long. The largest fish in the world is the whale shark.

Lesson Planner

Objective

Review how to collect data to create and interpret graphs.

Review Vocabulary

vote, graph

Materials: chart paper, stickers or sticky notes

Activate Prior Knowledge

Read and discuss the introduction and *Did You Know?* on p. 11.

- Lead a class discussion about the activities students would most like to do in the forest.
- Tell students that they are voting when they pick their favorite. Their answer is a **vote**.

Using student page 11.

- Tell students they will be taking a survey of five friends in Exercise 1. Then they will show their data or information on a **graph**.
- **If a friend told you her favorite activity was camping, which section would you color in?** the section after the picture of the tent
- **After your graph is complete, what will it show you?** which activity my friends like to do in the forest
- **Which activity do you think will be most popular? Least?** Answers should include camping, hiking, or having a picnic.

Name: _____

6 Data Analysis

Did you Know?

You can camp, picnic, or hike at the Shawnee National Forest.

Illinois Forest

A view of the Shawnee National Forest in Illinois

1. What do you like to do? Ask 5 friends.
   Color a picture to show each vote.

   Favorite Forest Activities

   Check students' work.

2. How many votes did each activity get? Check students' work.

   _____ votes   _____ votes   _____ votes

Start Smart   eleven   11

Options for Review

Concept	Review Options
Collect and Record Data	Kindergarten, Lesson 5-1
Graphing	Kindergarten, Lesson 5-2 Kindergarten, Lesson 5-4 Kindergarten, Lesson 5-5

3. What would you like to do at the lake? Ask 5 friends. Draw a | to show each vote.

Favorite Lake Activities

🎣	
🛶	
🏊	

Check students' work.

4. How many votes did each get? Check students' work.

🎣 _____ votes 🛶 _____ votes 🏊 _____ votes

5. Color a box on the graph to show each vote. Check students' work.

Favorite Lake Activities

🛶				
🏊				
🎣				

12   twelve

Using student page 12.

- In Exercises 3–5, have students create a graph based on the information they collect about the activities their friends like to do at the lake.
- Remind students that a vote for an activity will get a tally mark next to the drawing. Demonstrate how to make a tally mark on the board and how to make a set of five tally marks.
- Have students check to make sure the number of tally marks or votes they collect for each activity matches the graph they make. Some students may need help transferring the data they collect to their graph.
- Ask students to share their graphs in small groups.

Assess and Close

Class Graph Make a class graph of favorite snacks.

- Ask the students to brainstorm a list of five snacks. Create a graph on chart paper listing the five snacks vertically along the left side of the paper.
- Give each student a sticker or sticky note to represent their vote. Have students place their sticker or sticky note on the graph to vote for their favorite snack.
- Discuss the graph as a class.
- **Which snack is most popular? Which snack is least popular?** See students' answers.
- **How many votes did the most popular snack get?** See students' answers.
- **Did any snacks have the same number of votes? Which ones?** See students' answers.
- Have students share how their vote changed the graph.

More FUN Facts

- The Shawnee National Forest has all types of outdoor activities such as hiking, biking, horseback riding, fishing, and rock climbing.
- The Carlsbad Caverns National Park in New Mexico has one of the world's largest known caves.
- Redwood National Park in California has the world's tallest tree.
- Haleakala National Park in Hawaii cares for endangered species. Some of these animals only exist in this park.

Chapter Overview

Chapter-at-a-Glance

In Chapter 1, students will extend and create patterns and compare and order whole numbers to 20.

Lesson	Math Objective	State/Local Standards
1-1 **Extend a Pattern** (pp. 17–18)	Describe and extend a pattern.	
1-2 **Create a Pattern** (pp. 19–20)	Identify, describe, and create patterns.	
1-3 **Problem-Solving Strategy: Look for a Pattern** (pp. 21–22)	Use the *look for a pattern* strategy to solve the problems.	
1-4 **Numbers to 10** (pp. 23–26)	Count, read, and write whole numbers to 10.	
1-5 **Numbers 11 to 15** (pp. 27–28)	Count, read, and write whole numbers to 15.	
1-6 **Numbers 16 to 20** (pp. 29–30)	Count, read, and write whole numbers to 20.	
1-7 **Problem-Solving Investigation: Choose a Strategy** (pp. 33–34)	Choose the best strategy to solve a problem.	
1-8 **Compare Numbers** (pp. 35–36)	Use concrete and pictorial models to compare numbers.	
1-9 **Order Numbers** (pp. 39–40)	Use concrete and pictorial models to order whole numbers through 20.	

Describe and Compare Numbers

BIG Idea In kindergarten students began recognizing patterns based on characteristics such as size, shape, and color. In first grade, students build upon these concepts by identifying simple repeating patterns using shapes. In this chapter, students review reading, counting, and writing numbers up to 20. In addition, students extend their number sense by comparing and ordering numbers using the terms *greater than, less than,* and *equal to.*

Algebra Readiness Students prepare for algebra through extending and creating patterns. Lessons 1-1 and 1-2

Students are laying the foundation for solving inequalities by comparing numbers. Lesson 1-8

Geometry Readiness Students prepare for geometry through exposure to various two-dimensional figures. Lessons 1-1 and 1-2

Focal Points and Connections

G1-FP2   *Number and Operations:* Developing an understanding of whole number relationships, including grouping in tens and ones

Children compare and order whole numbers (at least to 100) to develop an understanding of and solve problems involving the relative sizes of these numbers. They think of whole numbers between 10 and 100 in terms of groups of tens and ones (especially recognizing the numbers 11 to 19 as 1 group of ten and particular numbers of ones). They understand the sequential order of the counting numbers and their relative magnitudes and represent numbers on a number line.

Skills Trace
Vertical Alignment

Kindergarten

In kindergarten, students learned to:

* Describe and extend a pattern with color, size, and shape.
* Count, read, and write whole numbers to 20.
* Compare and order whole numbers to 20.

First Grade

During this chapter, students will learn to:

* Describe and extend a pattern.
* Identify and create patterns.
* Count, read, and write whole numbers to 20.
* Compare and order whole numbers to 20.
* Choose appropriate problem solving strategies.

After this chapter, students learn to:

* Count, read, and write whole numbers to 99.
* Compare and order whole numbers to 99.

Second Grade

In second grade, students learn to:

* Describe and extend a pattern.
* Identify and create patterns.
* Count, read, and write whole numbers to 1000.

Backmapping and Vertical Alignment
McGraw-Hill's *Math Connects* program was conceived and developed with the final results in mind: student success in Algebra 1 and beyond. The authors, using the **NCTM Focal Points and Focal Connections** as their guide, developed this brand-new series by backmapping from Algebra 1 concepts, and vertically aligning the topics so that they build upon prior skills and concepts and serve as a foundation for future topics.

Math Vocabulary

The following math vocabulary words for Chapter 1 are listed in the glossary of the *Student Edition.* You can find interactive definitions in 13 languages in the *eGlossary* at macmillanmh.com.

after to follow in place or time (p. 39)

$$a \quad b \quad c \quad d$$
b is after a

before the square is before the triangle (p. 39)

between the triangle is between the two squares (p. 39)

is equal to (=) having the same value, is equal to (p. 35)

$$2 + 4 = 6$$
↑

is greater than (>) the number on the left side of the symbol is larger than the number on the right side, 7 > 2, 7 is greater than 2 (p. 35)

is less than (<) the number on the left side of the symbol is smaller than the number on the right side, 4 < 7, 4 is smaller than 7 (p. 35)

number tells how many, 1, 2, 3, 4, 5, 6, 7, 8, 9, 10, . . . (p. 23)

number line a line with numbers labels (p. 39)

```
←──┼──┼──┼──┼──┼──→
   0  1  2  3  4  5
```

order these numbers are in order:
1, 3, 6, 7, 9 (p. 39)

pattern an order that a set of objects or numbers follows over and over (p. 17)
A, A, B, A, A, B, A, A, B

pattern unit the part of the pattern that repeats (p. 17)

Visual Vocabulary Cards Use Visual Vocabulary Cards 23, 24, 30, and 33 to introduce and reinforce the vocabulary in this chapter. (The Define/Example/Ask routine is printed on the back of each card.)

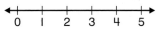

Chapter Planner

Suggested Pacing		
Instruction	**Review and Assessment**	**TOTAL**
9 days	2 days	**11 days**

✓ **Diagnostic Assessment**
Are You Ready? (p. 14)

	Lesson 1-1 Pacing: 1 day	**Lesson 1-2** Pacing: 1 day	**Lesson 1-3** Pacing: 1 day
Lesson/ Objective	**Extend a Pattern** (pp. 17–18) **Objective:** Describe and extend a pattern.	**Create a Pattern** (pp. 19–20) **Objective:** Identify, describe, and create patterns.	**Problem-Solving Strategy** **Look for a Pattern** (pp. 21–22) **Objective:** Use the *look for a pattern* strategy to solve problems.
State/Local Standards			
Math Vocabulary	**pattern** **pattern unit**		
Lesson Resources	**Materials** construction paper, glue **Manipulatives** pattern blocks **Other Resources** CRM Leveled Worksheets (pp. 6–10) Daily Reteach • 5-Minute Check Problem of the Day	**Materials** crayons **Manipulatives** pattern blocks, attribute blocks **Other Resources** CRM Leveled Worksheets (pp. 11–15) Daily Reteach • 5-Minute Check Problem of the Day	**Manipulatives** two-colored counters, pattern blocks **Other Resources** CRM Leveled Worksheets (pp. 16–20) Daily Reteach • 5-Minute Check Problem of the Day *Maps and Mail*
Technology Math Online ▷	Concepts in Motion	Concepts in Motion	
Reaching All Learners	Below Level, p. 17B **BL** English Learners, p. 17B **ELL** Early Finishers, p. 17B **OL** **AL**	Gifted and Talented, p. 19B **AL** English Learners, p. 19B **ELL** Early Finishers, p. 19B **OL** **AL**	Gifted and Talented, p. 21B **AL** English Learners, p. 21B **ELL** Early Finishers, p. 21B **OL** **AL**
Alternate Lessons	*Math Their Way*, p. 260 *IMPACT Mathematics*: Unit D	*Math Their Way*, pp. 265–266 *IMPACT Mathematics*: Unit D	

KEY
BL Below/ Approaching Level   **OL** On Level   **AL** Above/Beyond Level   **ELL** English Learners

SE Student Edition   **TE** Teacher Edition   **CRM** Chapter 3 Resource Masters   CD-Rom

Transparency   Flip Chart   Real-World Problem Solving Library

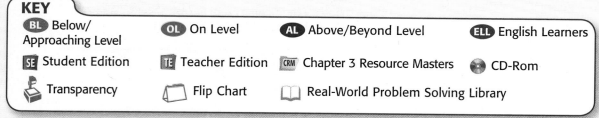

Lesson 1-4 **Pacing:** 1 day	Lesson 1-5 **Pacing:** 1 day	Lesson 1-6 **Pacing:** 1 day	
Numbers to 10 (pp. 23–26) **Objective:** Count, read, and write whole numbers to 10.	**Numbers 11 to 15** (pp. 27–28) **Objective:** Count, read, and write whole numbers to 15.	**Numbers 16 to 20** (pp. 29–30) **Objective:** Count, read, and write whole numbers to 20.	**Lesson/Objective**
			State/Local Standards
number			**Math Vocabulary**
Materials pencils or crayons, number cards, adding machine tape, notecards **Other Resources** [CRM] Leveled Worksheets (pp. 21–25) Daily Reteach • 5-Minute Check Problem of the Day	**Materials** pencils, crayons, craft sticks, rubber bands, pennies, cup **Other Resources** [CRM] Leveled Worksheets (pp. 26–30) Daily Reteach • 5-Minute Check Problem of the Day	**Materials** pencils or crayons, number cards, pennies **Manipulatives** two-colored counters **Other Resources** [CRM] Leveled Worksheets (pp. 31–35) Daily Reteach • 5-Minute Check Problem of the Day	**Lesson Resources**
♪ Math Adventures Concepts in Motion	♪ Math Song Track 10 Math Adventures Concepts in Motion	♪ Math Song Track 10 Concepts in Motion	**Technology** Math Online
Gifted and Talented, p. 23B **AL** English Learners, p. 23B **ELL** Early Finishers, p. 23B **OL AL**	Below Level, p. 27B **BL** English Learners, p. 27B **ELL** Early Finishers, p. 27B **OL AL**	Below Level, p. 29B **BL** English Learners, p. 29B **ELL** Early Finishers, p. 29B **OL AL**	**Reaching All Learners**
Math Their Way, p. 44	*Math Their Way*, p. 47	*Math Their Way*, p. 50	**Alternate Lessons**

Formative Assessment
- Mid-Chapter Check (p. 31)
- Spiral Review (p. 32)

Chapter Planner

	Lesson 1-7 — Pacing: 1 day	**Lesson 1-8** — Pacing: 1 day	**Lesson 1-9** — Pacing: 1 day
Lesson/ Objective	Problem-Solving Investigation **Choose a Strategy** (pp. 33–34) **Objective:** Choose the best strategy to solve a problem.	**Compare Numbers** (pp. 35–36) **Objective:** Use concrete and pictorial models to compare numbers to 20.	**Order Numbers** (pp. 39–40) **Objective:** Use concrete and pictorial models to order whole numbers to 20.
State/Local Standards			
Math Vocabulary		is greater than is less than is equal to	number line order before after between
Lesson Resources	**Other Resources** CRM Leveled Worksheets (pp. 36–40) Daily Reteach • 5-Minute Check Problem of the Day *Maps and Mail*	**Materials** number cards, animal pictures, checkers **Manipulatives** connecting cubes **Other Resources** CRM Leveled Worksheets (pp. 41–45) Daily Reteach • 5-Minute Check Problem of the Day	**Materials** pencils or crayons, strips of 1-inch grid paper, tape, scissors, number cards 1–20, ruler **Manipulatives** connecting cubes **Other Resources** CRM Leveled Worksheets (pp. 46–50) Daily Reteach • 5-Minute Check Problem of the Day
Technology Math Online	Math Adventures Concepts in Motion	♪ Math Song Track 10 Math Adventures Concepts in Motion	♪ Math Song Track 10 Math Adventures Concepts in Motion
Reaching All Learners	Below Level, p. 33B BL English Learners, p. 33B ELL Early Finishers, p. 33B OL AL	Gifted and Talented, p. 35B AL English Learners, p. 35B ELL Early Finishers, p. 35B OL AL	Below Level, p. 39B BL English Learners, p. 39B ELL Early Finishers, p. 39B OL AL
Alternate Lessons		*Math Their Way*, pp. 126–127	*Math Their Way*, p. 93

Extra Practice (p. 37)
Game Time: The Bigger the Better (p. 38)

Problem Solving in Science (p. 41)

✓ **Summative Assessment**
Chapter Review/Test (p. 43)
Test Practice (p. 45)

Assessment Options

✓ Diagnostic Assessment

- **SE** *Option 1:* Are You Ready? (p. 14)
  Option 2: Online Quiz macmillanmh.com
- **CRM** *Option 3:* Diagnostic Test (p. 54)
- **CRM** *Option 4:* Chapter Pretest (p. 55)

✓ Formative Assessment

- **TE** Alternate Teaching Strategies (every lesson)
- **SE** Talk About It (every lesson)
- **SE** Writing in Math (every lesson)
- **SE** Check (every lesson)
- **TE** Line Up (every lesson)
- **SE** Mid-Chapter Check (p. 31)
- **CRM** Mid-Chapter Test (p. 56)

✓ Summative Assessment

- **SE** Chapter Review/Test (pp. 43–44)
- **SE** Test Practice (pp. 45–46)
- **CRM** Vocabulary Test (p. 57)
- **CRM** Leveled Chapter Tests (pp. 64–72)
- **CRM** Cumulative Test Practice (p. 74)
- **CRM** Listening Assessment (p. 60)
- **CRM** Oral Assessment (p. 58)
- **◉** Exam*View®* Assessment Suite
- **A** Advance Tracker

McGraw Hill Professional Development

Targeted professional development has been articulated throughout the **McGraw-Hill's *Math Connects*** program. The **McGraw-Hill Professional Development Video Library** provides short videos that support the **NCTM Focal Points and Focal Connections.** For more information, visit macmillanmh.com.

| Model Lessons | Instructional Strategies |

The one-stop **Assessment Options** planner organizes the resources available for diagnostic, formative, and summative assessment in this chapter.

Teacher Notes

Learning Stations
Cross-Curricular Links

 Reading

Fishy Numbers

- Read *Fish Eyes: A Book You Can Count On*.
- Choose a number card from 1 to 20.
- Draw a picture showing the number of fish on your number card.

Teacher Note: After drawing their pictures, students can arrange their pictures in order from 1 fish to 20 fish.

Materials:
- drawing paper
- crayons
- *Fish Eyes: A Book You Can Count On* by Lois Ehlert
- number cards 1–20

Cross-curricular Learning Stations give students self-guided opportunities to explore chapter concepts.

 **Science**

Weather Watchers

- Find a card that shows what today's weather is like.
- Find today's date on the calendar.
- Put the weather card on the calendar.

Teacher Note: Review what yesterday's weather was. Predict what tomorrow's weather will be. At the end of the week, have students count and tally how many times each type of weather occurred during the week. At the end of the month, have students use weather symbols from the calendar to make a pictograph on chart paper and count the number of each type of weather day.

Materials:
- calendar cards with symbols for rain, snow, clouds, and sun
- class calendar

 Music

Sound Patterns

- Choose a musical instrument.
- Use your instruments to make a rhythm pattern.
- Share your pattern with the class.

Teacher Note: Challenge each group to create a different pattern.

Materials:
- musical instruments

Art

  group | **VISUAL/SPATIAL**

Pattern Art

- Choose shapes or other objects.
- Use the shapes or other objects to make a pattern.
- Glue your pattern onto construction paper.

Teacher Note: Extend the activity by having students combine parts of their patterns to make a larger pattern.

Materials:
- construction paper
- paper triangles, stars, and other shapes
- buttons
- stickers
- beans
- other small items

Language Arts

pair | **LOGICAL**

Greater Than, Less Than

- Find a partner.
- Place counters on one half of the paper and a different number of counters on the other half of the paper.
- Have your partner count the counters on each side of the paper.
- Place the *less than* or *greater than* pipe cleaner symbol on the paper.
- Take turns placing the counters and writing the correct statement.

Teacher Note: Make the activity more fun by allowing students to choose a number of different objects from the classroom to compare. Also encourage students to try using equal to.

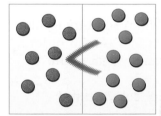

Materials:
- 11" x 14" paper creased down the middle to create 2-sided mat
- counters
- pipe cleaner

Calendar Time

Calendar Patterns

- Have students count the number of days from Sunday to Sunday and pick up a counter for each day you name.
- Have students count the number of days from Monday to Monday and pick up a counter for each day you name.
- Ask them to compare the number of counters in the two sets.
- Repeat for the other days of the week. Have them tell about the pattern you find.

Teacher Note: Have students read the days of the week in order for the entire month to hear the pattern repeating every seven days.

Introduce the Chapter

🌐 Real World: The Four Seasons

Materials: index cards, crayons

Divide the class into four groups. Assign each group a season: spring, summer, autumn, and winter. Allow the children to draw a representation of their season on their index cards. Explain that the seasons of the year change in a pattern.

- Have groups sit together holding their index cards.
- Have the children raise their index cards in the air when their season is called.
- Call out the seasons in order. Repeat several times to demonstrate the pattern.

Have students turn to p. 13.

- **Put your finger on your favorite balloon.**
- **What pattern do you see on that balloon?**
  Sample Answer: dark blue, light blue, light blue

Key Vocabulary

Introduce the key vocabulary in the chapter using the routine below.

Define: A **pattern** happens when something, like a shape or a number, repeats in a certain order.
Example: The days of the week repeat in the same order.
Ask: Can you find a pattern of colors in the classroom?

Key Vocabulary
pattern
pattern unit
number

Explore
How many balloons do you see? __14__ balloons

Chapter 1   thirteen   13

Foldables® are a unique way to enhance students' study skills. Encourage students to add to their Foldable as they work through the chapter and to use it to review for their chapter test.

FOLDABLES® **Dinah Zike's**
Study Organizer **Foldables**

Guide students to create their own Matchbook Foldables for number sense.

① Fold a sheet of $8\frac{1}{2}" \times 11"$ paper like a hamburger, but fold it so that one side is one inch longer than the other side.

② Fold the one-inch tab over the short side forming an envelopelike fold.

③ Cut the front flap in half toward the mountain top to create two flaps.

1   5

When to Use It Lessons 1-4, 1-5, 1-6, 1-8 and 1-9. (Additional instructions for using the Foldable with these lessons are found on pp. 31 and 43.)

✓ Are You Ready for Chapter 1?

1. Use a ◀▬crayon▬▶ to color the circle ○.
2. Use a ◀▬crayon▬▶ to color the square □.
3. Use a ◀▬crayon▬▶ to color the triangle △.

1–3. Check students' work.

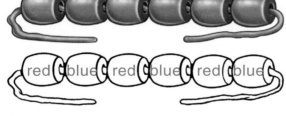

> Each chapter provides three options for **Diagnostic Assessment**. Based on the results, **Intervention Options** include suggestions for intensive and strategic students, as well as on-level and above-level students.

Copy the pattern.

4.

red | blue | red | blue | red | blue

5. How many ⬤ are in this group? Circle the number.

⬤ ⬤ ⬤

1   2   ③

This page checks skills needed for Chapter 1.

Diagnostic Assessment

Check for students' prerequisite skills before beginning the chapter.

- **Option 1:** *Are You Ready for Chapter 1?*
  SE Student Edition, p. 14

- **Option 2:** *Online Readiness Quiz*
  Math Online ▶ macmillanmh.com

- **Option 3:** *Diagnostic Test*
  CRM Chapter 1 Resource Masters, p. 54

RTI (Response to Intervention)

Apply the Results Based on the results of the diagnostic assessment on student p. 14, use the chart below to address individual needs before and during the chapter.

TIER 3 Intensive Intervention

If	students miss four or more of the exercises:
Then	use Chapters 4, 5, and 6 of *Math Triumphs*, an intensive math intervention program from McGraw-Hill

TIER 2 Strategic Intervention below/approaching grade level	**TIER 1 On-Level**	**Above/Beyond Level**
If students miss two or three in: **Exercises 1–5**	**If** students miss one in: **Exercises 1–5**	**If** students miss none in: **Exercises 1–5**
Then Choose a resource:	**Then** Choose a resource:	**Then** Choose a resource:
Strategic Intervention Guide (p. 36) **TE** Smart Start 2: Number and Operations (p. 3) **Math Online** ▶ Concepts in Motion	**TE** Learning Stations (pp. 13G–13H) **TE** Chapter Project (p. 15) **CRM** Game: *Showing Numbers* 🌎 Math Adventures **Math Online** ▶ Fact Dash	**TE** Learning Stations (pp. 13G–13H) **TE** Chapter Project (p. 15) 🌎 Math Adventures 📖 Real-World Problem Solving: *Maps and Mail* **Math Online** ▶ Fact Dash

Before you begin Chapter 1:

- Read the Math at Home letter found on student p. 15 with the class and have each child sign it.
- Send home copies of the Math at Home letter with each student.
- Use the Spanish letter on student p. 16 for students with Spanish-speaking parents or guardians.

WRITING IN ▶ MATH

Starting the Chapter

Have students think about the days of the week and the different activities they do during the week. For example, they go to school from Monday to Friday or they go to soccer practice on Tuesdays and Thursdays. Have children write about the patterns that repeat during their week.

Read-Aloud Anthology

For an optional reading activity to introduce this chapter's math concepts, see the Read-Aloud Anthology on p. TR24.

Chapter Projects apply chapter concepts and skills through extended activities and provide additional assessment opportunities.

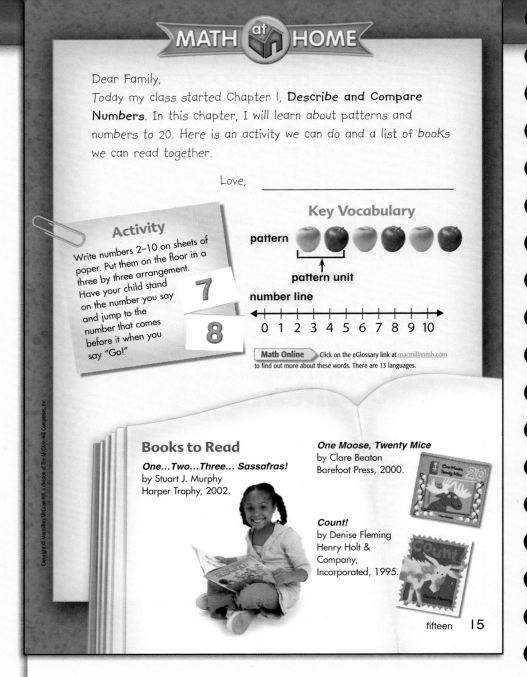

MATH at HOME

Dear Family,
Today my class started Chapter 1, **Describe and Compare Numbers**. In this chapter, I will learn about patterns and numbers to 20. Here is an activity we can do and a list of books we can read together.

Love, _____

Activity

Write numbers 2–10 on sheets of paper. Put them on the floor in a three by three arrangement. Have your child stand on the number you say and jump to the number that comes before it when you say "Go!"

7

8

Key Vocabulary

pattern

pattern unit

number line

0 1 2 3 4 5 6 7 8 9 10

Math Online Click on the eGlossary link at macmillanmh.com to find out more about these words. There are 13 languages.

Books to Read

One...Two...Three... Sassafras!
by Stuart J. Murphy
Harper Trophy, 2002.

One Moose, Twenty Mice
by Clare Beaton
Barefoot Press, 2000.

Count!
by Denise Fleming
Henry Holt & Company, Incorporated, 1995.

fifteen 15

✓ Chapter 1 Project

Pattern Mural

Have students create a mural to illustrate their understanding of concrete and pictorial patterns and numbers to 20.

- Have students draw an AB pattern on a 5-foot strip of paper.
- Make sure the students' patterns contain a total of twenty objects; therefore the pattern unit should be duplicated ten times.
- Once their patterns are complete, have students number each object of the pattern starting with 1 and ending with 20.

CRM *Refer to Chapter 1 Resource Masters, p. 62, for a rubric to assess students' progress on this project.*

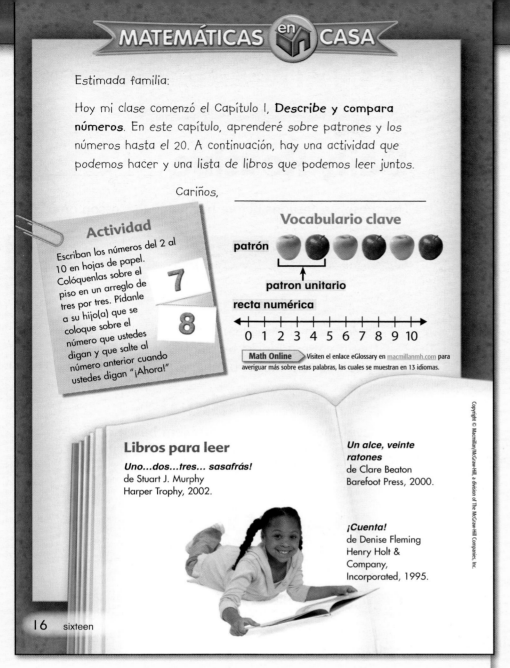

Estimada familia:

Hoy mi clase comenzó el Capítulo I, **Describe y compara números**. En este capítulo, aprenderé sobre patrones y los números hasta el 20. A continuación, hay una actividad que podemos hacer y una lista de libros que podemos leer juntos.

Cariños, _____

Actividad

Escriban los números del 2 al 10 en hojas de papel. Colóquenlas sobre el piso en un arreglo de tres por tres. Pídanle a su hijo(a) que se coloque sobre el número que ustedes digan y que salte al número anterior cuando ustedes digan "¡Ahora!"

7

8

Vocabulario clave

patrón

patron unitario

recta numérica

0 1 2 3 4 5 6 7 8 9 10

Math Online Visiten el enlace eGlossary en macmillanmh.com para averiguar más sobre estas palabras, las cuales se muestran en 13 idiomas.

Libros para leer

Uno...dos...tres... sasafrás!
de Stuart J. Murphy
Harper Trophy, 2002.

Un alce, veinte ratones
de Clare Beaton
Barefoot Press, 2000.

¡Cuenta!
de Denise Fleming
Henry Holt & Company, Incorporated, 1995.

Copyright © Macmillan/McGraw-Hill, a division of The McGraw-Hill Companies, Inc.

16 sixteen

Chapter 1 Literature List

Lesson	Book Title
1-1	**Pattern Fish** Trudy Harris
1-2	**Beep Beep, Vroom Vroom!** Stuart J. Murphy
1-3	**Icky Bug Numbers *1 2 3*** Jerry Pallotta
1-4	**Gray Rabbit's 1, 2, 3** Alan Baker
1-5	**The Icky Bug Book *1 2 3*** Jerry Pallotta
1-6	**Icky Bug Numbers *1 2 3*** Jerry Pallotta
1-8	**More, Fewer, Less** Tana Hoban
1-9	**One Hundred Is a Family** Pam Munoz Ryan
Any	**One Moose, Twenty Mice** Clare Beaton
Any	**Count!** Denise Fleming
Any	**One... Two... Three... Sassafrass!** Stuart J. Murphy

The **Literature List** presents all of the literature referenced in the chapter.

National ESL Standards Alignment for Chapter 1

Lesson, Page	ESL Standard	Modality	Level
1-1, p 17B	Goal 1, Standard 1, c	Auditory, Kinesthetic	Beginning
1-2, p 419B	Goal 1, Standard 3, b	Auditory, Visual/Spatial	Intermediate
1-3, p 21B	Goal 2, Standard 2, j	Kinesthetic	Intermediate
1-4, p 23B	Goal 1, Standard 1, a	Auditory, Kinesthetic	Beginning
1-5, p 27B	Goal 2, Standard 1, f	Kinesthetic, Visual/Spatial	Intermediate
1-6, p 29B	Goal 2, Standard 3, k	Kinesthetic, Auditory	Beginning
1-7, p 33B	Goal 1, Standard 3, e	Interpersonal	Intermediate
1-8, p 35B	Goal 1, Standard 3, c	Logical, Visual, Spatial	Intermediate
1-9, p 39B	Goal 2, Standard 2, f	Linguistic, Kinesthetic	Intermediate

The National ESL Standards can be found in the Teacher Reference Handbook.

Lesson Planner

Objective
Describe and extend a pattern.

Vocabulary
pattern, pattern unit

Resources
Materials: construction paper, glue

Manipulatives: pattern blocks

Literature Connection: *Pattern Fish* by Trudy Harris

Alternate Lesson: Use "Geoboard Number Patterns" on p. 260 of *Math Their Way* to provide practice describing and extending a pattern.
Use *IMPACT Mathematics:* Unit D to provide practice with extending patterns.

Teacher Technology
🔵 TeacherWorks • Concepts in Motion

Focus on Math Background

Sorting by a single attribute such as color, size, or shape is a foundation skill in both math and science (classifying) and leads to pattern recognition and creating by attributes. Understanding likenesses and differences in size and shape are essential for the concepts in geometry and measurement of perimeter and area. Pattern building with concrete objects sets the stage for looking at patterns with numbers: skip counting, odd and even, and greater than and less than. Many students have built patterns while stringing beads or working with shape blocks.

Daily Routine

Use these suggestions before beginning the lesson on p. 17.

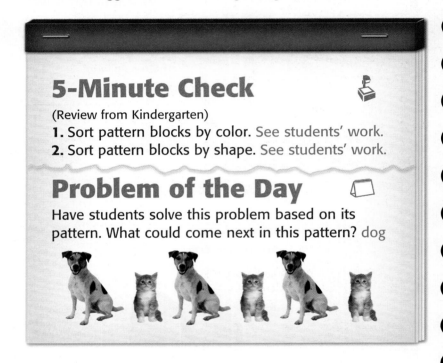

5-Minute Check
(Review from Kindergarten)
1. Sort pattern blocks by color. See students' work.
2. Sort pattern blocks by shape. See students' work.

Problem of the Day
Have students solve this problem based on its pattern. What could come next in this pattern? dog

LINE UP Ask students to line up in a boy/girl pattern. Ask students if there is another way they could line up in a pattern. Sample answers: long sleeves/short sleeves; shorts/pants

Building Math Vocabulary
Arrange six students in an AB **pattern** of standing and sitting. Ask additional students to continue lining up in the same way, "over and over." Write on the chalkboard the vocabulary word pattern and its definition.

- **What do you see over and over?** standing, sitting
- Write on the chalkboard the vocabulary word **pattern unit** and its definition.
- **What is the pattern unit in the red, yellow, red, yellow pattern?** red, yellow
- Display a pattern with pattern blocks. Have students name the pattern unit.

Visual Vocabulary Cards
Use Visual Vocabulary Card 33 to reinforce the vocabulary introduced in this lesson. (The Define/Example/Ask routine is printed on the back of each card.)

Differentiated Instruction

Small Group and Independent Work Options offer classroom flexibility for students who need additional help or self-directed activity suggestions after completing their work.

Small Group Options

Option 1 **Below/Approaching Level** BL

SPATIAL, AUDITORY

Materials: connecting cubes

- Model a concrete pattern using colored cubes.
- Point to each cube as you "read" the pattern.
- Have students identify what part is repeating.
- **What is the repeating part called?** pattern unit
- Repeat with other cubes in different patterns.

Option 2 **English Language Learners** ELL

AUDITORY, KINESTHETIC

Core Vocabulary: clap, again, tap
Common Use Verb: do/does

Hear Math This strategy uses restricted language with phonemic similarities and kinesthetic movement to connect background knowledge to vocabulary.

- Have students stand up.
- Clap hands and say: "**Clap**."
- Repeat a few times.
- Tap fingers to your nose and say: "**tap**."
- Create an AB pattern and repeat several times.
- Say: "**do it again**" and repeat, prompting the students to identify and mimic your actions.
- Extend the lesson by changing the actions or by having eight students lead their own AB pattern.

Each lesson includes suggestions ideas for **differentiating instruction** in your classroom with both remediation and extension ideas. These strategies are keyed for English language learners, students above grade level, struggling students, and students with special needs.

Independent Work Options

Option 1 **Early Finishers** OL AL

VISUAL, SPATIAL

Materials: adding machine tape, dot stickers

- Cut the adding machine tape in 6- to 8-inch strips, then use the dot stickers to make three pattern units of a pattern.
- Have each student take one strip and use dot stickers to extend the pattern by at least one pattern unit.
- Invite students to display the dot patterns on a bulletin board or wall.

Option 2 **Student Technology**

Math Online ▷ macmillanmh.com

Option 3 **Learning Station: Art** (p. 13H)

Direct students to the Art Learning Station for more opportunities to explore the lesson concept.

Option 4 **Problem-Solving Practice**

Reinforce problem-solving skills and strategies with the Problem-Solving Practice worksheet.

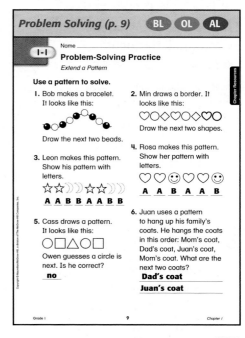

Problem Solving (p. 9) BL OL AL

1-1 **Problem-Solving Practice**
Extend a Pattern

Use a pattern to solve.

1. Bob makes a bracelet. It looks like this:
   Draw the next two beads.

2. Min draws a border. It looks like this:
   ♡♡◇♡♡◇♡○
   Draw the next two shapes.

3. Leon makes this pattern. Show his pattern with letters.
   ☆☆〉〉☆☆〉〉
   A A B B A A B B

4. Rosa makes this pattern. Show her pattern with letters.
   ♡♡☺♡♡☺
   A A B A A B

5. Cass draws a pattern. It looks like this:
   ○□△○□
   Owen guesses a circle is next. Is he correct?
   no

6. Juan uses a pattern to hang up his family's coats. He hangs the coats in this order: Mom's coat, Dad's coat, Juan's coat, Mom's coat. What are the next two coats?
   Dad's coat
   Juan's coat

Grade 1   9   Chapter 1

1-1

① Introduce

Activity Choice 1 • Hands-On

- Cut various shapes out of construction paper.
- Have the students create patterns with the shapes.
- Check that their patterns are correct. Then, have students paste the shapes to a piece of paper.
- Give the students time to share and describe their patterns to their classmates.

Activity Choice 2 • Literature

Introduce the lesson with *Pattern Fish* by Trudy Harris. For additional support, see p. TR42.

② Teach

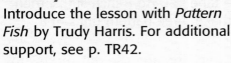

Use the overhead pattern blocks to display this pattern, using a single shape: yellow, blue, yellow, blue, yellow, blue.

- **What two colors do you see over and over?** yellow, blue
- **This is a pattern. The colors repeat over and over. Identify the color pattern you see.** yellow, blue, yellow, blue . . .
- **Describe the pattern unit.** yellow, blue
- Repeat the procedure with this pattern, using a single color: square, triangle, square, triangle, square, triangle.
- **Extend the pattern.** square, triangle

Get Ready Use the section at the top of p. 17 to reinforce the lesson concept.

Check Observe students as you work through Exercises 1–5 as a class.

Exercise 5 Assess student comprehension before assigning practice exercises.

> **Talk About** It exercises at the end of the **Check** section provide an informal assessment opportunity to gauge student comprehension.

⚠ COMMON ERROR!

If students misorder the objects in the pattern, have them say the pattern aloud and touch each item as they say its name.

17 **Chapter 1** Describe and Compare Numbers

Name _____

Extend a Pattern

Get Ready

Main Idea
I will identify, describe, and extend a pattern.

Vocabulary
pattern
pattern unit

These shapes make a **pattern**. △, ⬤ is the **pattern unit**. It repeats over and over.

pattern unit   pattern

> *Orange, blue, orange, blue is also a color pattern.*

> **New Vocabulary** is listed at the beginning of every lesson. **Review Vocabulary** is listed as necessary.

✓ Check

Identify the pattern unit. Circle it.

1.

2.

Identify the pattern unit. Circle it. Extend the pattern. **Draw** what comes next.

3.

4.

5. **Talk About It** Describe the pattern in Exercise 4. Sample answer: The pattern repeats colors and shapes: Purple square, purple square, green square

Chapter 1   Lesson 1   seventeen   17

Copyright © Macmillan/McGraw-Hill, a division of The McGraw-Hill Companies, Inc.

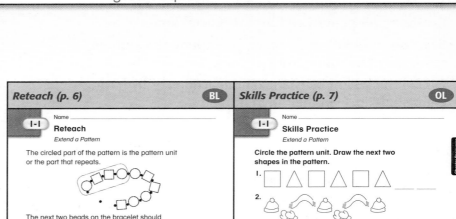

Reteach (p. 6) **BL**

Skills Practice (p. 7) **OL**

Practice

Identify the pattern unit.
Circle it. Extend the pattern.
Draw what comes next.

Remember
A pattern unit repeats over and over to make a pattern.

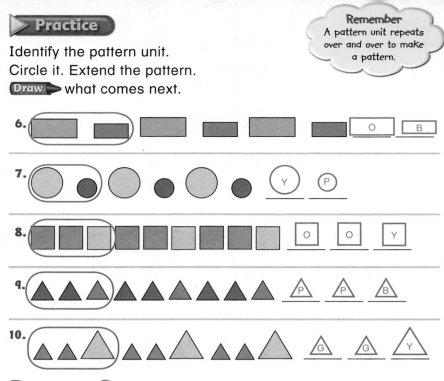

6.

7.

8.

9.

10.

Problem Solving

11. **Logical Reasoning**
Dave likes pizza. He does not like hot dogs. Should he buy lunch on Friday if the pattern repeats?

School Lunch Menu				
Monday	Tuesday	Wednesday	Thursday	Friday

Sample answer: Yes, Dave should buy his lunch on Friday. The pattern for school lunches is pizza, hot dog, pizza, hot dog, so Friday is a pizza day.

18   eighteen

Math at Home Activity: Make a pattern using sound. Ask your child to tell what part you are repeating to make the pattern.

Copyright © Macmillan/McGraw-Hill, a division of The McGraw-Hill Companies, Inc.

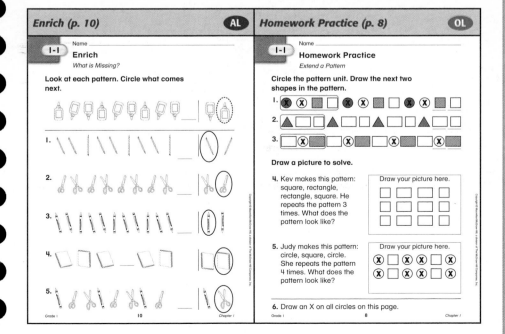

Enrich (p. 10) **AL**

1-1 Enrich
What is Missing?
Look at each pattern. Circle what comes next.

Homework Practice (p. 8) **OL**

1-1 Homework Practice
Extend a Pattern
Circle the pattern unit. Draw the next two shapes in the pattern.

BL Alternate Teaching Strategy

If students have trouble understanding a pattern unit . . .

Then use one of these reteaching options.

1 **CRM Daily Reteach Worksheet** (p. 6)

2 **Pattern Play** Display a pattern with three or four pattern units. Have students copy the pattern on strips of paper. Guide them in identifying the repeating part. Then help them cut the paper to divide the pattern into the separate pattern units. Have students lay the pattern units out in a vertical column to show that each section is the same.

3 Practice

Differentiate practice, using these leveled assignments for Exercises 6–11.

Level	Assignment
BL Below/Approaching Level	Guide students through the patterns, using pattern blocks.
OL On Level	Complete exercises independently using pattern blocks as needed.
AL Above/Beyond Level	Complete exercises independently.

4 Assess

Formative Assessment

• Model a pattern, using pattern blocks.
• Have students draw what comes next in the pattern. Repeat with another pattern.

WRITING IN ►MATH Have students describe a pattern they see in the classroom.

Quick Check **Are students continuing to struggle with simple repeating patterns?**

If Yes → Small Group Options (p. 17B)
If No → Independent Work Options (p. 17B)
   CRM Skills Practice Worksheet (p. 7)
   CRM Enrich Worksheet (p. 10)

Create a Pattern

Lesson Planner

Objective
Identify, describe, and create patterns.

Review Vocabulary
pattern, pattern unit

Resources

Materials: crayons

Manipulatives: pattern blocks, attribute blocks

Literature Connection:
Beep, Beep, Vroom Vroom!
by Stuart J. Murphy

Alternate Lesson: Use "Surrounding Patterns" on pp. 265 and 266 of *Math Their Way* to provide practice identifying and creating a pattern. Use *IMPACT Mathematics:* Unit D to provide practice with creating patterns.

Teacher Technology
TeacherWorks • Concepts in Motion

Focus on Math Background

Before working on creating patterns, students should have multiple opportunities to sort objects by attributes such as color, size, and shape. Identifying, extending, and creating patterns requires the ability to differentiate various characteristics by which objects can be sorted.

The 5-Minute Check provides a quick review and assessment of a previous lesson. Use the Problem of the Day to challenge students with additional review and higher-order questions.

Focus on Math Background provides background information for each lesson. This information would be especially valuable to new teachers or those new to teaching mathematics.

Daily Routine

Use these suggestions before beginning the lesson on p. 19.

5-Minute Check

(Reviews Lesson 1-1) 1-2. See students' drawings.
Draw or predict the next pattern unit.
1. circle, triangle, square, circle, triangle, square . . . circle
2. square, square, triangle, square, square, triangle . . . square

Problem of the Day

Use connecting cubes to create a pattern. Then draw the pattern. See students' work.

LINE UP Ask three students to line up. Have those students form a pattern unit by either clapping or stomping. Have the rest of the students continue the pattern as they join the line.

Review Math Vocabulary

Review the vocabulary words **pattern** and **pattern unit** from Lesson 1.
- Write the vocabulary words and their definitions on the chalkboard. Read the words aloud and discuss the definitions.
- Choose volunteers to draw, model, or act out an example of a pattern and a pattern unit.

Visual Vocabulary Cards

Use Visual Vocabulary Card 33 to reinforce the vocabulary reviewed in this lesson. (The Define/Example/Ask routine is printed on the back of each card.)

Differentiated Instruction

Small Group Options

Option 1: Gifted and Talented (AL)

VISUAL/SPATIAL, LOGICAL

Materials: nature pictures, including some that show patterns (such as flower petals and zebras) and others that do not show patterns

- Have students sort the pictures into two groups: those with patterns and those without patterns.
- After sorting, have students describe the patterns they see (zebra: black, white . . .).
- Ask students to think of and name other things they have seen that have patterns. Have students describe the patterns.

Option 2: English Language Learners (ELL)

AUDITORY, VISUAL/SPATIAL

Core Vocabulary: period (symbol), question (symbol), it
Common Use Verb: is

Hear Math This strategy introduces 2 phonemically similar high frequency words and the symbols for questions and statements, and applies them to tonal patterning.

- Write and say, "**it**" on the board.
- Repeat for "**is.**"
- Say, "**It is.**" and clap as you make the period.
- Walk around saying "it *is* ___" as you name various things and clap. Have the students chorally say "It *is.*"
- Repeat the process for "**Is *it*?**" using a rising tone as you write the question mark.
- Have students chorally chant the ABCBAD pattern with you.

Independent Work Options

Option 1: Early Finishers (OL) (AL)

KINESTHETIC, SPATIAL

Materials: paper, crayons, scissors, sentence strips

- Have students cut out shapes to create a concrete pattern unit. Then have them arrange it on a sentence strip.
- Ask students to repeat their pattern on a second sentence strip.
- Have students convert the concrete patterns into pictorial patterns.
- Ask questions about the number of each shape in their pattern.

Option 2: Student Technology

Math Online > macmillanmh.com

Option 3: Learning Station: Music (p. 13G)

Direct students to the Music Learning Station for more opportunities to explore the lesson concept.

Option 4: Problem-Solving Practice

Reinforce problem-solving skills and strategies with the Problem-Solving Practice worksheet.

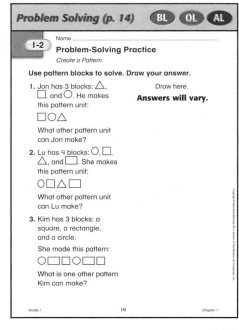

1-2

1 Introduce

Activity Choice 1 • Hands-On

- Have students use attribute blocks to create a concrete pattern.
- When all students have created a concrete pattern, have them exchange with a partner and try to identify their partner's pattern
- Have partners use attribute blocks to model and extend each other's pattern.

Activity Choice 2 • Literature

Introduce the lesson with *Beep Beep, Vroom Vroom!* by Stuart J. Murphy. For additional support, see p. TR42.

2 Teach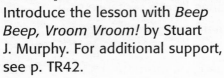

Display a simple pictorial pattern and have students copy the pattern. Ask them to circle the pattern unit.

- **What should you look for to extend the pattern?** pattern unit
- Have students think of two other shapes. **What pattern unit can you make with the shapes?**
- Have students draw their pattern unit and extend it.
- Have students switch papers with a neighbor. **Describe the pattern unit you see in the pattern your neighbor drew. Predict what will come next.**

Display your simple pattern again and leave out one part. Ask students to identify what is different.

Get Ready Use the section at the top of p. 19 to reinforce the lesson concept. Make sure students can identify and extend the pattern unit.

Check Observe students as you work through Exercises 1–3 as a class.

 Exercise 3 Assess student comprehension before assigning practice exercises.

! COMMON ERROR!

Students may leave out an element in one of the pattern units. Have students draw a box or circle around the first pattern unit so they can see what each pattern unit should look like.

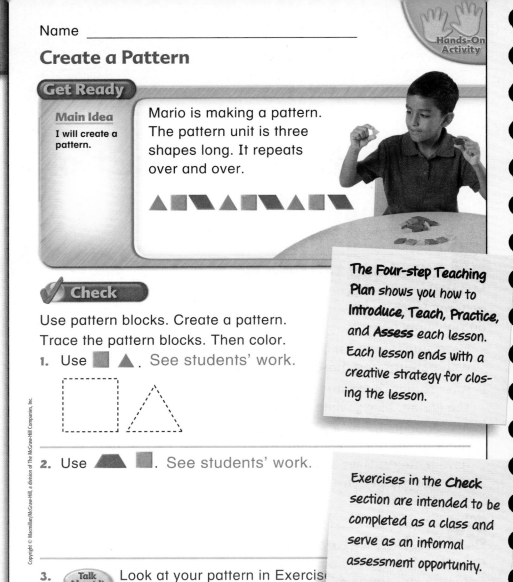

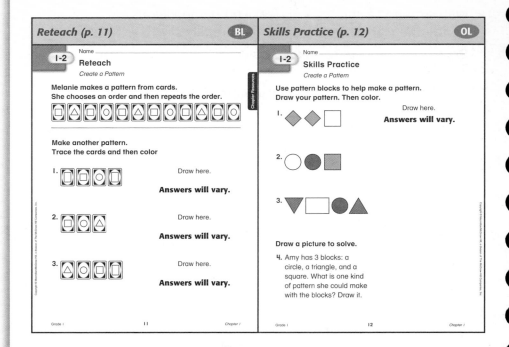

Practice

Use pattern blocks. Create a pattern.
Trace the pattern blocks. Then color.

4. Use  . See students' work.

Create a pattern. Use any pattern blocks.

5. See students' work.

6. See students' work.

7. **WRITING IN** ►**MATH** Use words to describe the pattern on the shirt.

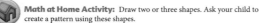

Sample answer:

The shirt has a color pattern.

Red, blue, red, blue, red, blue.

Copyright © Macmillan/McGraw-Hill, a division of The McGraw-Hill Companies, Inc.

20 twenty

Math at Home Activity: Draw two or three shapes. Ask your child to create a pattern using these shapes.

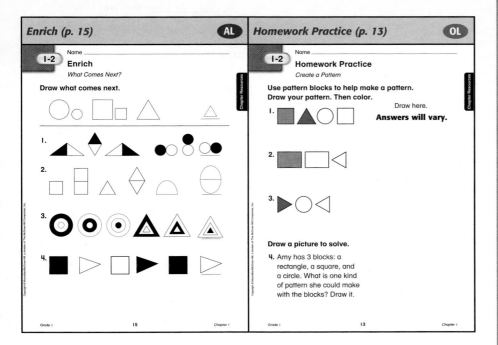

Enrich (p. 15) **AL**

1-2 Name _____
Enrich
What Comes Next?

Draw what comes next.

1.

2.

3.

4.

Grade 1   15   Chapter 1

Homework Practice (p. 13) **OL**

1-2 Name _____
Homework Practice
Create a Pattern

Use pattern blocks to help make a pattern.
Draw your pattern. Then color.

Draw here.
Answers will vary.

1.

2.

3.

Draw a picture to solve.

4. Amy has 3 blocks: a rectangle, a square, and a circle. What is one kind of pattern she could make with the blocks? Draw it.

Grade 1   13   Chapter 1

BL Alternate Teaching Strategy

If ► students have trouble creating a pattern . . .

Then ► use one of these reteach options.

1 **CRM** **Daily Reteach Worksheet** (p. 11)

2 **Move and Make Patterns** To support kinesthetic learners, display and read aloud a pattern of Xs and Os as students form each letter with their arms. Ask students to say and show the pattern unit. Then help students create and extend a new pattern unit with hand shapes (V, L, diamond, etc.).

Differentiated practice options provide suggestions for the exercises that are appropriate for below-level, on-level, or above-level students.

③ Practice

Differentiate practice, using these leveled assignments for Exercises 4–7.

Level	Assignment
BL Below/ Approaching Level	Guide students through the patterns, using pattern blocks.
OL On Level	Complete exercises independently.
AL Above/Beyond Level	Complete exercises without using pattern blocks.

④ Assess

✓ Formative Assessment

Draw a shirt on the board. Use the shirt's buttons to create a pattern. Make sure one button is missing from the pattern. **Which button is missing? Can you identify a pattern in order to solve the problem?** See students' work.

WRITING IN ►**MATH** Have students create a pattern they could use to decorate their room and describe it in their Math Journal.

Quick Check **Are students continuing to struggle with creating and describing patterns?**

If Yes → Strategic Intervention Guide (p. 50)

If No → Independent Work Options (p. 19B)

CRM Skills Practice Worksheet (p. 12)

CRM Enrich Worksheet (p. 15)

Lesson Planner _____

Objective

Use the *look for a pattern* strategy to solve problems.

Resources

Manipulatives: two-colored counters, pattern blocks

Literature Connection: *Icky Bug Numbers 1 2 3* by Jerry Pallotta

Teacher Technology
- 💿 TeacherWorks

📖 **Real-World Problem Solving Library**
Math and Social Studies: *Maps and Mail*
Use these leveled books to reinforce and extend problem-solving skills and strategies.

Leveled for:
- **OL** On Level
- **ELL** Sheltered English
- **SP** Spanish

For additional support, see the Real-World Problem Solving Teacher Guide.

The Real-World Problem Solving Readers, fiction and non-fiction leveled readers, extend problem-solving skills and strategies and make real-world connections.

Daily Routine _____

Use these suggestions before beginning the lesson on p. 21.

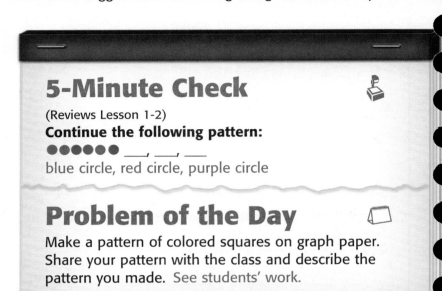

5-Minute Check

(Reviews Lesson 1-2)
Continue the following pattern:
●●●●●● ___, ___, ___
blue circle, red circle, purple circle

Problem of the Day

Make a pattern of colored squares on graph paper. Share your pattern with the class and describe the pattern you made. See students' work.

LINE UP When it is time for students to line up for recess, lunch, or dismissal, call them up in a way that makes a pattern. For example, call 2 boys, 2 girls, 3 boys, and 3 girls. Then ask students how to continue the pattern as they line up. 4 boys, 4 girls, 5 boys, 5 girls

Problem-Solving Strategy and Problem-Solving Investigations lessons help students learn different problem-solving skills and strategies for solving word problems.

Differentiated Instruction

Small Group Options

Option 1 — **Gifted and Talented** **AL**
LOGICAL

Materials: magazines, scissors, glue, paper

- Have small groups of students cut pictures out of magazines to use in making a pattern.
- Explain that students will glue their pictures onto paper in a pattern.
- Ask each group to give their pattern to another group to see whether the students can identify and describe the pattern.
- Once students identify the pattern, challenge them to find more magazine pictures, draw pictures, or write words to describe the pictures that should come next in the pattern.

Option 2 — **English Language Learners** **ELL**
KINESTHETIC

Core Vocabulary: jump, what, point
Common Use Verb: comes next

Do Math This strategy kinesthetically integrates patterns to vocabulary and requires students to predict what comes next.

- Demonstrate jump. Have the group jump while saying **"jump jump jump."** Repeat for clap and **point.**
- Prompt 3 students to stand in line.
- Have the 1st volunteer jump, the 2nd clap, and the 3rd reach, in line order. Add a volunteer to the line. Prompt them to extend the pattern and say: **"What *comes next?"*** The first student to identify the next action joins the line.
- Repeat as time permits.

Independent Work Options

Option 1 — **Early Finishers** **OL** **AL**
LOGICAL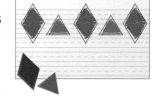

Materials: crayons or markers, paper, pencil, crayons, pattern blocks

- Have small groups of students use pattern blocks to form a pattern along the top edge of a sheet of paper.
- After their blocks are arranged, ask students to trace in pencil the outline of each shape.
- Next, have students color the traced shapes with crayons to make a color pattern.
- Invite students to exchange papers with another group member and trace and color pattern blocks to continue their partner's pattern along the bottom of the paper.

Option 2 — **Student Technology**

| Math Online | macmillanmh.com |

Option 3 — **Learning Station: Science** (p. 13G)

Direct students to the Science Learning Station for more opportunities to explore and extend the lesson concept.

① Introduce

Activity Choice 1 • Review

Use two-colored counters to make a pattern for students to see. For example, two red, one yellow, two red, one yellow, and so on. Tell them that they will extend the pattern.

- **What do we know?** The counters make a pattern.
- **What do we want to find?** which counter comes next
- Help students use counters to predict what comes next.
- **Which counters finish the pattern?** See students' work.

Lessons begin with two Activity Choices: a Hands-On activity suggestion and a Literature Connection.

Activity Choice 2 • Literature

Introduce the lesson with *Icky Bug Numbers 1 2 3* by Jerry Pallotta. For additional support, see p. TR42.

② Teach

Understand Using the questions, review what students know and what they need to find.

- **What do you need to find?** which bead is missing

Plan Have them discuss their strategy.

Solve Guide students to use *look for a pattern* to solve the problem.

- Point to the area where the bead is missing.
- **Which two beads start the pattern?** green, pink
- **Which two beads end the pattern?** pink, green

Check Have students look back at the problem to make sure that the answers fit the facts given.

- Repeat the bead pattern aloud.
- **Which bead is missing?** pink

 COMMON ERROR!

Students copy all the shapes in a long series without recognizing the shorter pattern that is repeating. Underline the first pattern unit and have students find and underline each set of shapes that repeats that pattern. Then have them draw shapes to make one more pattern unit like the others.

Name _____

Problem-Solving Strategy
Look for a Pattern

Main Idea
I will look for a pattern to solve a problem.

Lee made a bracelet. A bead fell off. Which bead is missing?

Understand ————
What do I need to find?
Circle the question.

Plan ————
How will I solve the problem?

Solve ————
Look for a pattern. See students' work.

Check ————
Look back.
Is my answer reasonable?
Check students' explanations.

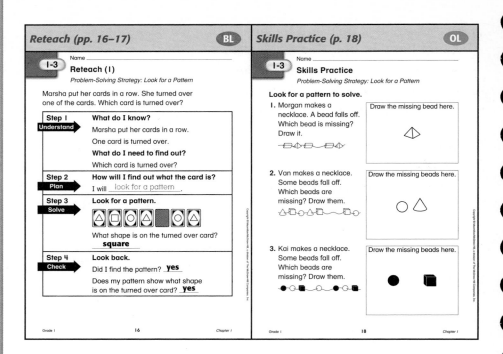

Try It

Look for a pattern to solve.

1. Ana made a necklace.
   A bead fell off.
   Which bead is missing?

green bead

2. Lucy was wearing a necklace.
   It broke and 2 of the beads are lost.
   Which beads are missing?

green and yellow beads

Your Turn

Look for a pattern to solve.

3. This is Meg's necklace.
   Two beads fell off.
   Which beads are missing?

two yellow beads

4. Juan is making a bracelet.
   He needs 2 more beads to finish.
   Which beads are needed?

yellow and green beads

The Alternate Teaching Strategy provides two suggestions for remediation for students did not grasp the concept.

22 twenty-two

Math at Home Activity: Look for patterns around your home. Ask your child to extend patterns found on clothes, blankets, towels, the walls, the floors, and so on.

Try It Observe students as you work through Exercises 1–2 as a class.

BL Alternate Teaching Strategy

If students have difficulty creating or extending a pattern . . .

Then use one of these reteaching options.

1. CRM **Daily Reteach Worksheet** (pp. 16–17)

2. **Create a Pattern** Ask students to make a pattern with two different colored blocks.
   - **Which color block will you use to start?**
   - Have students choose another color for their second block.
   - Ask students to extend the pattern by alternating the two colors of blocks.
   - Continue until students can make patterns with three and four colors of blocks.

③ Practice

Your Turn

Exercises 3–4 Have pattern blocks and crayons available if necessary for students to use to extend the pattern. Remind students that they should find the pattern unit first. Ask students to describe the rest of the patterns before they begin.

④ Assess

Formative Assessment

Have students draw a series of shapes to create a pattern, followed by three blank lines where missing shapes can be drawn. Ask them to trade papers with a partner.

- **How will you solve the problem? Which shapes can you use?** look at the shapes before the blanks; the shapes that are already in the pattern
- Have students draw shapes to finish the pattern.

Quick Check — **Are students continuing to struggle with looking for patterns?**

If Yes → Strategic Intervention Guide (p. 50)

If No → Independent Work Options (p. 21B)

CRM Skills Practice Worksheet (p. 18)

CRM Enrich Worksheet (p. 20)

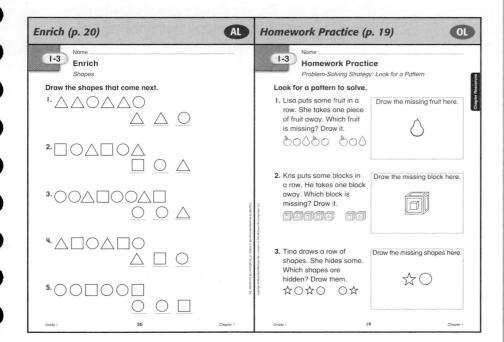

Lesson Planner

Objective
Count, read, and write whole numbers to 10.

Vocabulary
number

Resources
Materials: pencils or crayons, number cards, adding machine tape, notecards

Literature Connection: *Gray Rabbit's 1, 2, 3* by Alan Baker

Alternate Lesson: Use "Large Numeral Cards" on p. 44 of *Math Their Way* to provide practice identifying and creating a pattern.

Teacher Technology
TeacherWorks • Concepts in Motion

Focus on Math Background

The ability to count, read, and write numbers is an essential precursor skill to communicating mathematically. Students hear numbers used to describe their age, the number of students in the classroom, and time designated for specific events. Students see numerals on school doors, on addresses, and on packaging to designate quantities. The calendar is a daily reminder of written numerals designating an ordinal progression of dates.

Daily Routine

Use these suggestions before beginning the lesson on p. 23.

5-Minute Check
(Reviews Lesson 1-3) 1–2. See students' work.
Use connecting cubes to create the following patterns:
1. green, red, green, red . . .
2. blue, blue, red, blue, blue, red . . .

Problem of the Day
What should come next in these patterns?
blue, yellow, blue, yellow, blue . . . yellow
red, orange, white, red, orange, white, . . . red
green, green, pink, green, green, . . . pink

 Ask students to match numbers to rhyming words. **What number word rhymes with clue?** two Have the student who answers correctly line up.

Building Math Vocabulary
Write the numbers 1 through 10 on the chalkboard and below them the vocabulary word **number.** Remind students that a number tells how many.
- Place four counters on an overhead projector. **Count them with me: 1, 2, 3, 4.** Write the number 4 on the chalkboard and explain that 4 is the number that tells how many counters there are.
- Display other groups of counters and have volunteers tell the number in each group. Write on the chalkboard each number they mention.
- Have students write the word *number* and draw a picture to illustrate its meaning.

Building Math Vocabulary and Reviewing Math Vocabulary activities introduce and reinforce mathematics vocabulary

Differentiated Instruction

Small Group Options

Option 1 — Gifted and Talented (AL)

Materials: 3-column chart on a poster, classroom items

- Select several sets of classroom items to be inventoried. In the first column of the chart, draw pictures to represent each set.
- Have each student select a set of items from the poster.
- As students count the items in their set, have them record their results by making dots in the second column. Help students write in the third column the total number they count.
- Have a partner check the number by counting the same group of objects. If the results do not match, have partners count the objects together.

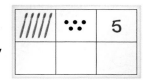

AUDITORY, KINESTHETIC

Option 2 — English Language Learners (ELL)

Core Vocabulary: #1–10, me, this is
Common Use Verb: show

Hear Math This strategy teaches English numbers and key high frequency words through action within a familiar context.

- Say: "**Show** me 1."
- Model showing one finger. Say: "**This is one.**"
- Pick up one counter and say: "This is 1."
- Repeat.
- Continue with numbers to 10, using fingers first and then a different manipulative.
- Finish by the students showing you a number (students hold up their fingers). Encouraging verbal responses—regardless of accuracy to the standard of "This is ____." Note: You can repeat this strategy for other number words.

Independent Work Options

LOGICAL, KINESTHETIC

Option 1 — Early Finishers (OL) (AL)

Materials: large sheets of drawing paper, cubes

- Fold drawing paper to create ten sections. Ask students to number the boxes from 0 to 9. Ask students to write the number name under each number.
- Have each student place the corresponding number of cubes in each box.

Option 2 — Student Technology

Math Online ▸ macmillanmh.com

Math Adventures

This program is supported by a wealth of technology options on CD-ROM, on DVD, and online.

Option 3 — Learning Station: Art (p. 13H)

Direct students to the Art Learning Station for more opportunities to explore the lesson concept.

Option 4 — Problem-Solving Practice

Reinforce problem-solving skills and strategies with the Problem-Solving Practice worksheet.

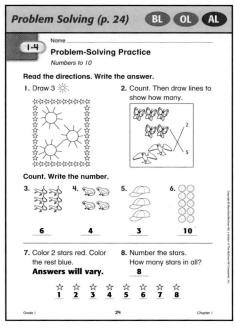

Problem Solving (p. 24) BL OL AL

 Introduce

Activity Choice 1 • Hands-On

- Have students place the **number** 0 on the left side of their desks and the number 10 on the right side of their desks.
- Students should continue placing number cards in between until all numbers are in order.
- Using the cards as a model, have students write the numbers in order on a strip of adding machine tape.

Activity Choice 2 • Literature

Introduce the lesson with *Gray Rabbit's 1, 2, 3* by Alan Baker. For additional support, see p. TR42.

② Teach

- Write each number 0 to 10 on a notecard. Then write each number name on a notecard.
- Mix-up the cards. Draw a card and show it to the class.
- Have the students write the corresponding number or number name.
- Use cubes to model the number or number name.
- First, model the number with cubes close together. Then, show the same number with cubes spread apart.
- Help students identify that the spacing of the same number of cubes does not affect the quantity (conservation).

Get Ready Use the section at the top of p. 23 to reinforce the lesson concept. In each row have the students count the item, say the name, and the number.

Check Observe students as you work through Exercise 1–9 as a class.

Exercise 9 Assess student comprehension before assigning practice exercises.

! COMMON ERROR!

If students have difficulty with the order of word tags, but understand the concepts of one-to-one correspondence and the "one more" pattern of counting, let them look at a number line while counting.

Name _____

Numbers to 10

Get Ready

Main Idea
I will read and write numbers to 10.

Vocabulary
number

A **number** tells how many.

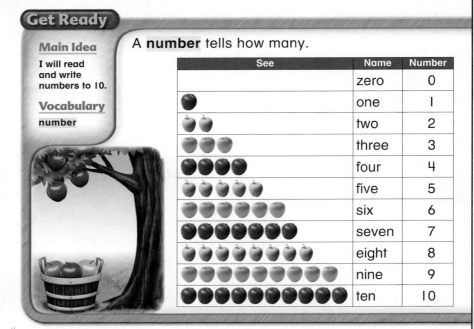

See	Name	Number
	zero	0
	one	1
	two	2
	three	3
	four	4
	five	5
	six	6
	seven	7
	eight	8
	nine	9
	ten	10

✓ Check

Read the number name.
Draw 🍎 to show the number.

1.

6
six

2. See students' drawings.

3
three

Reteach (p. 21)   BL

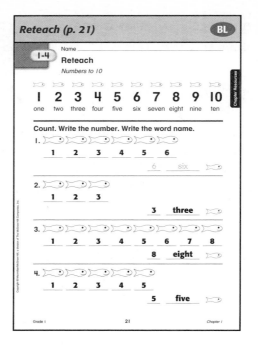

Read the number name.
Draw ● to show the number.

3. See students' drawings.

8
eight

4. See students' drawings.

5
five

Count. Write the number.
Write the number name.

0	zero
1	one
2	two
3	three
4	four
5	five
6	six
7	seven
8	eight
9	nine
10	ten

5. I one

6. 9 nine

7. 3 three

8. 8 eight

9. **Talk About It** How do you know which number to write?
Sample answer: by counting the objects.

GO on

Copyright © Macmillan/McGraw-Hill, a division of The McGraw-Hill Companies, Inc.

BL **Alternate Teaching Strategy**

If students have trouble counting to 10 . . .

Then use one of the following reteach options.

1 **CRM** **Daily Reteach Worksheet** (p. 21)

2 **Read and Write.** Have students find a partner. Have the first partner write the number names for 0 to 5 on a piece of paper. Have the second partner write the number names for 6 to 10. Then have partners switch papers and read each others list out loud.

Skills Practice (p. 22) **OL**

1-4 Name _____
Skills Practice
Numbers to 10

Count. Write the number. Write the word name.

1. 5 five
2. 3 three
3. 8 eight
4. 2 two
5. 10 ten
6. 6 six

Solve.

7. Stacy writes the numbers 1 and 10. Then she changes the words into numbers. What does she write?
1 one
10 ten

8. Julio is thinking of a number. The number is between six and eight. What number is Julio thinking of? Write the number and the word name.
7 seven

Grade 1   22   Chapter 1

Reteach, Skills Practice, Problem-Solving Practice, Enrich, and Homework Practice Masters are shown for each lesson in the Student Edition. These masters can be found in the **Chapter Resource Masters.**

3 Practice

Differentiate practice, using these leveled assignments for Exercises 10–18.

Level	Assignment
BL Below/ Approaching Level	Guide students to use counters as they count the objects and provide a writing model for the numbers.
OL On Level	Complete exercises independently, using counters if needed.
AL Above/Beyond Level	Complete exercises independently without counters.

Name _____

Practice

Count. Write the number.
Write the number name. Then read the name.

Remember
A number tells how many.

10. _____ 5 _ _ five _

11. _____ 7 _ _ seven _

12. _____ 2 _ _ two _

13. _____ 4 _ _ four _

14. _____ 6 _ _ six _

15. _____ 10 _ _ ten _

0	zero
1	one
2	two
3	three
4	four
5	five
6	six
7	seven
8	eight
9	nine
10	ten

Chapter 1   Lesson 4   twenty-five   **25**

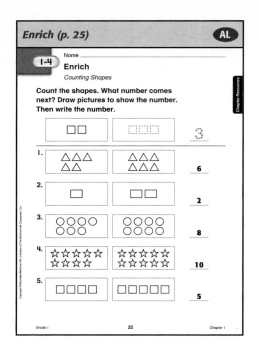

Enrich (p. 25)   **AL**

16. Read the numbers. Write these number names in order from one to ten.

seven	four	one	six	three
two	eight	five	ten	nine

one, two, three, four, five, six, seven, eight, nine, ten

Data File

The Stennis Space Center is in Mississippi. The center shows how people travel to outer space.

17. How many people are leaving for space? ___8___ people

18. How many people are inside the space shuttle? ___3___ people

Math at Home Activity: Say a number between 0 and 10. Have your child draw that many objects and write the number.

Homework Practice (p. 23) OL

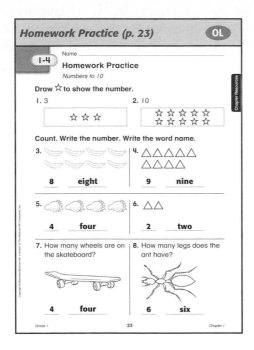

Name _____

1-4 **Homework Practice**
Numbers to 10

Draw ☆ to show the number.

1. 3   2. 10

Count. Write the number. Write the word name.

3. 8 eight   4. 9 nine

5. 4 four   6. 2 two

7. How many wheels are on the skateboard?   8. How many legs does the ant have?

4 four   6 six

Grade 1   23   Chapter 1

---

4 Assess

✓ Formative Assessment

Display a picture with one to ten different objects. **How can you find out how many _____ are in this picture?** Count them. Have students count the number of objects.

Have students use cubes to model the number of objects in each picture.

WRITING IN ►MATH Have students write in their Math Journal the number of pets they have or the number of pets they would like to have. Encourage students to use the number names.

Quick Check provides reteaching suggestions for students who continue to struggle.

Quick Check — **Are students continuing to struggle counting to 10?**

If Yes → Strategic Intervention Guide (p. 14)

If No → Independent Work Options (p. 23B)

  CRM Skills Practice Worksheet (p. 22)

  CRM Enrich Worksheet (p. 25)

Lesson Planner _____

Objective

Count, read, and write whole numbers to 15

Review Vocabulary

number

Resources

Materials: pencils, crayons, craft sticks, rubber bands, pennies, cup

Literature Connection: *The Icky Bug Book 1 2 3* by Jerry Pallotta

Alternate Lesson: Adapt "Numeral Sequencing Cards" on p. 47 of *Math Their Way* for practice with the concept of zero.

Teacher Technology

● TeacherWorks • Concepts in Motion • Math Songs Track 10 Lesson Plan

Focus on Math Background

Students have heard numbers used in various situations and should be making connections between the word, the number, and what it represents. Computational skills of adding and subtracting require the ability to count, read, and write numbers. Using counters to represent two numbers being added together is a natural progression from counting with counters.

Daily Routine _____

Use these suggestions before beginning the lesson on p. 27.

5-Minute Check

(Reviews Lesson 1-4) 1-4. See students' work.
Use counters to show each numbers:
1. five
2. eight
3. three
4. six

Problem of the Day

Draw pictures showing from 1 to 10 objects. Write the number of objects in each drawing. See students' work.

LINE UP Give each student a card with a number from 1 to 15. If needed, use a second set of numbers on another color paper. Have students use the number cards to line up in order.

Review Math Vocabulary

Review the vocabulary word **number** from Lesson 4. Write *number* on the chalkboard and point to it each time you use the word during this activity.

- Have three students stand at the front of the room.
- **The number 3 tells how many students.**
- Hold up six crayons and have students repeat after you: **The number 6 tells how many crayons.**
- Continue with other sets of objects, having students repeat the sentence **The number _____ tells how many _____.**

Differentiated Instruction

Small Group Options

Option 1 — SPATIAL, KINESTHETIC
Below/Approaching Level BL

Materials: dot cards for 11–15, number cards for 11–15, counters

- Display the dot card for 11. **What number is this?** 11 Have students count in unison as you point to each dot. Show the number card for 11.
- Repeat for numbers 12–15.
- After introducing the numbers, display the dot cards. Have volunteers match a number card to each dot card.
- Have students place counters on each dot to model each number.

Option 2 — KINESTHETIC/VISUAL/SPATIAL
English Language Learners ELL

Core Vocabulary: eleven, twelve, thirteen, fourteen, fifteen
Common Use Verb: scrunch down

Do Math This strategy teaches how to pronounce numbers with kinesthetic movement.

- Model moving an arm straight up over your head. Say: "Eeee." Repeat with the other arm. Say "leven." Prompt students to copy you.
- For 12, use a student standing straight and another kneeling and curving their arms like the number 2. Say: "Too-welve." Tap them sequentially but blend sounds together.
- For thirteen, have 3 students say: "thir" and then scrunch down and say: "teen."
- For fourteen, have 4 students stand with an arm up and the other bent at a right angle. Repeat the "four" and "teen" process.
- For fifteen, have 5 students stand with one arm out and a bent leg, toes to ankle. Repeat the "fif" and "teen" process.

Independent Work Options

Option 1 — SPATIAL, LOGICAL
Early Finishers OL AL

Materials: 16 pictures of groups of objects representing 0 to 15, 16 cards with numbers from 0 to 15.

- Have students display the pictures in one group and the numbers in another group.
- Have partners take turns picking a number card and the picture card that corresponds to it.
- After each turn, ask students to count to make sure their partner's choice is correct.

Option 2
Student Technology

Math Online — macmillanmh.com

♪ Math Songs, "The Number Line" Track 10
🌎 Math Adventures

Option 3
Learning Station: Science (p. 13G)

Direct students to the Science Learning Station for more opportunities to explore the lesson concept.

Option 4
Problem-Solving Practice

Reinforce problem-solving skills and strategies with the Leveled Problem-Solving Worksheet.

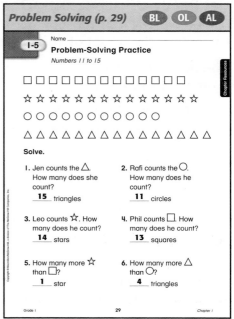

1 Introduce

Activity Choice 1 • Hands-On

- Have students count ten craft sticks, saying the numbers aloud as they count.
- Have students put a rubber band around their ten craft sticks. Tell them that bundle is a group of ten. Have students write the number ten.
- Have students place a craft stick next to the bundle. **You have a group of ten and one more. How many sticks do you have now? Write the number.** Model by pointing to the bundle as you read *ten*, then pointing to the other stick as you read *eleven*.
- Have students continue adding one stick at a time and writing down the total each time.

Activity Choice 2 • Literature

Introduce the lesson with *Icky Bug Numbers 1 2 3* by Jerry Pallotta. For additional support, see p. TR42.

2 Teach

Display 12 crayons.

- **How can we tell whether there are more than 10 crayons?** Count them.
- As you count, move the crayons to one side. When you reach 10, bundle them with a rubber band.
- Continue counting to 12. **Do we have more than 10 crayons?** yes

Get Ready Use the section at the top of p. 27 to reinforce the lesson concept. Make sure the students circle the set of 10 and count on.

Check Observe students as you work through Exercises 1–3 as a class.

 Exercise 3 Assess student comprehension before assigning practice exercises.

⚠ COMMON ERROR!

The base-ten system becomes confusing in the "teens." Provide plenty of practice counting, bundling, and using the number.

Name _____

Numbers 11 to 15

Main Idea
I will count and write numbers 11 to 15.

Numbers from 11 to 15 can be made with one group of 10 and some left over.

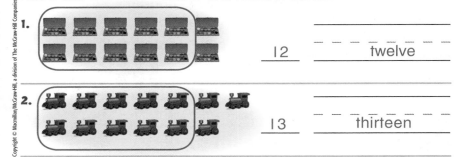

See	Name	Number
	eleven	11
	twelve	12
	thirteen	13
	fourteen	14
	fifteen	15

Check 3. Sample answer: They all have one group of 10 and some more.

Count. Circle a group of 10.
Read and write the number and number name.

1. _____
12 _____ twelve

2. _____
13 _____ thirteen

3. **Talk About It** What is the same about these numbers: 11, 12, 13, 14, 15?

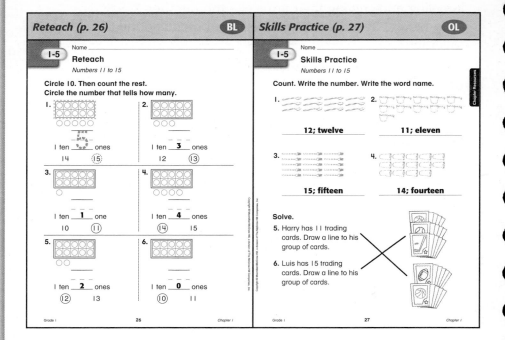

Reteach (p. 26) **BL**

1-5 Reteach
Numbers 11 to 15

Circle 10. Then count the rest.
Circle the number that tells how many.

Skills Practice (p. 27) **OL**

1-5 Skills Practice
Numbers 11 to 15

Count. Write the number. Write the word name.

Count. Circle a group of ten.
Read and write the number and number name.

11	eleven
12	twelve
13	thirteen
14	fourteen
15	fifteen

4.

11   eleven

5.

15   fifteen

6.

14   fourteen

Problem Solving

7. Number Sense
Use the picture.
Write how many.

5   0   2

28   twenty-eight

Math at Home Activity: Say a number between 10 and 15. Have your child draw that many objects and write the number.

Problem Solving exercises are found throughout the chapter to ensure continuous problem-solving practice.

Enrich (p. 30)   **AL**

Name _____
1-5 Enrich
Find Zero

Look at each picture. Read the question. Write the answer.

1. How many 🌴? **2**   How many ⚓? **0**

2. How many ❄? **0**   How many ☃? **1**

3. How many 🌿? **10**   How many 🐛? **0**

4. How many 🦋? **2**   How many 🐿? **0**

Grade 1   30   Chapter 1

Homework Practice (p. 29)   **OL**

Name _____
1-5 Problem-Solving Practice
Numbers 11 to 15

☐☐☐☐☐☐☐☐☐☐☐☐☐
☆☆☆☆☆☆☆☆☆☆☆☆☆☆
○○○○○○○○○○○○
△△△△△△△△△△△△△△△

Solve.

1. Jen counts the △. How many does she count?
15 triangles

2. Rafi counts the ○. How many does he count?
11 circles

3. Leo counts ☆. How many does he count?
14 stars

4. Phil counts ☐. How many does he count?
13 squares

5. How many more ☆ than ☐?
1 star

6. How many more △ than ○?
4 triangles

Grade 1   29   Chapter 1

BL **Alternate Teaching Strategy**

If ➤ Students have trouble counting to 15 . . .

Then ➤ use one of the following reteach options.

1 CRM **Daily Reteach Worksheet** (p. 26)

2 Coin Count Put 10 pennies in a cup and tell them you have a group of 10. Place one penny next to the cup. Ask students to write down how many pennies you have now. Continue to 15. Have students read their answers aloud to check that they are correct.

3 Practice

Differentiate practice, using these leveled assignments for Exercises 4–7.

Level	Assignment
BL Below/Approaching Level	Guide students in using counters and ten frames to count the objects. Provide a writing model for the numbers.
OL On Level	Complete exercises independently, using counters if needed.
AL Above/Beyond Level	Complete exercises independently without counters.

4 Assess

Formative Assessment

Show students a bundle of 10 craft sticks and a single craft stick. Have students count on to 11. Repeat for 12, 13, 14, and 15. Have the students write each number.

WRITING IN ➤ MATH Ask students to choose a number from 11 to 15. Have them make a list of items they might find that number of.

Quick Check   **Are students continuing to struggle counting to 15?**

If Yes ➤ Small Group Options (p. 27B)
     Strategic Intervention Guide (p. 22)

If No ➤ Independent Work Options (p. 27B)
     CRM Skills Practice Worksheet (p. 27)
     CRM Enrich Worksheet (p. 30)

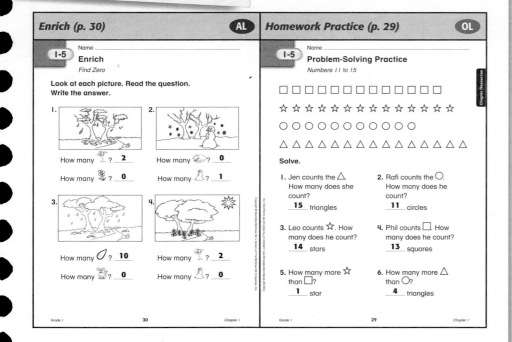

Numbers 16–20

Lesson Planner

Objective
Count, read, and write whole numbers to 20.

Review Vocabulary
number

Resources
Materials: pencils or crayons, number cards, pennies

Manipulatives: two-colored counters

Literature Connection: *Icky Bug Numbers 1 2 3* by Jerry Pallotta

Alternate Lesson: Adapt "Number Line Templates" on p. 50 of *Math Their Way* for practice with numbers 1 through 20.

Teacher Technology
- TeacherWorks • Concepts in Motion

Focus on Math Background

When students are learning to count from 1 to 20, they are developing a basic understanding of patterns in numbers. In this case, the pattern is adding one more each time. Understanding numbers and number patterns is a key component to developing algebraic reasoning.

Daily Routine

Use these suggestions before beginning the lesson on p. 29.

5-Minute Check
(Reviews Lesson 1-5)
Use 15 craft sticks and bundle a group of 10. Then, use the craft sticks to model the following numbers: 11, 12, 13, 14, and 15.
See students' work.

Problem of the Day
Write the number words for 11, 12, 13, 14, and 15. eleven, twelve, thirteen, fourteen, fifteen

LINE UP Place number cards 1 through 20 in a jar. Draw a card and give a clue to help students guess the number. The student who guesses the number, lines up. Continue until everyone has lined up.

Review Math Vocabulary
- Review the vocabulary word **number** from Lesson 4.
- Have each student write the word *number* on a sheet of drawing paper.
- Display numbers 1 through 15. Have students choose one of the numbers and write it on their paper.
- Ask students to draw a picture to model their number.

Differentiated Instruction

Small Group Options

Option 1
Below Level BL
SPATIAL, KINESTHETIC

Materials: index cards, dot stickers

- Give each student 20 index cards.
- Have students write the number 1 on one side of a card. **How many dots do you need to put on the other side to show the number 1?** Guide students in placing one dot sticker on the other side of the card.
- Repeat for numbers 2 through 20.
- Have students use the cards as flash cards to practice reading numbers to describe sets of objects.

Option 2
English Language Learners ELL
KINESTHETIC, AUDITORY

Core Vocabulary: 16–19, twenty, arms
Common Use Verb: spread

Hear Math This strategy teaches how to pronounce numbers with kinesthetic movement.

- Model 16 by curling your back. Say: "Six." Say: "teen" and scrunch down. Prompt students to copy you.
- For 17, forming a 7 with arms out and head bent. Say: "seven." Say: "teen" as you scrunch down. Blend sounds together.
- For 18, stand with elbows and knees out akimbo. Say: "eigh." Say "teen" and scrunch down.
- For 19, make a circle with your arms. Say: "nine." Say: "teen" as you scrunch down.
- For twenty, show two fingers and say: "twen." Spread your arms wide like a "t" and say: "tee."
- Repeat as time permits.

Use this worksheet to provide additional support for English Language Learners.

Independent Work Options

Option 1
Early Finishers OL AL
SPATIAL, LOGICAL

Materials: connecting cubes, paper, and pencil

- Give each student a handful of cubes.
- Have students sort the cubes by color. Then, ask students to count each group of cubes.
- On a piece of paper, ask students to write the number and number names of the amount of cubes in each group.

Option 2
Student Technology

Math Online macmillanmh.com

♪ Math Songs, "The Number Line" Track 10

Option 3
Learning Station: Reading (p. 13G)
Direct students to the Reading Learning Station for more opportunities to explore the lesson concept.

Option 4
Problem-Solving Practice
Reinforce problem-solving skills and strategies with the Problem-Solving Practice worksheet.

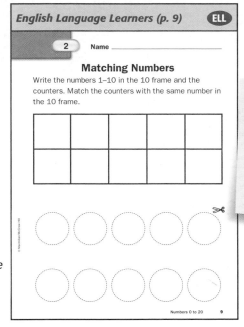

English Language Learners (p. 9) ELL

2 Name _____

Matching Numbers

Write the numbers 1–10 in the 10 frame and the counters. Match the counters with the same number in the 10 frame.

Worksheets for English Language Learners provide an additional support for ELL students.

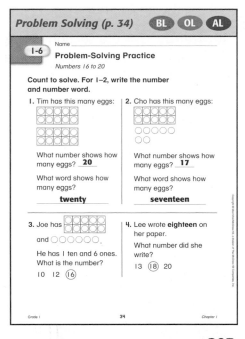

Problem Solving (p. 34) BL OL AL

1-6 Name _____
Problem-Solving Practice
Numbers 16 to 20

Count to solve. For 1–2, write the number and number word.

1. Tim has this many eggs:
   What number shows how many eggs? **20**
   What word shows how many eggs?
   twenty

2. Cho has this many eggs:
   What number shows how many eggs? **17**
   What word shows how many eggs?
   seventeen

3. Joe has and ○○○○○○○
   He has 1 ten and 6 ones. What is the number?
   10   12   ⑯

4. Lee wrote **eighteen** on her paper.
   What number did she write?
   13   ⑱   20

1 Introduce

Activity Choice 1 • Hands-On

- Give half of the students a card with a number 1 to 20.
- Give the other half a card with the number names for 1 to 20.
- Explain to the students that they need to find their match.
- After everyone has matched the numbers with the number names, ask each pair to draw a picture that models their number.

Activity Choice 2 • Literature

Introduce the lesson with *Icky Bug Numbers 1 2 3* by Jerry Pallotta. For additional support, see p. TR43.

2 Teach

Display sixteen counters on an overhead projector.

- **Is there a group of ten?** Have students count ten of the counters with you. Push the group of ten to one side. Ask the students to write *10* and *ten*
- **How many counters in all?** Point to the group of ten and say "ten." Then model counting on to count all sixteen counters. Write the number *16* and the word *sixteen* on the board.
- **What number and number name is this?** 16; sixteen Have students write the number in their Math Journal.
- Repeat with the numbers 17 through 20.

Get Ready Use the section at the top of p. 29 to reinforce the lesson concept. Make sure the students circle the set of ten and count on.

Check Observe students as you work through Exercises 1–3 as a class.

Exercise 3 Assess student comprehension before assigning practice exercises.

COMMON ERROR!

If students do not know the number names for 16 through 20, post the words beside the numerals.

Name _____

Numbers 16 to 20

Get Ready

Main Idea

I will count and write numbers 16 to 20.

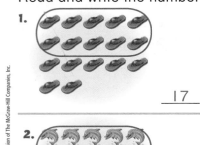

See		Name	Number
		sixteen	16
		seventeen	17
		eighteen	18
		nineteen	19
		twenty	20

Check

Count. Circle a group of 10.
Read and write the number and number name.

1. _____
   17   seventeen

2. _____
   19   nineteen

3. **Talk About It** What pattern do you see in the name of the numbers 13–19? Sample answer: They all have "teen" at the end of the number name.

Chapter 1   Lesson 6   twenty-nine   **29**

Copyright © Macmillan/McGraw-Hill, a division of The McGraw-Hill Companies, Inc.

Reteach (p. 31) **BL**

Name _____

Reteach
Numbers 16 to 20

Circle 10. Then count the others.
Circle the number that tells how many.

1.   2.

I ten **10** ones   I ten **7** ones
19 ⟨20⟩   ⟨17⟩ 18

3.   4.

I ten **9** ones   I ten **8** ones
18 ⟨19⟩   ⟨18⟩ 19

Grade 1   31   Chapter 1

Skills Practice (p. 32) **OL**

Name _____

Skills Practice
Numbers 16 to 20

Count. Write the number and word name.

1.   2.

16   sixteen   17   seventeen

3.   4.

20   twenty   18   eighteen

Solve.

5. Tanya writes the following numbers in order: sixteen, seventeen, eighteen, nineteen, twenty. Then, she changes the words into numbers. What did she write?
   16, 17, 18, 19, 20

Grade 1   32   Chapter 1

Count. Circle a group of 10.
Read and write the number and number name.

16	sixteen
17	seventeen
18	eighteen
19	nineteen
20	twenty

4.
_____
18   eighteen

5.
_____
13   thirteen

6.
_____
20   twenty

Problem Solving

Number Sense Choose a number from 16 to 20.
Use 🎲 to model the number.

7. Write the number. See students' answers.

8. Write the number name.

_____
See students' answers.
_____

30   thirty

Math at Home Activity: Say a number between 16 and 20. Have your child use pennies, beans, or other small objects to model the number.

BL Alternate Teaching Strategy

If ▶ students have trouble reading and writing numbers from 16 to 20 . . .

Then ▶ use one of the following reteach options:

1 CRM **Daily Reteach Worksheet** (p. 31)

2 **Use Manipulatives** Give pairs of students 20 pennies. Have them count out 15 pennies. Then have them work together to count another five pennies, writing 16, 17, 18, 19, 20 on their paper as they go.

3 Practice

Differentiate practice, using these leveled assignments for Exercises 4–6.

Level	Assignment
BL Below/ Approaching Level	Pair students with Above Level students for peer modeling.
OL On Level	Complete independently.
AL Above/Beyond Level	Model problems for Below Level students.

4 Assess

Formative Assessment

Give students twenty counters each. Show fifteen counters. **What number am I modeling if I put in one more counter?** 16

WRITING IN ▶MATH Have students choose a number from 16 to 20, then write anything they know about the number, such as *My brother is 16* or *My birthday is on June 18.*

Quick Check **Are students continuing to struggle counting to 20?**

If Yes → Small Group Options (p. 29B)
    Strategic Intervention Guide (p. 32)

If No → Independent Work Options (p. 29B)
    CRM Skills Practice Worksheet (p. 32)
    CRM Enrich Worksheet (p. 35)

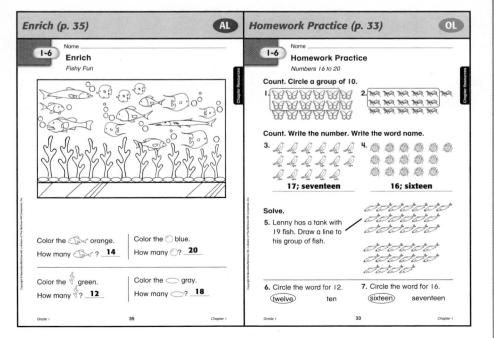

Mid-Chapter Check

Lessons 1-1 to 1-6

 Formative Assessment

Use the Mid-Chapter Check to assess student's progress in the first half of the chapter.

Assessment Suite

Customize and create multiple versions of your Mid-Chapter Check and the test answer keys.

FOLDABLES **Dinah Zike's Foldables**

Use these lesson suggestions to incorporate the Foldables during the chapter.

Lesson 1-4 Make ten Matchbook Foldables and use them for numbers 1–10.

Lesson 1-5 Make five Matchbook Foldables and use them for numbers 11–15.

Lesson 1-6 Make five Matchbook Foldables and use them for numbers 16–20.

Lesson 1-8 Use the Matchbook Foldables to make comparisons between the numbers 1 and 20.

Name _____

Identify the pattern unit. Circle it.
Extend the pattern. **Draw** what comes next.

1. [pattern blocks] | Y | B | Y |

2. Create a pattern. Use any pattern blocks.
   Check students' pattern.

3. If the weather pattern repeats, where will recess be on Friday? Circle it.

Monday	Tuesday	Wednesday	Thursday	Friday

(inside)
outside

Count. Write the number.

4.  ___13___

5. ___4___

Count. Write the number and number name.

6. ___2___ two _____

Data-Driven Decision-Making

Based on the results of the Mid-Chapter Check, use the following resources to review concepts that continue to give students problems.

> The Mid-Chapter Check reviews skills and concepts presented in previous lessons. Students' results can be used for Data-Driven Decision Making.

Exercises	State/Local Standards	What's the Math?	Error Analysis	Resources for Review
1–3 Lesson 1-1, 1-2		Identify, describe and extend patterns in order to make predictions and solve problems.	Does not draw three shapes. Does not continue same pattern.	Strategic Intervention Guide (p. 2) **CRM** Chapter 1 Resource Masters (Reteach Worksheets)
3–6 Lesson 1-4, 1-5		Count, read and write whole numbers to 20.	Counts incorrectly. Writes down wrong number.	Math Adventures **Math Online** Concepts in Motion

Copyright © Macmillan/McGraw-Hill, a division of The McGraw-Hill Companies, Inc.

Identify the pattern unit. Circle it.
Extend the pattern. **Draw** what comes next.

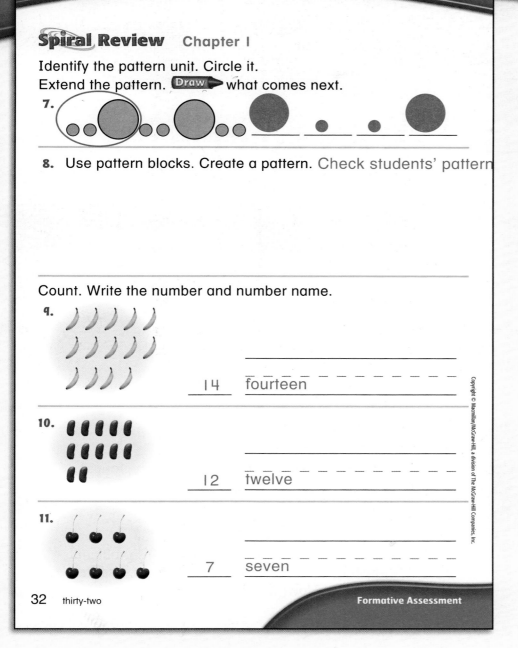

7.

8. Use pattern blocks. Create a pattern. Check students' pattern

Count. Write the number and number name.

9.

_14_ fourteen

10.

_12_ twelve

11.

_7_ seven

Formative Assessment

Spiral Review

Reviews Chapter 1

Objective: Review and assess mastery of skills and concepts from previous chapters.

Resources for Review

Based on student results, refer to these lessons for remediation.

- **Exercise 6: Lesson 1-1** (pp. 17–18)
- **Exercise 7: Lesson 1-2** (pp. 19–20)
- **Exercises 8–11: Lessons 1-4 and 1-5** (pp. 23–28)

Lesson Planner

Objective

Choose the best strategy to solve a problem.

Resources

Teacher Technology

- TeacherWorks

Real-World Problem Solving Library
Math and Social Studies: *Maps and Mail*
Use these leveled books to reinforce and extend
problem-solving skills and strategies.

Leveled for:

- **OL** On Level
- **ELL** Sheltered English
- **SP** Spanish

For additional support, see
the Real-World Problem
Solving Teacher Guide.

Daily Routine

Use these suggestions before beginning the lesson on p. 33.

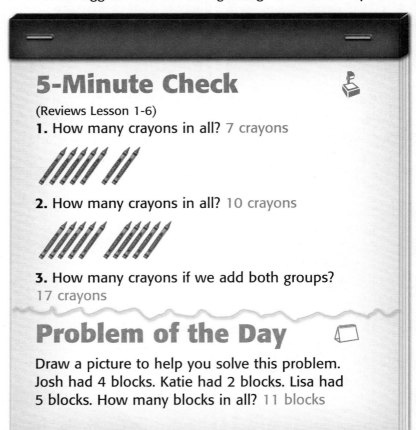

5-Minute Check

(Reviews Lesson 1-6)

1. How many crayons in all? 7 crayons

2. How many crayons in all? 10 crayons

3. How many crayons if we add both groups?
17 crayons

Problem of the Day

Draw a picture to help you solve this problem.
Josh had 4 blocks. Katie had 2 blocks. Lisa had
5 blocks. How many blocks in all? 11 blocks

LINE UP When students line up for recess, lunch, or
dismissal, ask them to hold up fingers to show
how to make various numbers: **Show me 4; show me 7;
show me 6;** and so on.

Differentiated Instruction

Small Group Options

Option 1
Below/Approaching Level **BL**   LOGICAL

Materials: paper, pencil, pattern blocks

- Have one group member create a pattern of shapes for other group members to complete.
- Explain that the student creating the pattern should trace pattern blocks to show the pattern, leaving a blank space for a missing shape in the middle of the pattern. The other group members should describe aloud in unison the pattern of shapes that come before and after the blank space to determine the missing shape.

- Continue until each group member has had a turn creating a pattern.

Option 2
English Language Learners **ELL**   INTERPERSONAL

Core Vocabulary: change, did, you/he/she
Common Use Verb: is/was

Do Math This lesson helps the student connect present and past tense language to math patterning.

- Demonstrate a simple AB pattern using movements such as claps, pats, foot stomps, or snaps.
- Have students mimic you.
- Ask a volunteer to switch your actions while keeping the AB pattern. Say: "**Change** the pattern." (NOTE: Even though the actions will change, you should still say: "A" "B.")
- Say: "How **did** (**you/he/she**) **change** the pattern?"
- Repeat with other volunteers as time permits.

Independent Work Options

Option 1
Early Finishers **OL** **AL**   LOGICAL, SOCIAL

Materials: math stories on index cards

- Have students choose a math story to solve in a small group.
- For each problem, students should begin by choosing a strategy to help them solve the problem.
- Group members should work together to use the strategy to solve the problem.

Option 2
Student Technology

Math Online ➤ macmillanmh.com

Math Adventures

Option 3
Learning Station: Music (p. 13G)

Direct students to the Music Learning Station for more opportunities to explore and extend the lesson concept.

1 Introduce

Activity • Review

Write and read aloud the following number story: *Six ladybugs were on a leaf. Three more ladybugs flew to the leaf. How many ladybugs are on the leaf?*

- Have students draw a picture to solve the problem.
- **How many ladybugs should you draw first?** 6 ladybugs
- **How many ladybugs should you draw next?** 3 ladybugs
- Have students count all the lady bugs.
- **How many ladybugs in all are on the leaf?** 9 ladybugs

2 Teach

Understand Using the questions, review what students know and what they need to find.

Plan Have them discuss and develop their strategy.

Solve Guide students to use a strategy to solve the problem.

- **What strategy can you use to help you solve the problem?** Sample answer: act it out using connecting cubes.
- **Where are the red beads?** on the ends
- **Where are the blue beads?** in the middle
- Have students use connecting cubes to model the necklace.

Check Have students look back at the problem to make sure that the answers fit the facts given.

- **Where are the yellow beads?** between each of the red and blue beads

! COMMON ERROR!

Rather than acting out the problem, some students may simply use connecting cubes to make up their own pattern. Have them read, and restate the problem in their own words. Have students place the cubes as described in a sentence before reading the next sentence.

Name _____

Problem-Solving Investigation

Main Idea
I will choose a strategy to solve a problem.

Your Mission: Find where the yellow beads are.

I have a necklace with 6 beads. There are 2 of each color: red, yellow, and blue. I have 1 red in the front and 1 red in the back. I have the 2 blue in the middle. Where are the yellow beads?

Understand
What do I need to find?
Circle it.

Plan
How will I solve the problem?

Solve
One way is to act it out.
See students' work.

One yellow bead is before the blue beads, and one yellow bead is after the blue beads.

Check
Look back.
Is my answer reasonable?

Check students' explanations.

Chapter 1   Lesson 7   thirty-three 33

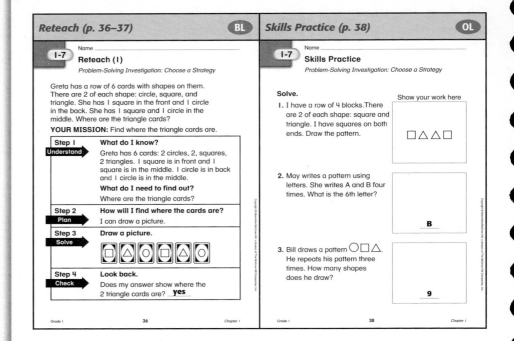

Reteach (p. 36–37) **BL**

1-7 Reteach (1)
Problem-Solving Investigation: Choose a Strategy

Greta has a row of 6 cards with shapes on them. There are 2 of each shape: circle, square, and triangle. She has 1 square in the front and 1 circle in the back. She has 1 square and 1 circle in the middle. Where are the triangle cards?

YOUR MISSION: Find where the triangle cards are.

Step 1 Understand	**What do I know?** Greta has 6 cards: 2 circles, 2 squares, 2 triangles. 1 square is in front and 1 square is in the middle. 1 circle is in back and 1 circle is in the middle. **What do I need to find out?** Where are the triangle cards?
Step 2 Plan	**How will I find where the cards are?** I can draw a picture.
Step 3 Solve	**Draw a picture.**
Step 4 Check	**Look back.** Does my answer show where the 2 triangle cards are? **yes**

Grade 1   36   Chapter 1

Skills Practice (p. 38) **OL**

1-7 Skills Practice
Problem-Solving Investigation: Choose a Strategy

Solve.

1. I have a row of 4 blocks. There are 2 of each shape: square and triangle. I have squares on both ends. Draw the pattern.

   Show your work here

2. May writes a pattern using letters. She writes A and B four times. What is the 6th letter? **B**

3. Bill draws a pattern ○□△. He repeats his pattern three times. How many shapes does he draw? **9**

Grade 1   38   Chapter 1

Choose a strategy. Solve.

1. Sumi made this pattern.
   How many stars did she use?

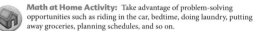

_____ 4 stars

2. Ally has 20 beads to make bracelets.
   Each bracelet has 10 beads.
   How many bracelets can she make?

_____ 2 bracelets

3. Doug and Ming play catch. Then Dion
   and Ella join them. How many children
   are playing catch?

_____ 4 children

4. The class seating chart went boy, girl,
   boy, girl, boy, girl. Who comes next?

_____ boy

34 thirty-four

Math at Home Activity: Take advantage of problem-solving opportunities such as riding in the car, bedtime, doing laundry, putting away groceries, planning schedules, and so on.

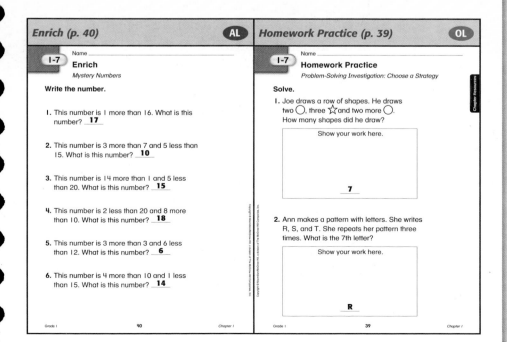

Problem-Solving Strategies
• Act it out
• Draw a picture
• Find a pattern

BL Alternate Teaching Strategy

If students have trouble choosing a strategy to solve problems . . .

Then use one of these reteaching options.

1 CRM **Daily Reteach Worksheet** (pp. 36–37)

2 **Use a Strategy** Read each problem to students. Ask them which strategy they would use to solve the problem.

• **How would you use that strategy to solve the problem?** Answers will vary depending on the problem and the strategy chosen.

3 Practice

Mixed Problem Solving

Exercise 1 Have the students touch the stars as they count them.

Exercise 2 Have the students use cubes to model the problem.

4 Assess

Formative Assessment

• **Look at Exercise 1. If Sumi adds five more figures to her pattern, how many stars would she use in all? Extend the pattern to solve the problem.** 6 stars

Share the following problem with students: *There were 4 bird nests. Each nest had 3 baby birds in it. How many baby birds are there?*

• **Which strategy would you use to solve this problem? Why?** Sample answer: I would draw a picture to find the total number of birds. After drawing the birds in each nest, I could count them.

Quick Check Are students continuing to struggle with choosing a strategy to solve a problem?

If Yes → CRM Reteach Worksheet (pp. 36–37)

If No → Independent Work Options (p. 33B)

CRM Skills Practice Worksheet (p. 38)

CRM Enrich Worksheet (p. 40)

Lesson Planner

Objective

Use concrete and pictorial models to compare numbers to 20.

Vocabulary

is greater than, **is less than**, **is equal to**

Resources

Materials: number cards, animal pictures, checkers

Manipulatives: connecting cubes

Literature Connection: *More, Fewer, Less* by Tana Hoban

Alternate Lesson: Adapt "Stack, Tell, Spin, and Win" on pp. 126 and 127 of *Math Their Way* for practice with the concept of greater than and less than.

Teacher Technology

🔘 TeacherWorks • Concepts in Motion • Math Songs Track 10 Lesson Plan

Focus on Math Background

Even the youngest students easily make visual comparisons of size. When comparing quantity first with concrete experiences and then pictorially, students need their skills in both counting and conservation of number. Students need to conserve the first number counted to make a comparison with the second number counted.

Students' understandings of equal are based on likenesses and differences, not initially on quantity, unless the comparison in sharing "equally" is made. When students begin to use number symbols for quantities they take the comparison and understandings of equality to an abstract level.

Daily Routine

Use these suggestions before beginning the lesson on p. 35.

5-Minute Check

(Reviews Lesson 1-7)
Display four pictures showing from 16 to 20 items. Have students count the items and write down the number for each of the four pictures. See students' work.

Problem of the Day

Write two numbers. Circle the greater number. See students' work.

LINE UP Pass out a number card to each student. Tell students that if their number is greater than 18, they should line up. Then tell students that if their number is less than 5 they should line up. Continue until all students are in line.

Building Math Vocabulary

Write on the chalkboard **is greater than**, **is less than**, and **is equal to**. Read aloud each vocabulary term and write the definition next to the term.

- Divide students into groups of two and give each group a number cube and twenty counters.
- Have students roll the number cube. Ask one student in each group to use counters to model a number less than the number rolled. The other student will model a number greater than the number rolled.
- Have students repeat with different numbers. Each time the students can switch roles.

Visual Vocabulary Cards

Use Visual Vocabulary Card(s) 23 and 24 to reinforce the vocabulary introduced in this lesson. (The Define/Example/Ask routine is printed on the back of each card.)

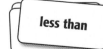
less than

Differentiated Instruction

Small Group Options

Option 1
SPATIAL, KINESTHETIC

Gifted and Talented (AL)

Materials: paper, magazine pictures with varying numbers of objects, glue

- Have students choose two pictures and count the number of objects in each picture.
- Help students glue the two pictures onto a sheet of paper. Ask them to write the number of objects in each picture below the picture.
- Have students decide which term, *greater than*, *less than*, or *equal to*, belongs between the two numbers. Students may write their answer in words between the numbers.

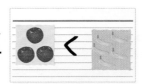

Option 2
LOGICAL, VISUAL/SPATIAL

English Language Learners (ELL)

Core Vocabulary: more, less, who
Common Use Verb: have/has

See Math This strategy introduces comparative vocabulary and activates background knowledge of greater and lesser amounts.

- Model getting blocks from a bucket with the cup. Place them on one side of the overhead. Have a student repeat and place on the other side.
- Say: "**Who has more?**"
- Count by 2s to show the one to one comparison.
- Say: "He **has more** (or **less**) than I **have**." Prompt your partner to say the reverse.
- Restate, saying: "Yes, you **have less** than I **have**."
- Repeat with pairs as time permits.

Use this worksheet to provide additional support for English Language Learners.

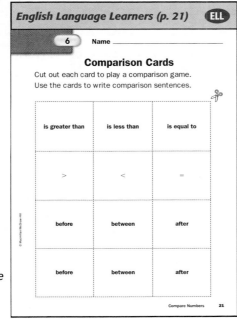

English Language Learners (p. 21) **ELL**

6 Name _____

Comparison Cards

Cut out each card to play a comparison game.
Use the cards to write comparison sentences.

is greater than	is less than	is equal to
>	<	=
before	between	after
before	between	after

Compare Numbers **21**

Independent Work Options

Option 1
SPATIAL, LOGICAL

Early Finishers (OL) (AL)

Materials: number cards from 0 to 11

- Have pairs of students shuffle the number cards and place them facedown on a table.
- Tell partners to each draw a card. Then they should lay the cards faceup, side by side.
- Have partners take turns saying the statement "X is greater than/less than Y" using the numbers turned up.

Option 2

Student Technology

Math Online macmillanmh.com

♪ Math Songs, "The Number Line" Track 10
🌐 Math Adventures

Option 3

Learning Station: Art (p.13H)

Direct students to the Art Learning Station for more opportunities to explore the lesson concept.

Option 4

Problem-Solving Practice

Reinforce problem-solving skills and strategies with the Problem-Solving Practice worksheet.

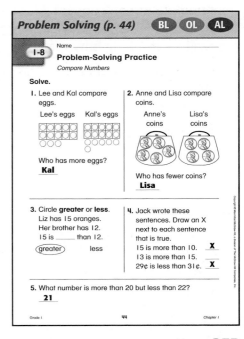

Problem Solving (p. 44) **BL** **OL** **AL**

Name _____

1-8 **Problem-Solving Practice**
Compare Numbers

Solve.

1. Lee and Kal compare eggs.

   Lee's eggs Kal's eggs

   Who has more eggs?
   Kal

2. Anne and Lisa compare coins.

   Anne's coins Lisa's coins

   Who has fewer coins?
   Lisa

3. Circle **greater** or **less**.
   Liz has 15 oranges.
   Her brother has 12.
   15 is _____ than 12.
   (greater)   less

4. Jack wrote these sentences. Draw an X next to each sentence that is true.
   15 is more than 10. **X**
   13 is more than 15.
   29¢ is less than 31¢. **X**

5. What number is more than 20 but less than 22?
   21

Grade 1   44   Chapter 1

1 Introduce

Activity Choice 1 • Hands-On

- Have each student use up to 20 animal pictures to make two "zoos" of different sizes.
- Place the "zoos" next to each other and help students make statements with "**is greater than**," "**is less than**," and "**is equal to**" to compare the number of animals in each "zoo".

Activity Choice 2 • Literature

Introduce the lesson with *More, Fewer, Less* by Tana Hoban. For additional support, see p. TR43.

MORE, FEWER, LESS
TANA HOBAN

2 Teach

Ask five students to stand at the front left of the room. Ask three other students to sit in chairs to the right of the first group.

- **Is the number of students standing *greater than, less than,* or *equal to* the number sitting?** greater than
- Have the groups switch sides so that the three students sitting are to the left.
- **Is the number of students sitting *greater than, less than,* or *equal to* the group standing?** less than
- **How can we move these students so there are equal numbers of students standing and sitting?** One student should move from sitting to standing.

Get Ready Use the section at the top of p. 35 to reinforce the lesson concept. Make sure students understand that when they compare numbers, they are really comparing how many.

Check Observe students as you work through Exercises 1–3 as a class.

 Exercise 3 Assess student comprehension before assigning practice exercises.

⚠ COMMON ERROR!

If students have difficulty with the concept of "greater than," remind them that they understand "more than." Twelve things is more than three things. The number 12 is greater than the number 3.

Name _____

Compare Numbers

Get Ready

Main Idea
I will compare numbers.

Vocabulary
is greater than
is less than
is equal to

12   **is greater than**   3

8   **is less than**   17

5   **is equal to**   5

✓ Check

Use 🎲 to model each number.
Compare. Circle the words.

Think
4 cubes are more than 2 cubes. So, 4 is greater than 2.

1.   4   _____   2
(is greater than)   is less than   is equal to

2.   8   _____   8
is greater than   is less than   (is equal to)

3. Talk About It   Is 11 less than 12? How do you know?

Sample answer: Yes. If I drew a picture of 11 objects and 12 objects there would be fewer objects in the group with 11.

Chapter 1   Lesson 8   thirty-five 35

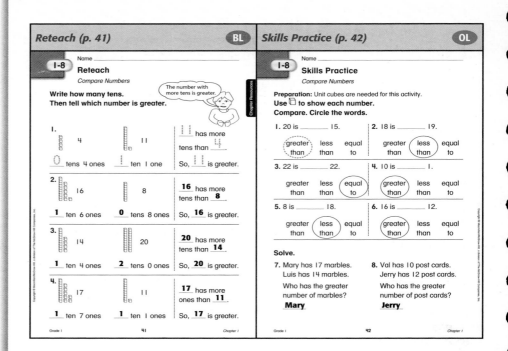

Reteach (p. 41) **BL**

Skills Practice (p. 42) **OL**

Use 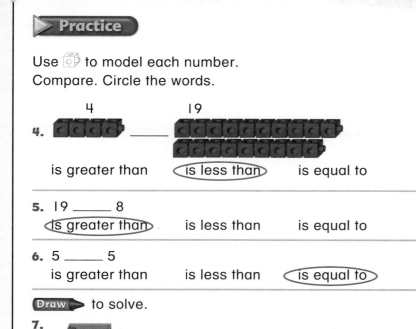 to model each number.
Compare. Circle the words.

4
19

4. _____

is greater than   (is less than)   is equal to

5. 19 _____ 8
   (is greater than)   is less than   is equal to

6. 5 _____ 5
   is greater than   is less than   (is equal to)

Draw ▶ to solve.

7.

is greater than

Sample answer: any number less than 13

8.

is less than

Sample answer: any number more than 4

H.O.T. Problem

> H.O.T. Problems require students to use Higher Order Thinking skills to solve problems.

9. **Thinking Math**

Julia has 4 marbles. Bill has 14 marbles.
Andrew has 11 marbles. Use 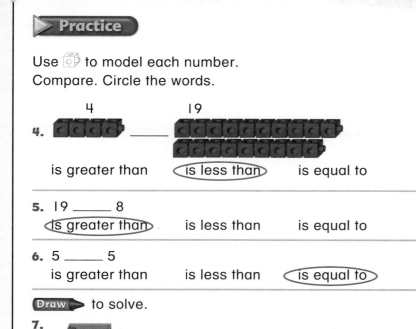 to model

Who has the most? _____Bill_____

Who has the least? _____Julia_____

36   thirty-six

Math at Home Activity: Say the number 15. Have your child give three numbers that are greater than 15 and three numbers that are less than 15.

Copyright © Macmillan/McGraw-Hill

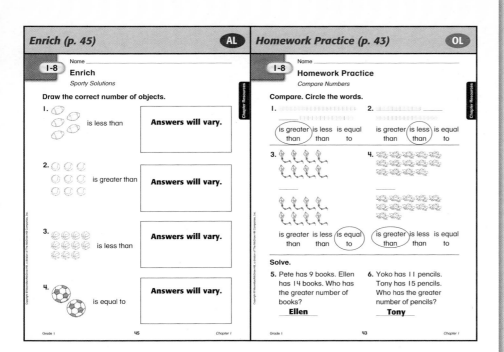

Enrich (p. 45) · **AL**

1-8 **Enrich**
Sporty Solutions

Draw the correct number of objects.

1. is less than · Answers will vary.

2. is greater than · Answers will vary.

3. is less than · Answers will vary.

4. is equal to · Answers will vary.

Grade 1   45   Chapter 1

Homework Practice (p. 43) · **OL**

1-8 **Homework Practice**
Compare Numbers

Compare. Circle the words.

1. (is greater than) / is less than / is equal to

2. is greater than / (is less than) / is equal to

3.

4.

is greater than / is less / (is equal to)

(is greater than) / is less / is equal to

Solve.

5. Pete has 9 books. Ellen has 14 books. Who has the greater number of books?
   Ellen

6. Yoko has 11 pencils. Tony has 15 pencils. Who has the greater number of pencils?
   Tony

Grade 1   43   Chapter 1

---

③ Practice

Differentiate practice, using these leveled assignments for Exercises 4–9.

Level	Assignment
BL Below/Approaching Level	Guide students in using counters to compare numbers.
OL On Level	Complete exercises independently, using counters as needed.
AL Above/Beyond Level	Complete exercises independently.

④ Assess

✓ Formative Assessment

Which number is greater—15 or 9? 15 **Is 12** *greater than* **or** *less than* **15?** less than Have students randomly choose two number cards and write a comparison number sentence with the cards.

WRITING IN ▶MATH Ask students if they have more shoes or more socks. Have them record their answers in their Math Journal.

Quick Check | **Are students continuing to struggle with comparing numbers?**

If Yes ⟶ Strategic Intervention Guide (p. 30)

If No ⟶ Independent Work Options (p. 35B)
[CRM] Skills Practice Worksheet (p. 42)
[CRM] Enrich Worksheet (p. 45)

Extra Practice

Review Lessons 1-4 to 1-8

Objective: Review and assess mastery of previous lessons' skills and concepts.

- Review with students how to compare numbers.
- Review *is greater than, is less than,* and *is equal to* with students.

Practice with Technology

Math Online ▷ Have students visit macmillanmh.com for additional practice with online activities, games, and quizzes.

Extra Practice is found in every chapter to give students additional review opportunities with chapter concepts and skills.

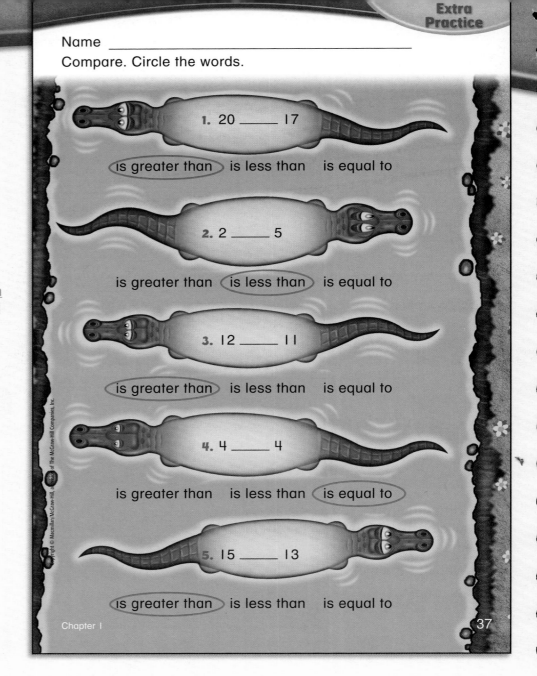

Name _____

Compare. Circle the words.

1. 20 _____ 17

(is greater than)   is less than   is equal to

2. 2 _____ 5

is greater than   (is less than)   is equal to

3. 12 _____ 11

(is greater than)   is less than   is equal to

4. 4 _____ 4

is greater than   is less than   (is equal to)

5. 15 _____ 13

(is greater than)   is less than   is equal to

Chapter 1   37

Game Time

The Bigger the Better
Comparing Numbers

Play with a partner.
- Put your ♟ on **START**.
- Choose a 🎲 Toss it the same time as your partner.
- Whoever rolls the greater number gets to move one space.
- If you roll the same number, roll again.
- The first person to reach **FINISH** wins.

You Will Need

START
1 2 3 4 5 6 7 8 9 10 11
FINISH

38 thirty-eight

Differentiated Practice

Use these leveling suggestions to differentiate the game for all learners.

Level	Assignment
BL Below/Approaching Level	Allow students to use connecting cubes to model each number rolled. Remind students that the more cubes used, the greater the number.
OL On Level	Have students play the game with the rules as written.
AL Above/Beyond Level	Have students move the same number of spaces as they roll on the number cube.

The Bigger the Better

Math Concept:
Comparing Numbers

Manipulatives: game pieces, two number cubes

Introduce the game on p. 38 to your students to play as a class, in small groups, or at a learning workstation to review concepts introduced in this chapter.

Instructions

- Put students into pairs.
- Give each student a number cube.
- Students should toss their number cubes at the same time.
- Whoever rolls the greater number gets to move one space.
- If students roll the same number, they can roll again.
- The first student to *Finish* wins.

Extend the Game

Have students continue playing, but head back towards *Start*.

> *Game Time* activities reinforce chapter concepts and skills. The Teacher Edition offers suggestions for differentiation and extension.

Lesson Planner

Objective
Use concrete and pictorial models to order whole numbers to 20.

Vocabulary
number line, order, before, after, between

Resources
Materials: pencils or crayons, strips of 1-inch grid paper, tape, scissors, number cards 1–20, ruler

Manipulatives: connecting cubes

Literature Connection: *One Hundred Is a Family* by Pam Munoz Ryan

Alternate Lesson: Use "Count and Turn" on p. 93 of *Math Their Way* to provide practice ordering numbers 1 through 20.

> *Concepts in Motion* are online animations of key concepts. They are also provided on StudentWorks Plus and TeacherWorks Plus.

Teacher Technology
- 💿 TeacherWorks • Concepts in Motion • Math Songs Track 10 Lesson Plan

Focus on Math Background
Young students come to school knowing their age. They easily tell you what age they used to be and what age they are going to be. They can also tell you that their older siblings and parents are "more" than they are and any younger siblings are "less" than they are. This is an opportunity to do an age number line "segment" comparing the ages in the classroom: 5, 6, 7, or 6, 7, 8. The math vocabulary for this lesson can be used along with pointing out that many students in the classroom are the "same age."

Daily Routine

Use these suggestions before beginning the lesson on p. 39.

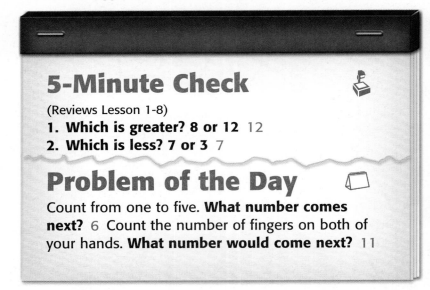

5-Minute Check
(Reviews Lesson 1-8)
1. **Which is greater? 8 or 12** 12
2. **Which is less? 7 or 3** 7

Problem of the Day
Count from one to five. **What number comes next?** 6 Count the number of fingers on both of your hands. **What number would come next?** 11

LINE UP Have students count off. Have a student with a number between 7 and 9 line up first. Then have students with numbers after 9 line up. Have students with numbers before 7 line up next. Finally, have students with the numbers right before and after 8 line up.

Building Math Vocabulary
- Write on the chalkboard the vocabulary words **number line, order, before, after, between** and the definitions.
- Encourage students to give examples or draw pictures to show what they know about each word.
- Show students how a 12-inch ruler can be a horizontal number line and how a thermometer can be a vertical number line.

Visual Vocabulary Cards
Use Visual Vocabulary Card 30 to reinforce the vocabulary introduced in this lesson. (The Define/Example/Ask routine is printed on the back of each card.)

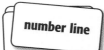
number line

Differentiated Instruction

Small Group Options

SPATIAL, KINESTHETIC

Option 1 — Below Level (BL)

Materials: number cards from 0 to 20, 2-ft length of adding machine tape

- Have pairs of students take turns choosing a number card and placing it on the adding machine tape.
- Explain that each time students draw a number, they should place it in order with the numbers already on the tape. Point out that they may need to move cards to make room to lay down their card in the correct order.

Option 2 — English Language Learners (ELL)

LINGUISTIC, KINESTHETIC

Core Vocabulary: before, after, in a line
Common Use Verb: is standing

Talk Math This strategy makes students respond and vocalize placement and relative position vocabulary.

- Prompt students to line up (one behind the other, all facing you).
- Pointing at each student, say: "(Student A) *is standing before* (Student B). (Student B) *is standing after* (Student A) and **before** (Student C)."
- Have students describe their position, e.g., Student A would say: "*I am standing* **after** Andres and **before** Luis."
- Have students line up in smaller groups and repeat the activity.

Use this worksheet to provide additional support for English Language Learners.

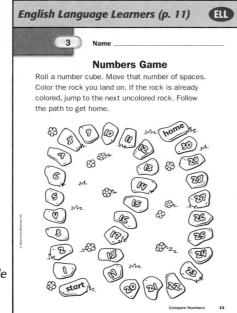

English Language Learners (p. 11) (ELL)

3 Name _____

Numbers Game

Roll a number cube. Move that number of spaces. Color the rock you land on. If the rock is already colored, jump to the next uncolored rock. Follow the path to get home.

Compare Numbers 11

Independent Work Options

SPATIAL, LOGICAL

Option 1 — Early Finishers (OL) (AL)

Materials: paper, markers, stapler

- Have students fold two sheets of paper in half to make a booklet. Staple the pages together on the fold.
- On the front cover, have students write *Picture Dictionary, Math Word Book,* or a similar title.
- Display the vocabulary terms. Have students write one term and its definition on each page of their book. Show students how to use the Glossary as a guide.
- Have students complete their book by drawing a picture to illustrate each term.

Option 2 — Student Technology

Math Online macmillanmh.com

♪ Math Songs, "The Number Line" Track 10

Math Adventures

Option 3 — Learning Station: Music (p. 13G)

Direct students to the Music Learning Station for more opportunities to explore the lesson concept.

Option 4 — Problem-Solving Practice

Reinforce problem-solving skills and strategies with the Problem-Solving Practice worksheet.

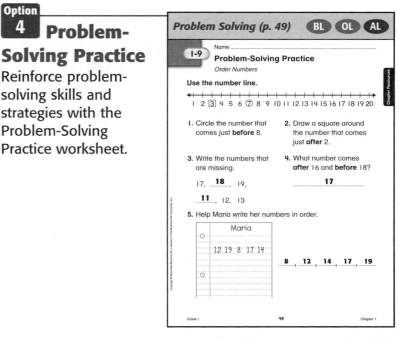

Problem Solving (p. 49) (BL) (OL) (AL)

1-9 Name _____
Problem-Solving Practice
Order Numbers

Use the number line.

1 2 ③ 4 5 6 ⑦ 8 9 10 11 12 13 14 15 16 17 18 19 20

1. Circle the number that comes just **before** 8.

2. Draw a square around the number that comes just **after** 2.

3. Write the numbers that are missing.

17, __18__, 19,

__11__, 12, 13

4. What number comes **after** 16 and **before** 18?

__17__

5. Help Maria write her numbers in order.

Maria

12 19 8 17 14

__8__, __12__, __14__, __17__, __19__

Grade 1   49   Chapter 1

① Introduce

Activity Choice 1 • Hands-On

- Have students make **number lines** by taping graph paper strips end-to-end to get twenty sections.
- Have students write the numbers 1 through 20 in the squares of their number line.
- Draw a number card and have students point to the number on their number line. Ask them to use the words **after, before,** and **between** to describe the **order** of the number.
- Have the students use cubes to model a number that comes before and a number that comes after the number on the card. **Which number did you use the most cubes to model?** See students' work.

Activity Choice 2 • Literature

Introduce the lesson with *One Hundred Is a Family* by Pam Munoz Ryan. For additional support, see p. TR43.

② Teach

- Display a vertical number line. Write 3 and 8 on the chalkboard. Then have students find both numbers on the number line.
- **Which number is lower?** 3 **Which number is higher?** 8
- Repeat the activity with various numbers.
- Have students describe how to move from least to greatest on a vertical number line.
- Explain to students that higher numbers are greater than the lower numbers.

Get Ready Use the section at the top of student p. 39 to teach the lesson concept.

Check Observe students as you work through Exercises 1–5 as a class.

 Exercise 5 Assess student comprehension before assigning practice exercises.

⚠ COMMON ERROR!

Students may have trouble ordering numbers that are not consecutive. To help students visualize the order, have them locate the numbers on a number line and point to the number that comes first.

Name _____

Order Numbers

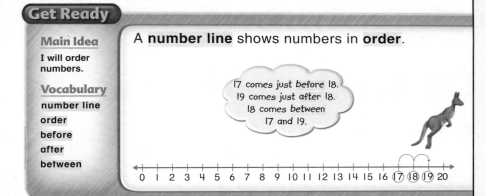

Get Ready

Main Idea
I will order numbers.

Vocabulary
number line
order
before
after
between

A **number line** shows numbers in **order**.

17 comes just before 18.
19 comes just after 18.
18 comes between 17 and 19.

0 1 2 3 4 5 6 7 8 9 10 11 12 13 14 15 16 ⑰ ⑱ ⑲ 20

✓ Check

Write the missing number.

0 1 2 3 4 5 6 7 8 9 10 11 12 13 14 15 16 17 18 19 20

1. 3 4 **5**

2. **11** 12 13

3. 8 **9** 10

4. 16 **17** 18

5. **Talk About It** How do you know which number comes just before 7? Look on the number line and one to the left. 6 comes before 7.

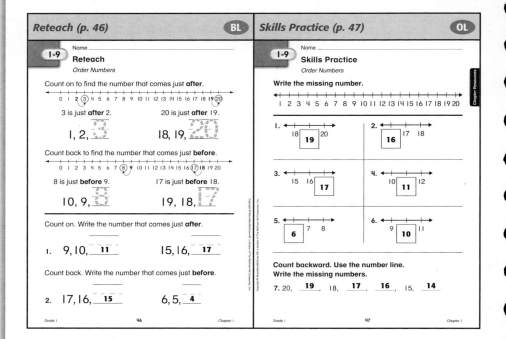

Reteach (p. 46) BL

1-9 Reteach
Order Numbers

Count on to find the number that comes just **after**.

0 1 2 ③ 4 5 6 7 8 9 10 11 12 13 14 15 16 17 18 19 ⑳

3 is just **after** 2.   20 is just **after** 19.

1, 2, __   18, 19, __

Count back to find the number that comes just **before**.

0 1 2 3 4 5 6 7 ⑧ 9 10 11 12 13 14 15 16 ⑰ 18 19 20

8 is just **before** 9.   17 is just **before** 18.

10, 9, __   19, 18, __

Count on. Write the number that comes just **after**.

1. 9, 10, **11**   15, 16, **17**

Count back. Write the number that comes just **before**.

2. 17, 16, **15**   6, 5, **4**

Grade 1   46   Chapter 1

Skills Practice (p. 47) OL

1-9 Skills Practice
Order Numbers

Write the missing number.

1 2 3 4 5 6 7 8 9 10 11 12 13 14 15 16 17 18 19 20

1. 18 **19** 20   2. **16** 17 18

3. 15 16 **17**   4. 10 **11** 12

5. **6** 7 8   6. 9 **10** 11

Count backward. Use the number line. Write the missing numbers.

7. 20, **19**, 18, **17**, **16**, 15, **14**

Grade 1   47   Chapter 1

Practice

Write the missing number.

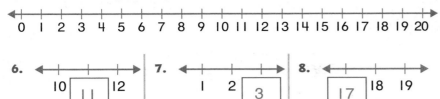

0 1 2 3 4 5 6 7 8 9 10 11 12 13 14 15 16 17 18 19 20

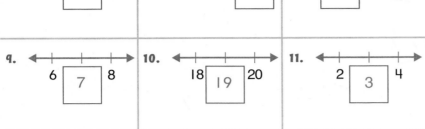

6. 10 **11** 12

7. 1 2 **3**

8. **17** 18 19

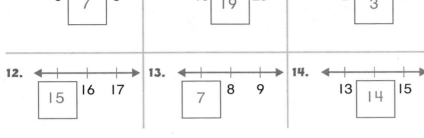

9. 6 **7** 8

10. 18 **19** 20

11. 2 **3** 4

12. **15** 16 17

13. **7** 8 9

14. 13 **14** 15

Problem Solving

Number Sense Count back. Write the missing numbers.

15. 10, 9, 8, __7__, 6, __5__, __4__

16. 17, 16, __15__, __14__, 13, 12, __11__

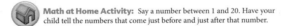

Math at Home Activity: Say a number between 1 and 20. Have your child tell the numbers that come just before and just after that number.

40   forty

Copyright © Macmillan/McGraw-Hill, a division of The McGraw-Hill Companies, Inc.

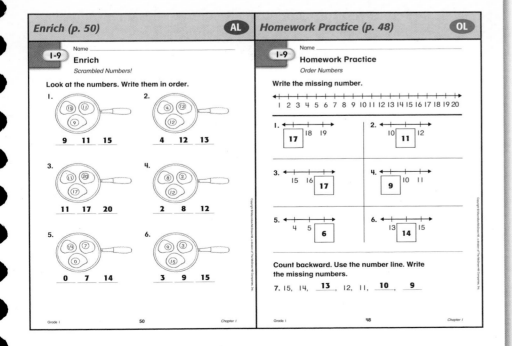

Enrich (p. 50) **AL**

Name _____
1-9 Enrich
Scrambled Numbers!

Look at the numbers. Write them in order.

1. 9 11 15

2. 4 12 13

3. 11 17 20

4. 2 8 12

5. 0 7 14

6. 3 9 15

Grade 1   50   Chapter 1

Homework Practice (p. 48) **OL**

Name _____
1-9 Homework Practice
Order Numbers

Write the missing number.

1 2 3 4 5 6 7 8 9 10 11 12 13 14 15 16 17 18 19 20

1. **17** 18 19

2. 10 **11** 12

3. 15 16 **17**

4. **9** 10 11

5. 4 5 **6**

6. 13 **14** 15

Count backward. Use the number line. Write the missing numbers.

7. 15, 14, __13__, 12, 11, __10__, 9

Grade 1   48   Chapter 1

BL Alternate Teaching Strategy

If students have trouble ordering numbers . . .

Then use one of these reteach options.

1 CRM **Daily Reteach Worksheet** (p. 46)

2 **Manipulatives** Have students use a ruler to find the numbers that they need to put in order.

3 Practice

Differentiate practice, using these leveled assignments for Exercises 6–16.

Level	Assignment
BL Below/ Approaching Level	Have students use their number lines to complete the lesson.
OL On Level	Complete exercises independently.
AL Above/Beyond Level	Complete exercises independently, adding a comparison statement when appropriate.

4 Assess

Formative Assessment

Provide number cards from 4 to 17. Have students draw a number card. **What three numbers come right before your number? What three numbers come right after your number?**

WRITING IN ►MATH Have students record in their Math Journal three things they do each morning in the correct order. Have students number their pictures.

Quick Check **Are students continuing to struggle with ordering numbers?**

If Yes → Strategic Intervention Guide (p. 26)

If No → Independent Work Options (p. 39B)
CRM Skills Practice Worksheet (p. 47)
CRM Enrich Worksheet (p. 50)

These animals have patterns too!

Circle the animal you think has more black stripes.

Butterfly   (Zebra)

D

The cross-curricular **Real-Word Problem Solving** lessons connect math to real-world applications.

Problem Solving
in Science

Real-World MATH

Patterns are everywhere! This coral snake has a pattern on it.

This book belongs to

_____

A

Lesson Planner

Objective

Identify and describe patterns found in nature.

National Standard

Students should develop an understanding of the characteristics of organisms.

Vocabulary

pattern

Activate Prior Knowledge

Before you turn students' attention to the pages, discuss how an animal's skin or coat protects it.

- **Why do animals have colors and designs on their skin and coats?** Sample answer: It helps them blend in with their surroundings.

- **What patterns have you seen on animals' skins and coats?** Sample answer: Fish have colors and designs on their skin.

Ask students to find out more about patterns on animals as they read the information in the lesson.

This caterpillar has a pattern too.

The caterpillar changes into this butterfly! Can you find a pattern on the butterfly?

B

Show a color pattern on the butterfly below.

Check students' drawings.

C

Create the Book

Guide students to create their book.

- Have them fold the page in half.
- Ask them to write their name on page A.
- Explain that page A is the front cover and page D is the back cover. If necessary, have them practice flipping through the book pages in order.
- Guide students in reading the information and problems on each page.

Use the Student Pages

Have students work individually or in pairs to answer the questions on pages B–D.

Page C Students can refer to the picture of the monarch on page C to help create their pattern. Help students see that the same design appears on each wing.

Page D Have students tell about the patterns on the caterpillar and the zebra.

WRITING IN ▶MATH Help students write a sentence describing the pattern on the snake, caterpillar, butterfly, or zebra.

Extend the Activity

Have students look through picture books or magazines to find other examples of animals with patterns on their skin or coat.

 **Dinah Zike's Foldables**

If students have not completed their Foldables, guide them to create and fill in the appropriate information using the information on pp. 13 and 31.

You may choose to use the Foldable to help students review the concepts presented in this chapter and as a tool for studying for the Chapter Test.

Lesson 1–9 Sequence the Matchbook Foldables to form a number line. Find numbers before, after, and between given numbers. Observe how a number line sequences numbers or places them "in order."

Vocabulary Review

Review chapter vocabulary using one of the following options.

- **Visual Vocabulary Cards** (23, 24, 30, and 33)
- **eGlossary** at macmillanmh.com

Vocabulary Test

CRM Chapter 1 Resource Masters (p. 57)
Assess Student comprehension of the chapter vocabulary with the Vocabulary Test.

Math Online > **Chapter Test**
Alternative summative assessment options are available online at macmillanmh.com.

The Chapter Review/Test can be used for practice or assessment. Five different forms of summative assessment are also found in the Chapter Resource Masters.

Name _____

Vocabulary

Complete the sentences.

Word Bank

number line
pattern unit

1. A _____ pattern unit _____ is a repeating part of a pattern.

2. A _____ number line _____ is a line with numbers on it.

Concepts

3. Identify the pattern unit. Circle it. Extend the pattern. **Draw** what comes next.

4. Use pattern blocks. Create a pattern. See students' drawings.

5. Draw the missing shape.

Chapter 1   forty-three **43**

✓ Chapter 1 Project

Pattern Mural

Alone, in pairs, or in small groups, have students discuss the results of their completed chapter project with the class. Assess their work using the Chapter Project rubric found in Chapter 1 Resource Masters on page 62.

Count. Write the number. Write the number name.

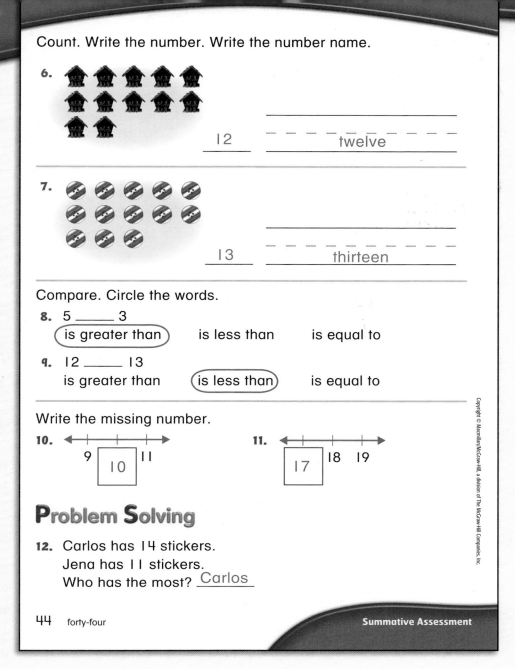

6. 12 twelve

7. 13 thirteen

Compare. Circle the words.

8. 5 _____ 3
(is greater than)   is less than   is equal to

9. 12 _____ 13
is greater than   (is less than)   is equal to

Write the missing number.

10. 9 [10] 11

11. [17] 18 19

Problem Solving

12. Carlos has 14 stickers.
Jena has 11 stickers.
Who has the most? Carlos

Summative Assessment

Summative Assessment

Use these alternate leveled chapter tests to differentiate assessment for the specific needs of your students.

Leveled Chapter 1 Tests			
Form	**Type**	**Level**	**CRM Pages**
1	Multiple Choice	BL	64–65
2A	Multiple Choice	OL	66–67
2B	Multiple Choice	OL	68–69
2C	Multiple Choice	AL	70–71
2D	Free Response	AL	72–73

BL = below/approaching grade level
OL = on grade level
AL = above/beyond grade level

ExamView Assessment Suite Customize and create multiple versions of your Chapter Test and their test answer keys.

Data-Driven Decision Making

Based on the results of the Chapter Test, use the following to review concepts that continue to present students with problems.

Exercises	State/Local Standards	What's the Math?	Error Analysis	Resources for Review
3–5		Identify and extend a pattern. Create a pattern.	Does not understand pattern. Does not draw correct number of shapes.	Strategic Intervention Guide (p. 34) CRM Chapter 1 Resource Masters (Reteach Worksheets)
6–7		Count, read, and write whole numbers.	Does not add correctly.	**Math Online** Concepts in Motion Math Adventures
8–9		Compare numbers using symbols for less than, equal to, and greater than.	Confuses symbols for less than, equal to, greater than and circles incorrect answer.	
10–11		Compare and order numbers. Use a number line.	Goes wrong way when filling in number line and writes incorrect answer.	

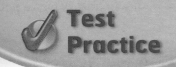

Test Practice

Formative Assessment

- Use Student Edition pp. 45–46 as practice and cumulative review. The questions are written in the same style as many state tests.
- You can also use these two pages to benchmark student progress, or as an alternate homework assignment.

Additional practice pages can be found in the Chapter 1 Resource Master.

[CRM] Chapter 1 Resource Masters
Cumulative Test Practice

- **Multiple Choice format** (pp. 64–69, 74)
- **Free Response format** (pp. 70–73, 75)

ExamView Assessment Suite Create practice worksheets or tests that align to your state standards.

Math Online For additional practice, visit macmillanmh.com.

Test Practice exercises help students solidify their knowledge of multiple choice format.

Name _____

Listen as your teacher reads each problem.
Choose the correct answer.

1.

2   3   5   6

4. ○ □ ♡ ○ □ ♡ ○ □

○   □   ☆   ♡

2.

5.
13   14   15

12   13   14   16

3.

4   6   7   8

6.

Chapter 1   forty-five **45**

Test-Taking Tips

For the Teacher

- It may be helpful to review the vocabulary words and provide examples.
- Tell students to work on one question at a time.

For the Student

- Tell students where to put their name on their test.
- Be sure to tell students to write their first and last name on their test.

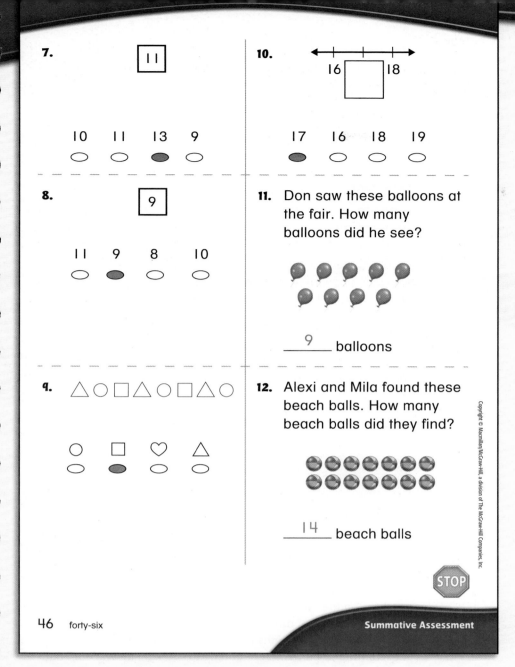

7.

11

10	11	13	9
○	○	●	○

8.

9

11	9	8	10
○	●	○	○

9. △○□△○□△○

○	□	♡	△
○	●	○	○

10.

16 [ ] 18

17	16	18	19
●	○	○	○

11. Don saw these balloons at the fair. How many balloons did he see?

_____9_____ balloons

12. Alexi and Mila found these beach balls. How many beach balls did they find?

_____14_____ beach balls

STOP

Summative Assessment

Test Directions for Teachers

Read the following directions to students before they begin the test. Then read each question followed by a pause to allow students time to work on the problem and choose an answer. The first test item can be worked as a class example.

- **Write your name at the top of the page.**
- **I am going to read each question to you. Listen carefully to the entire question before you choose your answer.**

Multiple Choice

1. Look at the bananas. How many bananas in all?
2. Look at the groups of cars. Which group has 4 cars? Mark the group.
3. John has 6 juice boxes. What number is 6?
4. Look at the pattern. What comes next in the pattern? Mark the shape.
5. Look at the number line. What number comes just before 15?
6. Look at the beach pails. Which group has 7 beach pails?

- **Turn the page over.**

7. What number is greater than 11?
8. What number is equal to 9?
9. Look at the pattern. What comes next in the pattern?
10. Look at the number line. What number comes between 16 and 18?

Short Response

11. Don saw these balloons at the fair. How many balloons did he see?
12. Alexi and Mila found these beach balls. How many beach balls did they find?

Chapter Overview

Chapter-at-a-Glance

In Chapter 2, the emphasis is on modeling and solving simple addition problems, writing addition sentences, and choosing a strategy to solve problems.

Lesson	Math Objective	State/Local Standards
2-1 **Addition Stories** (pp. 51–52)	Use counters to show addition stories.	
2-2 **Modeling Addition** (pp. 53–54)	Add by joining two groups.	
2-3 **Addition Sentences** (pp. 55–56)	Write addition sentences using + and =.	
2-4 **Adding Zero** (pp. 59–60)	Find sums by adding zero.	
2-5 **Problem-Solving Strategy: Write a Number Sentence** (pp. 61–62)	Use the *write a number sentence* strategy to solve problems.	
2-6 **Ways to Make 4, 5, and 6** (pp. 65–66)	Use counters to make sums of 4, 5, and 6.	
2-7 **Ways to Make 7, 8, and 9** (pp. 67–68)	Use counters to make sums of 7, 8, and 9.	
2-8 **Ways to Make 10, 11, and 12** (pp. 69–72)	Use a ten-frame and counters to make sums of 10, 11, and 12.	
2-9 **Problem-Solving Investigation: Choose a Strategy** (pp. 73–74)	Choose the best strategy to solve a problem.	
2-10 **Vertical Addition** (pp. 75–76)	Write addition facts horizontally and vertically.	

Develop Addition Concepts

BIG Idea Up to this point, the experiences students have had with addition have been very concrete. In first grade, addition becomes more abstract as students move from modeling addition to writing number sentences. They also become more familiar with the addition sign (+). In this chapter, students discover many ways to add single-digit numbers with sums up to 12. Students also learn to write addition facts vertically.

Algebra In Lesson 2-1, students begin using manipulatives to create addition stories. Using models will lay the foundation for using algebra tiles when learning equation concepts.

In Lesson 2-3, students begin to understand the idea of an equation as two balanced equalities.

Focal Points and Connections

G1-FP1 *Number and Operations* and *Algebra:* **Developing understandings of addition and subtraction and strategies for basic addition facts and related subtraction facts**

Children develop strategies for adding and subtracting whole numbers on the basis of their earlier work with small numbers. They use a variety of models, including discrete objects, length-based models (e.g., lengths of connecting cubes), and number lines, to model "part-whole," "adding to," "taking away from," and "comparing" situations to develop an understanding of the meanings of addition and subtraction and strategies to solve such arithmetic problems. Children understand the connections between counting and the operations of addition and subtraction (e.g., adding two is the same as "counting on" two). They use properties of addition (commutativity and associativity) to add whole numbers, and they create and use increasingly sophisticated strategies based on these properties (e.g., "making tens") to solve addition and subtraction problems involving basic facts. By comparing a variety of solution strategies, children relate addition and subtraction as inverse operations.

Skills Trace
Vertical Alignment

Kindergarten
In kindergarten, students learned to:
- Understand and describe simple addition problems.
- Use concrete objects to solve addition problems.
- Show different ways to solve to 9.

First Grade
In this chapter, students learn to:
- Model and solve addition problems.
- Write addition sentences.
- Use number sentences to solve problems.

After this chapter, students learn to:
- Use different strategies to solve sums to 12.
  (Chapter 5)
- Use different strategies to solve sums to 20.
  (Chapter 10)

Second Grade
In second grade, students learn to:
- Use properties to solve addition problems.
- Use different strategies to solve two-digit addition problems.
- Use different strategies to solve three-digit addition problems.

Backmapping and Vertical Alignment
McGraw-Hill's *Math Connects* program was conceived and developed with the final results in mind: student success in Algebra 1 and beyond. The authors, using the **NCTM Focal Points and Focal Connections** as their guide, developed this brand-new series by back-mapping from Algebra 1 concepts, and vertically aligning the topics so that they build upon prior skills and concepts and serve as a foundation for future topics.

Math Vocabulary
The following math vocabulary words for Chapter 2 are listed in the Glossary of the *Student Edition*. You can find interactive definitions in 13 languages in the *eGlossary* at macmillanmh.com.

add to join together sets to find the total, or sum (p. 53)

addition sentence an expression using numbers and the + and = sign (p. 55)

equals (=) having the same value or is the same as (p. 55)

plus (+) a symbol to show addition (p. 55)

sum the answer to an addition problem (p. 55)

$$2 + 4 = \overset{\downarrow}{6}$$

zero the number zero equals none or nothing (p. 59)

Visual Vocabulary Cards Use the Visual Vocabulary Cards 1, 16, 38, and 47 to introduce and reinforce the vocabulary in this chapter. (The Define/Example/Ask routine is printed on the back of each card.)

Chapter Planner

Suggested Pacing		
Instruction	**Review and Assessment**	**TOTAL**
10 days	2 days	**12 days**

✓ Diagnostic Assessment
Are You Ready? (p. 48)

	Lesson 2-1 Pacing: 1 day	**Lesson 2-2** Pacing: 1 day	**Lesson 2-3** Pacing: 1 day
Lesson/ Objective	**Addition Stories** (pp. 51–52) **Objective:** Use counters to show addition stories.	**Modeling Addition** (pp. 53–54) **Objective:** Add by joining two groups.	**Addition Sentences** (pp. 55–56) **Objective:** Write addition sentences using + and =.
State/Local Standards			
Math Vocabulary		**add**	**addition sentence plus (+) equals (=) sum**
Lesson Resources	**Materials** overhead projector **Manipulatives** two-colored counters **Other Resources** CRM Leveled Worksheets (pp. 6–10) 🖌 Daily Reteach • 5-Minute Check 📖 Problem of the Day	**Materials** WorkMat 3: Part-Part-Whole, paper, overhead projector **Manipulatives** two-colored counters **Other Resources** CRM Leveled Worksheets (pp. 11–15) 🖌 Daily Reteach • 5-Minute Check 📖 Problem of the Day	**Manipulatives** connecting cubes **Other Resources** CRM Leveled Worksheets (pp. 16–20) 🖌 Daily Reteach • 5-Minute Check 📖 Problem of the Day
Technology [Math Online]	🎵 Math Song Track 11 🌐 Math Adventures Concepts in Motion	🎵 Math Song Track 11 🌐 Math Adventures Concepts in Motion	🎵 Math Song Track 11 Concepts in Motion
Reaching All Learners	Gifted and Talented, p. 51B **AL** English Learners, p. 51B **ELL** Early Finishers, p. 51B **OL** **AL**	Gifted and Talented, p. 53B **AL** English Learners, p. 53B **ELL** Early Finishers, p. 53B **OL** **AL**	Gifted and Talented, p. 55B **AL** English Learners, p. 55B **ELL** Early Finishers, p. 55B **OL** **AL**
Alternate Lessons	*Math Their Way*, pp. 181–182 *IMPACT Mathematics*: Units A and C	*Math Their Way*, p. 174 *IMPACT Mathematics*: Units A and C	*Math Their Way*, pp. 238 *IMPACT Mathematics*: Units C and G
			Extra Practice (p. 57) **Game Time:** Snack Time (p. 58)

KEY
BL Below/ Approaching Level   **OL** On Level   **AL** Above/Beyond Level   **ELL** English Learners

SE Student Edition   **TE** Teacher Edition   **CRM** Chapter 3 Resource Masters   💿 CD-Rom

🖌 Transparency   📖 Flip Chart   📖 Real-World Problem Solving Library

Lesson 2-4
Pacing: 1 day

Adding Zero
(pp. 59–60)

Objective: Find sums by adding zero.

Math Vocabulary

zero

Materials
dominoes

Other Resources
- [CRM] Leveled Worksheets (pp. 21–25)
- Daily Reteach • 5-Minute Check
- Problem of the Day

- ♪ Math Song Track 11
- Math Adventures
- Concepts in Motion

Below Level, p. 59B **BL**
English Learners, p. 59B **ELL**
Early Finishers, p. 59B **OL** **AL**

Math Their Way, pp. 238–239
IMPACT Mathematics: Units A and G

Lesson 2-5
Pacing: 1 day

Problem-Solving Strategy
Write a Number Sentence
(pp. 61–62)

Objective: Use the *write a number sentence* strategy to solve problems.

Materials
blank transparency, overhead projector

Other Resources
- [CRM] Leveled Worksheets (pp. 26–30)
- Daily Reteach • 5-Minute Check
- Problem of the Day

Gifted and Talented, p. 61B **AL**
English Learners, p. 61B **ELL**
Early Finishers, p. 61B **OL** **AL**

Lesson 2-6
Pacing: 1 day

Ways to Make 4, 5, and 6
(pp. 65–66)

Objective: Use counters to make sums of 4, 5, and 6.

Materials
WorkMat 3: Part-Part-Whole, dominoes

Manipulatives
two-colored counters

Other Resources
- [CRM] Leveled Worksheets (pp. 31–35)
- Daily Reteach • 5-Minute Check
- Problem of the Day

- ♪ Math Song Track 11
- Math Adventures

Below Level, p. 65B **BL**
English Learners, p. 65B **ELL**
Early Finishers, p. 65B **OL** **AL**

Math Their Way, p. 246
IMPACT Mathematics: Unit A

Right column labels:

- Lesson/Objective
- State/Local Standards
- Math Vocabulary
- Lesson Resources
- Technology — Math Online
- Reaching All Learners
- Alternate Lessons

✓ Formative Assessment
- Mid-Chapter Check (p. 63)
- Spiral Review (p. 64)

	Lesson 2-7 Pacing: 1 day	**Lesson 2-8** Pacing: 1 day	**Lesson 2-9** Pacing: 1 day
Lesson/ Objective	**Ways to Make 7, 8, and 9** (pp. 67–68) **Objective:** Use counters to make sums of 7, 8, and 9.	**Ways to Make 10, 11, and 12** (pp. 69–72) **Objective:** Use a ten-frame and counters to make sums of 10, 11, and 12.	**Problem-Solving Investigation** **Choose a Strategy** (pp. 73–74) **Objective:** Choose the best strategy to solve a problem.
State/Local Standards			
Math Vocabulary			
Lesson Resources	**Manipulatives** two-colored counters **Other Resources** CRM Leveled Worksheets (pp. 36–40) Daily Reteach • 5-Minute Check Problem of the Day	**Materials** WorkMat 1: Ten-Frame, red crayons, yellow crayons, number cards **Manipulatives** two-colored counters, connecting cubes **Other Resources** CRM Leveled Worksheets (pp. 41–45) Daily Reteach • 5-Minute Check Problem of the Day	**Other Resources** CRM Leveled Worksheets (pp. 46–50) Daily Reteach • 5-Minute Check Problem of the Day *Healthful Snacks*
Technology Math Online	♪ Math Song Track 11 Math Adventures	♪ Math Song Track 11 Math Tool Chest, Counter Level 1 Concepts in Motion	
Reaching All Learners	Gifted and Talented, p. 67B **AL** English Learners, p. 67B **ELL** Early Finishers, p. 67B **OL** **AL**	Below Level, p. 69B **BL** English Learners, p. 69B **ELL** Early Finishers, p. 69B **OL** **AL**	Below Level, p. 73B **BL** English Learners, p. 73B **ELL** Early Finishers, p. 73B **OL** **AL**
Alternate Lessons	*Math Their Way*, p. 248 *IMPACT Mathematics*: Unit A	*Math Their Way*, p. 190 *IMPACT Mathematics*: Units A and H	

Lesson 2-10

Pacing: 1 day

Vertical Addition
(pp. 75–76)

Objective: Write addition facts horizontally and vertically.

Materials
white crayons, black construction paper, Work Mat 1: Ten-Frame, dominoes

Manipulatives
two-colored counters

Other Resources
CRM Leveled Worksheets (pp. 51–55)

Daily Reteach • 5-Minute Check

Problem of the Day

♪ Math Song Track 11

Below Level, p. 75B **BL**

English Learners, p. 75B **ELL**

Early Finishers, p. 75B **OL** **AL**

Math Their Way, p. 238
IMPACT Mathematics: Unit A

Problem Solving in Health
(p. 77)

Summative Assessment
• Chapter Review/Test (p. 79)
• Test Practice (p. 81)

Assessment Options

Diagnostic Assessment

SE *Option 1:* Are You Ready? (p. 48)
Option 2: Online Quiz macmillanmh.com
CRM *Option 3:* Diagnostic Test (p. 57)
CRM *Option 4:* Chapter Pretest (p. 58)

Formative Assessment

TE Alternate Teaching Strategies (every lesson)
SE Talk About It (every lesson)
SE Writing in Math (every lesson)
SE Check (every lesson)
TE Line Up (every lesson)
SE Mid-Chapter Check (p. 63)
CRM Mid-Chapter-Test (p. 59)

Summative Assessment

SE Chapter Review/Test (p. 79)
SE Test Practice (p. 81)
CRM Vocabulary Test (p. 60)
CRM Leveled Chapter Tests (pp. 67–76)
CRM Cumulative Test Practice (p. 77)
CRM Oral Assessment Interview (pp. 61–62)
CRM Listening Assessment (pp. 63–64)
Exam*View*® Assessment Suite
Advance Tracker

Mc Graw Hill Professional Development

Targeted professional development has been articulated throughout the *McGraw-Hill's Math Connects* program. The **McGraw-Hill Professional Development Video Library** provides short videos that support the **NCTM Focal Points and Focal Connections.** For more information, visit macmillanmh.com.

| Model Lessons | Instructional Strategies |

Learning Stations
Cross-Curricular Links

 Reading

 individual | **SPATIAL**

Button Addition

- Read *The Button Box.*
- Use the buttons in the box to write an addition sentence.
- Draw the buttons on paper and write the addition sentence below.

Teacher Note: Suggest writing a variety of number sentences.

Materials:
- *The Button Box* by Margarette S. Reid
- buttons
- paper
- crayons

 Art

individual | **SPATIAL**

Neat Numbers

- Select a number card.
- Write or draw the number on a piece of construction paper.
- Decorate your number with that number of items.
- Place your number in the correct pile: less than 10 or greater than 10.

Teacher Note: Put out as many materials as you would like for them to decorate with. Persuade students to fill the whole page with their number.

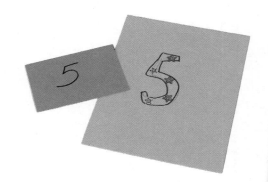

Materials:
- Number cards from 1 to 20
- construction paper
- decorating materials, such as stickers and buttons

 Language Arts

partners | **LOGICAL**

Stepping up a Story

- Choose and read a picture book with your partner.
- On your paper, list 3 things that happen in the story.
- Add a new event to the story. What could happen next?
- Draw an illustration to go with your story.

Teacher Note: Instead of having students write on a blank piece of paper, you may want to create a worksheet for them to fill in the blanks.

Materials:
- picture books
- paper
- crayons

Science

partners | KINESTHETIC, LOGICAL

Flower Power

- Select a flower with a partner.
- Count the number of petals on the flower.
- Write an addition problem for that number. For example: 4 petals + 6 petals = 10 petals. Draw an illustration to go with the addition problem.
- Repeat with another flower.

Teacher Note: If you do not want to use real flowers, have students draw flowers and then use their drawings.

Materials:
- paper
- crayons
- several flowers with easily countable petals, such as daisies

Social Studies

partners | LOGICAL

Community Helper Addition Problems

- Take a community card. Think of who works there.
- With your partner, write an addition problem for those people. For example: 3 doctors + 4 nurses = 7 people working in the hospital.
- Take 3 more cards and repeat.

Teacher Note: Be sure to list places in the community that the students are familiar with on the cards. Examples would be: school, grocery, hospital, or firehouse.

Materials:
- paper
- index cards listing places in the community

Calendar Time

2 Weeks of School Equal 10 Days

- Hand out calendar pages to each student with the current month and dates.
- Have students cut out 2 weeks of days and cut off the weekend days. Students will now have 2 weeks of school days–a ten-frame with 5 weekday blocks attached to the top of 5 other weekday blocks.
- Distribute 10 counters to students. Have them put a counter on every day of the 2 school weeks.
- Have students take off one counter and say that 1 + 9 = 10. Remove one more counter and say that 2 + 8 = 10, and so on.
- Once all 10 counters have been removed, have students put one counter on and say 9 + 1 = 10, and so on until all counters have been put back on.

Introduce the Chapter

🌎 Real World: How Many?

Tell students they are going to learn how to **add**. Explain that when they add, they join groups or numbers together.

- Ask students how many students are sitting at a particular table or in a certain row of desks.
- **How did you find this number?** counted the students
- **How could you find the total number of students at two tables or in two rows of desks?** Count all the students.

Have students turn to p. 47.

- **How many puppies are in the photo?** three puppies
- **If two more puppies came to play, how could you find out how many puppies there are altogether?** Start with three, and count on two more.

Key Vocabulary

Introduce key vocabulary in the chapter using the routine below.

<u>Define:</u> The **sum** is the answer you get when you add numbers.

<u>Example:</u> The sum of 2 + 2 is 4.

<u>Ask:</u> Add the number 2 to your age. What is the sum?

Develop Addition Concepts

Key Vocabulary
add
addition sentence
plus (+)
equals (=)
sum

Copyright © Macmillan/McGraw-Hill, a division of The McGraw-Hill Companies, Inc.

Explore
Tell a number story about this picture. Write how many animals there are in all.

____4____ animals

Chapter 2   forty-seven **47**

 **Dinah Zike's Foldables**

Guide students to create their 5-Pocket Book Foldable for developing addition concepts.

① Fold a 8 ½' × 11"sheet of paper in half like a hamburger.

② Open the folded paper and fold one of the long sides up two inches to form a pocket. Refold along the hamburger fold so that the newly formed pockets are on the inside.

③ Glue the outer edges of the two-inch fold with a small amount of glue.

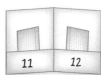

④ Repeat steps 1-3 for 4 more sheets of paper. Attach all 5 pocket books by gluing each one side-by-side. Glue a cover around the multi-paged pocket book.

When to Use It Lessons 2–4, 2–6, 2–7, and 2–8. (Additional instructions for using the Foldable with these lessons are found on pp. 63 and 79.)

Glue Pocket Books back to front.

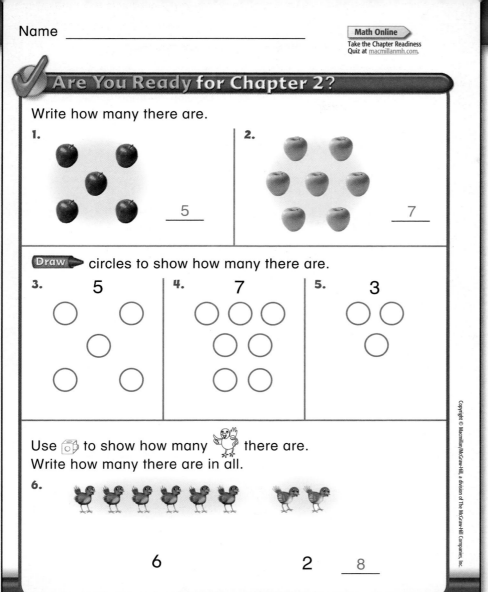

Are You Ready for Chapter 2?

Write how many there are.

1. _5_

2. _7_

Draw circles to show how many there are.

3. **5**

4. **7**

5. **3**

Use 🎲 to show how many 🐦 there are.
Write how many there are in all.

6.

6   2   _8_

This page checks skills needed for Chapter 2.

Copyright © Macmillan/McGraw-Hill, a division of The McGraw-Hill Companies, Inc.

Diagnostic Assessment

Check for students' prerequisite skills before beginning the chapter.

- **Option 1:** *Are You Ready for Chapter 2?*
  SE Student Edition, p. 48

- **Option 2:** *Online Readiness Quiz*
  Math Online   macmillanmh.com

- **Option 3:** *Diagnostic Test*
  CRM Chapter 2 Resource Masters, p. 57

RTI (Response to Intervention)

Apply the Results Based on the results of the diagnostic assessment on student p. 48, use the chart below to address individual needs before beginning the chapter.

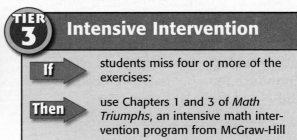

TIER 3   Intensive Intervention

If students miss four or more of the exercises:

Then use Chapters 1 and 3 of *Math Triumphs*, an intensive math intervention program from McGraw-Hill

TIER 2   Strategic Intervention
below/approaching grade level

If students miss two or three in:
Exercises 1–6

Then choose a resource:

Strategic Intervention Guide (pp. 6–11)

CRM Chapter 1 Resource Masters
(Reteach Worksheets)

Math Online   Concepts in Motion

TIER 1   On-Level

If students miss one in:
Exercises 1–6

Then choose a resource:

TE Learning Stations (pp. 47G–47H)

TE Chapter Project (p. 49)

CRM Game: *Addition Tic-Tac-Toe*

Math Adventures
My Math Zone Chapter 1

Math Online   Fact Dash

Above/Beyond Level

If students miss none in:
Exercises 1–6

Then choose a resource:

TE Learning Stations (pp. 47G–47H)

TE Chapter Project (p. 49)

📖 Real-World Problem Solving: *Healthful Snacks*

Math Adventures
My Math Zone Chapter 1, 2

Math Online

Before you begin Chapter 2:

- Read the Math at Home letter found on p. 49 with the class and have each child sign it.
- Send home copies of the Math at Home letter with each student.
- Use the Spanish letter on p. 50 for students with Spanish-speaking parents or guardians.

WRITING IN ▶ MATH

Starting the Chapter

- Tell students that for breakfast, you ate 2 orange slices and then ate 3 more orange slices. **How many orange slices did you eat at breakfast?**
  5 orange slices
- Divide students into pairs or small groups.
- Have each student write an addition story about breakfast. Another student should attempt to answer each question.
- Assist students by writing on the board some common breakfast foods, such as pancakes, cereal, juice, toast, and eggs.

Read-Aloud Anthology For an optional reading activity to introduce this chapter's math concepts, see the Read-Aloud Anthology on p. TR25.

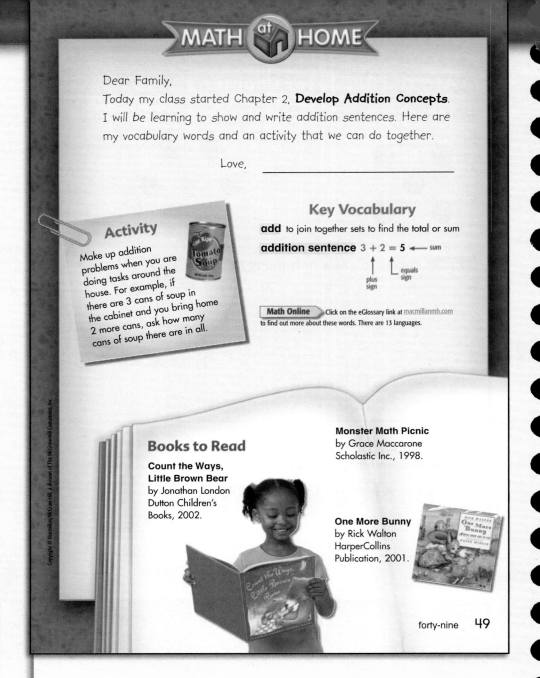

MATH at **HOME**

Dear Family,
Today my class started Chapter 2, **Develop Addition Concepts**. I will be learning to show and write addition sentences. Here are my vocabulary words and an activity that we can do together.

Love, _____

Activity

Make up addition problems when you are doing tasks around the house. For example, if there are 3 cans of soup in the cabinet and you bring home 2 more cans, ask how many cans of soup there are in all.

Key Vocabulary

add to join together sets to find the total or sum

addition sentence $3 + 2 = 5$ ◄— sum
↑ plus sign   ↑ equals sign

Math Online Click on the eGlossary link at macmillanmh.com to find out more about these words. There are 13 languages.

Books to Read

Count the Ways, Little Brown Bear
by Jonathan London
Dutton Children's Books, 2002.

Monster Math Picnic
by Grace Maccarone
Scholastic Inc., 1998.

One More Bunny
by Rick Walton
HarperCollins Publication, 2001.

forty-nine **49**

✔ Chapter 2 Project

Treasure Hunt

- Have small groups work on writing addition stories as clues about locations in the classroom. Each group needs to write on index cards a total of five addition stories. A sample clue might be: "At Table One, there are 2 boys and 3 girls. How many students sit at Table One?"
- The team should write an addition sentence and solve the clue, then go to Table One to receive their next clue.
- Determine a location in the classroom, such as your desk, where each group should end up at the end of its last clue.
- Prepare a treasure, such as a sticker, at the final location so groups will be rewarded for succeeding in their hunt.

CRM *Refer to Chapter 2 Resource Masters, p. 65 for rubric to assess students' progress on this project.*

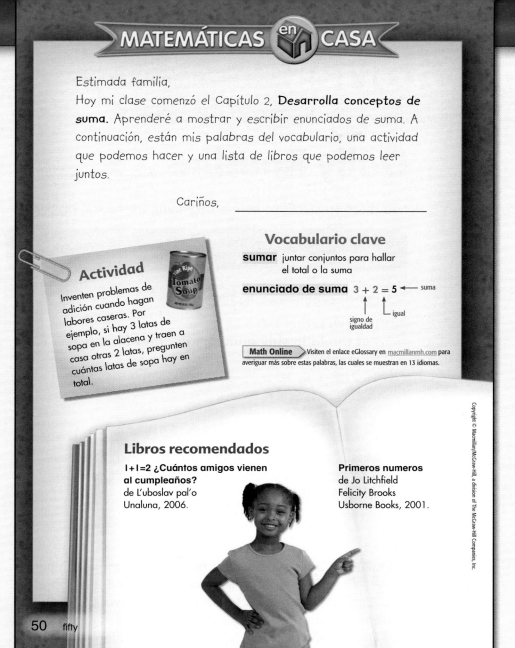

MATEMÁTICAS en CASA

Estimada familia,

Hoy mi clase comenzó el Capítulo 2, **Desarrolla conceptos de suma.** Aprenderé a mostrar y escribir enunciados de suma. A continuación, están mis palabras del vocabulario, una actividad que podemos hacer y una lista de libros que podemos leer juntos.

Cariños,

_____

Actividad

Inventen problemas de adición cuando hagan labores caseras. Por ejemplo, si hay 3 latas de sopa en la alacena y traen a casa otras 2 latas, pregunten cuántas latas de sopa hay en total.

Vocabulario clave

sumar juntar conjuntos para hallar el total o la suma

enunciado de suma $3 + 2 = 5$ ← suma

signo de igualdad ↑ ↑ igual

Math Online Visiten el enlace eGlossary en macmillanmh.com para averiguar más sobre estas palabras, las cuales se muestran en 13 idiomas.

Libros recomendados

1+1=2 ¿Cuántos amigos vienen al cumpleaños?
de L'uboslav pal'o
Unaluna, 2006.

Primeros numeros
de Jo Litchfield
Felicity Brooks
Usborne Books, 2001.

50 fifty

Chapter 2 Literature List

Lesson	Book Title
2-1	**The Gingerbread Boy** Richard Egielski
2-2	**Mama Cat Has Three Kittens** Denise Fleming
2-3	**Rooster's Off to See the World** Eric Carle
2-4	**A House for Hermit Crab** Eric Carle
2-5	**Quack and Count** Keith Baker
2-6	**Anno's Counting Book** Mitsumasa Anno
2-7	**Quack and Count** Keith Baker
2-8	**Anno's Counting Book** Mitsumasa Anno
2-10	**Counting in the Garden** Kim Parker
Any	**Count the Ways, Little Brown Bear** Jonathan London
Any	**Monster Math Picnic** Grace Maccarone
Any	**One More Bunny** Rick Walton

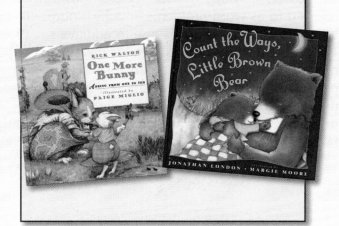

ELL National ESL Standards Alignment for Chapter 2

Lesson, Page	ESL Standard	Modality	Level
2-1, p 51B	Goal 2, Standard 4, H	Visual/Spatial, Linguistic	Intermediate
2-2, p 53B	Goal 1, Standard 2, D	Visual/Spatial, Kinesthetic	Beginning
2-3, p 55B	Goal 1, Standard 2, C	Visual/Spatial, Kinesthetic	Intermediate
2-4, p 59B	Goal 1, Standard 3, K	Visual, Kinesthetic	Beginning
2-5, p 61B	Goal 2, Standard 3, H	Visual, Linguistic	Advanced
2-6, p 65B	Goal 2, Standard 2, F	Visual, Spatial, Social	Intermediate
2-7, p 67B	Goal 2, Standard 3, E	Logical, Visual, Spatial	Intermediate
2-8, p 69B	Goal 3, Standard 1, A	Auditory	Intermediate
2-9, p 73B	Goal 2, Standard 2, I	Auditory, Visual	Intermediate
2-10, p 75B	Goal 2, Standard 2, E	Visual, Spatial	Intermediate

The National ESL Standards can be found in the Teacher Reference Handbook.

Addition Stories

Lesson Planner

Objective
Use counters to show addition stories.

Review Vocabulary
number

Resources
Materials: overhead projector

Manipulatives: two-colored counters

Literature Connection: *The Gingerbread Boy* by Richard Egielski

Alternate Lessons: Use "Lift the Bowl" on pp. 181 and 182 of *Math Their Way* to provide practice using manipulatives to show number stories.

Use *IMPACT Mathematics:* Units A and C to provide practice modeling addition stories.

Teacher Technology
TeacherWorks • Concepts in Motion • Math Songs Track 11 Lesson Plan

---

Focus on Math Background

This lesson introduces students to stories, commonly referred to as word problems, in which numbers and amounts undergo changes due to additive situations. The basic structure of these stories involves a starting number that increases by a particular action, such as putting together. The end result is a number greater than the starting quantity. By solving these word problems, students are able to visualize how addition takes place in real world situations.

Daily Routine

Use these suggestions before beginning the lesson on p. 51.

5-Minute Check
(Reviews Lesson 1-9)
Put the following numbers in order from least to greatest.
1. 2, 8, 4, 6, 10   2, 4, 6, 8, 10
2. 5, 13, 1, 9, 21   1, 5, 9, 13, 21

Problem of the Day
Miguel ate 6 of his carrot sticks for lunch. He gave 4 to Kim. How many carrot sticks did Miguel have when lunch began?   10 carrot sticks

---

LINE UP Choose a group of five students in line. Separate the group into a group of four and a group of one. Encourage students to count the two groups using this pattern: "A group of 4 and a group of 1 makes a group of 5 in all." Ask a student to put the five students in two different groups and count the groups in the same way.

Review Math Vocabulary
- Review the term **number** with students.
- Explain that numbers tell how many of something we have.
- Ask students to find places around the room where numbers can be found.
- Draw on the chalkboard a number line from 0–20.
- Call three students up to the front of the classroom and have them stand in a line. Instruct the class that there are three students standing there.
- **Using the number line, how many students do you need to add to equal 5?** 2 students
- Add two more students to the line. Have all the students count off.
- **Does it equal 5?** yes

Differentiated Instruction

Small Group Options

Option 1 — Gifted and Talented (AL)

Materials: counting stories or picture books

- Have students select a counting story or picture book to read.
- Ask one student to read the story aloud to the other.
- After the story has been read, students should talk about the story and write addition stories about the characters, actions, and events in the book.
- Have students write and answer questions to go with their addition stories.

Option 2 — English Language Learners (ELL)

VISUAL/SPATIAL, LINGUISTIC

Core Vocabulary: six, seven, eight, nine, ten, I found ___, Did you find ____?

Common Use Verb: find/found

Talk Math This strategy uses the math skill to introduce question forms in past tense with two high frequency irregular verbs.

- Count 6 items. Encourage choral response.
- Give each student ten manipulatives.
- Write and say: "**Find six**" (command form), "**Did you find six**?" and "**I found six.**" (Underline **find,** past tense form **found,** and the past tense auxiliary verb **did** used to form questions.)
- Repeat for numbers up to ten.
- Allow students to practice counting and verifying in pairs or small groups.

Independent Work Options

Option 1 — Early Finishers (OL) (AL)

VERBAL/KINESTHETIC/LOGICAL

Materials: number spinner, red and purple connecting cubes

- Have students take turns spinning the number spinner two times.
- Ask one student to use red cubes to model the first number.
- Ask another student to use purple cubes to model the second number.
- Invite a student to tell a number story using the numbers.

Option 2 — Student Technology

| Math Online | macmillanmh.com |

♪ Math Song, "The Addition Boogie" Track 11

Math Adventures

Option 3 — Learning Stations: Science (p. 47H)

Direct students to the Science Learning Station for opportunities to explore and extend the lesson concept.

Option 4 — Problem-Solving Practice

Reinforce problem-solving skills and strategies with the Problem-Solving Practice worksheet.

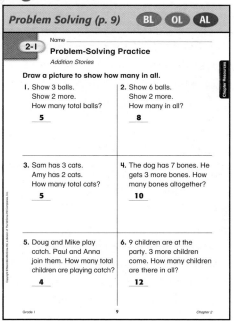

Problem Solving (p. 9) — BL OL AL

2-1 Name _____

Problem-Solving Practice
Addition Stories

Draw a picture to show how many in all.

1. Show 3 balls. Show 2 more. How many total balls?
   5
2. Show 6 balls. Show 2 more. How many in all?
   8
3. Sam has 3 cats. Amy has 2 cats. How many total cats?
   5
4. The dog has 7 bones. He gets 3 more bones. How many bones altogether?
   10
5. Doug and Mike play catch. Paul and Anna join them. How many total children are playing catch?
   4
6. 9 children are at the party. 3 more children come. How many children are there in all?
   12

Grade 1   9   Chapter 2

1 Introduce

Activity Choice 1 • Hands-On

Call five students to the front of the classroom. Pick students with similarities and differences in clothing so you can group them in a variety of ways.

- Have students count how many are wearing (long sleeves, sneakers). Write that number on the board.
- Have students count how many are wearing (short sleeves, no sneakers). Write that number on the board.

Activity Choice 2 • Literature

Introduce the lesson with *The Gingerbread Boy* by Richard Egielski. For additional support, see p. TR43.

2 Teach

Model the following story on an overhead projector with squares and triangles.

- **Three children were playing in the sandbox. Two more joined them. How many are there now?** 5 children

Have students use square and triangle shapes to solve the following problems. Model each problem on an overhead projector.

- **Jose found 5 rocks. Then he found 2 more. How many does he have in all?** 7 rocks
- **Sarah put 2 plates on the table. Then she added 4 more plates. How many plates are on the table?** 6 plates
- **Three ducks were in a pond. Four more ducks joined them. How many ducks are in the pond now?** 7 ducks

Get Ready Use this section at the top of student p. 51 to reach the lesson concept.

Check Observe students as you work through Exercises 1–3 as a class.

Exercise 3 Assess students' comprehension before assigning practice exercises.

⚠ COMMON ERROR!

Students may miscount when doing Exercises 1 and 2. Encourage them to count aloud or raise fingers as they point to or touch the pictures and two-colored counters.

Name _____

Addition Stories

Get Ready

Main Idea

I will use counters to model addition stories.

> I have 1 red apple on the table. I put 2 yellow apples on the table. There are 3 apples on the table.

✓ Check

Tell a number story to your partner. Use ⬤◯.
Write how many there are.

1.
<u>5</u> birds

2.
<u>6</u> turtles

3. **Talk About It** What happens when you put groups together?
Sample answer: When more is added to a group, the group becomes larger.

Chapter 2   Lesson 1   fifty-one   51

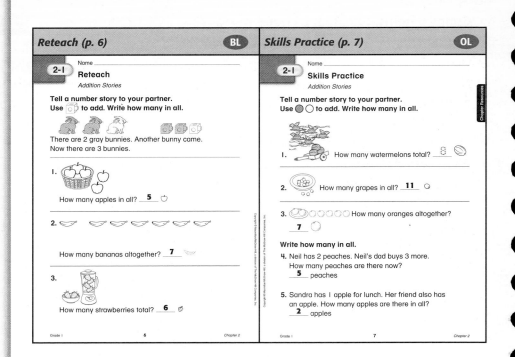

Reteach (p. 6)   **BL**

2-1 **Reteach**
Addition Stories

Tell a number story to your partner.
Use 🐰 to add. Write how many in all.

There are 2 gray bunnies. Another bunny came.
Now there are 3 bunnies.

1. How many apples in all? __5__

2. How many bananas altogether? __7__

3. How many strawberries total? __6__

Grade 1   6   Chapter 2

Skills Practice (p. 7)   **OL**

2-1 **Skills Practice**
Addition Stories

Tell a number story to your partner.
Use ⬤◯ to add. Write how many in all.

1. How many watermelons total? __8__

2. How many grapes in all? __11__

3. How many oranges altogether? __7__

Write how many in all.

4. Neil has 2 peaches. Neil's dad buys 3 more. How many peaches are there now? __5__ peaches

5. Sandra has 1 apple for lunch. Her friend also has an apple. How many apples are there in all? __2__ apples

Grade 1   7   Chapter 2

Practice

Tell a number story to your partner. Use .
Write how many.

4.

<u> 4 </u> foxes

5.

<u> 2 </u> deer

6.

<u> 7 </u> crabs

Problem Solving

7. **Visual Thinking** Draw⟶ 6 gray cats and 3 cats with stripes. How many cats are there in all? Tell a number story about your picture.

See students' drawings.

<u> 9 </u> cats

52 fifty-two

Math at Home Activity: Tell addition stories to your child. Have your child use buttons or pennies to model the story.

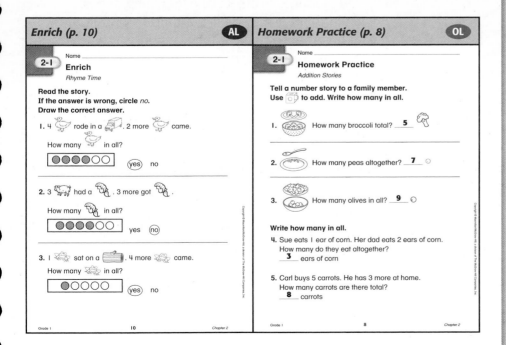

---

3 Practice

Differentiate practice, using these leveled assignments for Exercices 4–7.

Level	Assignment
BL Below/Approaching Level	Pair students with Above Level students for peer modeling.
OL On Level	Complete independently.
AL Above/Beyond Level	Complete exercises without the counters. Model problems for Below Level students.

Exercise 7 This exercise asks students to create their own number story using the given numbers– the foundation for learning how to create problem situations from given number sentences. Students have not previously created their own situation, so you may want to work as a class first. As students learn new skills during the year, use this type of question to further their understanding.

4 Assess

Formative Assessment

Tell the following addition story:

Two students missed their school bus. Three more students overslept. How many students were late for school?

- **How will you solve the problem?** Sample answers: Model the problem with counters; draw a picture; add the numbers.

Quick Check **Are students continuing to struggle with modeling addition?**

If Yes ⟶ Strategic Intervention Guide (p. 52)

If No ⟶ Independent Work Options (p. 51B)
　　CRM Skills Practice Worksheet (p. 7)
　　CRM Enrich Worksheet (p. 10)

Modeling Addition

Lesson Planner

Objective
Add by joining two groups.

Vocabulary
add

Resources
Materials: WorkMat 3: Part-Part-Whole, paper, overhead projector

Manipulatives: two-colored counters

Literature Connection: *Mama Cat Has Three Kittens* by Denise Fleming

Alternate Lessons: Adapt "Beans" on p. 174 of *Math Their Way* for practice in addition as part-part-whole. Use *IMPACT Mathematics:* Units A and C, to provide practice modeling addition.

Teacher Technology
TeacherWorks • Concepts in Motion • Math Songs Track 11 Lesson Plan

Focus on Math Background

In this lesson students focus on the meaning of addition by using manipulative materials to represent story structures or to model actions that involve a joining situation. Two types of story structures are introduced:

1. *part-part-whole*—John has two red balls and six blue balls. How many does he have altogether?
2. *joining*—John had two marbles. Sue gave him four marbles. How many marbles does John have now?

Daily Routine

Use these suggestions before beginning the lesson on p. 53.

5-Minute Check

(Reviews Lesson 2-1)
Daniel had 8 model cars. His grandmother gave him 2 model cars for his birthday. How many model cars does Daniel have now? 10 cars

Problem of the Day

Jeff and Amy are playing volleyball. Sarah, Dave, and Kim come to play with them. How many friends are playing volleyball? 5 friends

LINE UP Assign each student a number beginning with 1 and going up to the number of students. Have them line up in number order.

Building Math Vocabulary

Review with students how to **add**. Show that two parts added together make a whole.

- Show students two sets of connecting cubes. Explain that each set is like a train car. Bring the cars together to make a longer train. Show that each train car is a part by itself. Put them together to show how the new train becomes a whole.
- Have the class help you label *part*, *part*, and *whole* on the connecting cube "train."

Visual Vocabulary Cards
Use Visual Vocabulary Card 1 to reinforce the vocabulary introduced in this lesson. (The Define/Example/Ask routine is printed on the back of each card.)

Differentiated Instruction

Small Group Options

Option 1 — Gifted and Talented (AL)

Materials: set of number cards from 1 to 10

- Have one of the partners deal out the cards one at a time facedown so that each partner gets five cards total.
- Have students count to three and flip over the top card in their facedown pile.
- Have students put their cards next to each other and add the numbers together.
- After the numbers are added together, have students put the two cards in a discard pile.
- Have students continue until all cards have been added together.

VISUAL/SPATIAL, KINESTHETIC

Option 2 — English Language Learners (ELL)

Materials: large poster with "whole" written across the back and precut into pieces, tape
Core Vocabulary: part, whole, a puzzle piece
Common Use Verb: will put together

See Math This strategy models the concept of addition.

- Say: "This is a whole. It is together." Display the back of the poster.
- Say: "**Parts** of a **puzzle** are called **pieces**" as you disassemble.
- Have each student write their name on a puzzle piece and decorate the front.
- Say: "Now we **will put** the **pieces** back **together**."
- Model re-assembling the backside with "whole" on it.

Use this worksheet to provide additional support for English Language Learners.

English Language Learners (p. 49) ELL

13   Name _____

Adding Counters

Draw counters in two groups.
Use a different color for each group.
Use numbers to write the addition sentence.
Answers will vary.

		PLUS		EQUALS	SUM
●● ○○○	2	+	3	=	5

Addition to 10   49

Independent Work Options

Option 1 — Early Finishers (OL) (AL)

Materials: number cubes, two-colored counters

- Ask a student to roll the number cube two times.
- Have another student use two-colored counters to model each number rolled.
- Have another student say the addition sentence.
- Ask students to work together to find and say the sum of the number sentence.

Option 2 — Student Technology

 Math Online ▶ macmillanmh.com

🎵 Math Song, "The Addition Boogie" Track 11

🌀 Math Adventures

Option 3 — Learning Stations: Art (p. 47G)

Direct students to the Art Learning Station for opportunities to explore and extend the lesson concept.

Option 4 — Problem-Solving Practice

Reinforce problem-solving skills and strategies with the leveled Problem-Solving Practice worksheet.

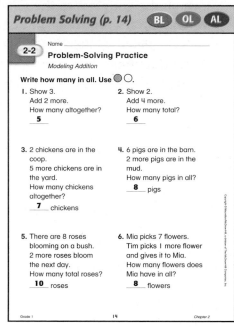

Problem Solving (p. 14) BL OL AL

Name _____

2-2   **Problem-Solving Practice**
Modeling Addition

Write how many in all. Use ● ○.

1. Show 3.
   Add 2 more.
   How many altogether?
   __5__

2. Show 2.
   Add 4 more.
   How many total?
   __6__

3. 2 chickens are in the coop.
   5 more chickens are in the yard.
   How many chickens altogether?
   __7__ chickens

4. 6 pigs are in the barn.
   2 more pigs are in mud.
   How many pigs in all?
   __8__ pigs

5. There are 8 roses blooming on a bush.
   2 more roses bloom the next day.
   How many total roses?
   __10__ roses

6. Mia picks 7 flowers.
   Tim picks 1 more flower and gives it to Mia.
   How many flowers does Mia have in all?
   __8__ flowers

Grade 1   14   Chapter 2

1 Introduce

Activity Choice 1 • Hands-On

Have students fold a piece of paper in half and keep it closed. Have them draw three yellow circles on one side and two red circles on the other side. Have students open the paper and count the number of circles.

- **How many yellow circles did you draw?** 3 yellow circles
- **How many red circles did you draw?** 2 red circles
- **How many circles did you draw in all?** 5 circles
- Tell students that 2 and 3 are the parts.
- Tell students that 5 is the whole.
- **We added the parts to find the whole.**

Activity Choice 2 • Literature

Introduce the lesson with *Mama Cat Has Three Kittens* by Denise Fleming. For additional support, see p. TR43.

2 Teach

Place a part-part-whole workmat on an overhead projector. Place three red counters in one part and four yellow counters in the other part.

- **How many red counters are there?** 3 red counters Count the red counters together.
- **How many yellow counters are there?** 4 yellow counters Count the yellow counters together.
- Move all the counters to the whole box. **How many counters are there in all?** 7 counters Count the counters together and write 7 in the box.
- Explain that when two parts are joined together, you **add** them to make the whole.

Get Ready Use this section at the top of student p. 53 to teach the lesson concept.

Check Observe students as you work through Exercises 1–5 as a class.

> **Exercise 5** Assess students' comprehension before assigning practice exercises.

! COMMON ERROR!

Students may try to work in the wrong boxes on their workmats. Make sure that all students place their workmats in the correct position.

Name _____

Modeling Addition

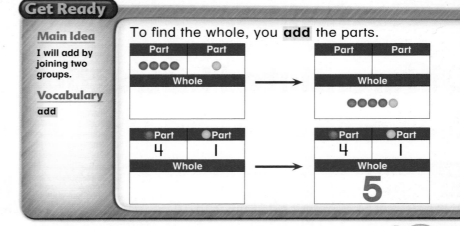

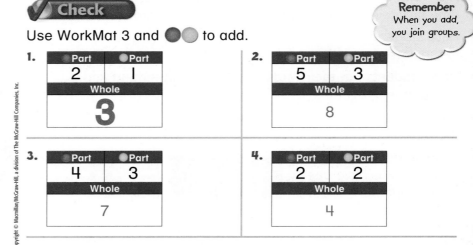

Chapter 2   Lesson 2

fifty-three   53

Reteach (p. 11) BL

2-2 **Reteach**
Modeling Addition

Use WorkMat 3 and ⊚ ○ to add.
Use counters to show parts.
Add parts to find the whole.

1. Whole 8
2. Whole 6
3. Whole 7
4. Whole 10

Skills Practice (p. 12) OL

2-2 **Skills Practice**
Modeling Addition

Use WorkMat 3 and ⊚ ○ to add.

1. Whole 5
2. Whole 9
3. Whole 6
4. Whole 8

Write how many. Use ⊚ ○.

5. Show 2.
Add 3 more.
How many in all? **5**

6. Show 4.
Add 4 more.
How many altogether? **8**

7. Show 5.
Add 2 more.
How many total? **7**

8. Show 3.
Add 1 more.
How many in all? **4**

Practice

Use WorkMat 3 and  to add.

6.

Part	Part
3	2
Whole	
5	

7.

Part	Part
4	5
Whole	
9	

8.

Part	Part
6	2
Whole	
8	

9.

Part	Part
5	5
Whole	
10	

10.

Part	Part
1	3
Whole	
4	

11.

Part	Part
4	2
Whole	
6	

12.

Part	Part
1	2
Whole	
3	

13.

Part	Part
3	3
Whole	
6	

H.O.T. Problems

Algebra Write the missing part. Use .

Sample answers:

14.

Part	Part
3	4
Whole	
7	

15.

Part	Part
2	3
Whole	
5	

54 fifty-four

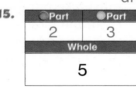 **Math at Home Activity:** Draw 2 red circles and 4 yellow circles. Have your child add to find the sum.

---

③ Practice

Differentiate practice, using these leveled assignments for Exercises 6–15.

Level	Assignment
BL Below/Approaching Level	Model additional problems, having students help you.
OL On Level	Complete independently.
AL Above/Beyond Level	Complete exercises without the workmat and counters.

④ Assess

Formative Assessment

Give each student a blank workmat. Have them place three red counters in one part and five yellow counters in the other part.

- **Tell how you can find the whole.** Possible answer: I counted all the counters. I added the numbers.

WRITING IN ►MATH Have students brainstorm objects in the classroom or at home that are in parts, but together make a whole. Example: Each wheel is a part. The seat is a part, the handle bar is a part, and the bike is the whole.

Quick Check **Are students continuing to struggle with modeling addition?**

If Yes → Strategic Intervention Guide (pp. 54–59)

If No → Independent Work Options (p. 53B)

CRM Skills Practice Worksheet (p. 12)

CRM Enrich Worksheet (p. 15)

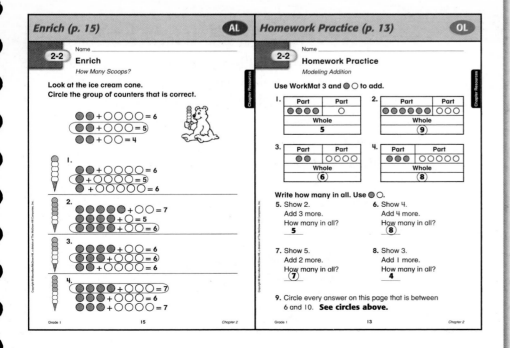

Lesson Planner

Objective
Write addition sentences using + and =.

Vocabulary
addition sentence, equals (=), plus (+), sum

Resources
Manipulatives: connecting cubes

Literature Connection: *Rooster's Off to See the World* by Eric Carle

Alternate Lessons: Use "Peek Through the Wall" on p. 238 of *Math Their Way* to provide practice writing number sentences for addition.

Use *IMPACT Mathematics:* Units C and G to provide practice with writing addition sentences.

Teacher Technology
TeacherWorks • Concepts in Motion • Math Songs Track 11 Lesson Plan

Focus on Math Background

The students' work in this lesson focuses on relating numerical expressions (addition sentences) to additive situations modeled in story problems. The students will learn that the plus sign (+) stands for the combining of two sets, and that the equal sign (=) indicates the result of this joining action. A fundamental component of algebra is the use of symbols to represent mathematical situations, such as addition.

Daily Routine

Use these suggestions before beginning the lesson on p. 55.

5-Minute Check
(Reviews Lesson 2-2)
Use WorkMat 3 and counters to find the whole.
1. Part 2, Part 2 4
3. Part 3, Part 2 5
2. Part 5, Part 1 6
4. Part 6, Part 3 9

1–4. See students' work.

Problem of the Day
Ali and Khadija have chores to do every week. Ali must take out the trash, wash the dishes and clean the birdcage. Khadija must fold the laundry and put away the dishes. How many chores do they have altogether? 5 chores

LINE UP When in the hallway, call on students to create addition sentences for things they see. For example, 3 windows + 2 more windows = 5 total windows.

Building Math Vocabulary
Discuss the term **addition sentence** with students. Explain that it includes two numbers (parts), a **plus** sign, an **equals** sign, and a **sum** (the whole).

- List the following on the chalkboard: 6, 9, 3, +, =.
- **What addition sentence can be made using these numbers and symbols?** 6 + 3 = 9 or 3 + 6 = 9
- **Read the addition sentence aloud to the class.**
- Repeat as time allows.

Visual Vocabulary Cards
Use Visual Vocabulary Card 16 to reinforce the vocabulary introduced in this lesson. (The Define/Example/Ask routine is printed on the back of each card.)

equals (=)

Differentiated Instruction

Small Group Options

LOGICAL, SOCIAL

Option 1 — Gifted and Talented (AL)

Materials: red number cubes, paper, pencil, crayons

- Divide students into groups of two and give each student a red number cube.
- Have students roll their number cubes. Ask partners to write an addition sentence with the numbers they rolled.
- Challenge students to draw a picture to model their number sentence.

Option 2 — English Language Learners (ELL)

VISUAL, SPATIAL, KINESTHETIC

Materials: supermarket flyers with pictures of food, scissors (per each), construction paper, sentence strips or adding tape (should be in long strips), glue
Core Vocabulary: and (+), eat/ate, your/my meal
Common Use Verb: would like

See Math This strategy uses conditional tense and question forms to help students decode word problems.

- Say: "What **would you like** to **eat**?"
- Show pictures of your typical dinner. Post the strip of pictures of what you ate. Say: "I **ate** a hamburger, green beans and an apple" as you pantomime the action.
- Write an addition sentence under the picture sentence that ends "= my meal"
- Have students make their own addition picture strips. Discuss the verb placements for "would like", "eat", and "ate" in questions and statements.

  = my meal

Independent Work Options

Option 1 — Early Finishers (OL) (AL)

INDIVIDUAL, KINESTHETIC, SPATIAL

Materials: resealable plastic sandwich bags, number cards (0–10), symbol cards (+ and =)

- Make addition bags containing three numbers and the symbol cards + and = so students can form addition sentences with sums up to 10.
- Invite students to select a bag and use the cards inside to build as many addition sentences as they can, whether the sentence is correct or not.
- Have students record their number sentences on paper and then check their work by circling the true addition sentences.

Option 2 — Student Technology

| Math Online | macmillanmh.com |

♪ Math Song, "The Addition Boogie" Track 11

Option 3 — Learning Stations: Language Arts (p. 47G)

Direct students to the Language Arts Learning Station for opportunities to explore and extend the lesson concept.

Option 4 — Problem-Solving Practice

Reinforce problem-solving skills and strategies with the Problem-Solving Practice worksheet.

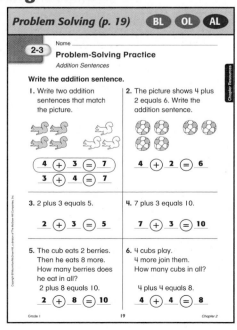

① Introduce

Activity Choice 1 • Hands-On

- Give each student five yellow and five purple connecting cubes and a two-column chart.
- Have the students put one purple cube in the left column and two yellow cubes in the right column. **How many purple parts?** 1 part **How many yellow parts?** 2 parts **Snap them together. How many parts altogether?** 3 parts
- Repeat with additional combinations with sums up to 6.

Activity Choice 2 • Literature

Introduce the lesson with *Rooster's Off to See the World* by Eric Carle. For additional support, see p. TR44.

② Teach

- Write an **addition sentence** on the board. Draw arrows and label the **plus** sign, the **equals** sign, and the **sum**.
- Draw an empty addition sentence on the board: ____ + ____ = ____. List the numbers 2, 4, and 6 above the empty sentence.
- **What addition sentence can we make from these numbers?** 2 + 4 = 6 or 4 + 2 = 6
- **Can we rearrange the numbers to make a different addition sentence?** yes, 4 + 2 = 6 or 2 + 4 = 6
- List 5, 3, and 2 on the board. Have students create an addition sentence from these numbers. 2 + 3 = 5; 3 + 2 = 5
- Repeat with different number sets.

Get Ready Use this section at the top of student p. 55 to reinforce the lesson concept.

Check Observe students as you work through Exercises 1–5 as a class.

💬 **Exercise 5** Assess students' comprehension before assigning practice exercises.

⚠️ **COMMON ERROR!**

Make sure students do not repeat numbers when counting. For example, when solving 4 + 2, students should count by saying "5 . . . 6." Students should not repeat the 4 by saying "4 . . . 5."

Name _____

Addition Sentences

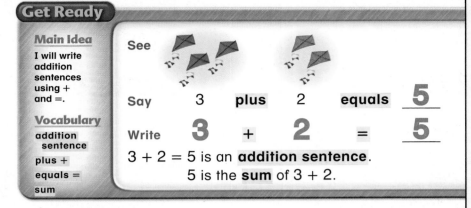

Get Ready

Main Idea

I will write addition sentences using + and =.

Vocabulary

addition sentence

plus +

equals =

sum

See

Say   3   **plus**   2   **equals**   5

Write   3   +   2   =   5

3 + 2 = 5 is an **addition sentence**.
5 is the **sum** of 3 + 2.

✓ **Check**

Write the addition sentence.

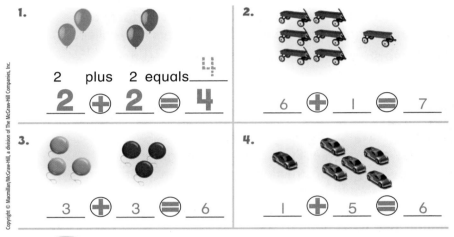

1.
2 plus 2 equals____
2 ⊕ 2 ⊜ 4

2.
6 ⊕ 1 ⊜ 7

3.
3 ⊕ 3 ⊜ 6

4.
1 ⊕ 5 ⊜ 6

5. 💬 **Talk About It** What does + mean? Sample answer: The symbol means plus, join, add, or and.

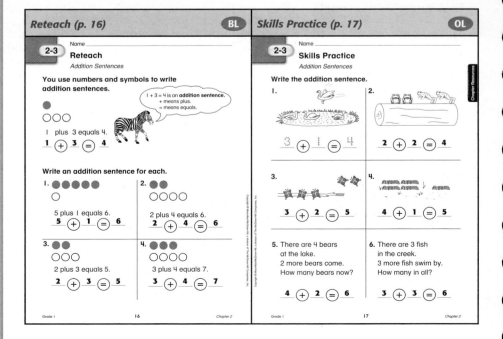

Reteach (p. 16)   **BL**

2-3 Name ___
Reteach
Addition Sentences

You use numbers and symbols to write addition sentences.

💭 1 + 3 = 4 is an **addition sentence**.
+ means plus.
= means equals.

○ ○○○

1 plus 3 equals 4.
1 ⊕ **3** ⊜ **4**

Write an addition sentence for each.

1. ●●●●●
○
5 plus 1 equals 6.
5 ⊕ **1** ⊜ **6**

2. ●●
○○○○
2 plus 4 equals 6.
2 ⊕ **4** ⊜ **6**

3. ●●
○○○
2 plus 3 equals 5.
2 ⊕ **3** ⊜ **5**

4. ●●●
○○○○
3 plus 4 equals 7.
3 ⊕ **4** ⊜ **7**

Grade 1   16   Chapter 2

Skills Practice (p. 17)   **OL**

2-3 Name ___
Skills Practice
Addition Sentences

Write the addition sentence.

1.
3 ⊕ 1 ⊜ 4

2.
2 ⊕ 2 ⊜ 4

3.
3 ⊕ 2 ⊜ 5

4.
4 ⊕ 1 ⊜ 5

5. There are 4 bears at the lake. 2 more bears come. How many bears now?
4 ⊕ **2** ⊜ **6**

6. There are 3 fish in the creek. 3 more fish swim by. How many in all?
3 ⊕ **3** ⊜ **6**

Grade 1   17   Chapter 2

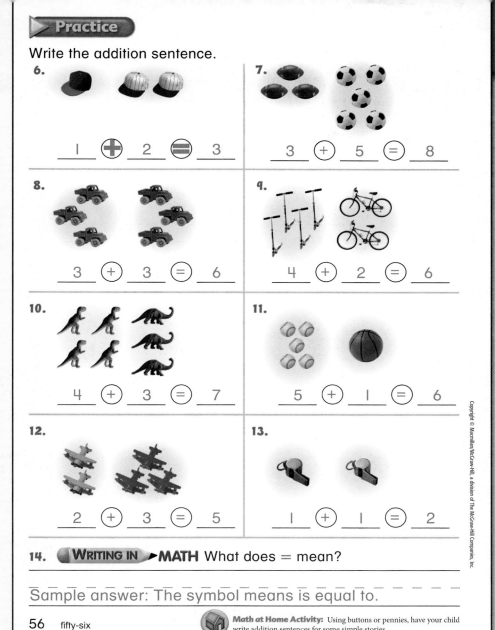

Practice

Write the addition sentence.

6. ___ 1 + 2 = 3

7. ___ 3 + 5 = 8

8. ___ 3 + 3 = 6

9. ___ 4 + 2 = 6

10. ___ 4 + 3 = 7

11. ___ 5 + 1 = 6

12. ___ 2 + 3 = 5

13. ___ 1 + 1 = 2

14. **WRITING IN ►MATH** What does = mean?

Sample answer: The symbol means is equal to.

56 fifty-six

Math at Home Activity: Using buttons or pennies, have your child write addition sentences for some simple stories.

Copyright © Macmillan/McGraw-Hill, a division of The McGraw-Hill Companies, Inc.

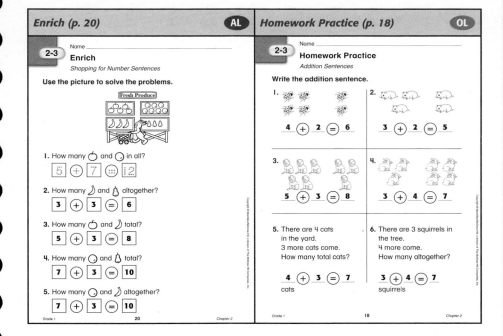

Enrich (p. 20) (AL)

2-3 Name ___
Enrich
Shopping for Number Sentences

Use the picture to solve the problems.

Fresh Produce

1. How many 🍎 and 🍊 in all?
   5 + 7 = 12

2. How many 🍌 and 🍐 altogether?
   3 + 3 = 6

3. How many 🍎 and 🍌 total?
   5 + 3 = 8

4. How many 🍊 and 🍐 total?
   7 + 3 = 10

5. How many 🍊 and 🍌 altogether?
   7 + 3 = 10

Grade 1   20   Chapter 2

Homework Practice (p. 18) (OL)

2-3 Name ___
Homework Practice
Addition Sentences

Write the addition sentence.

1. ___ 4 + 2 = 6

2. ___ 3 + 2 = 5

3. ___ 5 + 3 = 8

4. ___ 3 + 4 = 7

5. There are 4 cats in the yard. 3 more cats come. How many total cats?
   4 + 3 = 7 cats

6. There are 3 squirrels in the tree. 4 more come. How many altogether?
   3 + 4 = 7 squirrels

Grade 1   18   Chapter 2

Copyright © Macmillan/McGraw-Hill, a division of The McGraw-Hill Companies, Inc.

(BL) Alternate Teaching Strategy

If students have trouble writing an addition sentence . . .

Then use one of the following reteach items:

1 [CRM] **Daily Reteach Worksheet** (p. 16)

2 **Unscramble the Addition Sentence:** Give students an envelope with two symbol cards (+, =) and three number cards. The three number cards should be a part of the same fact family. Ask students to unscramble the cards to make an addition sentence.

③ Practice

Differentiate practice, using these leveled assignments for Exercises 6–14.

Level	Assignment
(BL) Below/ Approaching Level	Have students use two-colored counters to give them a hands-on approach.
(OL) On Level	Complete work independently.
(AL) Above/Beyond Level	Have students write each number sentence backwards as well. Ask them to explain whether the sentence makes sense that way.

④ Assess

Formative Assessment

Write the addition sentence 3 + 4 = 7 on the board.

- **How do we know this is an addition sentence?** It has a plus sign.

- **Which part of the sentence is the sum?** 7

WRITING IN ►MATH Have students write addition sentences for things they see around the classroom. For example, 5 markers + 3 markers = 8 markers.

Quick Check **Are students continuing to struggle with addition sentences?**

If Yes ➙ Strategic Intervention Guide (pp. 54–59)
If No ➙ Independent Work Options (p. 55B)
  [CRM] Skills Practice Worksheet (p. 17)
  [CRM] Enrich Worksheet (p. 20)

Extra
Practice

Review Lesson 2-1 to 2-3

Objective: Review and assess mastery of previous lessons' skills and concepts.

- Review with students that addition is a joining of two parts to make a whole or sum.
- Display on the chalkboard a plus sign and an equals sign.
- Students may wish to use two-colored counters and WorkMat 3 to help with their arithmetic.

Practice with Technology

Math Online Have students visit macmillanmh.com for additional practice with online activities, games, and quizzes.

Name _____

Write the addition sentence.

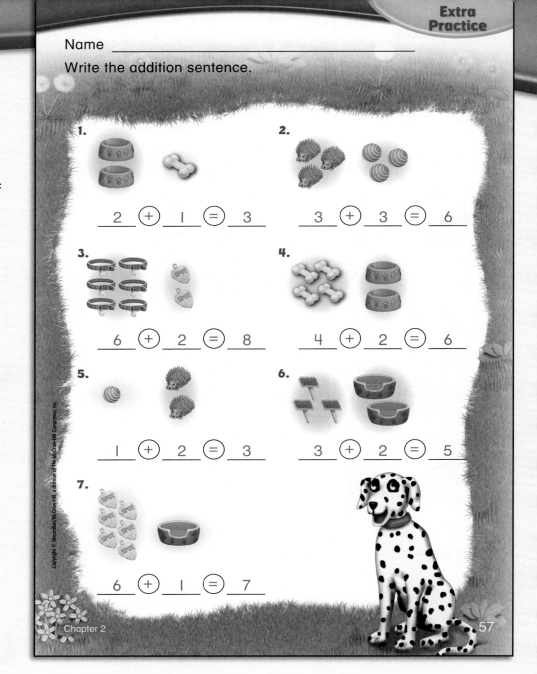

1. 2 (+) 1 (=) 3

2. 3 (+) 3 (=) 6

3. 6 (+) 2 (=) 8

4. 4 (+) 2 (=) 6

5. 1 (+) 2 (=) 3

6. 3 (+) 2 (=) 5

7. 6 (+) 1 (=) 7

Chapter 2   57

Snack Time
Addition

Play with a partner.
- Put the ⚪ ⚫ on START.
- Take turns. Toss the 🎲.
- Move that many spaces.
- Find how many in all.
- If you are wrong, you lose a turn.
- The first player to reach END wins.

You Will Need
🎲 ⚪ ⚫

START

Move ahead 1 space.

2 + 6

3 + 1

3 + 2

1 + 2

2 + 4

Move back 1 space.

END

1 + 3

4 + 1

5 + 2

2 + 3

2 + 2

Copyright © Macmillan/McGraw-Hill, a division of The McGraw-Hill Companies, Inc.

58 fifty-eight

Differentiated Practice
Use these leveling suggestions to differentiate the game for all learners.

Level	Assignment
BL Below/Approaching Level	Allow students to use connecting cubes or two-colored counters to help find the sum.
OL On Level	Have students play the game with the rules as written.
AL Above/Beyond Level	After students find the sum of each addition sentence, have them roll the number cube and add that number to the sum to continue.

Snack Time

Math Concept:
Solve Addition Sentences
Manipulatives: two-colored counters, red number cubes

Instructions
Introduce the game on p. 58 to students to play as a class, in small groups, or at a learning station to review concepts introduced in this chapter.

- Assign each student a color.
- Students play in pairs and take turns moving their counters along the path.
- Students write the addition sentence and the sum on a separate piece of paper.
- If they are wrong, the other player goes twice in a row.
- You may choose to have an addition fact sheet or counters for each pair to check answers.

Extend the Game
This game can easily be adapted to other math concepts. As students study subtraction in Chapter 3 and more complex addition strategies in Chapter 5, have them play this game with the problems suitable for these chapters.

Lesson Planner

Objective
Find sums by adding zero.

Vocabulary
zero

Resources

Materials: dominoes

Literature Connection: *A House for Hermit Crab* by Eric Carle

Alternate Lessons: Use Adapt "The Old Games" on pp. 238 and 239 of *Math Their Way* for practice with addition using zero.

Use *IMPACT Mathematics:* Units A and G to provide practice with adding zero.

Teacher Technology
⊙ TeacherWorks • Concepts in Motion • Math Songs Track 11 Lesson Plan

Focus on Math Background

In this lesson students will analyze the effect of adding zero to any number. After repeated practice and concrete experiences with this concept, the students will begin to generalize how adding zero makes no change to a quantity. Learning these types of numerical relationships and labeling them into categories—*e.g., any number plus zero*—helps students transition to more efficient computational strategies and acquire facility with basic number facts.

Daily Routine

Use these suggestions before beginning the lesson on p. 59.

5-Minute Check

(Reviews Lesson 2-3)
Write an addition sentence and solve.
1. Ben eats 3 green beans and 2 carrots. How many vegetables does he eat? $3 + 2 = 5$, 5 vegetables
2. Kelly gets 2 awards. Jim receives 1 award. How many awards in all? $2 + 1 = 3$, 3 awards

Problem of the Day

Do the patterns below equal each other? Explain.
2, 4, 6, 8, 10 . . .
$2 + 0, 0 + 4, 6 + 0, 8 + 0, 0 + 10$ . .
Yes, because if you solve the addition problems in the second pattern, they equal the same numbers in the same order in the first pattern.

LINE UP While standing in line, have students "pass zero back." Have the first student in line say, "I have zero _____" (e.g., wings). The second student in line says, "I have zero _____ and _____," repeating what the first student said and adding something new. Have students keep passing zero back until the chain breaks down or each student in line participates.

▷ Building Math Vocabulary

Discuss the term **zero** and write it on the board. Write the number 0 on the board. **The number zero equals none or nothing.**

- On the board write, $4 + 0 =$ _____ .
- **What is the sum?** 4
- **Why is the sum the same number as one of the addends?** Sample answer: We added zero or nothing, so the addend does not change.
- Have students write a number sentence that shows adding zero. Students may also illustrate their number sentences.

Differentiated Instruction

Small Group Options

Option 1
Below/Approaching Level BL
VISUAL, SPATIAL, LOGICAL

Materials: two-colored counters , flash cards with the zero facts to 9 + 0

Model one fact for students. Say, "Six plus zero." Say, "Here is six," and place six counters on the desk. Say, "Now I will add zero." Act as though you are placing a counter but do not. Say, "The answer is six."

- Have one student in each pair read aloud the fact on the flash card and the other student model adding zero. Have students switch roles as they work through the facts.

- Would the answer change if we wrote the zero first in a problem? For example, 0 + 3 instead of 3 + 0? No, the answer stays the same.

Option 2
English Language Learners ELL
VISUAL, KINESTHETIC

Materials: beads, some strung beads tied off, some empty strings tied off

Core Vocabulary: how many, any, zero

Common Use Verb: have/don't have

Talk Math This strategy introduces zero with positive and negative forms of "to have," and allows for speed practice with the vocabulary and counting skills.

- Show 5 beads on a table. Count along with student and say: "I *have* five beads." Have students repeat.

- Remove all the beads and say: "I *don't have* any beads. I *have* zero beads.

- Pass out the strung and empty strings. Have students sit in a circle and pass to the left. Say: "I *have* 3 beads", "I *have* zero beads", or "I *don't have* any beads."

Use this worksheet to provide additional support for English Language Learners.

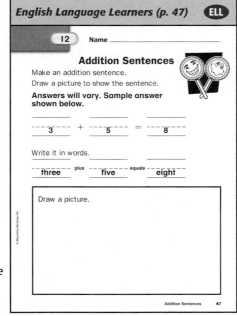

Independent Work Options

Option 1
Early Finishers OL AL
SMALL GROUP, VISUAL, SPATIAL, SOCIAL

Materials: four-part spinner, addition flash cards with sums of 2, 3, 4, or 5

- Have students spread the flash cards facedown on a table.

- Have students take turns spinning the spinner and turning over one card.

- If the sum of the card matches the number on the spinner, the student keeps the card. If the sum and spinner do not match, the student turns the card facedown again.

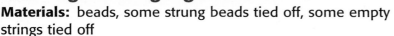

Option 2
Student Technology

Math Online > macmillanmh.com

♪ Math Songs, "The Addition Boogie" Track 11

Math Adventures

Option 3
Learning Stations: Science (p. 47H)

Direct students to the Science Learning Station for opportunities to explore and extend the lesson concept.

Option 4
Problem-Solving Practice

Reinforce problem-solving skills and strategies with the Problem-Solving Practice worksheet.

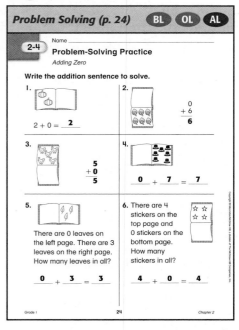

2-4

1 Introduce

Activity Choice 1 • Hands-On

Pass out dominoes to small groups. Explore the domino. Have them find all the dominoes that have **zero** on one side.

- Draw a domino on the chalkboard. Put three dots on one end and zero on the other end.
- **How many dots are on this end?** 3 dots
- **How many dots are on the other end?** 0 dots
- **What addition sentence could we write for this domino?** 3 + 0 = 3
- Have students write addition sentences for their dominoes with zero.

Activity Choice 2 • Literature

Introduce the lesson with *A House for Hermit Crab* by Eric Carle. For additional support, see p. TR44.

2 Teach

- Call two students up to the board. Give a pencil to one student. **How many pencils does this student have?** 1 pencils **How many pencils does the other student have?** 0 pencils **What addition sentence could we write to show the total number of pencils?** 1 + 0 = 1
- Call two different students up to the board. Give four pencils to one student. **How many pencils does this student have?** 4 pencils **How many pencils does the other student have?** 0 pencils **What addition sentence could we write to show the total number of pencils?** 4 + 0 = 4
- Repeat, using different students and objects.

Get Ready Use the section at the top of student p. 59 to teach the lesson concept.

Check Observe students as you work through Exercises 1–5 as a class.

Exercise 5 Assess students' comprehension before assigning practice exercises.

⚠ COMMON ERROR!

Once students learn the concept of zero, they will often start counting manipulatives at zero. Make sure students are not pointing to a manipulative and counting, "0 . . . 1 . . . ."

Name _____

Adding Zero

Get Ready

Main Idea
I will find sums by adding zero.

Vocabulary
zero

When you add **zero**, the sum is the same as the other number.

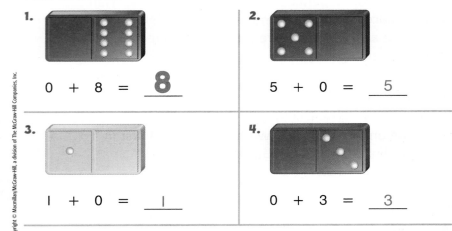

$4 + 0 = $ __4__ $0 + 2 = $ __2__

✓ Check

Find each sum.

1.

$0 + 8 = $ __8__

2.

$5 + 0 = $ __5__

3.

$1 + 0 = $ __1__

4.

$0 + 3 = $ __3__

5. **Talk About It** What happens when you add zero to a number? Why? Sample answer: The number stays the same because it is adding no more.

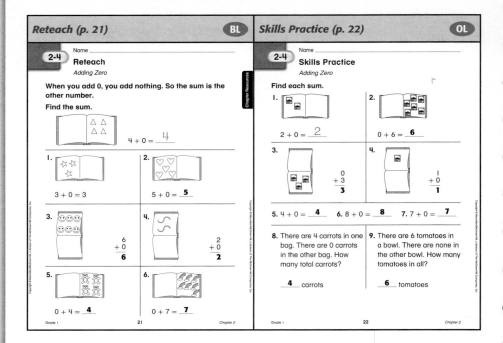

Reteach (p. 21)   **BL**

2-4 Reteach
Adding Zero

When you add 0, you add nothing. So the sum is the other number.
Find the sum.

$4 + 0 = $ __4__

1. $3 + 0 = 3$

2. $5 + 0 = $ __5__

3. $\begin{array}{r} 6 \\ + 0 \\ \hline 6 \end{array}$

4. $\begin{array}{r} 2 \\ + 0 \\ \hline 2 \end{array}$

5. $0 + 4 = $ __4__

6. $0 + 7 = $ __7__

Grade 1   21   Chapter 2

Skills Practice (p. 22)   **OL**

2-4 Skills Practice
Adding Zero

Find each sum.

1. $2 + 0 = $ __2__

2. $0 + 6 = $ __6__

3. $\begin{array}{r} 0 \\ + 3 \\ \hline 3 \end{array}$

4. $\begin{array}{r} 1 \\ + 0 \\ \hline 1 \end{array}$

5. $4 + 0 = $ __4__   **6.** $8 + 0 = $ __8__   **7.** $7 + 0 = $ __7__

8. There are 4 carrots in one bag. There are 0 carrots in the other bag. How many total carrots?

__4__ carrots

9. There are 6 tomatoes in a bowl. There are none in the other bowl. How many tomatoes in all?

__6__ tomatoes

Grade 1   22   Chapter 2

Practice

Find each sum.

Remember
When you add zero, you add none.

6.

$7 + 0 = \underline{7}$

7.

$0 + 6 = \underline{6}$

---

8. $4 + 2 = \underline{6}$ **9.** $3 + 1 = \underline{4}$ **10.** $8 + 0 = \underline{8}$

11. $3 + 0 = \underline{3}$ **12.** $2 + 3 = \underline{5}$ **13.** $3 + 3 = \underline{6}$

14. $2 + 1 = \underline{3}$ **15.** $0 + 5 = \underline{5}$ **16.** $0 + 4 = \underline{4}$

17. $1 + 3 = \underline{4}$ **18.** $2 + 2 = \underline{4}$ **19.** $5 + 1 = \underline{6}$

H.O.T. Problem

20. Make It Right
Taylor adds $6 + 0$ like this.
Tell why Taylor is wrong.
Make it right.

$6 + 0 = 0$

Sample answer: When you add zero to a number, the sum is the same as the other number. $6 + 0 = 6$.

60   sixty

 Math at Home Activity: Hold some pennies in one hand. Hold both hands out to your child. Ask your child to tell you which hand has zero pennies.

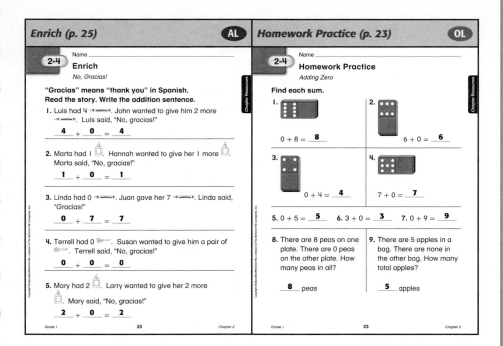

Enrich (p. 25) **AL**

2-4 Name _____
Enrich
No, Gracias!

"Gracias" means "thank you" in Spanish.
Read the story. Write the addition sentence.

1. Luis had 4 🖍. John wanted to give him 2 more 🖍. Luis said, "No, gracias!"

$\underline{4} + \underline{0} = \underline{4}$

2. Marta had 1 🧴. Hannah wanted to give her 1 more 🧴. Marta said, "No, gracias!"

$\underline{1} + \underline{0} = \underline{1}$

3. Linda had 0 🖍. Juan gave her 7 🖍. Linda said, "Gracias!"

$\underline{0} + \underline{7} = \underline{7}$

4. Terrell had 0 🧤. Susan wanted to give him a pair of 🧤. Terrell said, "No, gracias!"

$\underline{0} + \underline{0} = \underline{0}$

5. Mary had 2 🧴. Larry wanted to give her 2 more 🧴. Mary said, "No, gracias!"

$\underline{2} + \underline{0} = \underline{2}$

Grade 1   25   Chapter 2

Homework Practice (p. 23) **OL**

2-4 Name _____
Homework Practice
Adding Zero

Find each sum.

1. $0 + 8 = \underline{8}$

2. $6 + 0 = \underline{6}$

3. $0 + 4 = \underline{4}$

4. $7 + 0 = \underline{7}$

5. $0 + 5 = \underline{5}$ **6.** $3 + 0 = \underline{3}$ **7.** $0 + 9 = \underline{9}$

8. There are 8 peas on one plate. There are 0 peas on the other plate. How many peas in all?

$\underline{8}$ peas

9. There are 5 apples in a bag. There are none in the other bag. How many total apples?

$\underline{5}$ apples

Grade 1   23   Chapter 2

BL Alternate Teaching Strategy

If students have trouble adding zero . . .

Then use one of the following reteach items:

1 🖥 **Daily Reteach Worksheet** (p. 21)

2 Play a Game: Show students a classroom board game or ask students to turn to p. 94. Show a red number cube with the zero face up. Ask students how many spaces forward they would move with this roll. Be sure students understand that they would not move forward; they would same on the same space. Explain that this is just like adding zero to a number; the addend stays the same.

③ Practice

Differentiate practice, using these leveled assignments for Exercises 6–20.

Level	Assignment
BL Below/Approaching Level	Use two-colored counters to find the sums.
OL On Level	Complete independently.
AL Above/Beyond Level	Pair with Below-Level students for peer-modeling.

④ Assess

✓ Formative Assessment

- **How many is zero?** none

- **When you add zero to a number, why is the sum the same as the number?** You are not adding anything to the number.

WRITING IN ▶MATH Have students make a list of things they have zero of. For example, "I have zero brothers."

Quick Check | **Are students continuing to struggle with adding zero?**

If Yes → Small Group Options (p. 59B)
Strategic Intervention Guide (pp. 60–61)

If No → Independent Work Options (p. 59B)
🖥 Skills Practice Worksheet (p. 22)
🖥 Enrich Worksheet (p. 25)

Lesson Planner

Objective

Use the *write a number sentence* strategy to solve problems.

Resources

Materials: blank transparency, overhead projector

Literature Connection: *Quack and Count* by Keith Baker

Teacher Technology
 TeacherWorks

📖 **Real-World Problem Solving Library**
Math and Science: *Healthful Snacks*
Use these leveled books to reinforce and extend problem-solving skills and strategies.

Leveled for:
- **OL** On Level
- **ELL** Sheltered English
- **SP** Spanish

For additional support, see the Real-World Problem Solving Teacher Guide.

Daily Routine

Use these suggestions before beginning the lesson on p. 61.

5-Minute Check

(Reviews Lesson 2-4)
Solve.
1. Julia has three baseballs and did not buy any more. How many baseballs does she have? 3 baseballs
2. Mara has 4 toy airplanes. Luca has no toy airplanes. How many do they have altogether? 4 toy airplanes

Problem of the Day

Asher's mom baked 12 muffins. Asher ate 3 muffins. Carmen ate 2 muffins. How many muffins were eaten? 5 muffins

LINE UP Assign each student a number. Instruct students to line up in reverse order, placing the greatest number first and the least number last. Then have them line up in the correct number order, least number first and the greatest number last.

Differentiated Instruction

Small Group Options

Option 1 — Gifted and Talented

Materials: several index cards with addition problems adding 0, 1, 2, or 3 on each card, drawing paper, pencil.

- Pairs of students sit together with index cards, paper, and pencils.
- One partner chooses an index card with an addition problem and then draws a picture to represent the problem.
- The other partner will then take the drawing and will write the addition problem they think that the drawing represents.
- The students check answers and then change roles.

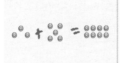

Option 2 — English Language Learners (ELL)

VISUAL, LINGUISTIC

Core Vocabulary: sentence, write, number sentence
Common Use Verb: can read
See Math This strategy helps students recognize, read, and write word and number sentences.

- Draw two red and three yellow counters. Underneath write "There are two red counters and three yellow counters." Say: "This is a **sentence** of words."
- Write: "2 + 3 = 5" and say: "This is also a **sentence**. It is a **sentence** of numbers. We can *read* each."
- Read each.
- Have students throw counters, draw them, and write a sentence about them.
- Repeat as time permits, extending the pictures and sentences into number sentences as the students better understand sentences.

Independent Work Options

SOCIAL/KINESTHETIC

Option 1 — Early Finishers (OL) (AL)

Materials: number cards 1-10, green and yellow connecting cubes, white board, dry erase marker

- Ask students to mix up the set of number cards.
- Have students take turns picking two cards.
- Ask students to work together to use green and yellow connecting cubes to model the two numbers.
- Have students write the number sentence they made on the white board. Remind students to use the plus and equals symbols in their number sentence.
- Encourage students to continue until all cards have been used.

Option 2 — Student Technology

Math Online macmillanmh.com

Option 3 — Learning Stations: Social Studies (p. 47H)

Direct students to the Social Studies Learning Station for opportunities to explore and extend the lesson concept.

① Introduce

Activity Choice 1 • Review

On a blank transparency, draw a repeating border pattern of a circle, triangle, star three times.

- Explain that Fala made a get-well card with this border for her classmate. **We need to finish the card. What strategy can we use to finish the card?** Look for a pattern.
- **What pattern do you see?** circle, triangle, star
- Ask individual students to name the next shape in the pattern. Draw the shapes on the transparency and check each answer before moving to the next.

Activity Choice 2 • Literature

Introduce the lesson with *Quack and Count* by Keith Baker. For additional support, see p. TR44.

② Teach

Have students read the problem on p. 61. Guide them through the problem-solving steps.

Understand Using the questions, review what students know and need to find.

Plan Have students discuss their strategy.

Solve Guide students to *write a number sentence* to solve the problem.

- **What do we do to the parts to find how many children in all?** Join or add the numbers together.
- **What number comes after the equals sign?** the total; the whole; the number that tells how many in all; the sum

Check Have students look back at the problem to make sure that the answer fits the facts given.

- **Should the whole number be greater than either of the parts?** yes **Why?** Adding makes a number bigger.

⚠ COMMON ERROR!

Students may get confused on what mathematical operation they are going to use when solving word problems. Show students how the problem starts with one part. Then it tells about another part. The question asks students to find the whole.

Name _____

Problem-Solving Strategy
Write a Number Sentence

Main Idea

I will write number sentences to solve problems.

2 children paint a fence. 4 more children help. How many children are painting in all?

Understand

What do I need to find?
Circle the question.

Plan

How will I solve the problem?

Solve

Write a number sentence.

Sample answer:
2 + 4 = 6

_____6_____ children

Check

Look back.
Is my answer reasonable?

Check students' explanations.

Chapter 2   Lesson 5

sixty-one   61

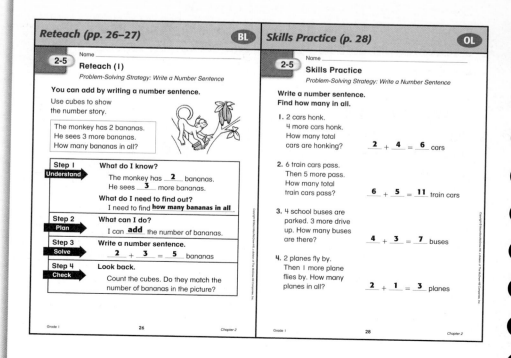

Reteach (pp. 26–27) **BL**

2-5   Name _____
Reteach (1)
Problem-Solving Strategy: Write a Number Sentence

You can add by writing a number sentence.

Use cubes to show the number story.

The monkey has 2 bananas.
He has 3 more bananas.
How many bananas in all?

Step 1 Understand	What do I know?
	The monkey has **2** bananas.
	He sees **3** more bananas.
	What do I need to find out?
	I need to find **how many bananas in all**
Step 2 Plan	What can I do?
	I can **add** the number of bananas.
Step 3 Solve	Write a number sentence.
	2 + **3** = **5** bananas
Step 4 Check	Look back.
	Count the cubes. Do they match the number of bananas in the picture?

Grade 1   26   Chapter 2

Skills Practice (p. 28) **OL**

2-5   Name _____
Skills Practice
Problem-Solving Strategy: Write a Number Sentence

Write a number sentence.
Find how many in all.

1. 2 cars honk.
4 more cars honk.
How many total
cars are honking?   **2** + **4** = **6** cars

2. 6 train cars pass.
Then 5 more pass.
How many total
train cars pass?   **6** + **5** = **11** train cars

3. 4 school buses are
parked. 3 more drive
up. How many buses
are there?   **4** + **3** = **7** buses

4. 2 planes fly by.
Then 1 more plane
flies by. How many
planes in all?   **2** + **1** = **3** planes

Grade 1   28   Chapter 2

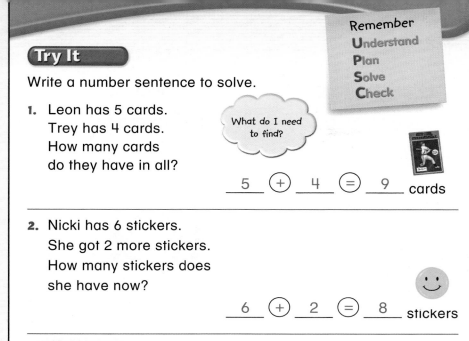

Try It

Write a number sentence to solve.

1. Leon has 5 cards.
Trey has 4 cards.
How many cards
do they have in all?

What do I need to find?

$\underline{}\ 5\ (+)\ \underline{}\ 4\ (=)\ \underline{}\ 9$ cards

2. Nicki has 6 stickers.
She got 2 more stickers.
How many stickers does
she have now?

$\underline{}\ 6\ (+)\ \underline{}\ 2\ (=)\ \underline{}\ 8$ stickers

Your Turn

Write a number sentence to solve.

3. Maria has 2 cats.
Marta has 5 cats.
How many cats do
they have in all?

$\underline{}\ 2\ (+)\ \underline{}\ 5\ (=)\ \underline{}\ 7$ cats

4. Isi saw 6 cars.
Jamaal saw 3 cars.
How many cars did
Isi and Jamaal see?

$\underline{}\ 6\ (+)\ \underline{}\ 3\ (=)\ \underline{}\ 9$ cars

62 sixty-two

Math at Home Activity: Have your child write number sentences about things in the house, such as their toys and their siblings toys.

Remember

Understand
Plan
Solve
Check

Try It Observe students as you work through Exercises 1–2 as a class.

BL Alternate Teaching Strategy

If students have trouble writing a number sentence to solve problems . . .

Then use one of the following reteach items.

1 CRM **Daily Reteach Worksheet** (pp. 26–27)

2 Read Problems Aloud Have students fill in the blanks in the addition sentence as you read the problem aloud. Point out that any numbers they hear will be the parts.

③ Practice

Your Turn

Exercises 3–4 Make sure students can read and understand the problems. Use manipulatives to model the problems if needed. Remind students they are joining two groups or parts to find how many parts there are in all.

④ Assess

Formative Assessment

Tell the following addition story:
Marcos plays basketball. He made 2 shots in a row. Then he made 3 more shots. How many shots did he make in all?

- **How will you solve this problem?** Write a number sentence.

- **From the problem, do you know the parts or the whole?** the parts

- Have students write an addition sentence to solve the problem. $2 + 3 = 5$

Quick Check **Are students continuing to struggle with writing number sentences?**

If Yes → Strategic Intervention Guide (pp. 54–59)

If No → Independent Work Options (p. 61B)
CRM Skills Practice Worksheet (p. 28)
CRM Enrich Worksheet (p. 30)

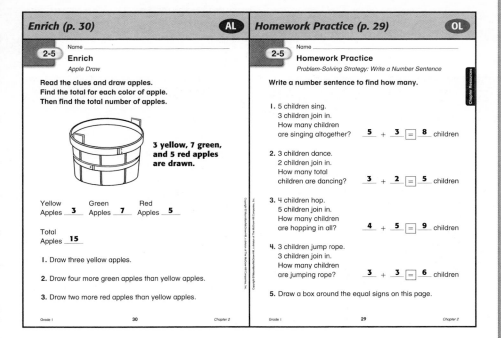

Enrich (p. 30) **AL**

2-5 Name ___
Enrich
Apple Draw

Read the clues and draw apples.
Find the total for each color of apple.
Then find the total number of apples.

3 yellow, 7 green, and 5 red apples are drawn.

Yellow Apples **3** Green Apples **7** Red Apples **5**

Total Apples **15**

1. Draw three yellow apples.

2. Draw four more green apples than yellow apples.

3. Draw two more red apples than yellow apples.

Grade 1   30   Chapter 2

Homework Practice (p. 29) **OL**

2-5 Name ___
Homework Practice
Problem-Solving Strategy: Write a Number Sentence

Write a number sentence to find how many.

1. 5 children sing.
3 children join in.
How many children
are singing altogether?   **5** + **3** = **8** children

2. 3 children dance.
2 children join in.
How many total
children are dancing?   **3** + **2** = **5** children

3. 4 children hop.
5 children join in.
How many children
are hopping in all?   **4** + **5** = **9** children

4. 3 children jump rope.
3 children join in.
How many children
are jumping rope?   **3** + **3** = **6** children

5. Draw a box around the equal signs on this page.

Grade 1   29   Chapter 2

Reviews Lessons 2-1 to 2-5

 Formative Assessment

Use the Mid-Chapter Check to assess students' progress in the first half of the chapter.

ExamView Assessment Suite Customize and create multiple versions of your Mid-Chapter Check and the test answer keys.

FOLDABLES Dinah Zike's Foldables

Use these suggestions to incorporate the Foldable during the chapter.

Lesson 2-4 Label the first pocket 5-Pocket Foldable "0." Have students dictate what they learn about addition with "0" and record their observations on 3"x 5" index cards. Place the information cards and examples of addition problems with "0" in the pocket.

Lesson 2-6 Label the second pocket "4", the third pocket "5", and the fourth pocket "6." Use 3"x 5" index cards to make addition sentence flashcards with sums of 4, 5, and 6 and store them in the appropriate pockets of the Foldable.

Name _____

Add.

1.
● Part	● Part
2	4
Whole	
6	

2.
● Part	● Part
3	5
Whole	
8	

Write the addition sentence.

3.
$\underline{5}\ (+)\ \underline{2}\ (=)\ \underline{7}$

4.
$\underline{4}\ (+)\ \underline{2}\ (=)\ \underline{6}$

Find each sum.

5. $0 + 2 = \underline{2}$

6. $4 + 1 = \underline{5}$

7. $0 + 4 = \underline{4}$

8. $6 + 2 = \underline{8}$

9. $1 + 5 = \underline{6}$

10. $5 + 0 = \underline{5}$

11. $2 + 2 = \underline{4}$

12. $5 + 1 = \underline{6}$

13. **Draw** a picture of 4 balls.
Draw 2 more balls.
Write how many balls there are in all.

$\underline{6}$ balls

Data-Driven Decision-Making

Based on the results of the Mid-Chapter Check, use the following resources to review concepts that continue to give students problems.

Exercises	State/ Local Standards	What's the Math?	Error Analysis	Resources for Review
1-2 Lesson 2-2		Add by joining two groups.	Does not model addends correctly.	Strategic Intervention Guide (p. 52)
3-4 Lesson 2-3		Write an addition sentence.	Does not count pictures correctly. Does not add the two numbers correctly. Does not fill in answer.	Chapter 2 Resource Masters (Reteach Worksheets) **Math Online** Concepts in Motion
5-12 Lesson 2-3 Lesson 2-4		Solve addition sentences with operational symbols.	Does not add correctly or know the word "sum." Puts numbers together to make a two digit number.	Math Adventures
13 Lesson 2-1		Create problem situations that lead to given number sentences.	Does not draw the correct number of balls. Does not answer the question.	

Circle the pattern unit.
Draw what two shapes should come next.

14. △ ■ △ ■ △ ■   △ □

_____

15. Use pattern blocks. Make a pattern. Trace the blocks.
    See students' drawings.

_____

Color the answer.

16. 7 _____ 14

| is greater than | **is less than** | is equal to |

17. 4 _____ 4

| is greater than | is less than | **is equal to** |

18. 18 _____ 2

| **is greater than** | is less than | is equal to |

14. 12 _____ 19

| is greater than | **is less than** | is equal to |

64   sixty-four

Formative Assessment

Spiral Review

Reviews Chapters 1 to 2

Objective: Review and assess mastery of skills and concepts from previous chapters.

Resources for Review

Based on students' results, refer to these lessons for remediation.

- **Exercise 14: Lesson 1-1** (p. 17)
- **Exercise 15: Lesson 1-2** (p. 19)
- **Exercises 16–19: Lesson 1-8** (p. 35)

Lesson Planner

Objective
Use counters to make sums of 4, 5, and 6.

Review Vocabulary
sum

Resources
Materials: WorkMat 3: Part-Part-Whole, dominoes

Manipulatives: two-colored counters

Literature Connection: *Anno's Counting Book* by Mitsumasa Anno

Alternate Lessons: Use "Addition with Unifix Cubes" on p. 246 of *Math Their Way* to provide practice with addition sentences with sums of 4, 5, and 6.

Use *IMPACT Mathematics:* Unit A to provide practice with using manipulatives to make sums of 4, 5, and 6.

Teacher Technology

TeacherWorks • Concepts in Motion • Math Songs Track 11 Lesson Plan

Focus on Math Background

This lesson introduces students to all of the different number combinations that are equivalent to 4, 5, and 6. By first grade, students should be able to quantify smaller quantities up to 6 without counting by simply identifying the whole as a sum of its parts. This skill, known as subitizing, occurs when a child instantly sees, for example, a set of 5 objects in chunks of 3 and 2 or 1 and 4.

Daily Routine

Use these suggestions before beginning the lesson on p. 65.

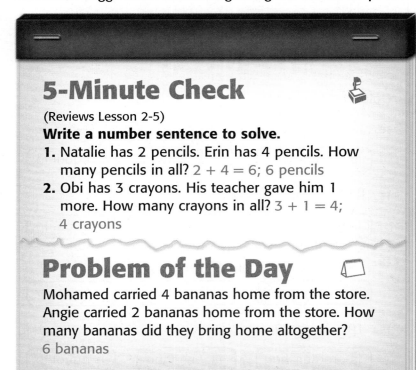

5-Minute Check
(Reviews Lesson 2-5)

Write a number sentence to solve.
1. Natalie has 2 pencils. Erin has 4 pencils. How many pencils in all? $2 + 4 = 6$; 6 pencils
2. Obi has 3 crayons. His teacher gave him 1 more. How many crayons in all? $3 + 1 = 4$; 4 crayons

Problem of the Day
Mohamed carried 4 bananas home from the store. Angie carried 2 bananas home from the store. How many bananas did they bring home altogether? 6 bananas

LINE UP Have students line up to equal sums of 4, 5, or 6. For example, have three girls line up with one boy or four boys line up with two girls. Have students name the addition sentence for their group of students.

Review Math Vocabulary

- On the chalkboard, write the following addition sentence: $4 + 2 = 6$. Have students read the problem aloud.
- Circle the 6. **What does the 6 tell you?** how many in all
- Tell students that the answer to an addition sentence is called the **sum.** Write *sum* on the chalkboard. **Can anyone remember what a sum is?** the answer to an addition sentence
- Call on students to write on the chalkboard addition sentences with sums of 4, 5, or 6. Have students circle the sums

Visual Vocabulary Cards
Use Visual Vocabulary Card 47 to reinforce the vocabulary introduced in this lesson. (The Define/Example/Ask routine is printed on the back of each card.)

sum

Differentiated Instruction

Small Group Options

Option 1 — Below/Approaching Level (BL)

AUDITORY, SOCIAL

Materials: flash cards with sums of 4, 5, and 6, two-colored counters

Give each pair of students four two-colored counters and flash cards with sums of 4.

- Have one student read the first number sentence aloud, saying "blank" instead of the second addend. For example, "1 + blank = 4."
- Have the other student show the named addend with a red counter, turn over the remaining counters to the yellow side, and count the yellow counters aloud.
- Repeat for sums of 5 and 6. Have partners switch roles.

Option 2 — English Language Learners (ELL)

VISUAL, SPATIAL, SOCIAL

Materials: domino tiles, scaffold poster with a drawing of a blank domino and "_____ and _____ makes _____ altogether"

Core Vocabulary: match, spot, altogether

Common Use Verb: makes (a given number)

Do Math This strategy activates background knowledge and uses it to practice addition skills and word problems.

- Show a domino tile, and ask: "How many spots are on the left side?" Write that number on the board. Repeat for the right side.
- Write "and" in between the 2 numbers.
- Ask: "How many **spots** are there **altogether**?"
- Circle both numbers and write "makes" (leave a space) "altogether" outside the circle.
- Have students pull a domino and write the addition problems using the scaffold.
- Match up dominos to the correct problems as time permits.

Independent Work Options

Option 1 — Early Finishers (OL) (AL)

PAIRS, KINESTHETIC, LOGICAL

Materials: sheets of empty addition sentences, rods of connecting four cubes

- Have one student break the rod into two parts by removing the leftmost cube. The other student should fill in an empty addition sentence for the parts.
- Have students repeat breaking and reassembling the rod, but break it one cube to the right of the previous time. In this way, all the sums up to 4 can be found.

$$\underline{\ 3\ } + \underline{\ 1\ } = \underline{\ 4\ }$$

Option 2 — Student Technology

Math Online macmillanmh.com

♪ Math Songs, "The Addition Boogie" Track 11

🌀 Math Adventures

Option 3 — Learning Stations: Reading (p. 47G)

Direct students to the Reading Learning Station for opportunities to explore and extend the lesson concept.

Option 4 — Problem-Solving Practice

Reinforce problem-solving skills and strategies with the Problem-Solving Practice worksheet.

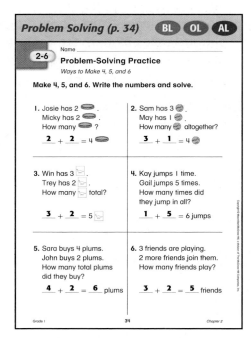

Problem Solving (p. 34) BL OL AL

Name

2-6 **Problem-Solving Practice**
Ways to Make 4, 5, and 6

Make 4, 5, and 6. Write the numbers and solve.

1. Josie has 2. Micky has 2. How many?
$\underline{2} + \underline{2} = 4$

2. Sam has 3. May has 1. How many altogether?
$\underline{3} + \underline{1} = 4$

3. Win has 3. Trey has 2. How many total?
$\underline{3} + \underline{2} = 5$

4. Kay jumps 1 time. Gail jumps 5 times. How many times did they jump in all?
$\underline{1} + \underline{5} = 6$ jumps

5. Sara buys 4 plums. John buys 2 plums. How many total plums did they buy?
$\underline{4} + \underline{2} = \underline{6}$ plums

6. 3 friends are playing. 2 more friends join them. How many friends play?
$\underline{3} + \underline{2} = \underline{5}$ friends

Grade 1   34   Chapter 2

2-6

① Introduce

Activity Choice 1 • Hands-On

- Give each student 6 two-colored counters.
- Ask the students to use any combination of counters to make 4. Then ask students to tell you about the combinations they made. Write an addition sentence for each combination.
- Repeat with combinations of 5 and 6.

Activity Choice 2 • Literature

Introduce the lesson with *Anno's Counting Book* by Mitsumasa Anno. For additional support, see p. TR44.

② Teach

Display WorkMat 3: Part-Part-Whole. Place two red counters in one part and two yellow counters in the other.

- **How many red counters?** 2 counters Write *2*.
- **How many yellow counters?** 2 counters Write *+ 2*.
- Move all the counters to the whole section. **How many counters in all?** 4 counters Write *= 4*.
- Have students read the number sentence with you. Do not erase the number sentence.
- Reverse the number of yellow and red counters on the workmat and repeat the procedure. **What are two ways to make 4?**
- Continue the activity with: 3 +1, 1 + 3, 4 + 0, 0 +4.
- **What patterns do you see?** You can reverse the order of the parts, and the sum does not change. Students might notice that when one part increases by one, the other must decrease by one for the sum to remain the same.
- Continue with sums of 5 and 6.

Get Ready Use the section at the top of student p. 65 to reinforce the lesson concept.

Check Observe students as you work through Exercises 1-4 as a class.

 Exercise 4 Assess student comprehension before assigning practice exercises.

⚠ COMMON ERROR!

Students may have difficulty showing their work. Remind students to check their work by reading the number sentence aloud while pointing to the appropriate counters.

65 **Chapter 2** Develop Addition Concepts

Name _____

Ways to Make 4, 5, and 6

Get Ready

Main Idea

I will use counters to make sums of 4, 5, and 6.

There are different ways to make a sum. Here are two ways to make 4.

I can add 2 and 2 to make 4. 2 + 2 = 4

I can add 1 and 3 to make 4. 1 + 3 = 4

✓ Check

Use WorkMat 1. Put ●◯ in two groups to make 4. Color the ◯. Write the numbers.

Sample answers:

Ways to Make 4				
●	plus	◯	equals	sum
1.	1	+	3	=	4
2.	3	+	1	=	4
3.	2	+	2	=	4

4. **Talk About It** What is another way to make 4?
Sample answers: 0 + 4 = 4, 4 + 0 = 4

Chapter 2   Lesson 6   sixty-five   65

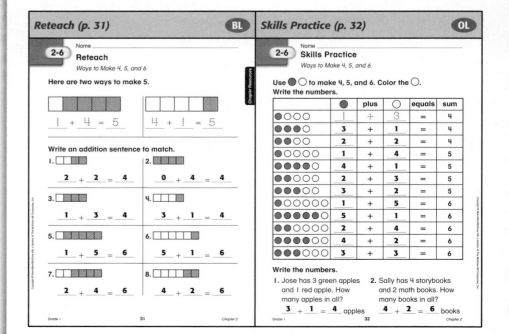

Reteach (p. 31) BL

2-6 **Reteach**
Ways to Make 4, 5, and 6

Here are two ways to make 5.

1 + 4 = 5   4 + 1 = 5

Write an addition sentence to match.

1. 2 + 2 = 4   2. 0 + 4 = 4

3. 1 + 3 = 4   4. 3 + 1 = 4

5. 1 + 5 = 6   6. 5 + 1 = 6

7. 2 + 4 = 6   8. 4 + 2 = 6

Grade 1   31   Chapter 2

Skills Practice (p. 32) OL

2-6 **Skills Practice**
Ways to Make 4, 5, and 6

Use ●◯ to make 4, 5, and 6. Color the ◯.
Write the numbers.

●	plus	◯	equals	sum
1	+	3	=	4
3	+	1	=	4
2	+	2	=	4
1	+	4	=	5
4	+	1	=	5
2	+	3	=	5
3	+	2	=	5
1	+	5	=	6
5	+	1	=	6
2	+	4	=	6
4	+	2	=	6
3	+	3	=	6

Write the numbers.

1. Jose has 3 green apples and 1 red apple. How many apples in all?
3 + 1 = 4 apples

2. Sally has 4 storybooks and 2 math books. How many books in all?
4 + 2 = 6 books

Grade 1   32   Chapter 2

Use WorkMat 1. Put ⬤◯ in two groups.
Color the ◯. Write the numbers.

Ways to Make 5			
Sample answers: ⬤ plus ◯ equals sum			

	⬤	plus	◯	equals	sum
5.	⬤⬤⬤⬤◯	4	+	1	=	5
6.	⬤◯◯◯◯	1	+	4	=	5
7.	⬤⬤◯◯◯	2	+	3	=	5

Ways to Make 6			
Sample answers: ⬤ plus ◯ equals sum			

	⬤	plus	◯	equals	sum
8.	⬤⬤⬤◯◯◯	3	+	3	=	6
9.	⬤⬤◯◯◯◯	2	+	4	=	6
10.	⬤⬤⬤⬤◯◯	4	+	2	=	6

H.O.T. Problem

11. **Make It Right**
This is what Dylan wrote
for the sum of 6.

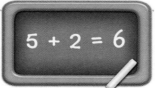
5 + 2 = 6

Tell why Dylan is wrong. Make it right.

Sample answer: Dylan added wrong. 5 + 2 = 7

Math at Home Activity: Give your child six objects. Have your child show different ways to make two groups and show 4 in all, 5 in all, or 6 in all.

Copyright © Macmillan/McGraw-Hill, a division of The McGraw-Hill Companies, Inc.

Enrich (p. 35) **AL**

Name _____

2-6 Enrich
Math Stars

Draw the missing stars. Write the addition sentence.

1. ☆☆ / ☆ ☆   __3__ + __1__ = 4

2. ☆ ☆☆ ☆   __2__ + __2__ = 4

3. ☆☆ / ☆☆ ☆   __5__ + __1__ = 6

4. ☆☆ ☆ / ☆ ☆   __4__ + __2__ = 6

5. ☆ ☆ ☆ / ☆   __2__ + __3__ = 5

6. ☆ / ☆☆ ☆   __1__ + __4__ = 5

Grade 1   35   Chapter 2

Homework Practice (p. 33) **OL**

Name _____

2-6 Homework Practice
Ways to Make 4, 5, and 6

Use ⬤ ◯ to make 5 and 6. Color the ◯.
Write the numbers.

	⬤	plus	◯	equals	sum
⬤◯◯◯◯	1	+	4	=	5
⬤⬤⬤⬤◯	4	+	1	=	5
⬤⬤◯◯◯	2	+	3	=	5
⬤⬤⬤◯◯	3	+	2	=	5
⬤◯◯◯◯◯	1	+	5	=	6
⬤⬤⬤⬤⬤◯	5	+	1	=	6
⬤⬤◯◯◯◯	2	+	4	=	6
⬤⬤⬤⬤◯◯	4	+	2	=	6
⬤⬤⬤◯◯◯	3	+	3	=	6

Solve.

1. Juan has 2 green dinosaurs. He also has 3 brown ones. How many dinosaurs does he have in all?

__2__ + __3__ = __5__ dinosaurs

2. Lisa has 3 toy trucks. She also has 3 toy cars. How many toys does she have altogether?

__3__ + __3__ = __6__ toys

Grade 1   33   Chapter 2

BL Alternate Teaching Strategy

If students have trouble making sums of 4, 5, or 6 . . .

Then use one of the following reteach items:

1 **CRM** **Daily Reteach Worksheet** (p. 31)

2 **Use Dominoes:** Give all the dominoes with total sums of 4, 5, or 6 to a student. Have him or her separate the dominoes into three piles based on the sums.

③ Practice

Differentiate practice, using these leveled assignments for Exercises 5–11.

Level	Assignment
BL Below/ Approaching Level	Work with students in pairs, modeling for them how to count the counters and record the information.
OL On Level	Complete independently.
AL Above/Beyond Level	Have students complete the exercises without the counters and workmat.

④ Assess

✔ Formative Assessment

Ask students to model these addition problems using counters and WorkMat 3.

- 2 + 4 = 6
- 1 + 3 = 4
- 4 + 0 = 4
- 3 + 2 = 5

WRITING IN ▶**MATH** Have students describe four, five, or six favorite foods that could be eaten in two separate meals.

Quick Check Are students continuing to struggle with finding all of the combinations to make 4, 5, and 6?

If Yes → Small Group Options (p. 65B)
Strategic Intervention Guide (pp. 54–55)

If No → Independent Work Options (p. 65B)
CRM Skills Practice Worksheet (p. 32)
CRM Enrich Worksheet (p. 35)

Lesson 2-6 Ways to Make 4, 5, and 6   **66**

Lesson Planner

Objective
Use counters to make sums of 7, 8, and 9.

Review Vocabulary
add

Resources
Manipulatives: two-colored counters

Literature Connection: *Quack and Count* by Keith Baker

Alternate Lessons: Use "The Magic Box" on p. 248 of *Math Their Way* to provide practice with addition sentences with sums of 7, 8, and 9.

Use *IMPACT Mathematics:* Units A and G to provide practice with using manipulatives to make sums of 7, 8, and 9.

Teacher Technology
TeacherWorks • Concepts in Motion • Math Songs Track 11 Lesson Plan

Focus on Math Background

In this lesson students continue their work representing equivalent forms of the same number through the use of physical models, diagrams, and number expressions. Unlike the previous lesson, however, the students will focus on number combinations that make larger quantities of 7, 8, and 9. Understanding how 8 can be expressed as 4 + 4 or 6 + 2 helps students to make sense of the concept of equivalency, another hallmark of algebraic reasoning.

Daily Routine

Use these suggestions before beginning the lesson on p. 67.

5-Minute Check
(Reviews Lesson 2-6)
Solve. Tell another way to make each sum.
1. $1 + 4 =$ _____ 5; Possible answer: $3 + 2 = 5$
2. $3 + 3 =$ _____ 6; Possible answer: $1 + 5 = 6$

Problem of the Day

	blue	yellow	green	purple	red	orange
Ahmed	2	4				
Latoya			4	3		
Madison					2	5

Which two children have the same number of marbles? Latoya and Madison How many marbles do they have? 7 marbles.

 Assign each student an addition fact with sums of 7, 8, or 9. Call students to line up by their sums.

Review Math Vocabulary
- **Remember that adding puts two numbers together. What numbers can you add together to get a sum of 7?** $1 + 6$; $2 + 5$; $3 + 4$; $0 + 7$
- Call on students to write on the board addition sentences with a sum of 7.
- Repeat the activity for sums of 8 and 9.

Visual Vocabulary Cards
Use Visual Vocabulary Card 1 to reinforce the vocabulary reviewed in this lesson. (The Define/Example/Ask routine is printed on the back of each card.)

Differentiated Instruction

Small Group Options

Option 1 — Gifted and Talented (AL)

Materials: grid paper, crayons, scissors
Distribute a 10 × 10 grid to each student.

- Have students color the first row in red and yellow to show a sum to 7, 8, or 9. Have them write the related addition sentence in the second row. Have students repeat until all the rows are full.

- Pair students. Have them cut the rows on their grid apart. Have each pair mix all the colored strips in one pile, and all the addition sentences in another pile.

- Have pairs work together to match the addition sentences to the colored strips.

Option 2 — English Language Learners (ELL)

Materials: attribute blocks
Core Vocabulary: help us remember, ways, new
Common Use Verb: help/helped

See Math This strategy attaches vocabulary and memory devices to addition skills.

- Use 7 attribute blocks to make a shape. Say: "Shapes or patterns can *help us remember ways* to make 7."

- Have students show 7 in a way that helps them remember 7 combinations.

- Say: **"Draw or show something that *helps* us remember ways** to make 7." Post.

- Say: "You ***helped* us remember** 7 by…"

- Repeat for 8 and 9.

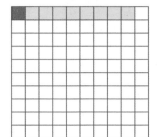

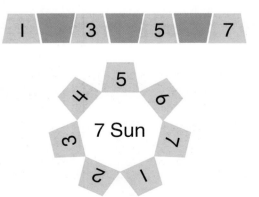

Independent Work Options

Option 1 — Early Finishers (OL) (AL)

Materials: Workmat 3: Part-Part-Whole, two-colored counters

- Have students use WorkMat 3: Part-Part-Whole to model ways to make 7.

- Ask students to take turns using counters to show two different parts that make 7 when added together.

- Encourage students to continue the activity making 8 and 9.

Option 2 — Student Technology

Math Online ▸ macmillanmh.com

♪ Math Songs, "The Addition Boogie" Track 11

🌐 Math Adventures

Option 3 — Learning Stations: Art (p. 47G)

Direct students to the Art Learning Station for opportunities to explore and extend the lesson concept.

Option 4 — Problem-Solving Practice

Reinforce problem-solving skills and strategies with the Problem-Solving Practice worksheet.

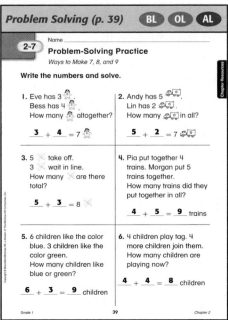

1 Introduce

Activity Choice 1 • Hands-On

- Give each student 9 two-colored counters. Ask the students to use any combination of counters to make 7. Then ask students to tell you about the combinations they made and write an addition sentence for each combination.
- Repeat with combinations of 8 and 9.

Activity Choice 2 • Literature

Introduce the lesson with *Quack and Count* by Keith Baker. For additional support, see p. TR44.

2 Teach

- Create recording sheets divided into three columns, labeled *red, yellow,* and *in all.*
- Have students place 8 two-colored counters in a cup, shake the cup, and empty the counters onto their desks.
- Show students how to sort their counters by color. **How many yellow counters are there? How many red counters are there? How many counters in all?** See students' work.
- Demonstrate on the chalkboard how to record the totals for each column on the recording sheets.
- Continue until students have each found several possible combinations that make 8.
- Have students repeat the activity with nine counters.

Get Ready Use the section at the top of student p. 67 to teach the lesson concept.

Check Observe students as you work through Exercises 1–6 as a class.

 Exercise 6 Assess students' comprehension before assigning practice exercises.

⚠ COMMON ERROR!

Students may overlook reversing the addends to create a new fact. For example, a student may find that $1 + 6 = 7$, but may not realize that $6 + 1 = 7$. Demonstrate this fact by switching piles of counters from right to left on a desk.

Name _____

Ways to Make 7, 8, and 9

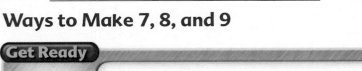

Get Ready

Main Idea
I will use counters to make sums of 7, 8, and 9.

	$1 + 6 = 7$
	$2 + 5 = 7$
	$3 + 4 = 7$

✓ **Check**   6. Student responses should be different from answers in the chart and should total 7.

Use WorkMat 1. Put ⬤◯ in two groups to make 7. Write the numbers.

Sample answers:

There are many ways to make 7.

Ways to Make 7

	⬤ plus	◯	equals	sum
1.	0	+ 7	=	7
2.	4	+ 3	=	7
3.	5	+ 2	=	7
4.	2	+ 5	=	7
5.	6	+ 1	=	7

6. **Talk About It** What is another way to make 7?

Chapter 2   Lesson 7   sixty-seven   **67**

Reteach (p. 36)   **BL**

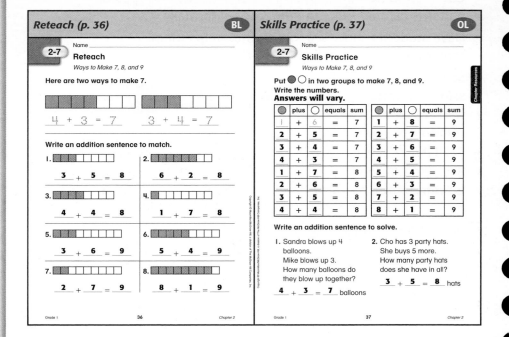

2-7 Reteach
Ways to Make 7, 8, and 9

Here are two ways to make 7.

$4 + 3 = 7$ $3 + 4 = 7$

Write an addition sentence to match.

1. $3 + 5 = 8$ 2. $6 + 2 = 8$
3. $4 + 4 = 8$ 4. $1 + 7 = 8$
5. $3 + 6 = 9$ 6. $5 + 4 = 9$
7. $2 + 7 = 9$ 8. $8 + 1 = 9$

Grade 1   36   Chapter 2

Skills Practice (p. 37)   **OL**

2-7 Skills Practice
Ways to Make 7, 8, and 9

Put ⬤◯ in two groups to make 7, 8, and 9.
Write the numbers.
Answers will vary.

⬤	plus	◯	equals	sum		⬤	plus	◯	equals	sum
1	+	6	=	7		1	+	8	=	9
2	+	5	=	7		2	+	7	=	9
3	+	4	=	7		3	+	6	=	9
4	+	3	=	7		4	+	5	=	9
1	+	7	=	8		5	+	4	=	9
2	+	6	=	8		6	+	3	=	9
3	+	5	=	8		7	+	2	=	9
4	+	4	=	8		8	+	1	=	9

Write an addition sentence to solve.

1. Sandra blows up 4 balloons. Mike blows up 3. How many balloons do they blow up together?
$4 + 3 = 7$ balloons

2. Cho has 3 party hats. She buys 5 more. How many party hats does she have in all?
$3 + 5 = 8$ hats

Grade 1   37   Chapter 2

Practice

Use WorkMat 1. Put  in two groups to make the sum shown.
Write the numbers. Sample answers:

Ways to Make 8				
	⬤	plus	⚪ equals	sum
7.	4	+	4 =	8
8.	5	+	3 =	8
9.	3	+	5 =	8
10.	6	+	2 =	8
11.	2	+	6 =	8
12.	1	+	7 =	8
13.	0	+	8 =	8

Ways to Make 9				
	⬤	plus	⚪ equals	sum
14.	5	+	4 =	9
15.	4	+	5 =	9
16.	8	+	1 =	9
17.	1	+	8 =	9
18.	7	+	2 =	9
19.	3	+	6 =	9
20.	9	+	0 =	9

Problem Solving

21. **Number Sense** Tell an addition story about the number of dogs shown. Write a number sentence for the story.

Sample answer:

<u> 6 </u> + <u> 3 </u> = <u> 9 </u>

68   sixty-eight

Math at Home Activity: Give your child 9 objects. Then have your child show different ways to make two groups and show 7 in all, 8 in all, or 9 in all.

Alternate Teaching Strategy

If ▶ students have trouble using two-colored counters to find sums of 7, 8, and 9 . . .

Then ▶ use one of the following reteach items:

1 **CRM** **Daily Reteach Worksheet** (p. 36)

2 **Work Backwards** Have students start with 7, 8, or 9 counters all with the same color showing. Tell students to flip the counters one at a time as they count backwards.

③ Practice

Differentiate practice, using these leveled assignments for Exercises 7–21.

Level	Assignment
BL Below/Approaching Level	Have students start with a connected stack of 7, 8, or 9 connecting cubes.
OL On Level	Complete work independently.
AL Above/Beyond Level	Have students complete the exercises without the workmat and counters.

④ Assess

✓ Formative Assessment

- **List the ways you can make sums of 7.**
  1 + 6, 2 + 5, 3 + 4, 0 + 7

- **List the ways you can make sums of 9.**
  1 + 8, 2 + 7, 3 + 6, 4 + 5, 0 + 9

WRITING IN ▶ MATH Have students write one addition sentence for each of the following sums: 7, 8, and 9. Then have them illustrate each sentence with pictures of their choice.

Quick Check **Are students continuing to struggle with ways to make 7, 8, and 9?**

If Yes → Strategic Intervention Guide (pp. 58–59)

If No → Independent Work Options (p. 67B)
    CRM Skills Practice Worksheet (p. 37)
    CRM Enrich Worksheet (p. 40)

Enrich (p. 40) **AL**

2-7 Name _____
Enrich
Sum of Each

Read the story. Color 2 ways to solve the problem. Write the addition sentence.

1. Lamar has 7 toy 🚗. Some are orange. Some are blue.

☐ + ☐ = 7   ☐ + ☐ = 7
Answers will vary.

2. Jill has 8 toy 🚌. Some are green. Some are yellow.

☐ + ☐ = 8   ☐ + ☐ = 8
Answers will vary.

3. Jose has 9 toy ✗. Some are black. Some are blue.

☐ + ☐ = 9   ☐ + ☐ = 9
Answers will vary.

Grade 1   40   Chapter 2

Homework Practice (p. 38) **OL**

2-7 Name _____
Homework Practice
Ways to Make 7, 8, and 9

Put ⬤⚪ in two groups to make 7, 8, and 9. Write the numbers.   **Answers will vary.**

⬤	plus	⚪	equals	sum
1	+	6	=	7
2	+	5	=	7
3	+	4	=	7
4	+	3	=	7
1	+	7	=	8
2	+	6	=	8
3	+	5	=	8
4	+	4	=	8
2	+	7	=	9
3	+	6	=	9
4	+	5	=	9
5	+	4	=	9

Write an addition sentence to solve.

1. 3 pandas are eating. 5 more join in. How many pandas are eating now?

<u> 3 </u> + <u> 5 </u> = <u> 8 </u> pandas

Grade 1   38   Chapter 2

Lesson 2-7 Ways to Make 7, 8, and 9   **68**

Ways to Make 10, 11, and 12

Lesson Planner

Objective
Use a ten-frame and counters to make sums of 10, 11, and 12.

Review Vocabulary
equals (=), plus (+)

Resources
Materials: WorkMat 1: Ten-Frame, red crayons, yellow crayons, number cards

Manipulatives: two-colored counters, connecting cubes

Literature Connection: *Anno's Counting Book* by Mitsumasa Anno

Alternate Lessons: *Use* "Listen and Count" on p. 198 of *Math Their Way* to provide practice with addition sentences with the sums of 10.

Use *IMPACT Mathematics:* Units A and H to provide practice with using manipulatives to make sums of 10, 11, and 12.

Teacher Technology
💿 TeacherWorks • Concepts in Motion • 🔲 Math Tool Chest • Math Songs Track 11 Lesson Plan

Focus on Math Background

Different ways to compose 10, 11, and 12 is the focus of this lesson. Knowing all of the combinations of 10 is an important foundation for future work adding two-digit numbers that equal 100. For example, if a student knows a basic fact, such as $3 + 7 = 10$, the child can apply this knowledge to help him or her figure out $30 + 70$. The focus of this lesson is also on increasing the students' familiarity with different ways to make 11 and 12. Through concrete experiences composing numbers with other number combinations, first graders will notice patterns and discover relationships in our number system, such as how $4 + 8$ is the same as $8 + 4$, and eventually commit these number facts to memory.

Daily Routine

Use these suggestions before beginning the lesson on p. 69.

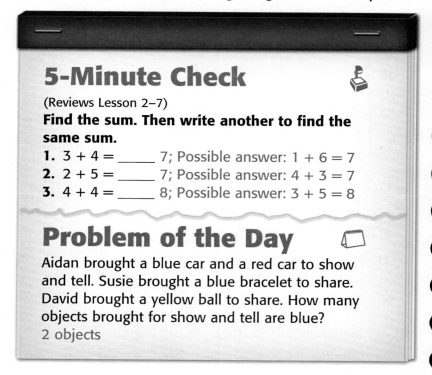

5-Minute Check
(Reviews Lesson 2–7)
Find the sum. Then write another to find the same sum.
1. $3 + 4 =$ _____ 7; Possible answer: $1 + 6 = 7$
2. $2 + 5 =$ _____ 7; Possible answer: $4 + 3 = 7$
3. $4 + 4 =$ _____ 8; Possible answer: $3 + 5 = 8$

Problem of the Day
Aidan brought a blue car and a red car to show and tell. Susie brought a blue bracelet to share. David brought a yellow ball to share. How many objects brought for show and tell are blue?
2 objects

LINE UP Call students to line up in groups that make 10. For example, call on two students to line up, and then call on eight students to line up. **What addition sentence describes the students that just lined up?** $2 + 8 = 10$ Repeat with other combinations for sums to 11 and 12.

Review Math Vocabulary
- Have students name different addition sentences with sums of 7, 8, or 9. Write the addition sentences on the board, reviewing the **plus** and **equals** symbols.
- Show students a ten-frame on an overhead projector and write the term ten-frame above it. Explain that the *ten-frame* is a tool to help find sums of 10. Point to each square and have students count as you point. **How many squares are there on the ten-frame?** 10 squares

Visual Vocabulary Cards
Use Visual Vocabulary Card 38 to reinforce the vocabulary reviewed in this lesson. (The Define/Example/Ask routine is printed on the back of each card.)

plus

Differentiated Instruction

Small Group Options

Option 1
Below/Approaching Level **BL**

KINESTHETIC, LOGICAL

Materials: common classroom objects

Assign two small, common classroom objects to each pair of students (e.g., pencils and markers). Have pairs independently collect about 12 of each object.

- Model the activity by showing two groups of objects that make a total of 11.
- **How many ___ are there?** See students' work.
- **How many ___ are there?** See students' work.
- **How many ___ and ___ are there in all?** 11 in all
- Have pairs work to find ways to make 11 with their manipulatives.
- Repeat the activity to make a total of 12.

Option 2
English Language Learners **ELL**

AUDITORY

Materials: two-colored counters, ten-frame
Core Vocabulary: plus
Common Use Verb: add up

Hear Math This strategy uses music as a memory device to remember the ways to make 10, 11, and 12.

- Give each pair of students 10 counters. Ask them to put them into 2 groups.
- Allow students a minute to divide the counters and then ask each pair how many they have in each group. Write answers on the board. "4 **plus** 6"
- Sing the following song to Row, Row, Row Your Boat: Ways, ways, ways to make, ways to make 10 ___ **plus** ___ or ___ **plus** ___. Now add them up again.
- Repeat for all answers with the number 10.
- Repeat for numbers 11 and 12 if time permits.

Independent Work Options

Option 1
Early Finishers **OL** **AL**

PAIRS, LOGICAL, SOCIAL

Materials: addition flash cards with sums to 9, 10, 11, and 12, four-part spinner

Label the parts of the spinner 9, 10, 11, and 12. Place flash cards faceup on a desk.

- Have one student spin the spinner to find the sum.
- Ask the other student to find two flash cards with addition facts that equal that sum.
- Have students take turns and continue until all sentences have been paired up.

1+8=9
2+7=9

Option 2
Student Technology

Math Online ➤ macmillanmh.com

♪ Math Songs, "The Addition Boogie" Track 11

🍰 Math Tool Chest

Option 3
Learning Stations: Social Studies (p. 47H)

Direct students to the Social Studies Learning Station for opportunities to explore and extend the lesson concept.

Option 4
Problem-Solving Practice

Reinforce problem-solving skills and strategies with the Problem-Solving Practice worksheet.

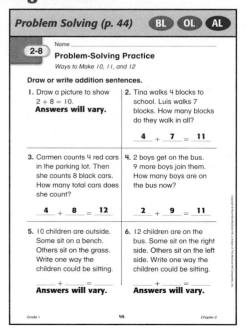

Problem Solving (p. 44) **BL** **OL** **AL**

Name ____

2-8
Problem-Solving Practice
Ways to Make 10, 11, and 12

Draw or write addition sentences.

1. Draw a picture to show $2 + 8 = 10$.
   Answers will vary.

2. Tina walks 4 blocks to school. Luis walks 7 blocks. How many blocks do they walk in all?
   $4 + 7 = 11$

3. Carmen counts 4 red cars in the parking lot. Then she counts 8 black cars. How many total cars does she count?
   $4 + 8 = 12$

4. 2 boys get on the bus. 9 more boys join them. How many boys are on the bus now?
   $2 + 9 = 11$

5. 10 children are outside. Some sit on a bench. Others sit on the grass. Write one way the children could be sitting.
   ___ + ___ = ___
   Answers will vary.

6. 12 children are on the bus. Some sit on the right side. Others sit on the left side. Write one way the children could be sitting.
   ___ + ___ = ___
   Answers will vary.

Grade 1   44   Chapter 2

① Introduce

Activity Choice 1 • Hands-On

Play the game "Concentration Tens." For each group, provide four sets of number cards labeled from 1 to 9.

- Tell students that each card's value is the number shown on it. Have groups spread their cards out on a desk and turn the cards number-side down.

- On a player's turn, he or she turns over two cards. If the sum of the two cards is 10, the player gets to keep them. If the sum is not 10, the cards are returned facedown to their original location.

- Players take turns until there are no possibilities left.

Activity Choice 2 • Literature

Introduce the lesson with *Anno's Counting Book* by Mitsumasa Anno. For additional support, see p. TR45.

② Teach

- Give pairs of students connecting cubes in two colors and a three-column table. Label the columns *starting number*, *prediction*, and *addition sentence*.

- Have pairs choose a number from 1 to 9 to start with and record it under the *starting number* column. Have students predict what number they would add to their starting number to make 10.

- Then have them use connecting cubes to see if their prediction is correct. Have students record correct addition sentences in the last column.

- Have students repeat the activity until each pair finds three or four ways to make 10, then 11 and 12.

Get Ready Use the section on p. 69 to teach the lesson concept.

Check Observe students as you work through Exercises 1–7 as a class.

Exercise 7 Assess students' comprehension before assigning practice exercises.

Ways to Make 10, 11, and 12

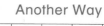

Get Ready

Main Idea

I will use a ten-frame and counters to make sums of 10, 11, and 12.

There are many ways to make 10.

One Way   Another Way

There are many ways to make 11.

One Way   Another Way

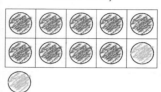 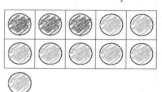

There are many ways to make 12.

One Way   Another Way

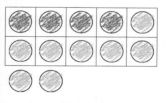 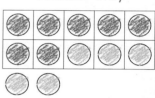

Chapter 2   Lesson 8   sixty-nine   **69**

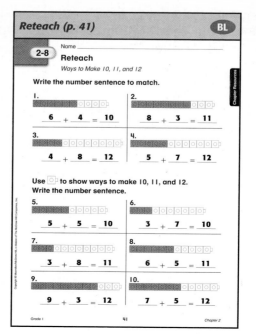

Reteach (p. 41) **BL**

2-8 Name _____
Reteach
Ways to Make 10, 11, and 12

Write the number sentence to match.

1.
__6__ + __4__ = __10__

2.
__8__ + __3__ = __11__

3.
__4__ + __8__ = __12__

4.
__5__ + __7__ = __12__

Use ⬚ to show ways to make 10, 11, and 12.
Write the number sentence.

5.
__5__ + __5__ = __10__

6.
__3__ + __7__ = __10__

7.
__3__ + __8__ = __11__

8.
__6__ + __5__ = __11__

9.
__9__ + __3__ = __12__

10.
__7__ + __5__ = __12__

Grade 1   41   Chapter 2

Check   1–6. See students' work.

Use  and WorkMat 1. Draw the ◯.
Write the numbers.

1.

$\underline{\ 3\ }$ + $\underline{\ 7\ }$ = 10

2.

_____ + _____ = 10

3.

_____ + _____ = 11

4.

_____ + _____ = 11

5.

_____ + _____ = 12

6.

_____ + _____ = 12

7. **Talk About It** Why do you get the same sum
when you add 8 + 2 and 7 + 3?
There are different ways to make 10.

70   seventy

 GO on

Copyright © Macmillan/McGraw-Hill, a division of The McGraw-Hill Companies, Inc.

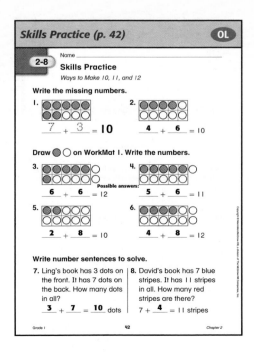

Skills Practice (p. 42)   **OL**

BL **Alternate Teaching Strategy**

If students have trouble making the sums
10, 11, and 12 . . .

Then use one of these reteaching options:

1 **CRM** **Daily Reteach Worksheet** (p. 41)

2 **Use a Ten-Frame and Counters** Have students
fill a ten-frame with two-colored counters and
then place 1 or 2 more counters outside the
frame to make 11 or 12.

3 🖥 Have students use Math Tool Chest to help
complete the problem-solving exercises.

⚠ **COMMON ERROR!**

Students will often overlook the facts involving
zero. Highlight the facts 0 + 10 = 10 and 10 +
0 = 10 with dominoes or a ten-frame filled
with one color of counter. (Note: Some
domino sets go up to only 9 pips.)

3 Practice

Differentiate practice, using these leveled assignments for Exercises 8–20.

Level	Assignment
BL Below/Approaching Level	Have students count red and yellow counters from the ten-frame aloud. Transfer only one number at a time to the addition sentence.
OL On Level	Complete work independently.
AL Above/Beyond Level	Have students complete the addition sentences without the ten-frame and counters.

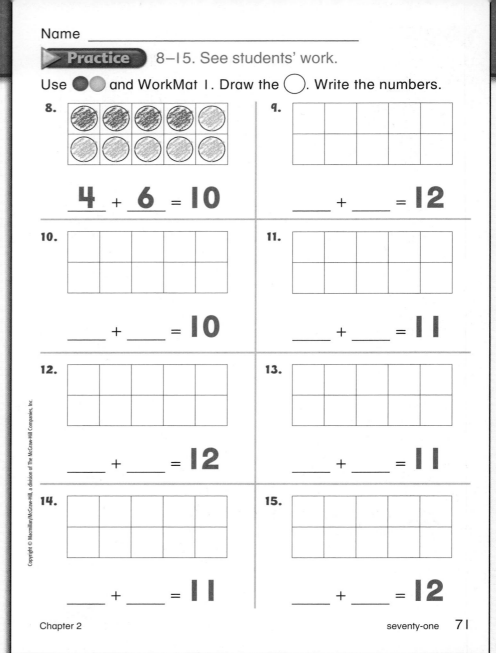

Name _____

▶ **Practice** 8–15. See students' work.

Use ⬤◯ and WorkMat 1. Draw the ◯. Write the numbers.

8.
__4__ + __6__ = 10

9.
____ + ____ = 12

10.
____ + ____ = 10

11.
____ + ____ = 11

12.
____ + ____ = 12

13.
____ + ____ = 11

14.
____ + ____ = 11

15.
____ + ____ = 12

Chapter 2   seventy-one   71

Copyright © Macmillan/McGraw-Hill, a division of The McGraw-Hill Companies, Inc.

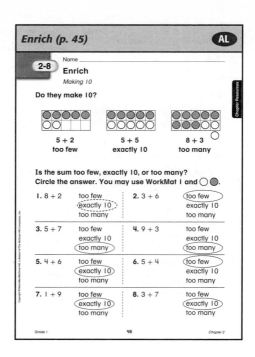

Enrich (p. 45)   **AL**

2-8 Enrich
Making 10

Do they make 10?

5 + 2   5 + 5   8 + 3
too few   exactly 10   too many

Is the sum too few, exactly 10, or too many?
Circle the answer. You may use WorkMat 1 and ◯⬤.

1. 8 + 2	too few / (exactly 10) / too many	2. 3 + 6	(too few) / exactly 10 / too many
3. 5 + 7	too few / exactly 10 / (too many)	4. 9 + 3	too few / exactly 10 / (too many)
5. 4 + 6	too few / (exactly 10) / too many	6. 5 + 4	(too few) / exactly 10 / too many
7. 1 + 9	too few / (exactly 10) / too many	8. 3 + 7	too few / (exactly 10) / too many

Grade 1   45   Chapter 2

16–19. See students' work.

Use and WorkMat 1. Draw the ◯. Write the numbers.

16.

____ + ____ = **10**

17.

____ + ____ = **11**

18.

____ + ____ = **12**

19.

____ + ____ = **10**

Data File

Bronx Zoo, New York	
Tigers	8
Giraffe	6
Polar bears	4
Sea lions	6

20. Use the chart. Write an addition sentence about the number of tigers and polar bears.

__8__ + __4__ = __12__ animals

72 seventy-two

Math at Home Activity: Give your child 12 pennies. Ask your child to use heads and tails and show different ways to make 10, 11, and 12.

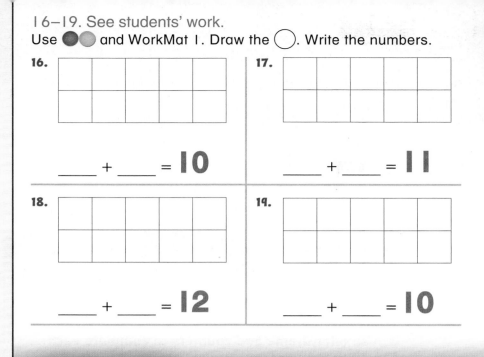

④ Assess

Formative Assessment

Eight plus 3 is 11. I want to change one of the parts so the sum is 12. What can I do to 8 or 3 to change the sum to 12? Add 1. **How do you know?** Twelve is one more than 11, so you have to add 1 to one of the parts.

WRITING IN ►MATH Have students respond to the following prompt: One dozen is the same as twelve. What are some things you see or can buy that are in a dozen? Draw pictures to show your answers.

Homework Practice (p. 43) **OL**

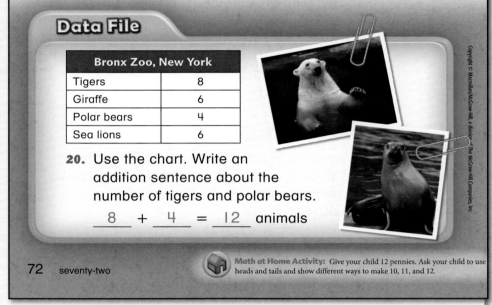

Quick Check **Are students continuing to struggle with finding 10, 11, and 12?**

If Yes → Small Group Options (p. 69B)
Strategic Intervention Guide (pp. 62–63)

If No → Independent Work Options (p. 69B)
CRM Skills Practice Worksheet (p. 42)
CRM Enrich Worksheet (p. 45)

Lesson 2-8 Ways to Make 10, 11, and 12 **72**

Lesson Planner

Objective

Choose the best strategy to solve a problem.

Resources

Teacher Technology

 TeacherWorks

📖 **Real-World Problem Solving Library
Math and Science: *Healthful Snacks***
Use these leveled books to reinforce and extend
problem-solving skills and strategies.

Leveled for:

OL On Level

ELL Sheltered English

SP Spanish

For additional support, see the
Real-World Problem Solving
Teacher Guide.

Daily Routine

Use these suggestions before beginning the lesson on p. 73.

5-Minute Check

(Reviews Lesson 2-8)

**Use a ten-frame and counters to complete each
addition sentence.**

1. 4 + _____ = 10 6
2. 8 + _____ = 10 2
3. 5 + _____ = 10 5
4. 3 + _____ = 10 7
5. 9 + _____ = 10 1

Problem of the Day

There are 4 children playing kickball. Two more
children come to play. Then 3 more come to play
with them. How many children are playing
kickball? 9 children

LINE UP While the class waits in line, tell students you
are thinking of a number between 1 and 20.
Call on students to guess numbers. Tell the class whether
the number is more than or less than the number guessed.
When a student guesses the mystery number, it is his or
her turn to line up and think of a new mystery number.

Differentiated Instruction

Small Group Options

Option 1 LOGICAL
Below/Approaching Level BL
Materials: 10 index cards with numbers 1 through 10, scrap paper, pencil.

- Have students work alone or in pairs with a set of index cards with numbers 1 through 10.
- The cards should be in a pile with the number side down. The student needs to pick two cards, and with these two cards, the student should make an addition sentence.
- The students should use the scrap paper to write the number sentence and figure out the answer.
- The activity should be repeated several times.

Option 2 AUDITORY, VISUAL
English Language Learners ELL
Materials: overhead with word problems
Core Vocabulary: then, they, left
Common Use Verb: see/saw
Hear Math This strategy shelters vocabulary to practice visualizing and understanding word problems.

- Read and show the first problem: Ben saw 3 lions at the zoo. Then he saw 2 lions. How many lions did he see altogether?
- Act out the problem line by line as students draw it. Solve together and review answers. Discuss any missteps in listening or translation.
- Repeat for the following problems, as time permits.
- Jeannie saw 4 walruses. Eli saw 5 walruses. How many did they see altogether?
- There are 14 shells in the bucket. Bea threw 4 shells on the sand. How many shells are there in the bucket?

Independent Work Options

Option 1 LINGUISTIC/KINESTHETIC
Early Finishers OL AL
Materials: number story cards, connecting cubes

- Have students mix up the number story cards.
- Ask students to take turns picking a card and reading it to the group.
- Have students work together to choose a strategy to solve the problem.
- Allow students to use connecting cubes to model the story.
- Encourage students to share one of the number stories they solved with the class and the strategy they used to solve it.

Option 2
Student Technology
| Math Online | macmillanmh.com |

Option 3
Learning Stations: Science (p. 47H)
Direct students to the Science Learning Station for opportunities to explore and extend the lesson concept.

1 Introduce

Activity • Review

Write the following addition story on the chalkboard:

Two penguins chased 4 fish through the water. How many animals were in the chase?

- **What do you know in this story?** the number of penguins and fish
- **What do you want to know in this story?** how many animals
- **What problem-solving strategies can you use to answer the question?** Possible answer: Draw a picture or write an addition sentence.
- **Write an addition sentence using a plus sign and an equals sign.** $2 + 4 = 6$ **How many animals were involved in the chase?** 6 animals

2 Teach

Have students read the problem on p. 73. Guide them through the problem-solving steps.

Understand Using the questions, review what students know and need to find.

Plan Have students discuss their strategy.

Solve Guide students to *draw a picture* to solve the problem.

- **How many brown shells does the girl have?** 6 brown shells **Draw 6 brown shells.**
- **How many pink and brown shells does she have in all?** 10 pink and brown shells
- Tell students to draw pink shells until there are 10 shells in all.
- **How many pink shells are there?** 4 pink shells

Check Have students look back at the problem to make sure that the answer fits the facts given.

! COMMON ERROR!

Students often simply add together all the numbers mentioned in the problem. Encourage students to read problems carefully to find which numbers represent parts and which number is the whole.

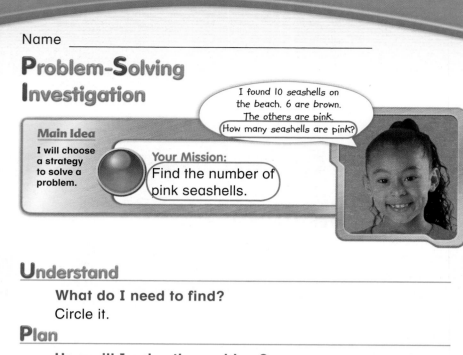

Name _____

Problem-Solving Investigation

I found 10 seashells on the beach. 6 are brown. The others are pink. How many seashells are pink?

Main Idea
I will choose a strategy to solve a problem.

Your Mission:
Find the number of pink seashells.

Understand

What do I need to find?
Circle it.

Plan

How will I solve the problem?

Solve

One way is to draw a picture.

See students' drawings.
4 pink seashells

Check

Look back.
Is my answer reasonable? Check students' explanations.

Copyright © Macmillan/McGraw-Hill, a division of The McGraw-Hill Companies, Inc.

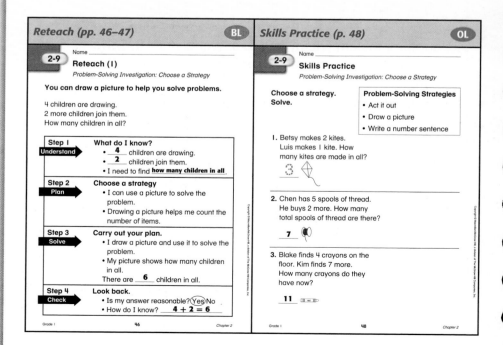

Reteach (pp. 46–47) BL

2-9 Reteach (1)
Problem-Solving Investigation: Choose a Strategy

You can draw a picture to help you solve problems.

4 children are drawing.
2 more children join them.
How many children in all?

Step 1 Understand	What do I know?
	• __4__ children are drawing.
	• __2__ children join them.
	• I need to find **how many children in all**.

Step 2 Plan	Choose a strategy
	• I can use a picture to solve the problem.
	• Drawing a picture helps me count the number of items.

Step 3 Solve	Carry out your plan.
	• I draw a picture and use it to solve the problem.
	• My picture shows how many children in all.
	There are __6__ children in all.

Step 4 Check	Look back.
	• Is my answer reasonable? (Yes) No
	• How do I know? __4 + 2 = 6__

Grade 1   46   Chapter 2

Skills Practice (p. 48) OL

2-9 Skills Practice
Problem-Solving Investigation: Choose a Strategy

Choose a strategy. Solve.

Problem-Solving Strategies
- Act it out
- Draw a picture
- Write a number sentence

1. Betsy makes 2 kites. Luis makes 1 kite. How many kites are made in all?

3

2. Chen has 5 spools of thread. He buys 2 more. How many total spools of thread are there?

7

3. Blake finds 4 crayons on the floor. Kim finds 7 more. How many crayons do they have now?

11

Grade 1   48   Chapter 2

Mixed Problem Solving

Problem-Solving Strategies
- Draw a picture
- Act it out
- Write a number sentence

Choose a strategy. Solve.

1. There are 5 boats in the water.
   There are 5 boats in the sand.
   How many boats are there in all?

   __10__ boats

2. 5 children have pails.
   The girls have 2 pails.
   How many pails do the boys have?

   __3__ pails

3. Alex has 2 shovels.
   Kary has 2 shovels.
   How many shovels do Kary
   and Alex have?

   __4__ shovels

4. There are 3 birds and 2 crabs
   on the beach. 6 more birds join them.
   How many birds are on the beach?

   __9__ birds

Copyright © Macmillan/McGraw-Hill, a division of The McGraw-Hill Companies, Inc.

Math at Home Activity: Take advantage of problem-solving opportunities during daily routines such as riding in the car, bedtime, doing laundry, putting away groceries, planning schedules, and so on.

74   seventy-four

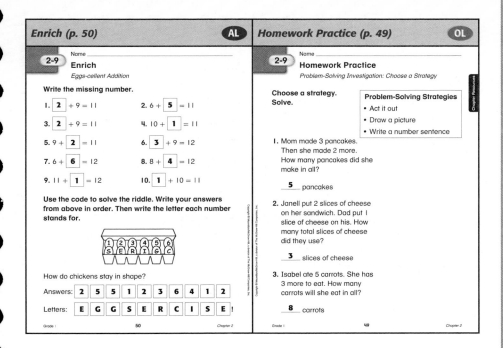

BL **Alternate Teaching Strategy**

> **If** students have trouble deciding what the story problem is asking . . .

> **Then** use one of the following reteach items:

1. **CRM** **Daily Reteach Worksheet** (pp. 46–47)

2. **Use a Table:** Give students a table with two columns: *What I Know* and *What I Need to Find.* Encourage them to find that information and ignore the rest. Explain that *What I Need to Find* is usually in a sentence with a question mark.

③ Practice

Mixed Problem Solving

Exercise 2 Remind students that they already know the total number of sand pails. Explain that they are to find a missing part.

Exercise 3 Make sure students can read the problem correctly and understand what they are trying to find.

④ Assess

Formative Assessment

Stephanie has 3 beads. Her sister has 5 beads. How many beads do they have altogether?

- **Describe how you would solve the problem.** Sample answers: draw a picture; act it out

- **What do you know?** Stephanie has 3 beads. Her sister has 5 beads.

- **What do you need to find?** The number of beads Stephanie and her sister have altogether.

- **What is the answer?** 8 beads

Quick Check Are students continuing to struggle with solving number sentences?

If Yes → Small Group Options (p. 73B)
If No → Independent Work Options (p. 73B)
  CRM Skills Practice Worksheet (p. 48)
  CRM Enrich Worksheet (p. 50)

Lesson 2-9 Problem-Solving Investigation   **74**

Vertical Addition

Lesson Planner

Objective
Write addition facts horizontally and vertically.

Review Vocabulary
add, plus, equals, sum

Resources

Materials: white crayons, black construction paper, WorkMat 1: Ten-Frame, dominoes

Manipulatives: two-colored counters

Literature Connection: *Counting in the Garden* by Kim Parker

Alternate Lessons: Adapt "Peek Through the Wall" on page 238 of *Math Their Way* for practice with addition facts, in horizontal or vertical form.

Use *IMPACT Mathematics:* Unit A to provide practice with writing number sentences both vertically and horizontally.

Teacher Technology
TeacherWorks • Concepts in Motion • Math Songs Track 11 Lesson Plan

Focus on Math Background

Students are comfortable in learning to write number sentences in a horizontal format because they are learning to read and write in English from left to right in the same horizontal manner. Introducing the game of dominoes (use double six dominoes for the initial games) shows students that one can match dominoes horizontally or vertically throughout the game. The recognition of composing numbers in either direction contributes later to an understanding of the commutative property of addition. Displaying both vertical (like a thermometer or goal chart) and horizontal number lines assists students in seeing identical order but different directions.

Daily Routine

Use these suggestions before beginning the lesson on p. 75.

5-Minute Check
(Reviews Lesson 2-9)
Keith planted 12 flowers. Four of the flowers are yellow. The rest of the flowers are white. How many flowers are white? 8 flowers

Problem of the Day
Julie has 5 books. Shannon has 2 more books than Julie. How many books does Shannon have? 7 books

LINE UP As students line up, show flash cards for addition math facts to 12. Encourage students to name the sums as quickly as they can.

Review Math Vocabulary
Review the terms **add , plus (+), equals (=),** and **sum.**

- Write 3 + 5 on the chalkboard. Remind students that the + symbol means *add*. Tell students they should say *plus* when they see + in a math problem.

- Write the symbol = after the 5. Remind students that this symbol shows that the number that follows is the answer. Tell students they should say *equals* when they see = in a math problem.

- **5 + 3 equals what number?** 8 Write the answer.

- Have students use the symbols to practice writing other addition facts.

Visual Vocabulary Cards
Use Visual Vocabulary Card 47 to reinforce the vocabulary reviewed in this lesson. (The Define/Example/Ask routine is printed on the back of each card.)

sum

Differentiated Instruction

Small Group Options

Option 1 — Below/Approaching Level BL

Materials: red number cube, yellow and green connecting cubes

- Have students work in pairs to practice adding two numbers.
- One student rolls the red number cube and uses yellow connecting cubes to show that number.
- The other student repeats the process with green connecting cubes to show the second addend.
- Partners join their bars of cubes together to make a horizontal train and find the sum.
- Partners stand the connecting cubes up to make a vertical tower and find the sum.
- Students repeat the activity several times

Option 2 — English Language Learners ELL

Materials: connecting cubes
Core Vocabulary: across, up/down, light/dark color
Common Use Verb: go

Write Math This strategy uses models to explore horizontal and vertical forms of addition.

- Pass out dark and light cubes to students. Specify "dark" and "light," then model connecting $3 + 5$ and $5 + 3$.
- Call up 4 students.
- Write: "3 + 5." Have two students show it horizontally (5 + 3). Stress "**across.**"
- Have the remaining 2 repeat vertically stressing up/down. Write 3 and 5
      $+5$ $+3$

Use this worksheet to provide additional support for English Language Learners.

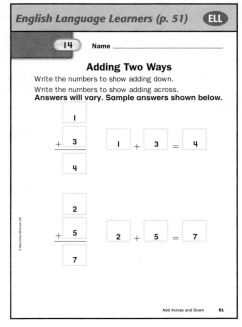

English Language Learners (p. 51) ELL

14 Name _____

Adding Two Ways
Write the numbers to show adding down.
Write the numbers to show adding across.
Answers will vary. Sample answers shown below.

$\begin{array}{r} 1 \\ +\ 3 \\ \hline 4 \end{array}$ $1 + 3 = 4$

$\begin{array}{r} 2 \\ +\ 5 \\ \hline 7 \end{array}$ $2 + 5 = 7$

Add Across and Down   51

Independent Work Options

Option 1 — Early Finishers OL AL

Materials: white board, dry erase marker, number cubes, two-colored counters

- Students draw a blank horizontal number sentence on the left side of their white board and a blank vertical number sentence on the right side of their white board.
- Have students take turns rolling a number cube and using the numbers rolled as addends. Have students write the problem horizontally and vertically.
- Students then work together to find the sum.

Option 2 — Student Technology

Math Online > macmillanmh.com

♪ Math Songs, "The Addition Boogie" Track 11

Option 3 — Learning Stations: Science (p. 47H)

Direct students to the Science Learning Station for more opportunities to explore and extend the lesson concept.

Option 4 — Problem-Solving Practice

Reinforce problem-solving skills and strategies with the Problem-Solving Practice worksheet.

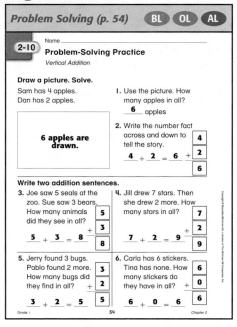

Problem Solving (p. 54) BL OL AL

Name _____

2-10 **Problem-Solving Practice**
Vertical Addition

Draw a picture. Solve.
Sam has 4 apples. Dan has 2 apples.

6 apples are drawn.

1. Use the picture. How many apples in all?
   __6__ apples

2. Write the number fact across and down to tell the story.
   $4 + 2 = 6$ $\begin{array}{r} 4 \\ +\ 2 \\ \hline 6 \end{array}$

Write two addition sentences.

3. Joe saw 5 seals at the zoo. Sue saw 3 bears. How many animals did they see in all?
   $5 + 3 = 8$ $\begin{array}{r} 5 \\ +\ 3 \\ \hline 8 \end{array}$

4. Jill drew 7 stars. Then she drew 2 more. How many stars in all?
   $7 + 2 = 9$ $\begin{array}{r} 7 \\ +\ 2 \\ \hline 9 \end{array}$

5. Jerry found 3 bugs. Pablo found 2 more. How many bugs did they find in all?
   $3 + 2 = 5$ $\begin{array}{r} 3 \\ +\ 2 \\ \hline 5 \end{array}$

6. Carla has 6 stickers. Tina has none. How many stickers do they have in all?
   $6 + 0 = 6$ $\begin{array}{r} 6 \\ +\ 0 \\ \hline 6 \end{array}$

Grade 1   54   Chapter 2

1 Introduce

Activity Choice 1 • Hands-On

- Have students make a domino, using a piece of black construction paper.
- Ask students to fold the paper in half "hamburger" style.
- Have students use a white crayon to draw from zero to six dots on each side of the fold. Have students rotate the paper to see the dots horizontally and vertically.
- **What is the sum of the dots on your domino?** Answers will vary. Answers should reflect the total number of dots on the domino.

Activity Choice 2 • Literature

Introduce the lesson with *Counting in the Garden* by Kim Parker. For additional support, see p. TR45.

2 Teach

Write the problem $3 + 4 = 7$ horizontally and vertically on the chalkboard.

- Point to the horizontal problem. **What is the sum?** 7
- Point to the vertical problem. **What is the sum?** 7
- **How are the problems different?** One is written across and the other is written down.
- **Are the addends in the problems the same?** yes
- Use connecting cubes to demonstrate how students can join cubes horizontally and vertically when adding.

Get Ready Use the section at the top of student p. 75 to teach the lesson concept.

Check Observe students as you work through Exercises 1-5 as a class.

 Exercise 5 Assess student comprehension before assigning practice exercises.

⚠ COMMON ERROR!

Students may write addends in reverse order from what the domino shows. Have them lay a domino alongside their blank number sentence and use the number from the left side or top of the domino as the first addend.

Name _____

Vertical Addition

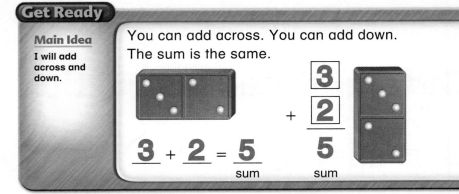

Get Ready

Main Idea
I will add across and down.

You can add across. You can add down. The sum is the same.

$3 + 2 = 5$

$3 + 2 = 5$ sum   sum

✓ Check

5. 8; Sample answer: You get the same sum no matter which way you add.

Write the numbers. Add.

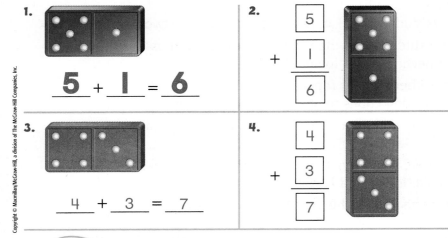

1. $5 + 1 = 6$

2. $5 + 1 = 6$

3. $4 + 3 = 7$

4. $4 + 3 = 7$

5. **Talk About It** $5 + 3 = 8$ If you add down, what is the sum? Why?

Reteach (p. 51) BL

2-10 **Reteach**
Vertical Addition

Draw the dots to show the numbers. Then write the sum.

You can add **across** or **down**.

1. $3 + 1 = 4$ sum

2. $4 + 2 = 6$ sum

3. $3 + 2 = 5$ sum

Grade 1   51   Chapter 2

Skills Practice (p. 52) OL

2-10 **Skills Practice**
Vertical Addition

Write the numbers. Add across and down.

1. $5 + 1 = 6$

2. $4 + 3 = 7$

3. $5 + 4 = 9$

Write two addition sentences. Add.

4. There are 3 birds in the nest. 2 more fly to the nest. How many birds are in the nest altogether?
$3 + 2 = 5$

Grade 1   52   Chapter 2

Write the numbers. Add.

6.
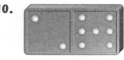

$\underline{\quad 6 \quad} + \underline{\quad 1 \quad} = \underline{\quad 7 \quad}$

7.

$\begin{array}{r} 6 \\ + 1 \\ \hline 7 \end{array}$

8.

$\underline{\quad 5 \quad} + \underline{\quad 3 \quad} = \underline{\quad 8 \quad}$

9.

$\begin{array}{r} 5 \\ + 3 \\ \hline 8 \end{array}$

10.

$\underline{\quad 2 \quad} + \underline{\quad 7 \quad} = \underline{\quad 9 \quad}$

11.
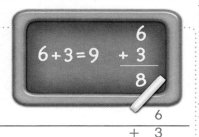

$\begin{array}{r} 2 \\ + 7 \\ \hline 9 \end{array}$

H.O.T. Problem

12. Make it Right

Amelia added these numbers.
Tell why Amelia is wrong.
Make it right.

$$6 + 3 = 9 \qquad \begin{array}{r} 6 \\ + 3 \\ \hline 8 \end{array}$$

Sample answer: She added wrong. $6 + 3 = 9$ and

$$\begin{array}{r} 6 \\ + 3 \\ \hline 9 \end{array}$$

76 seventy-six

Math at Home Activity: Give your child an addition sentence. Have your child show how to add across and then down.

Copyright © Macmillan/McGraw-Hill, a division of The McGraw-Hill Companies, Inc.

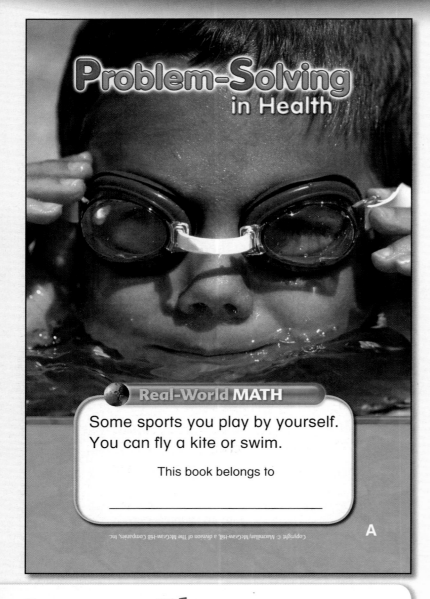

Problem-Solving
in Health

Real-World MATH

Some sports you play by yourself.
You can fly a kite or swim.

This book belongs to

_____

A

Sometimes you need 2 people to play a sport.

How many children are
playing catch?

$$\underline{\quad 1 \quad} + \underline{\quad 1 \quad} = \underline{\quad 2 \quad}$$

How many skaters are there in all?

$$\underline{\quad 1 \quad} + \underline{\quad 1 \quad} = \underline{\quad 2 \quad}$$

B

Lesson Planner

Objective

Use information given in real-world examples to write and solve addition sentences.

National Standard

Students will demonstrate the ability to practice health-enhancing behaviors and reduce health risks.

Vocabulary

addition sentence, sum

Activate Prior Knowledge

Before you turn students' attention to the pages, discuss several ways that numbers are important in sports.

- **What are some different ways people keep score in sports?** Possible answer: In basketball, each basket counts for two points or three points.

- **Why is it important to know the number of players on each team when you play a sport?** Sample answer: To make sure each team has the same number of people.

Some sports are fun to do with family and friends.

How many bike riders are there now?

$\underline{2} + \underline{2} = \underline{4}$

C

Goals

	Goals		
Red Team	I	I	I
Blue Team	I		

Look at the chart.
How many total soccer goals?

$\underline{3} + \underline{I} = \underline{4}$ goals

D

FOLD DOWN

Create the Book

Guide students to create their book.

- Have them fold the page in half.
- Ask them to write their name on page A.
- Explain that page A is the front cover and page D is the back cover. If necessary, have them practice flipping through the book in order.
- Guide them in reading the information and word problems on each page.

Use the Student Pages

Have students work individually or in pairs to solve the word problems on pages B–D.

Page C If students have difficulty with this problem, allow them to use two-colored counters or another manipulative.

Page D Explain to students that each tally mark equals one goal.

WRITING IN ►MATH Have students write an addition story about basketball, football, or another sport.

Extend the Activity

Organize a game of kickball or T-ball and keep score by using a tally chart. Have students write an addition sentence for the results. Each team's points will sum to the total number of points.

FOLDABLES® Dinah Zike's Foldables

Use these lesson suggestions to incorporate the Foldable during the chapter. Students can then use their Foldable to review for the test.

Lesson 2-7 Label the fifth, sixth, and seventh pockets of their 5-Pocket Foldable with the numbers 7, 8, and 9. Use 3" x 5" index cards to make addition sentence flashcards with sums of 7, 8, and 9 and store them in the appropriate pockets of the Foldable.

Lesson 2-8 Label the eighth, ninth, and tenth pockets with the numbers 10, 11, and 12. Use 3" x 5" index cards to make addition sentence flashcards with sums of 10, 11, and 12 and store them in the appropriate pockets.

Vocabulary Review

Review chapter vocabulary using one of the following options.

- **Visual Vocabulary Cards** (1, 16, 38, and 47)
- **eGlossary** at macmillanmh.com

Vocabulary Test

CRM **Chapter 2 Resource Masters** (p. 60)
Assess student comprehension of the chapter vocabulary with the Vocabulary Test.

Math Online ⟩ **Chapter Test**
Alternative summative assessment options are available online at macmillanmh.com.

Name _____

Vocabulary

Draw lines to match.

1. **addition sentence**   a. +
2. **equals**   b. 3 + 5 = 8
3. **zero**   c. =
4. **plus**   d. 0

Concepts

Write the addition sentence that describes the picture.

5.

    _7_ (+) _0_ (=) _7_

6.

    _3_ (+) _3_ (=) _6_

Add.

7. 1 + 6 = __7__   8. 9 + 0 = __9__

9. 3 + 2 = __5__   10. 4 + 4 = __8__

11. 5 + 1 = __6__   12. 0 + 3 = __3__

13.   4   14.   3   15.   5   16.   2
    + 1   + 1   + 4   + 6
    ___   ___   ___   ___
      5   4   9   8

✓ Chapter 2 Project

Treasure Hunt

Alone, in pairs, or in small groups, have students discuss the results of their completed chapter project with the class. Assess their work using the Chapter Project rubric found in Chapter 2 Resource Masters on page 65.

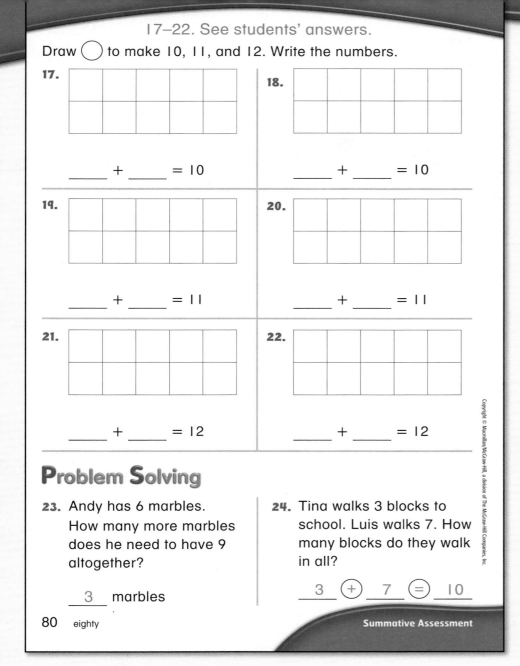

17–22. See students' answers.

Draw ◯ to make 10, 11, and 12. Write the numbers.

17.

_____ + _____ = 10

18.

_____ + _____ = 10

19.

_____ + _____ = 11

20.

_____ + _____ = 11

21.

_____ + _____ = 12

22.

_____ + _____ = 12

Problem Solving

23. Andy has 6 marbles. How many more marbles does he need to have 9 altogether?

___3___ marbles

24. Tina walks 3 blocks to school. Luis walks 7. How many blocks do they walk in all?

__3__ ⊕ __7__ ⊜ __10__

Copyright © Macmillan/McGraw-Hill, a division of The McGraw-Hill Companies, Inc.

Summative Assessment

Use these alternate leveled chapter tests to differentiate assessment for the specific needs of your students.

Leveled Chapter 2 Tests			
Form	**Type**	**Level**	**CRM Pages**
1	Multiple Choice	BL	67–68
2A	Multiple Choice	OL	69–70
2B	Multiple Choice	OL	71–72
2C	Multiple Choice	AL	73–74
2D	Free Response	AL	75–76

BL = below/approaching grade level
OL = on grade level
AL = above/beyond grade level

ExamView Assessment Suite Customize and create multiple versions of your Chapter Test and their test answer keys.

Data-Driven Decision Making

Based on the results of the Chapter Review Test, use the following to review concepts that continue to present students with problems.

Exercises	State/Local Standards	What's the Math?	Error Analysis	Resources for Review
5–6		Use pictures to write an addition sentence.	Does not count pictures correctly. Does not add the numbers correctly. Does not fill in the answer.	Strategic Intervention Guide (p. 52) CRM Chapter 2 Resource Masters (Reteach Worksheets)
7–16		Solve addition sentences with plus symbols.	Does not add correctly or know the word "sum." Puts numbers together to make a two digit number.	**Math Online** Concepts in Motion Math Adventures
17–22		Represent equivalent forms of the numbers 10, 11, and 12.	Writes incorrect numbers to make sums of 10, 11, or 12.	

Chapter 2 Summative Assessment **80**

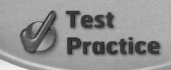 **Test Practice**

 ## Formative Assessment

- Use Student Edition pp. 81–82 as practice and cumulative review. The questions are written in the same style as many state tests.

- You can use these two pages to benchmark student progress, or as an alternative homework assignment.

Additional practice pages can be found in the Chapter 2 Resource Masters.

CRM **Chapter 2 Resource Masters**
Cumulative Test Practice

- Multiple Choice format (pp. 67–72, 77)
- Free Response format (pp. 73–76, 78)

ExamView Assessment Suite Create practice worksheets or tests that align to your state standards.

Math Online For additional practice visit macmillanmh.com.

Name _____

Listen as your teacher reads each problem.
Choose the correct answer.

1.

2	4	6	8
○	●	○	○

4. $2 \bigcirc 5 = 7$

=	+	−	×
○	●	○	○

2. $3 + 7 = \square$

3	4	10	11
○	○	●	○

5. $2 + 4 = \square$

2	4	6	8
○	○	●	○

3. $1 \bigcirc 4 = 5$

=	+	−	×
○	●	○	○

6. $2 + 3$

4 + 4	1 + 5	5 + 0	1 + 2
○	○	●	○

Copyright © Macmillan/McGraw-Hill, a division of The McGraw-Hill Companies, Inc.

Chapter 2   eighty-one   81

Test-Taking Tips

For the Teacher

- Before starting a test, tell students about how much time the test or each section will take.

- It may be helpful to remind students to double check that they put their first and last name on their test.

For the Student

- Tell students to be neat so everyone can read their answers.

- Encourage students to answer all the questions on the test.

- Tell students that if they cannot answer a question, cross out the answer choices they know are wrong, then choose an answer from the choices that remain.

7. $\boxed{11 + 0}$

$11 + 1$ ⚪ $7 + 5$ ⚪

$5 + 6$ ⬬ $6 + 6$ ⚪

8.

$6 + 6 = \square$

4 ⚪   6 ⚪   8 ⚪   12 ⬬

9.

$3 + 8 \bigcirc 11$

$=$ ⬬ $+$ ⚪ $-$ ⚪ $>$ ⚪

10.   10 _____ 3

is greater than ⬬   is equal to ⚪

is less than ⚪   in all ⚪

---

11. There are 2 bugs on the plant. 3 more bugs join them. How many bugs in all?

_____5_____ bugs

---

12. 3 people are on the bus. 3 more people get on. How many people are on the bus now?

_____6_____ people

82   eighty-two   **Summative Assessment**

Copyright © Macmillan/McGraw-Hill, a division of The McGraw-Hill Companies, Inc.

Test Directions for Teachers

Read the following directions to students before they begin the test. Then read each question followed by a pause to allow students time to work on the problem and choose an answer. The first test item can be worked as a class example.

- **Write your name at the top of the page.**
- **I am going to read each question to you. Listen carefully to the entire question before you choose an answer.**

Multiple Choice

1. How many rabbits in all?
2. What is the sum of 3 and 7?
3. Which sign makes the number sentence true?
4. Which sign makes the number sentence true?
5. What is the sum of 2 plus 4?
6. What is another way to get the sum of 5?

- **Turn the page over.**

7. What is another way to get the sum of 11?
8. What is the sum of 6 plus 6?
9. Which sign makes the number sentence true?
10. What words make the sentence true?

Short Response

11. There are 2 bugs on the plant. 3 more bugs join them. How many bugs in all?
12. Three people are on the bus. 3 more people get on. How many people are on the bus now?

CHAPTER 3

Chapter Overview

Chapter-at-a-Glance

In Chapter 3, the emphasis is on modeling and solving simple subtraction problems, writing subtraction sentences, and using strategies and skills to solve problems.

Lesson	Math Objective	State/Local Standards
3-1 **Subtraction Stories** (pp. 87–88)	Use counters to model subtraction stories.	
3-2 **Modeling Subtraction** (pp. 89–90)	Use counters to subtract and show how many are left.	
3-3 **Subtraction Sentences** (pp. 91–92)	Use pictures and the symbols minus (–) and equals (=) to write subtraction sentences.	
3-4 **Subtract Zero and All** (pp. 95–96)	Write number sentences subtracting zero or find a difference of zero.	
3-5 **Problem-Solving Strategy: Draw a Picture** (pp. 97–98)	Use the *draw a picture* strategy to solve problems.	
3-6 **Subtract from 4, 5, and 6** (pp. 101–102)	Use connecting cubes to subtract from 4, 5, and 6.	
3-7 **Subtract from 7, 8, and 9** (pp. 103–104)	Use connecting cubes to subtract from 7, 8, and 9.	
3-8 **Problem-Solving Investigation: Choose a Strategy** (pp. 105–106)	Choose the best strategy to solve a problem.	
3-9 **Subtract from 10, 11, and 12** (pp. 107–110)	Use connecting cubes to subtract from 10, 11, and 12.	
3-10 **Vertical Subtraction** (pp. 111–112)	Write subtraction facts in horizontal and vertical form.	

Develop Subtraction Concepts

BIG Idea Because addition and subtraction are opposite operations, it is no surprise that many concepts in this chapter mirror those in the previous chapter. Students begin by using modeling to solve subtraction stories and problems, and then move to a more abstract representation of subtraction involving writing complete subtraction sentences with minus (–) and equals (=) symbols. In addition, students subtract from numbers up to 12 and learn to vertically align subtraction problems.

Algebra In Lesson 3-3, students prepare for Algebra by using number sentences with pictures and the minus (–) and equals (=) symbols to solve problems.

In Lesson 3-4, students prepare for Algebra by developing a sense of the meaning of zero and how it applies to addition and subtraction.

Focal Points and Connections

G1-FP1 *Number and Operations* and *Algebra:* **Developing understandings of addition and subtraction and strategies for basic addition facts and related subtraction facts**

Children develop strategies for adding and subtracting whole numbers on the basis of their earlier work with small numbers. They use a variety of models, including discrete objects, length-based models (e.g., lengths of connecting cubes), and number lines, to model "part-whole," "adding to," "taking away from," and "comparing" situations to develop an understanding of the meanings of addition and subtraction and strategies to solve such arithmetic problems. Children understand the connections between counting and the operations of addition and subtraction (e.g., adding two is the same as "counting on" two). They use properties of addition (commutativity and associativity) to add whole numbers, and they create and use increasingly sophisticated strategies based on these properties (e.g., "making tens") to solve addition and subtraction problems involving basic facts. By comparing a variety of solution strategies, children relate addition and subtraction as inverse operations.

Skills Trace
Vertical Alignment

Kindergarten
In kindergarten, students learned to:
- Model subtraction as taking away from or separating sets of objects.
- Use concrete objects to solve subtraction problems.
- Use concrete objects to show different ways to solve to 9.

First Grade
During this chapter, students learn to:
- Model and solve subtraction problems.
- Write subtraction problems.
- Use strategies and skills to solve problems.

After this chapter, students learn to:
- Use different strategies to solve differences to 20.
- Use doubles to subtract. (Chapter 6)
- Relate addition and subtraction. (Chapter 6)
- Compare and order numbers to 100. (Chapter 13)

Second Grade
In second grade, students learn to:
- Estimate differences.
- Use two-digit and three-digit subtraction strategies such as regrouping.
- Subtract money.

Backmapping and Vertical Alignment
McGraw-Hill's *Math Connects* program was conceived and developed with the final results in mind: student success in Algebra 1 and beyond. The authors, using the **NCTM Focal Points and Focal Connections** as their guide, developed this brand-new series by back-mapping from Algebra 1 concepts, and vertically aligning the topics so that they build upon prior skills and concepts and serve as a foundation for future topics.

Math Vocabulary

The following math vocabulary words for Chapter 3 are listed in the glossary of the *Student Edition.* You can find interactive definitions in 13 languages in the *eGlossary* link at macmillanmh.com.

difference the answer to a subtraction problem (p. 91)

minus the sign used to show subtraction (p. 91)

$$3 - 1 = 2$$

subtract to take away, take apart, separate, or find the difference between two sets (p. 89)

subtraction sentence an expression using numbers and the − and = signs. (p. 91)

Visual Vocabulary Cards
Use Visual Vocabulary Cards to introduce and reinforce the vocabulary in this chapter. (The Define/Example/Ask routine is printed on the back of each card.)

Chapter Planner

Suggested Pacing		
Instruction	**Review and Assessment**	**TOTAL**
10 days	2 days	**12 days**

🔔 **Diagnostic Assessment**
Are You Ready? (p. 84)

	Lesson 3-1 Pacing: 1 day	**Lesson 3-2** Pacing: 1 day	**Lesson 3-3** Pacing: 1 day
Lesson/ Objective	**Subtraction Stories** (pp. 87–88) 🖐 **Objective:** Use counters to model subtraction stories.	**Modeling Subtraction** (pp. 89–90) 🖐 **Objective:** Use counters to subtract and show how many are left.	**Subtraction Sentences** (pp. 91–92) **Objective:** Use pictures and the symbols minus (−) and equals (=) to write subtraction sentences.
State/Local Standards			
Math Vocabulary		subtract	difference minus subtraction sentence
Lesson Resources	**Materials** cup, small plastic bags **Manipulatives** two-colored counters, connecting cubes **Other Resources** CRM Leveled Worksheets (pp. 6–10) 🖌 Daily Reteach 📖 Problem of the Day	**Materials** WorkMat: Part-Part-Whole **Manipulatives** two-colored counters, connecting cubes **Other Resources** CRM Leveled Worksheets (pp. 11–15) 🖌 Daily Reteach 📖 Problem of the Day	**Materials** number and symbol cards **Manipulatives** number cubes **Other Resources** CRM Leveled Worksheets (pp. 16–20) 🖌 Daily Reteach 📖 Problem of the Day
Technology Math Online ▶	🎵 Math Song Track 15 🎮 Math Adventures	🎵 Math Song Track 15 🎮 Math Adventures Concepts in Motion	🎵 Math Song Track 15 🎮 Math Adventures
Reaching All Learners	Gifted and Talented, p. 87B **AL** English Learners, p. 87B **ELL** Early Finishers, p. 87B **OL AL**	Below Level, p. 89B **BL** English Learners, p. 89B **ELL** Early Finishers, p. 89B **OL AL**	Gifted and Talented, p. 91B **AL** English Learners, p. 91B **ELL** Early Finishers, p. 91B **OL AL**
Alternate Lessons	*Math Their Way*, pp. 188–189 *IMPACT Mathematics:* Units A and C	*Math Their Way*, p. 192 *IMPACT Mathematics:* Units A and C	*Math Their Way*, p. 180 *IMPACT Mathematics:* Units A, C, and G

Extra Practice (p. 93)
Game Time: Subtracting to Swim (p. 94)

KEY
- **BL** Below/ Approaching Level
- **OL** On Level
- **AL** Above/Beyond Level
- **ELL** English Learners
- **SE** Student Edition
- **TE** Teacher Edition
- **CRM** Chapter 3 Resource Masters
- CD-Rom
- 🖌 Transparency
- 📖 Flip Chart
- 📖 Real-World Problem Solving Library

Lesson 3-4
Pacing: 1 day

Subtract Zero and All
(pp. 95–96)

Objective: Write number sentences subtracting zero or find a difference of zero.

Materials
whiteboard, dominoes

Manipulatives
two-colored counters

Other Resources
- CRM Leveled Worksheets (pp. 21–25)
- Daily Reteach
- Problem of the Day

- ♪ Math Song Track 15
- Math Adventures

Below Level, p. 95B **BL**
English Learners, p. 95B **ELL**
Early Finishers, p. 95B **OL** **AL**

Math Their Way, pp. 193–194
IMPACT Mathematics: Units A and G

Lesson 3-5
Pacing: 1 day

Problem-Solving Strategy
Draw a Picture
(pp. 97–98)

Objective: Use the *draw a picture* strategy to solve problems.

Materials
paper, pencils

Other Resources
- CRM Leveled Worksheets (pp. 26–30)
- Daily Reteach
- Problem of the Day
- *What Do They Eat*

Below level, p. 97B **BL**
English Learners, p. 97B **ELL**
Early Finishers, p. 97B **OL** **AL**

Lesson 3-6
Pacing: 1 day

Subtract from 4, 5, and 6
(pp. 101–102)

Objective: Use connecting cubes to subtract from 4, 5, and 6.

Materials
small plastic bags, dominoes

Manipulatives
connecting cubes, two-colored counters

Other Resources
- CRM Leveled Worksheets (pp. 31–35)
- Daily Reteach
- Problem of the Day

- ♪ Math Song Track 15
- Math Adventures

Math Online

Gifted and Talented, p. 101B **AL**
English Learners, p. 101B **ELL**
Early Finishers, p. 101B **OL** **AL**

Math Their Way, p. 190
IMPACT Mathematics: Unit A

Lesson/Objective

State/Local Standards

Math Vocabulary

Lesson Resources

Technology

Reaching All Learners

Alternate Lessons

✓ Formative Assessment
- Mid-Chapter Check (p. 99)
- Spiral Review (p. 100)

Chapter Planner

	Lesson 3-7 *Pacing: 1 day*	**Lesson 3-8** *Pacing: 1 day*	**Lesson 3-9** *Pacing: 1 day*
Lesson/ Objective	**Subtract from 7, 8, and 9** (pp. 103–104) **Objective:** Use connecting cubes to subtract from 7, 8, and 9.	**Problem-Solving Investigation** **Use a Model** (pp. 105–106) **Objective:** Choose the best strategy to solve a problem.	**Subtract from 10, 11, and 12** (pp. 107–110) **Objective:** Use connecting cubes to subtract from 10, 11, and 12.
State/Local Standards			
Math Vocabulary			
Lesson Resources	**Materials** plastic cup, white board, small plastic bags, number cards **Manipulatives** connecting cubes, two-colored counters **Other Resources** CRM Leveled Worksheets (pp. 36–40) Daily Reteach Problem of the Day	**Materials** paper, pencils **Manipulatives** connecting cubes, two-colored counters **Other Resources** CRM Leveled Worksheets (pp. 41–45) Daily Reteach Problem of the Day *What Do They Eat*	**Materials** Workmat 1: Ten-Frame, small plastic bags **Manipulatives** two-colored counters, connecting cubes **Other Resources** CRM Leveled Worksheets (pp. 46–50) Daily Reteach Problem of the Day
Technology [Math Online]	♪ Math Song Track 15 Math Adventures		♪ Math Song Track 15 Math Tool Chest Math Adventures Concepts in Motion
Reaching All Learners	Gifted and Talented, p. 103B **AL** English Learners, p. 103B **ELL** Early Finishers, p. 103B **OL** **AL**	Gifted and Talented, p. 105B **AL** English Learners, p. 105B **ELL** Early Finishers, p. 105B **OL** **AL**	Below Level, p. 107B **BL** English Learners, p. 107B **ELL** Early Finishers, p. 107B **OL** **AL**
Alternate Lessons	*Math Their Way*, p. 188 *IMPACT Mathematics:* Unit A		*Math Their Way*, p. 192 *IMPACT Mathematics:* Unit A

Lesson 3-10

Pacing: 1 day

Vertical Subtraction
(pp. 111–112)

Objective: Write subtraction facts in horizontal and vertical form.

Materials
dominoes, sticky notes

Manipulatives
two-colored counters, connecting cubes

Other Resources
- CRM Leveled Worksheets (pp. 51–55)
- Daily Reteach
- Problem of the Day

♪ Math Song Track 15

Concepts in Motion

Gifted and Talented, p. 111B **AL**
English Learners, p. 111B **ELL**
Early Finishers, p. 111B **OL** **AL**

Math Their Way, p. 249
IMPACT Mathematics: Unit A

Problem Solving in Social Studies (p. 113)

Summative Assessment
- Chapter Review/Test (p. 115)
- Test Practice (p. 117)

Assessment Options

Diagnostic Assessment

- SE *Option 1:* Are You Ready? (p. 84)
  Option 2: Online Quiz macmillanmh.com
- CRM *Option 3:* Diagnostic Test (p. 57)
- CRM *Option 4:* Chapter Pretest (p. 58)

Formative Assessment

- TE Alternate Teaching Strategies (every lesson)
- TE Line Up (every lesson)
- SE Talk About it (every lesson)
- SE Writing in Math (every lesson)
- SE Check What You Know (every lesson)
- SE Mid-Chapter Check (p. 99)
- CRM Mid-Chapter Test (p. 59)

Summative Assessment

- SE Chapter Review/Test (p. 115)
- SE Test Practice (p. 117)
- CRM Vocabulary Test (p. 60)
- CRM Leveled Chapter Tests (p. 67–76)
- CRM Cumulative Test Practice (p. 77)
- CRM Listening Assessment (pp. 63–64)
- CRM Oral Assessment (pp. 61–62)
- ● Exam*View*® Assessment Suite
- ✕ Advance Tracker

Mc Graw Hill Professional Development

Targeted professional development has been articulated throughout the *McGraw-Hill's Math Connects* program. The **McGraw-Hill Professional Development Video Library** provides short videos that support the **NCTM Focal Points and Focal Connections.** For more information, visit macmillanmh.com.

| Model Lessons | Instructional Strategies |

Learning Stations
Cross-Curricular Links

 Music

 pair | **AUDITORY**

Musical Subtraction

- Make a sound with your body.
- Begin with everyone in the group making their sound together.
- Have one person stop at a time.
- Listen to how the music changes as there are fewer sounds.
- Try again with instruments.

Teacher Note: Suggest different body percussion sounds to students, such as clapping, stomping, patting, or snapping.

Materials:
- various musical instruments

 Art

individual | **VISUAL/ SPATIAL**

Draw the Number

- Roll the blue number cube. Choose that many crayons from the box. Draw a picture of your number.
- Roll the red number cube. Draw a picture of your number. Return that many crayons to the box.
- How many crayons do you have left? Draw a picture of that number with the crayons you have left.

Teacher Note: Encourage students to write a number sentence that reflects the situation they have drawn.

Materials:
- red and blue number cubes
- construction paper
- box of crayons

 Health

individual | **LOGICAL**

A Healthy Breakfast

- Make a fruit salad! There are 6 strawberries, 8 apple slices, and 10 grapes.
- Write down the fruits you want to put in your salad. Be sure to say how many.
- Subtract to find out how much fruit is left. For example, if you took 3 grapes there are 7 left. 10 − 3 = 7
- Write out number sentences to show your answers.

Teacher Note: Help students by providing cut-outs of each piece of fruit to manipulate.

Materials:
- paper
- pencil or crayons

Science

individual | **INTER-PERSONAL**

Leafy Tree

- Draw a tree. Draw a trunk and branches. Draw 10 big green leaves.
- Think about what happens in the fall. Leaves turn colors and fall off of the trees. Draw 4 brown leaves falling off your tree.
- If 4 leaves fell off of your tree, how many are left?
- Write a number sentence to find out.

Materials:
- paper
- pencil or crayons

Language Arts

pair | **SOCIAL, LINGUISTIC**

A Story with Numbers

- Copy the story below on your paper. Use the number cards to fill in the blanks.

    I am _____ years old. I go to school at _____ o'clock. I had _____ books. I gave _____ books to my friend, Gabriel. Now, I only have _____ books left.

- Subtract to find how many books you have left.

Teacher Note: Give below-level students or English learners the option of drawing a picture that contains the number they have chosen.

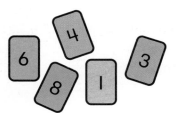

Materials:
- number cards 1–10
- paper
- pencil or crayons

Calendar Time

Tally the Days

- Fill in this month's days on a calendar poster or on the chalkboard.
- Write the names of the students in your class on various days across the calendar.
- **How many days are there from today to the day that has your name on it?** See students' work.
- Show students a calendar year.
- **How many months are there from [current month] to the end of the school year? to the fourth of July?** See students' work.

Introduce the Chapter

🌐 Real World: How Many Left?

Share with students that they are going to learn about subtraction. Explain that when you **subtract** you take away some from a starting number.

- Have students divide into groups of 5 or fewer. Give each group 6 pencils. Put all the pencils in the center of the group. Allow students, one at a time, to take 1 pencil.

- **How many pencils are left in the center?** Sample answer: 2 pencils

- **How did you solve the problem?** Sample answers: counted them all; subtracted

Have students turn to p. 83.

- Discuss what is happening in the picture. Have students use the picture to solve the Explore problem.

- **How many birds will be in the nest if 2 more birds fly away?** 2 birds

Key Vocabulary Introduce key vocabulary in the chapter using the routine below.

Define: To **subtract** means to take away.

Example: I subtracted two stickers when I gave them to Becky and Lee.

Ask: When do you subtract at home?

Key Vocabulary
subtract
subtraction
 sentence
difference
minus (−)

Explore
There were 5 birds sitting.
Then 1 bird flew away.
How many birds are left?

_4_

Chapter 3   eighty-three **83**

 **Dinah Zike's Foldables**

Guide students to create their 5-Pocket Book Foldable for developing subtraction concepts.

① Fold an 8 ½″ x 11″ sheet of paper in half like a hamburger.

② Open the folded paper and fold one of the long sides up two inches to form a pocket. Refold along the hamburger fold so that the newly formed pockets are on the inside.

③ Glue the outer edges of the two-inch fold with a small amount of glue.

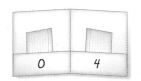

④ Repeat steps 1–3 for 4 more sheets of paper. Attach all 5 pocket books by gluing each one side-by-side. Glue a cover around the multi-paged pocket book.

When to Use It Lessons 3-4, 3-6, 3-7, and 3-9. (Additional instructions for using the Foldable with these lessons are found on pp. 99 and 115.)

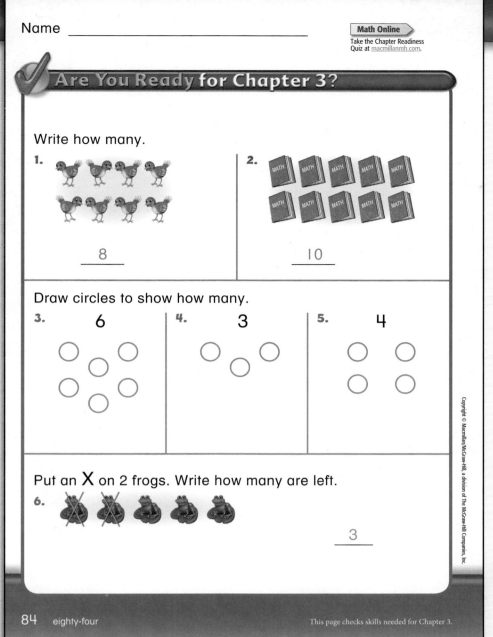

Math Online
Take the Chapter Readiness
Quiz at macmillanmh.com.

Are You Ready for Chapter 3?

Write how many.

1.

_____8_____

2.

_____10_____

Draw circles to show how many.

3. **6**

4. **3**

5. **4**

Put an X on 2 frogs. Write how many are left.

6.

_____3_____

84   eighty-four

This page checks skills needed for Chapter 3.

Copyright © Macmillan/McGraw-Hill, a division of The McGraw-Hill Companies, Inc.

Diagnostic Assessment

Check for students' prerequisite skills before beginning the chapter.

- **Option 1:** *Are You Ready for Chapter 3?*
  SE Student Edition, p. 84

- **Option 2:** *Online Assessment*
  Math Online macmillanmh.com

- **Option 3:** *Diagnostic Test*
  CRM Chapter 3 Resource Masters, p. 57

RTI (Response to Intervention)

Apply the Results Based on the results of the diagnostic assessment on student p. 84, use the chart below to address individual needs before beginning the chapter.

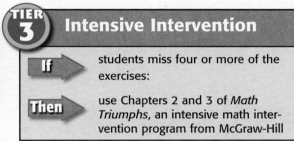

TIER 3 **Intensive Intervention**

| **If** | students miss four or more of the exercises: |
| **Then** | use Chapters 2 and 3 of *Math Triumphs*, an intensive math intervention program from McGraw-Hill |

TIER 2 **Strategic Intervention**
below/approaching grade level

If students miss two or three in:
Exercises 1–6

Then choose a resource:

Strategic Intervention Guide (p. 70)

CRM Chapter 3 Resource Masters
(Reteach Worksheets)

Math Online Concepts in Motion

TIER 1 **On-Level**

If students miss one in:
Exercises 1–6

Then choose a resource:

TE Learning Stations (pp. 83G–83H)

TE Chapter Project (p. 85)

CRM Game: *Follow the Arrow*

Math Adventures

My Math Zone Chapter 1

Math Online Fact Dash

Above/Beyond Level

If students miss none in:
Exercises 1–6

Then choose a resource:

TE Learning Stations (pp. 83G–83H)

TE Chapter Project (p. 85)

Math Adventures

Real-World Problem Solving: *What Do They Eat?*

My Math Zone Chapters 2, 3

Math Online Games

Before you begin Chapter 3:
- Read the Math at Home letter found on p. 85, with the class and have each student sign it.
- Send home copies of the Math at Home letter with each student.
- Use the Spanish letter on p. 86 for students with Spanish-speaking parents or guardians.

WRITING IN ▶MATH

Starting the Chapter
Ask students to write each of the chapter's vocabulary words in their Math Journal. Have them draw a simple illustration to represent each word. Then ask them to write the definition for each word using their glossaries.

Real-Aloud Anthology
For an optional reading activity to introduce this chapter's math concepts, see the Real-Aloud Anthology on p. TR26.

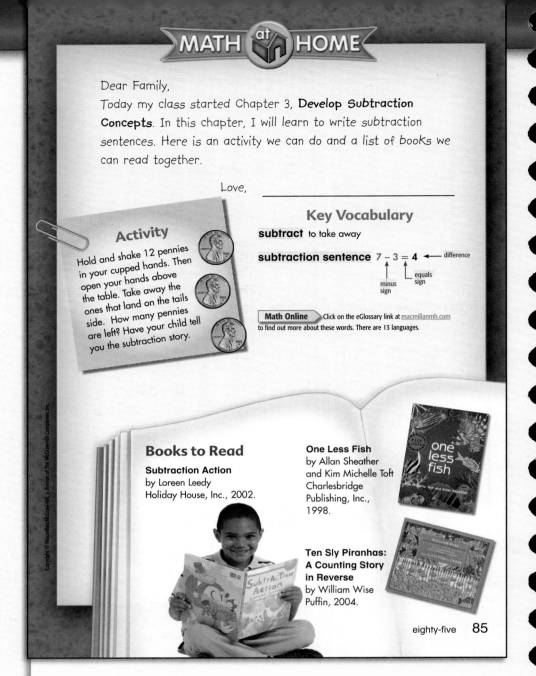

MATH at HOME

Dear Family,
Today my class started Chapter 3, **Develop Subtraction Concepts**. In this chapter, I will learn to write subtraction sentences. Here is an activity we can do and a list of books we can read together.

Love, _____

Activity
Hold and shake 12 pennies in your cupped hands. Then open your hands above the table. Take away the ones that land on the tails side. How many pennies are left? Have your child tell you the subtraction story.

Key Vocabulary
subtract to take away

subtraction sentence $7 - 3 = 4$ ⟵ difference

minus sign / equals sign

Math Online Click on the eGlossary link at macmillanmh.com to find out more about these words. There are 13 languages.

Books to Read
Subtraction Action
by Loreen Leedy
Holiday House, Inc., 2002.

One Less Fish
by Allan Sheather
and Kim Michelle Toft
Charlesbridge
Publishing, Inc.,
1998.

Ten Sly Piranhas: A Counting Story in Reverse
by William Wise
Puffin, 2004.

eighty-five 85

✔ Chapter 3 Project

Subtraction Number Storybook

- Have students work independently or with a partner to create a subtraction number storybook.
- Each page of the book should include a subtraction number story that includes three sentences, the corresponding number sentence, and an illustration of the story.
- When students have written five to seven stories, they may design a cover for their book.
- Ask students to share their book and subtraction number stories with the class or have books on display for parents at an open house or during parent/teacher conferences.

CRM *Refer to Chapter 3 Resource Masters, p. 65 for a rubric to assess students' progress on this project.*

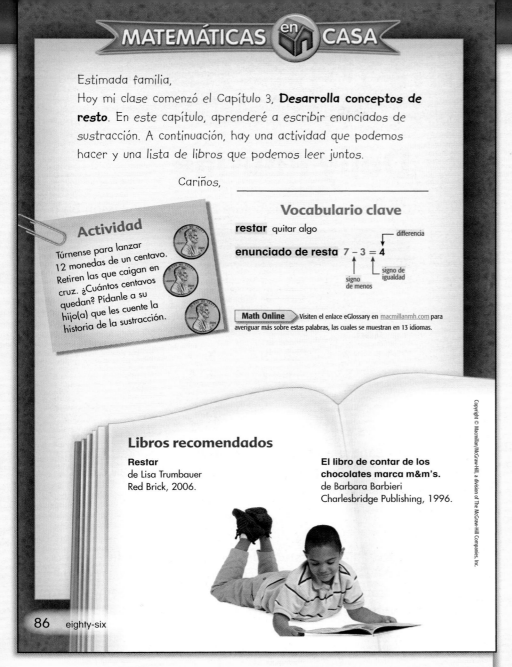

MATEMÁTICAS en CASA

Estimada familia,

Hoy mi clase comenzó el Capítulo 3, **Desarrolla conceptos de resto**. En este capítulo, aprenderé a escribir enunciados de sustracción. A continuación, hay una actividad que podemos hacer y una lista de libros que podemos leer juntos.

Cariños, _____

Actividad

Túrnense para lanzar 12 monedas de un centavo. Retiren las que caigan en cruz. ¿Cuántos centavos quedan? Pídanle a su hijo(a) que les cuente la historia de la sustracción.

Vocabulario clave

restar quitar algo

enunciado de resta 7 − 3 = 4

diferencia ↑

signo de menos ↑   ↑ signo de igualdad

Math Online Visiten el enlace eGlossary en macmillanmh.com para averiguar más sobre estas palabras, las cuales se muestran en 13 idiomas.

Libros recomendados

Restar
de Lisa Trumbauer
Red Brick, 2006.

El libro de contar de los chocolates marca m&m's.
de Barbara Barbieri
Charlesbridge Publishing, 1996.

86 eighty-six

Chapter 3 Literature List

Lesson	Book Title
3-1	**Anno's Counting House** Mitsumasa Anno
3-2	**Rooster's Off to See the World** Eric Carle
3-3	**Ten Tiny Monsters** Sheila White Samton
3-4	**Five Little Monkeys Jumping on the Bed** Eileen Christelow
3-5	**Six Snowy Sheep** Judith Ross Enderle and Stephanie Gordon Tessler
3-6	**Anno's Counting Book** Mitsumasa Anno
3-7	**Ten Black Dots** Donald Crews
3-9	**Ten Seeds** Ruth Brown
3-10	**Ten Sly Piranhas** William Wise
Any	**Subtraction Action** Loreen Leedy
Any	**One Less Fish** Allan Sheather and Kim Toft

ELL National ESL Standards Alignment for Chapter 3

Lesson, Page	ELL Standard	Modality	Level
3-1, p 87B	Goal 2, Standard 2, D	Visual, Spatial	Intermediate
3-2, p 89B	Goal 1, Standard 3, C	Visual, Social	Intermediate
3-3, p 91B	Goal 2, Standard 2, D	Visual, Spatial	Intermediate
3-4, p 95B	Goal 1, Standard 2, D	Auditory, Kinesthetic	Advanced
3-5, p 97B	Goal 3, Standard 1, F	Auditory, Visual	Advanced
3-6, p 101B	Goal 1, Standard 1, C	Kinesthetic, Visual	Beginning
3-7, p 103B	Goal 2, Standard 2, G	Auditory, Linguistic	Intermediate
3-8, p 105B	Goal 2, Standard 2, C	Spatial, Interpersonal	Advanced
3-9, p 107B	Goal 2, Standard 3, E	Visual/Spatial, Logical	Beginning
3-10, p 111B	Goal 2, Standard 1, F	Kinesthetic, Social	Intermediate

The National ESL Standards can be found in the Teacher Reference Handbook.

Lesson Planner

Objective
Use counters to model subtraction stories.

Review Vocabulary
number line

Resources
Materials: cup, plastic bags

Manipulatives: two-colored counters, connecting cubes

Literature Connection: *Anno's Counting House* by Mitsumasa Anno

Alternate Lesson: Use "The Whale Game" on pages 188 and 189 of *Math Their Way* to provide practice using manipulatives to show subtraction.
Use *IMPACT Mathematics:* Unit A and C to provide practice with using manipulatives to model subtraction stories.

Teacher Technology
- 💿 TeacherWorks • Math Song Track 15 Lesson Plan

Focus on Math Background

This lesson introduces students to the concept of subtraction through the context of stories, referred to in formal mathematics as word problems. By visualizing how quantities decrease due to situations involving the comparison of sets or the separation of parts from a whole, students will begin to make sense of and use subtraction as a strategy to solve problems in everyday events that involve operations with numbers.

Daily Routine

Use these suggestions before beginning the lesson on p. 87.

5-Minute Check
(Reviews Lesson 2-10)

Add.

1.	**2.**	**3.**	**4.**
7	9	7	6
+ 2	+ 2	+ 4	+ 6
9	11	11	12

Problem of the Day

Sandra and her mother go to the market. They buy 3 red peppers and 3 green peppers. How many peppers do they buy in all? 6 peppers

LINE UP Have students line up and show five fingers. Ask them to cover up two fingers. Describe the subtraction. For example, say, "You have five fingers. You covered up two. You now have three fingers showing."

Review Math Vocabulary

Review the vocabulary term **number line** and write it on the chalkboard.
- Ask students to look at WorkMat 4: Number Lines.
- Tell students to point to the number 5. Have them count back to number 3.
- **How many did you count back from 5 to get to 3?** 2
- Tell them that 2 subtracted from 5 is 3.
- Explain that a number line can help students with subtraction stories.

Visual Vocabulary Cards

Use Visual Vocabulary Card 30 to reinforce the vocabulary reviewed in this lesson. (The Define/Example/Ask routine is printed on the back of each card.)

number line

Differentiated Instruction

Small Group Options

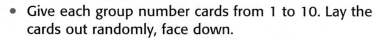

Option 1
Gifted and Talented **AL**
LOGICAL

Materials: set of number cards 1–10

- Give each group number cards from 1 to 10. Lay the cards out randomly, face down.
- Have each student take a turn by drawing two number cards and making up a subtraction story with the numbers. Another student in the group should provide the answer.
- **Can the greater number be the taking away number in a story? Why or why not?** No; you would take away more than you started with.

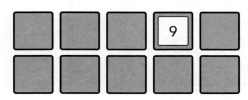

Option 2
English Language Learners **ELL**
VISUAL, SPATIAL

Core Vocabulary: on the paper, on the desk, still
Common Use Verb: take

Do Math This strategy allows students to respond to oral directions to increase their understanding and listening skills.

- Give each student 5 blocks and a paper circle. Draw a circle on the overhead.
- Say: "Put 5 blocks **on the paper**" while modeling the same on the overhead.
- Repeat for: "**Take** 2 blocks from the paper and put them **on the desk**."
- Ask: "How many blocks **are still on the paper**?" Model answer: "Three blocks are **still on the paper**."
- Repeat as time permits, avoiding zero.

Independent Work Options

Option 1
Early Finishers **OL** **AL**
VISUAL, SPATIAL

Materials: red and yellow crayons, two-colored counters

- Ask students to think of as many subtraction problems as they can that would use five counters.
- Have students show each subtraction sentence on a sheet of paper by drawing circles to show the starting amount and then drawing an X through those that were taken away.

Option 2
Student Technology

Math Online macmillanmh.com

🎵 Math Songs, "Take It Away" Track 15 • 🌐 Math Adventures

Option 3
Learning Station: Health (p. 83G)

Direct students to the Health Learning Station for more opportunities to explore and extend the lesson concept.

Option 4
Problem-Solving Practice

Reinforce problem-solving skills and strategies with the Problem-Solving Practice worksheet.

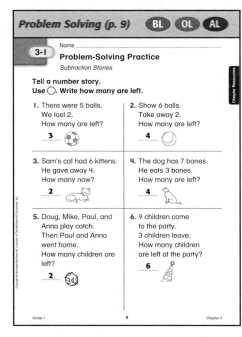

1 Introduce

Activity Choice 1 • Hands-On

Explain the rules of musical chairs to your class in case they are unfamiliar with the game. Have six students volunteer to play musical chairs.

- **Once the music stops for the first time, how many students get to sit down?** 5 students
- **How many chairs are taken away each time?** 1 chair
- **After four chairs are taken away, how many students get to sit down?** 1 student

Activity Choice 2 • Literature

Introduce the lesson with *Anno's Counting House* by Mitsumasa Anno. For additional support, see p. TR45.

2 Teach

Give each child a cup, a bag of two-colored counters, and a sheet of paper. Tell stories that students can act out on their papers with the counters. The following are some sample questions:

- **Five children were playing in the sandbox. Two went home. How many are left?** 3 children
- **Jose found seven rocks. Then he lost two. How many does he have left?** 5 rocks
- **Maria saw four squirrels in the tree. Then one ran away. How many are left?** 3 squirrels
- Introduce the term "are left" and explain that all these problems have to do with leftovers.

Get Ready Use the section at the top of p. 87 to teach the lesson concept.

Check Observe students as you work through Exercises 1–3 as a class.

Exercise 3 Assess student comprehension before assigning practice exercises.

 COMMON ERROR!

Students may not recognize the total in each picture and therefore how many counters to start with. For example, explain that in Exercise 1 all the kites had been flying. Then some fell to the ground. All the kites in the picture are the total.

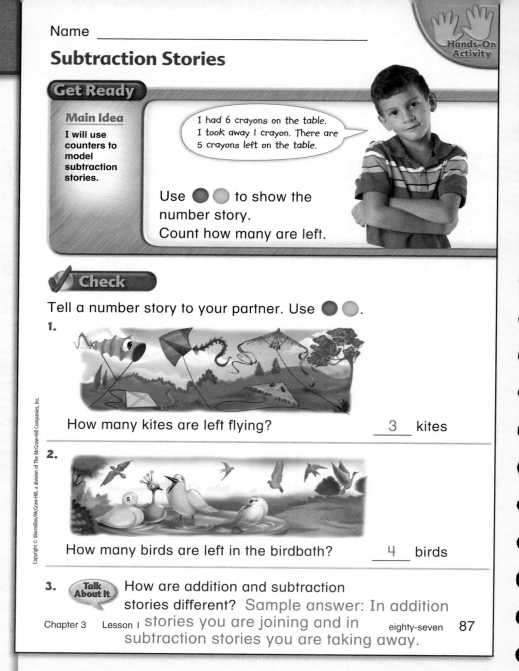

Name _____

Subtraction Stories

Get Ready

Main Idea
I will use counters to model subtraction stories.

I had 6 crayons on the table. I took away 1 crayon. There are 5 crayons left on the table.

Use ⬤ ⬤ to show the number story.
Count how many are left.

Check

Tell a number story to your partner. Use ⬤ ⬤.

1.

How many kites are left flying? ___3___ kites

2.

How many birds are left in the birdbath? ___4___ birds

3. *Talk About It* How are addition and subtraction stories different? Sample answer: In addition stories you are joining and in subtraction stories you are taking away.

Chapter 3   Lesson 1   eighty-seven   87

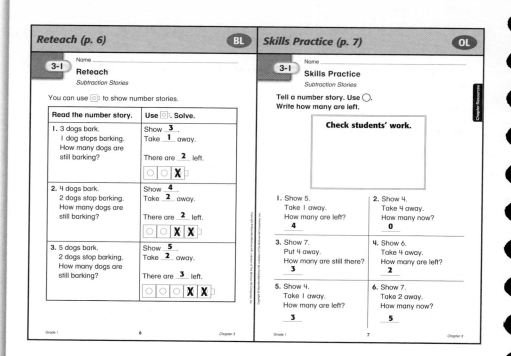

Reteach (p. 6) **BL**

3-1 Name _____
Reteach
Subtraction Stories

You can use ⬚ to show number stories.

Read the number story.	Use ⬚. Solve.
1. 3 dogs bark. 1 dog stops barking. How many dogs are still barking?	Show **3**. Take **1** away. There are **2** left. ⬚⬚**X**
2. 4 dogs bark. 2 dogs stop barking. How many dogs are still barking?	Show **4**. Take **2** away. There are **2** left. ⬚⬚**X X**
3. 5 dogs bark. 2 dogs stop barking. How many dogs are still barking?	Show **5**. Take **2** away. There are **3** left. ⬚⬚⬚**X X**

Grade 1   6   Chapter 3

Skills Practice (p. 7) **OL**

3-1 Name _____
Skills Practice
Subtraction Stories

Tell a number story. Use ◯.
Write how many are left.

Check students' work.

1. Show 5. Take 1 away. How many are left? **4**	2. Show 4. Take 4 away. How many now? **0**
3. Show 7. Put 4 away. How many are still there? **3**	4. Show 6. Take 4 away. How many are left? **2**
5. Show 4. Take 1 away. How many are left? **3**	6. Show 7. Take 2 away. How many now? **5**

Grade 1   7   Chapter 3

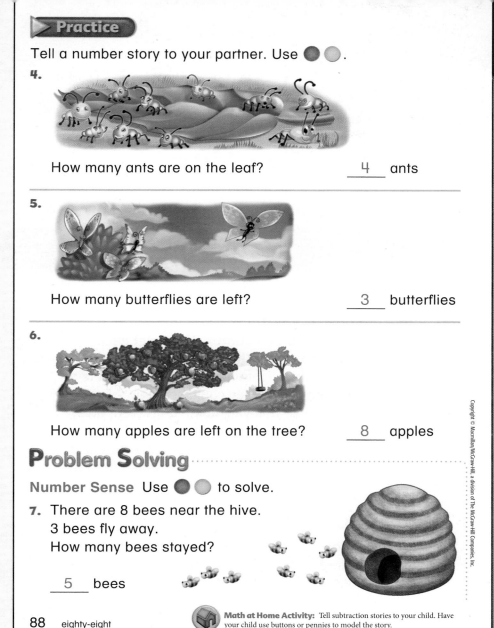

Practice

Tell a number story to your partner. Use ⬤ ◯.

4.

How many ants are on the leaf? ___4___ ants

5.

How many butterflies are left? ___3___ butterflies

6.

How many apples are left on the tree? ___8___ apples

Problem Solving

Number Sense Use ⬤ ◯ to solve.

7. There are 8 bees near the hive.
3 bees fly away.
How many bees stayed?

___5___ bees

88 eighty-eight

Math at Home Activity: Tell subtraction stories to your child. Have your child use buttons or pennies to model the story.

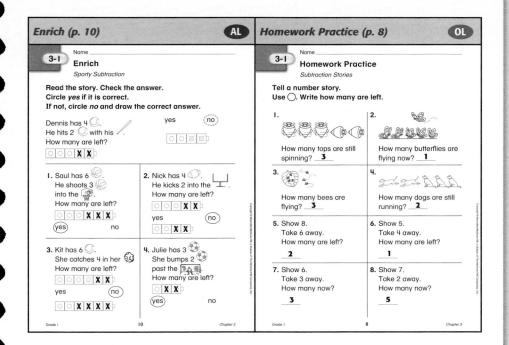

Enrich (p. 10) — AL

3-1 Enrich
Sporty Subtraction

Read the story. Check the answer.
Circle *yes* if it is correct.
If not, circle *no* and draw the correct answer.

Dennis has 4. He hits 2 with his. How many are left? yes / **no**

1. Saul has 6. He shoots 3 into the. How many are left? **yes** / no
2. Nick has 4. He kicks 2 into the. How many are left? yes / **no**
3. Kit has 6. She catches 4 in her. How many are left? yes / **no**
4. Julie has 3. She bumps 2 past the. How many are left? **yes** / no

Homework Practice (p. 8) — OL

3-1 Homework Practice
Subtraction Stories

Tell a number story.
Use ◯. Write how many are left.

1. How many tops are still spinning? **3**
2. How many butterflies are flying now? **1**
3. How many bees are flying? **3**
4. How many dogs are still running? **2**
5. Show 8. Take 6 away. How many are left? **2**
6. Show 5. Take 4 away. How many are left? **1**
7. Show 6. Take 3 away. How many now? **3**
8. Show 7. Take 2 away. How many now? **5**

Alternate Teaching Strategy

If students have trouble using counters to show subtraction stories . . .

Then use one of these reteach options.

1. **CRM Daily Reteach Worksheet** (p. 6)

2. **Use Connecting Cube** Assist students by using connecting cubes to show the total in each picture. Then allow students to break the cubes into two groups.

③ Practice

Differentiate practice using these leveled assignments for Exercises 4–7.

Level	Assignment
BL Below/Approaching Level	Have students work in groups. Encourage them to take their time with the exercises and use the two-colored counters.
OL On Level	Complete the exercises independently.
AL Above/Beyond Level	Have students write a subtraction sentence for each exercise.

④ Assess

✎ Formative Assessment

Have students model one of the practice questions.
- **Why did you start with that many counters?**
  Sample answer: That is all the pictures in the story.

WRITING IN ▶MATH Have students draw a picture showing one of the practice problems.

Quick Check **Are students continuing to struggle with showing subtraction stories?**

If Yes → Strategic Intervention Guide (p. 70)

If No → Independent Work Options (p. 87B)
  CRM Skills Practice Worksheet (p. 7)
  CRM Enrich Worksheet (p. 10)

Lesson Planner

Objective
Use counters to subtract and show how many are left.

Vocabulary
subtract

Resources
Materials: WorkMat 3: Part-Part-Whole

Manipulatives: two-colored counters, connecting cubes

Literature Connection: *Rooster's Off to See the World* by Eric Carle

Alternate Lesson: Use "The Cave" on page 192 of *Math Their Way* to provide practice for subtraction.
Use *IMPACT Mathematics:* Unit A and C to provide practice with modeling subtraction.

Teacher Technology
TeacherWorks • Concepts in Motion • Math Song Track 15 Lesson Plan

Focus on Math Background

In this lesson, students continue to make sense of subtraction by using manipulative materials and models to represent situations involving the separation of parts from a whole or the comparison of two sets. First graders need a strong conceptual understanding of all number operations, including subtraction, before moving to more abstract representations of these situations using symbols and procedural operations, such as regrouping.

Daily Routine

Use these suggestions before beginning the lesson on p. 89.

5-Minute Check

(Reviews Lesson 3-1)
Use two-colored counters to model each subtraction story. Then solve.

1. Vijay saw 6 lightning bugs in the sky. A few minutes later, Vijay could see only 2 lightning bugs. How many lightning bugs went away?
   4 lightning bugs

2. Seven ducks swam in the pond. Four ducks flew away. How many ducks were left in the pond? 3 ducks

Problem of the Day

On Monday, Johnny's mother told him to go to the pet store and purchase 1 dog treat for each day of the week. How many dog treats does Johnny need to buy? 7 dog treats

---

LINE UP Have a group of three students line up. Ask six students to get in another line. Explain that there are two parts, 3 and 6. Ask students to name what whole the two parts make. Repeat with different numbers until all students are in line.

Building Math Vocabulary

- On the board draw eight birds. Draw a second picture with only six birds.
- Tell students that 2 birds were **subtracted** from the 8, leaving a difference of 6.
- Start a discussion by asking students about other groups of objects that can be subtracted from to get a difference.

Visual Vocabulary Cards
Use Visual Vocabulary Cards 13 and 46 to reinforce the vocabulary introduced in this lesson. (The Define/Example/Ask routine is printed on the back of each card.)

difference

Differentiated Instruction

Small Group Options

Option 1

VISUAL, SPATIAL

Below/Approaching Level BL

Materials: two-foot pieces of string, straws

- Give each student a piece of two-foot string and ten straws.
- Have students form a circle with the string and place their straws inside the circle.
- Ask students oral subtraction problems. **You have 10 straws in your circle. Take 5 straws out of the circle. How many straws are left inside the circle?** 5 straws
- Repeat oral subtraction problems using the numbers 1 though 10.
- Students should put all 10 straws back into the circle after each problem.

Option 2

VISUAL, SOCIAL

English Language Learners ELL

Materials: An orange, orange objects, a picture of fruit with orange on it.
Core Vocabulary: these are, orange color, oranges
Common Use Verb: find

See Math This strategy helps visualize subtraction.

- Show oranges to students. Say: "These are **oranges.**"
- Say: "**This orange** has pieces."
- Count the segments and write the number.
- Give 3 students an orange segment. Write a subtraction sentence. Repeat until each student has "subtracted" a segment.

Use this worksheet to provide additional support for English Language Learners.

English Language Learners (p. 67) ELL

20 Name _____

Subtraction Sentences

Color the animals. Cut out the pictures. Make some subtraction sentences using the animal cards.
Answers will vary.

Subtraction to 10   67

Independent Work Options

Option 1

KINESTHETIC, LOGICAL

Early Finishers OL AL

Materials: subtraction flash cards, two-colored counters

- Have students take turns picking a subtraction flash card.
- Ask students to use connecting cubes to model the problem to find the difference.
- Have students continue the activity until all flash cards have been used.

Option 2

Student Technology

Math Online macmillanmh.com

♪ Math Songs, "Take It Away" Track 15 • 🌐 Math Adventures

Option 3

Learning Station: Art (p. 83G)

Direct students to the Art Learning Station for more opportunities to explore and extend the lesson concept.

Option 4

Problem-Solving Practice

Reinforce problem-solving skills and strategies with the Problem-Solving Practice worksheet.

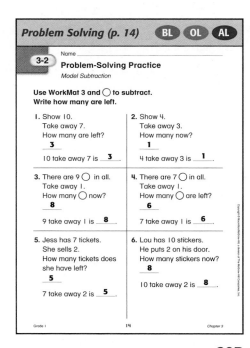

Problem Solving (p. 14) BL OL AL

Name _____

3-2 **Problem-Solving Practice**
Model Subtraction

Use WorkMat 3 and ◯ to subtract.
Write how many are left.

1. Show 10.
   Take away 7.
   How many are left?
   3

   10 take away 7 is __3__

2. Show 4.
   Take away 3.
   How many now?
   1

   4 take away 3 is __1__

3. There are 9 ◯ in all.
   Take away 1.
   How many ◯ now?
   8

   9 take away 1 is __8__

4. There are 7 ◯ in all.
   Take away 1.
   How many ◯ are left?
   6

   7 take away 1 is __6__

5. Jess has 7 tickets.
   She sells 2.
   How many tickets does she have left?
   5

   7 take away 2 is __5__

6. Lou has 10 stickers.
   He puts 2 on his door.
   How many stickers now?
   8

   10 take away 2 is __8__

Grade 1   14   Chapter 3

1 Introduce

Activity Choice 1 • Hands-On

- Have items available for the whole class to see such as rulers, pencils, staplers, and books.
- Call up two children at a time to model the subtraction process. Give each some rulers and then say: Sally has 6 rulers, and she gives Juan 5 rulers. How may rulers does Sally have left?
- As you write the equation $6 - 5 = 1$ on the board, point out that you are **subtracting** five rulers from the original six.

Activity Choice 2 • Literature

Introduce the lesson with *Rooster's Off to See the World* by Eric Carle. For additional support, see p. TR45.

2 Teach

- Have five students walk to the front of the class. Count the students aloud with the class.
- Ask two of the students to sit.
- **How many students are still standing?** 3 students
- **Is this addition or subtraction? How do you know?** Subtraction; Sample answer: We ended with less than we began with.
- **We subtracted 2 from 5. The difference is 3. How could you show this?** Sample answers: counters, connecting cubes, blocks

Get Ready Use the section at the top of p. 89 to teach the lesson concept.

Check Observe students as you work through Exercises 1–4 as a class.

> **Exercise 4** Assess student comprehension before assigning practice exercises.

⚠ COMMON ERROR!

Students may place the counters in the wrong area of WorkMat 3. Show them that the "Whole" section is larger than the two "Part" sections. Remind student that when two parts make a whole, the whole is always the greatest number.

Modeling Subtraction

 Hands-On Activity

Get Ready

Main Idea
I will subtract using counters.

Vocabulary
subtract

When you know the whole and a part, you can **subtract** to find the other part.

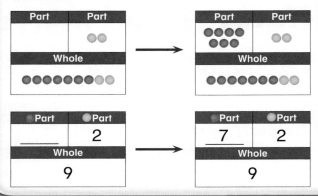

✓ Check

Use WorkMat 3 and ⬤⬤ to subtract.

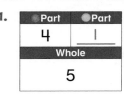 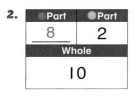 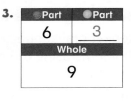

1.
● Part	● Part
4	1
Whole	
5	

2.
● Part	● Part
8	2
Whole	
10	

3.
● Part	● Part
6	3
Whole	
9	

4. **Talk About It** You have 10 counters in all. 3 of the counters are yellow. Do you have more than 7 red counters? Explain. No. 3 yellow counters and 7 red counters make 10 counters in all.

Chapter 3   Lesson 2   eighty-nine   89

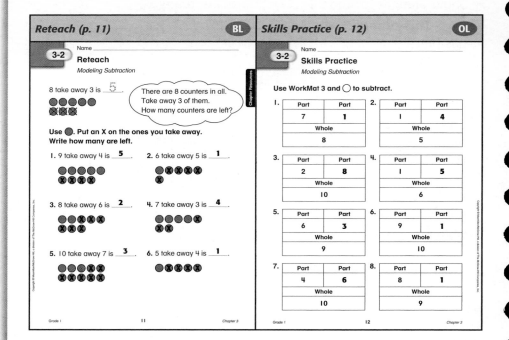

Reteach (p. 11) — BL

Skills Practice (p. 12) — OL

► Practice

Use WorkMat 3 and ⬤ ⬤ to subtract.

5.

⬤ Part	⬤ Part
3	5
Whole	
8	

6.

⬤ Part	⬤ Part
4	3
Whole	
7	

7.

⬤ Part	⬤ Part
4	5
Whole	
9	

8.

⬤ Part	⬤ Part
3	1
Whole	
4	

9.

⬤ Part	⬤ Part
4	2
Whole	
6	

10.

⬤ Part	⬤ Part
2	3
Whole	
5	

11.

⬤ Part	⬤ Part
1	6
Whole	
7	

12.

⬤ Part	⬤ Part
5	2
Whole	
7	

13. **WRITING IN ►MATH** How many will you have left if you take 10 away from 10? Explain.

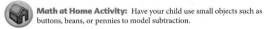 Sample answer: 0, because you have taken all away.

90   ninety

Math at Home Activity: Have your child use small objects such as buttons, beans, or pennies to model subtraction.

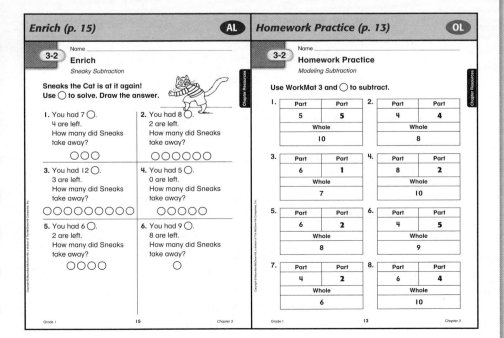

If ➤ students have trouble using connecting cubes to model subtraction . . .

Then ➤ use one of these reteach options.

1 [CRM] **Daily Reteach Worksheet** (p. 11)

2 **Domino Math** Give each student a domino and a sticky note. Ask students to count the total number of dots on the domino. Explain that the total is the "whole". Have them use a sticky note to cover one side of the domino. Explain that each side is a "part".

❸ Practice

Differentiate practice using these leveled assignments for Exercises 5–13.

Level	Assignment
BL Below/Approaching Level	Have students work in groups as you guide them.
OL On Level	Complete the exercises independently.
AL Above/Beyond Level	Write the corresponding subtraction sentence for each exercise.

❹ Assess

✎ Formative Assessment

- **Use connecting cubes to show 6 taken away from 10.** Student should show 4 cubes.
- **Show 3 taken away from 8.** Student should show 5 cubes.

WRITING IN ►MATH Have students draw a picture that illustrates Exercise 10.

Quick Check   **Are students continuing to struggle with modeling subtraction?**

If Yes → Small Group Options (p. 89B)
     Strategic Intervention Guide (p. 70)

If No → Independent Work Options (p. 89B)
     [CRM] Skills Practice Worksheet (p. 12)
     [CRM] Enrich Worksheet (p. 15)

Subtraction Sentences

Lesson Planner

Objective

Use pictures and the symbols minus (−) and equals (=) to write subtraction sentences.

Vocabulary

subtraction sentence, **difference**, **minus (−)**

Resources

Materials: number and symbol cards

Manipulatives: blue and red number cubes

Literature Connection: *Ten Tiny Monsters* by Sheila White Samton

Alternate Lesson: Use "Lift the Bowl" on page 180 of *Math Their Way* to provide practice in subtraction. Use *IMPACT Mathematics:* Unit A, C, and G to provide practice with writing subtraction sentences.

Teacher Technology
⬤ TeacherWorks • 🚂 Math Tool Chest • Math Songs Track 15 Lesson Plan

Focus on Math Background

Using number sentences to represent subtraction situations modeled in word problems is the focus of this lesson. Students will learn that the minus sign (−) corresponds to actions where there is a "taking away" of an amount from a larger set or a separation of parts from a whole. Moreover, students will use the equal sign (=) to indicate the end result of these actions involving separating, decomposing, or taking away situations.

Daily Routine

Use these suggestions before beginning the lesson on p. 91.

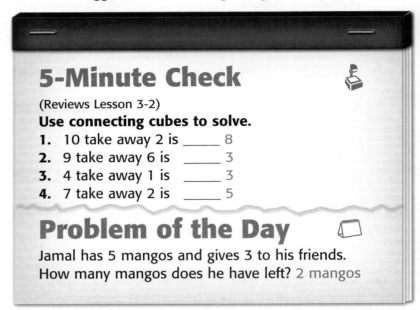

5-Minute Check

(Reviews Lesson 3-2)

Use connecting cubes to solve.

1. 10 take away 2 is _____ 8
2. 9 take away 6 is _____ 3
3. 4 take away 1 is _____ 3
4. 7 take away 2 is _____ 5

Problem of the Day

Jamal has 5 mangos and gives 3 to his friends. How many mangos does he have left? 2 mangos

LINE UP Have students create subtraction sentences as a group. Have the first student choose a number. Write it on the board. As you move down the line, each student completes a part of the sentence. When a sentence is complete, have students read it in unison. Repeat down the line with another sentence.

Building Math Vocabulary

Write the **subtraction sentence** 5 − 4 = 1 on the board.

• Use connecting cubes to model the subtraction.
• Explain that 1 is the **difference**.
• Have students draw seven circles on their whiteboards. Then have them erase three of the circles.
• **How many circles are left?** 4 circles **So, 4 is the difference.**
• Have students copy you as you write the subtraction sentence 7 − 3 = 4. Once they have written the sentence on their whiteboards, have them circle the **minus (−)** sign and the equals (=) sign.

Visual Vocabulary Cards

Use Visual Vocabulary Card 25 to reinforce the vocabulary introduced in this lesson. (The Define/Example/Ask routine is printed on the back of each card.)

minus

Differentiated Instruction

Small Group Options

LOGICAL, SOCIAL

Option 1
Gifted and Talented (AL)

Materials: pencil, paper, connecting cubes

- Have each student choose a number less than 10 and write five missing-number subtraction sentences using that number.

- Show that the missing number can be in two positions in the sentence. Out of their five sentences, students should give two examples of each kind of missing number subtraction sentence.

- Have students exchange papers and solve the problems. Have the group work together to model several of the sentences with connecting cubes.

$$7 - \quad = 2$$
$$5 - \quad = 4$$
$$9 - \quad = 4$$

Option 2
English Language Learners (ELL)

VISUAL, SPATIAL

Materials: marker for overhead
Core Vocabulary: grapes, there were, ate
Common Use Verb: were left

See Math This strategy uses scaffolding to teach subtraction sentences.

- Demonstrate the story on the scaffold using overhead materials. *There were 7 grapes. Maria ate _____ (4) grapes. 3 were left.*

- Model how to fill in missing information.

- Model writing story problems for the scaffold vertically and horizontally.

- Repeat with new name and numbers, switch which part of the problem is blank as time permits.

Use this worksheet to provide additional support for English Language Learners.

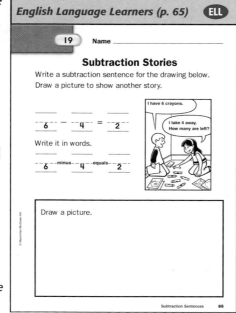

Independent Work Options

KINESTHETIC, LOGICAL

Option 1
Early Finishers (OL) (AL)

Materials: number cubes, connecting cubes, white board, dry erase marker

- Have students roll the number cube two times.

- Have students write the greater number on a white board, leave a space, and write the lesser number.

- Ask students to write a minus (−) sign between the numbers and an equals sign after the second number.

- Have students use connecting cubes to find and write the difference after the equals sign.

Option 2
Student Technology

Math Online > macmillanmh.com

♪ Math Songs, "Take It Away" Track 15 • 🌐 Math Adventures

Option 3
Learning Station: Music (p. 83G)

Direct students to the Music Learning Station for more opportunities to explore and extend the lesson concept.

Option 4
Problem-Solving Practice

Reinforce problem-solving skills and strategies with the Problem-Solving Practice worksheet.

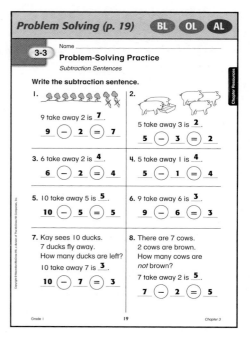

1 Introduce

Activity Choice 1 • Hands-On

- Have students roll a blue number cube and write the number followed by a minus sign. Then have them roll a red number cube and write that number after the minus sign.
- Have them solve their **subtraction sentence.**
- **What do you get if you add the difference to the number you subtracted?** Sample answer: You get the original number you rolled.

Activity Choice 2 • Literature

Introduce the lesson with *Ten Tiny Monsters* by Sheila White Samton. For addition support, see p. TR45.

2 Teach

- Ask eight students to stand and count off. Tell students that the whole is eight. Then have two students sit.
- Tell students still standing to count off again.
- **How many students are still standing?** 6 students
- Write a blank subtraction sentence on the chalkboard. Point to the **minus sign. What does this symbol tell you to do?** subtract
- **What number goes in the first blank?** 8 **What number goes in the second blank?** 2 **This is the taking-away number. What number goes in the third blank?** 6 **This is the difference.**

Get Ready Use the section at the top of p. 91 to teach the lesson concept.

Check Observe students as you work through Exercises 1–5 as a class.

> **Exercise 5** Assess student comprehension before assigning practice exercises.

⚠ COMMON ERROR!

Students may use the number of crossed-out items and the number of not–crossed-out items for the first two numbers in their sentences. Explain that the first number in a subtraction sentence should be the *total* number of items.

Name _____

Subtraction Sentences

Get Ready

Main Idea
I will write subtraction sentences.

Vocabulary
subtraction sentence
difference
minus (−)

5 − 2 = 3 is a **subtraction sentence.**
3 is the **difference.**

See

Say	5	minus	2	equals	3
Write	5	−	2	=	3

✓ Check

Write the subtraction sentence.

1.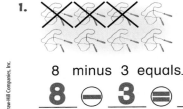

8 minus 3 equals **5**.

8 ⊖ **3** ⊜ **5**

2.

___5___ ⊖ ___1___ ⊜ ___4___

3.

___3___ ⊖ ___2___ ⊜ ___1___

4.

___10___ ⊖ ___7___ ⊜ ___3___

5. **Talk About It** What does − mean? − means minus; to subtract

---

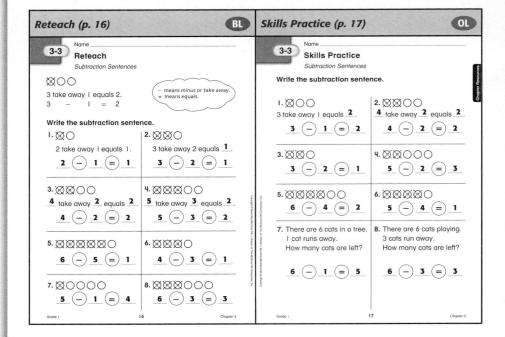

Reteach (p. 16) — BL

3-3 Reteach
Subtraction Sentences

⊠○○
3 take away 1 equals 2.
3 − 1 = 2

− means minus or take away.
= means equals.

Write the subtraction sentence.

1. ⊠○
2 take away 1 equals 1.
2 ⊖ 1 ⊜ 1

2. ⊠⊠○
3 take away 2 equals **1**.
3 ⊖ 2 ⊜ 1

3. ⊠⊠○○
4 take away **2** equals **2**.
4 ⊖ 2 ⊜ 2

4. ⊠⊠⊠○○
5 take away **3** equals **2**.
5 ⊖ 3 ⊜ 2

5. ⊠⊠⊠⊠⊠○
6 ⊖ 5 ⊜ 1

6. ⊠⊠⊠○
4 ⊖ 3 ⊜ 1

7. ⊠○○○○
5 ⊖ 1 ⊜ 4

8. ⊠⊠⊠○○○
6 ⊖ 3 ⊜ 3

Grade 1   16   Chapter 3

Skills Practice (p. 17) — OL

3-3 Skills Practice
Subtraction Sentences

Write the subtraction sentence.

1. ⊠○○
3 take away 1 equals **2**.
3 ⊖ 1 ⊜ 2

2. ⊠⊠○○
4 take away 2 equals **2**.
4 ⊖ 2 ⊜ 2

3. ⊠⊠○
3 ⊖ 2 ⊜ 1

4. ⊠⊠○○○
5 ⊖ 2 ⊜ 3

5. ⊠⊠⊠⊠○○
6 ⊖ 4 ⊜ 2

6. ⊠⊠⊠⊠○
5 ⊖ 4 ⊜ 1

7. There are 6 cats in a tree. 1 cat runs away. How many cats are left?
6 ⊖ 1 ⊜ 5

8. There are 6 cats playing. 3 cats run away. How many cats are left?
6 ⊖ 3 ⊜ 3

Grade 1   17   Chapter 3

Write the subtraction sentence.

Remember
The things that are not crossed out are the difference.

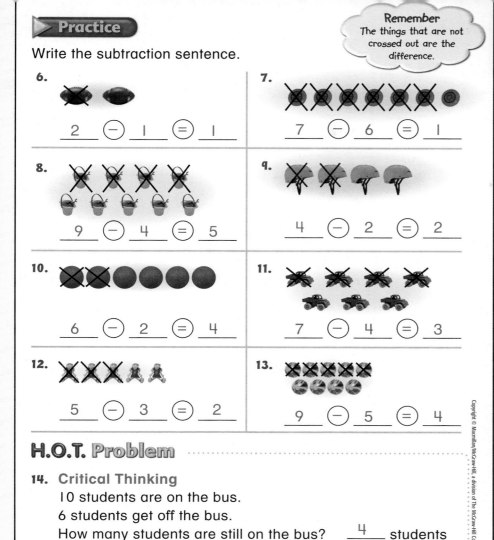

6.
2 ⊖ 1 ⊜ 1

7.
7 ⊖ 6 ⊜ 1

8.
9 ⊖ 4 ⊜ 5

9.
4 ⊖ 2 ⊜ 2

10.
6 ⊖ 2 ⊜ 4

11.
7 ⊖ 4 ⊜ 3

12.
5 ⊖ 3 ⊜ 2

13.
9 ⊖ 5 ⊜ 4

H.O.T. Problem

14. Critical Thinking

10 students are on the bus.

6 students get off the bus.

How many students are still on the bus? ___4___ students

Write the number sentence. ___10___ ⊖ ___6___ ⊜ ___4___

92 ninety-two

Math at Home Activity: Using buttons, beans, or pennies, have your child write subtraction sentences for some simple subtraction stories.

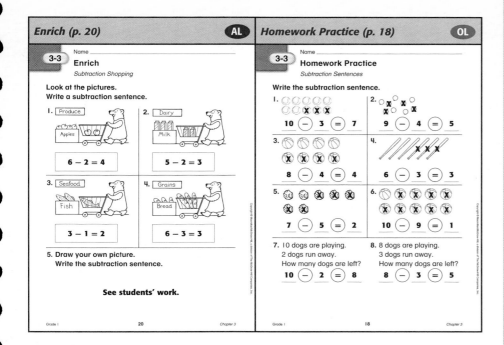

Enrich (p. 20) **AL**

Name _____
3-3 **Enrich**
Subtraction Shopping

Look at the pictures.
Write a subtraction sentence.

1. Produce
6 − 2 = 4

2. Dairy
5 − 2 = 3

3. Seafood
3 − 1 = 2

4. Grains
6 − 3 = 3

5. Draw your own picture.
Write the subtraction sentence.

See students' work.

Grade 1   20   Chapter 3

Homework Practice (p. 18) **OL**

Name _____
3-3 **Homework Practice**
Subtraction Sentences

Write the subtraction sentence.

1.
10 ⊖ 3 ⊜ 7

2.
9 ⊖ 4 ⊜ 5

3.
8 ⊖ 4 ⊜ 4

4.
6 ⊖ 3 ⊜ 3

5.
7 ⊖ 5 ⊜ 2

6.
10 ⊖ 9 ⊜ 1

7. 10 dogs are playing.
2 dogs run away.
How many dogs are left?
10 ⊖ 2 ⊜ 8

8. 8 dogs are playing.
3 dogs run away.
How many dogs are left?
8 ⊖ 3 ⊜ 5

Grade 1   18   Chapter 3

BL **Alternate Teaching Strategy**

If ▶ students have trouble writing subtraction sentences . . .

Then ▶ use one of these reteach options.

1 CRM **Daily Reteach Worksheet** (p. 16)

2 **Use Number and Symbol Cards** Allow students to arrange number cards and symbol cards for minus (−) and equals (=) on their desks. Once the cards are in the correct order, students can write the answer on their student pages.

③ Practice

Differentiate practice using these leveled assignments for Exercises 6–14.

Level	Assignment
BL Below/Approaching Level	Guide students by writing in the numbers or the − and = signs.
OL On Level	Complete the exercises independently.
AL Above/Beyond Level	Complete the exercises on a separate sheet of paper without the sentence frames.

④ Assess

Formative Assessment

Have students write a subtraction sentence for the following:

Tiffany blows up seven balloons on her birthday. Two balloons pop. How may balloons does Tiifany have? $7 - 2 = 5$

WRITING IN ▶**MATH** Have students describe what the minus sign and equals sign mean in a number sentence.

Quick Check **Are students continuing to struggle with writing subtraction sentences?**

If Yes ➞ Strategy Intervention Guide (p. 70)

If No ➞ Independent Work Options (p. 91B)

CRM **Skills Practice Worksheet** (p. 17)

CRM **Enrich Worksheet** (p. 20)

Extra Practice

Review Lessons 3-1 to 3-3

Objective: Review and assess mastery of previous lessons' skills and concepts.

- Review with students subtraction vocabulary and the form of a subtraction sentence.
- Students may wish to use connecting cubes to work through the problems.
- Students may wish to arrange number cards and minus-sign and equals-sign cards to create their sentences.
- Demonstrate how to translate a subtraction problem into a subtraction sentence. Remind students that the first number in a subtraction sentence is the total number of items in the picture, or the number you started with.

Practice with Technology

Math Online > Have students visit macmillanmh.com for additional practice with online activities, games, and quizzes.

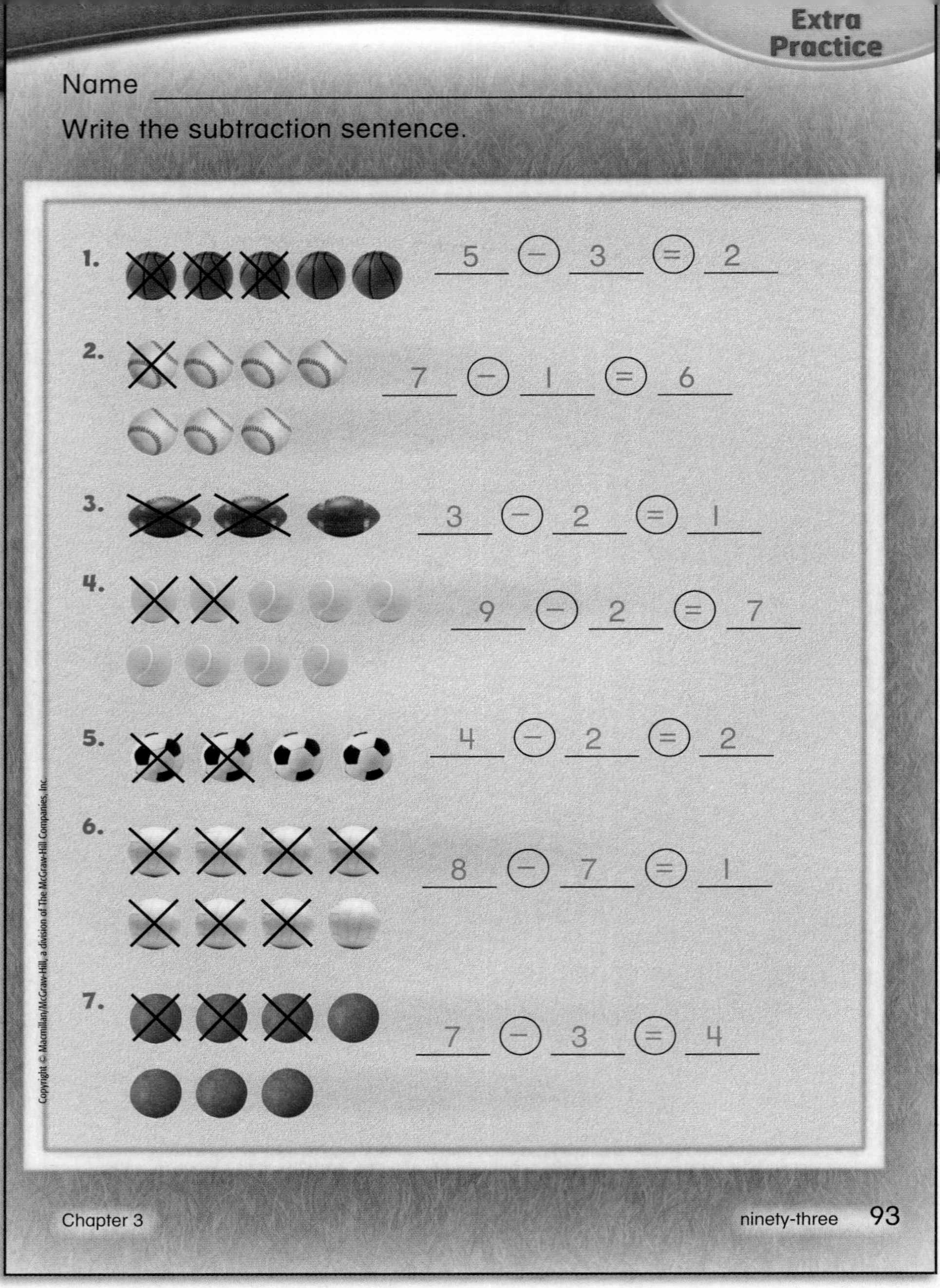

Name _____

Write the subtraction sentence.

1. $5 - 3 = 2$

2. $7 - 1 = 6$

3. $3 - 2 = 1$

4. $9 - 2 = 7$

5. $4 - 2 = 2$

6. $8 - 7 = 1$

7. $7 - 3 = 4$

Chapter 3   ninety-three 93

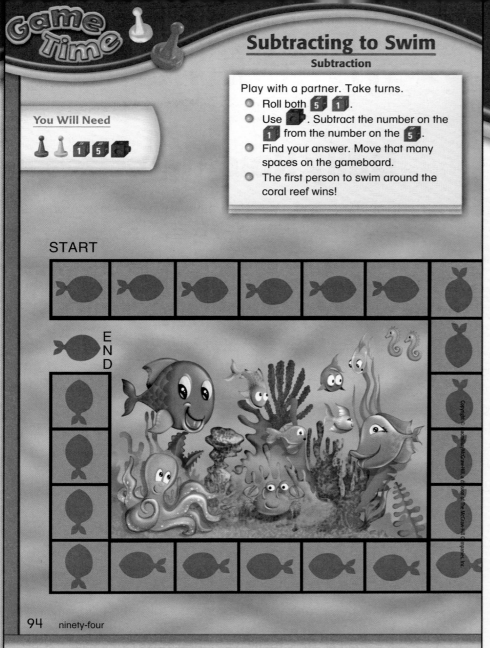

Subtracting to Swim
Subtraction

Play with a partner. Take turns.
- Roll both 5 1.
- Use ⬛. Subtract the number on the 1 from the number on the 5.
- Find your answer. Move that many spaces on the gameboard.
- The first person to swim around the coral reef wins!

You Will Need

🎲 🎲 1 5 ⬛

START

END

94 ninety-four

Differentiated Practice

Use these leveling suggestions to differentiate the game for all learners.

Level	Assignment
BL Below/Approaching Level	Allow students to use two-colored counters or connecting cubes to find the difference.
OL On Level	Have students play the game with the rules as written.
AL Above/Beyond Level	Have students set a timer for each turn. If a player has not found the correct difference when time runs out, the player does not move on that turn.

Subtracting to Swim

Math Concept:
Modeling Subtraction

Materials: game pieces
Manipulatives: red and blue number cubes, connecting cubes

Introduce the game on page 94 to your students to play as a class, in small groups, or at a learning workstation to review concepts introduced in this chapter.

Instructions

- Assign each student a game piece.
- Students take turns moving their game piece along the path.
- Students roll both the blue and red number cubes.
- Instruct students to use the connecting cubes to help them subtract the number on the red number cube from the number on the blue number cube.
- Students find the answer and move that many spaces on the game board.
- The first player to swim around the reef wins!

Extend the Game

The game ends when a game piece moves onto the space marked End. Players must continue to roll the cubes and create sentences until they get the exact number of spaces required to reach End. For example, if a player is three spaces from End, the player must roll numbers that subtract exactly to three.

Subtract Zero and All

Lesson Planner

Objective

Write number sentences subtracting zero or find a difference of zero.

Review Vocabulary

zero

Resources

Materials: whiteboard, dominoes

Manipulatives: two-colored counters

Literature Connection: *Five Little Monkeys Jumping on the Bed* by Eileen Christelowe

Alternate Lesson: Adapt "Subtraction Cards" on pages 193 and 194 of *Math Their Way* for practice with subtraction with zero.
Use *IMPACT Mathematics:* Units A and G to provide practice with subtraction.

Teacher Technology

　TeacherWorks • Math Songs Track 15 Lesson Plan

Focus on Math Background

This lesson revisits the concept of zero introduced in the previous chapter on addition. In this lesson, however, the focus is on the unchanging effect of *subtracting* zero from any number as well as the end result of removing all objects from a set. Through concrete experiences and models, students will eventually come to generalize an important rule of arithmetic—that subtracting any number from itself results in a difference of zero.

Daily Routine

Use these suggestions before beginning the lesson on p. 95.

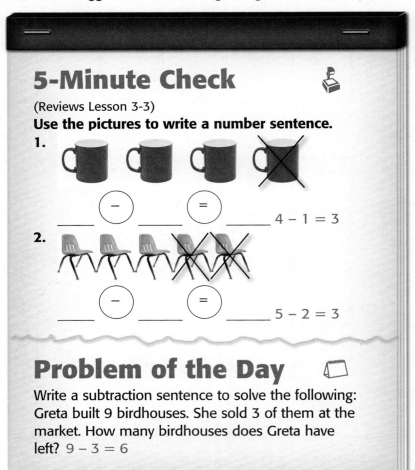

5-Minute Check

(Reviews Lesson 3-3)

Use the pictures to write a number sentence.

1.

___ (−) ___ (=) ___ $4 - 1 = 3$

2.

___ (−) ___ (=) ___ $5 - 2 = 3$

Problem of the Day

Write a subtraction sentence to solve the following: Greta built 9 birdhouses. She sold 3 of them at the market. How many birdhouses does Greta have left? $9 - 3 = 6$

LINE UP After students are in line, have them count off to find the total number of students. Explain if they all sat down, the number of students in line would be zero. If no one sat down, the number of students in line would remain the same. (Sitting down indicates subtraction.)

Review Math Vocabulary

Write the vocabulary term **zero** on the board and review its meaning with students.

- **The number zero equals none or nothing. What is something you have zero of?** See students' explanations.
- Ask students to draw the number that represents zero. Then have them write *zero* next to the number.
- Initiate a brainstorming discussion about other words and phrases that also mean "none."

Differentiated Instruction

Small Group Options

Option 1 Below/Approaching Level BL

Materials: number and symbol cards (0–5, −, =)

Gather or create cards with two each of the numbers from 0 to 5 and the symbols − and =. Give a set to each group.

- Have group members take turns starting a subtraction sentence with two numbers, the minus sign, and the equals sign. The other students will sort through the number cards to find the solution.
- Instruct students to continue until they have used all the numbers from 0 to 5 in several sentences.
- Encourage students to find two ways to use two of the same number in one sentence.

5 − 5 =
5 − 0 =

Option 2 English Language Learners ELL

Core Vocabulary: no one, everyone, get on/off the bus
Common Use Verb: pretend

Hear Math This strategy allows students to act out vocabulary they hear.

- Line up chairs and tell students to pretend this is a bus. Pantomime driving the bus until the students understand the idea of "pretend."
- Ask: "How many students are on **the bus**?" Respond with "No one is on the bus!"
- Call one or two students at a time to sit on the chairs. Continue with all students. Say: "Everyone is on the bus."
- Repeat for all students getting off the bus.

Independent Work Options

Option 1 Early Finishers OL AL

Materials: number spinner, connecting cubes

- Ask students to model the number they spin using connecting cubes.
- Have students subtract 0 cubes and say the number sentence.
- Have students subtract all cubes and say the number sentence.

Option 2 Student Technology

Math Online macmillanmh.com

♪ Math Songs, "Take It Away" Track 15 • Math Adventures

Option 3 Learning Station: Language Arts (p. 83H)

Direct students to the Language Arts Learning Station for more opportunities to explore and extend the lesson concept.

Option 4 Problem-Solving Practice

Reinforce problem-solving skills and strategies with the Problem-Solving Practice worksheet.

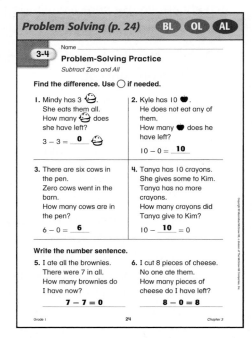

Problem Solving (p. 24) BL OL AL

3-4 Problem-Solving Practice
Subtract Zero and All

Find the difference. Use ◯ if needed.

1. Mindy has 3 🍪. She eats them all. How many 🍪 does she have left?
$3 − 3 = $ **0** 🍪

2. Kyle has 10 🍪. He does not eat any of them. How many 🍪 does he have left?
$10 − 0 = $ **10**

3. There are six cows in the pen. Zero cows went in the barn. How many cows are in the pen?
$6 − 0 = $ **6**

4. Tanya has 10 crayons. She gives some to Kim. Tanya has no more crayons. How many crayons did Tanya give to Kim?
$10 − $ **10** $ = 0$

Write the number sentence.

5. I ate all the brownies. There were 7 in all. How many brownies do I have now?
7 − 7 = 0

6. I cut 8 pieces of cheese. No one ate them. How many pieces of cheese do I have left?
8 − 0 = 8

Grade 1   24   Chapter 3

① Introduce

Activity Choice 1 • Hands-On

- Have students stand to play a few rounds of Simon Says.
- Have students sit if they make a mistake.
- Incorporate subtraction and use the term *all* in the game.
- For example, "Simon says put all your fingers on your head. Simon says take one finger off."

Activity Choice 2 • Literature

Introduce the lesson with *Five Little Monkeys Jumping on the Bed* by Eileen Christelowe. For additional support, see p. TR46.

② Teach

Give each pair of students a white board and a set of dominoes. Ask them to find all the dominoes that have zero in one half. Then have them record those number sentences with 0 as a subtraction problem on their white boards.

- Once every pair of children has completed this task, ask the class to gather in front of the board. Write on the board the number sentences that the children wrote.
- **What do you notice is happening?** When you subtract 0 from a number, the number stays the same.
- Now give the children counters. Tell subtraction stories similar to the ones in the *Hands-On* activity above. Be sure to include problems that subtract 0 and subtract all.

Get Ready Use the section at the top of p. 95 to teach the lesson concept.

Check Observe students as you work through Exercises 1–5 as a class.

Exercise 5 Assess student comprehension before assigning practice exercises.

⚠ COMMON ERROR!

Students may remember that two of the numbers in a subtraction-with-zero sentence are the same but think that the zero is repeated. Emphasize that adding or subtracting zero does not change the other number, so the number that is not zero is repeated.

Name _____

Subtract Zero and All

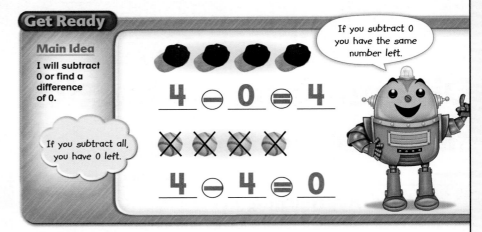

Get Ready

Main Idea
I will subtract 0 or find a difference of 0.

If you subtract all, you have 0 left.

If you subtract 0 you have the same number left.

$$4 - 0 = 4$$

$$4 - 4 = 0$$

✓ Check

Find the difference.
Write the subtraction sentence.

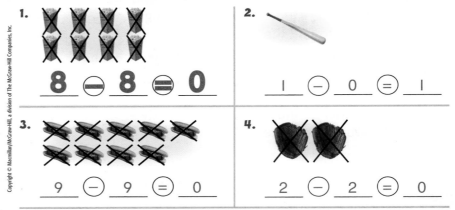

1. $8 - 8 = 0$

2. $1 - 0 = 1$

3. $9 - 9 = 0$

4. $2 - 2 = 0$

5. **Talk About It** Why do you get zero when you subtract all?
Sample answer: Because there is nothing left.

Chapter 3   Lesson 4   ninety-five   **95**

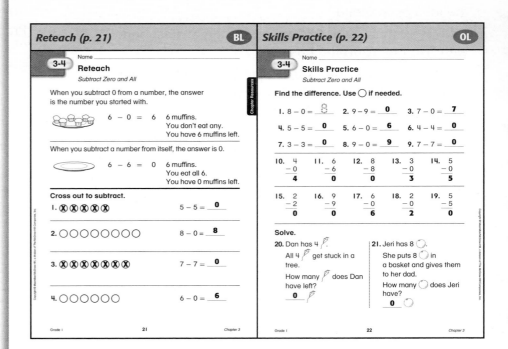

Reteach (p. 21) **BL**

3-4 **Reteach**
Subtract Zero and All

When you subtract 0 from a number, the answer is the number you started with.

6 − 0 = 6   6 muffins.
You don't eat any.
You have 6 muffins left.

When you subtract a number from itself, the answer is 0.

6 − 6 = 0   6 muffins.
You eat all 6.
You have 0 muffins left.

Cross out to subtract.

1. ⊗⊗⊗⊗⊗   5 − 5 = **0**

2. ○○○○○○○○   8 − 0 = **8**

3. ⊗⊗⊗⊗⊗⊗⊗   7 − 7 = **0**

4. ○○○○○○   6 − 0 = **6**

Grade 1   21   Chapter 3

Skills Practice (p. 22) **OL**

3-4 **Skills Practice**
Subtract Zero and All

Find the difference. Use ○ if needed.

1. $8 - 0 = $ **8**   2. $9 - 9 = $ **0**   3. $7 - 0 = $ **7**

4. $5 - 5 = $ **0**   5. $6 - 0 = $ **6**   6. $4 - 4 = $ **0**

7. $3 - 3 = $ **0**   8. $9 - 0 = $ **9**   9. $7 - 7 = $ **0**

10. 4 −0	11. 6 −6	12. 8 −8	13. 3 −0	14. 5 −0
4	**0**	**0**	**3**	**5**

15. 2 −2	16. 9 −9	17. 6 −0	18. 2 −0	19. 5 −5
0	**0**	**6**	**2**	**0**

Solve.

20. Dan has 4 🍃. All 4 🍃 get stuck in a tree. How many 🍃 does Dan have left?
0 🍃

21. Jeri has 8 ○. She puts 8 ○ in a basket and gives them to her dad. How many ○ does Jeri have?
0 ○

Grade 1   22   Chapter 3

Practice

Find the difference.
Write the subtraction sentence.

6. 

3 − 0 = 3

7. 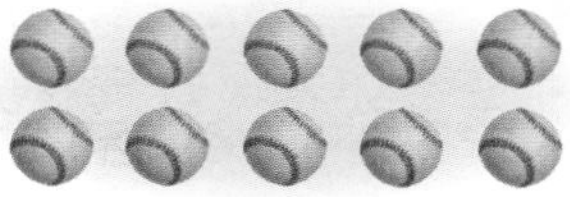

10 − 0 = 10

8. 

5 − 5 = 0

9. 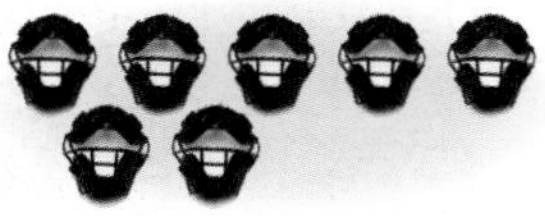

7 − 0 = 7

Find the difference. Use two-colored counters if needed.

10. 1 − 0 = 1
11. 9 − 9 = 0
12. 4 − 2 = 2
13. 3 − 0 = 3
14. 6 − 1 = 5
15. 2 − 0 = 2

Problem Solving

Number Sense Write the number sentence.

16. There are 9 baseball players in the locker room. All 9 players run to the baseball field. How many players are left in the locker room?

9 − 9 = 0

Copyright © Macmillan/McGraw-Hill, a division of The McGraw-Hill Companies, Inc.

Math at Home Activity: Give your child 3 objects, have them show 3 − 0 and 3 − 3 using the objects.

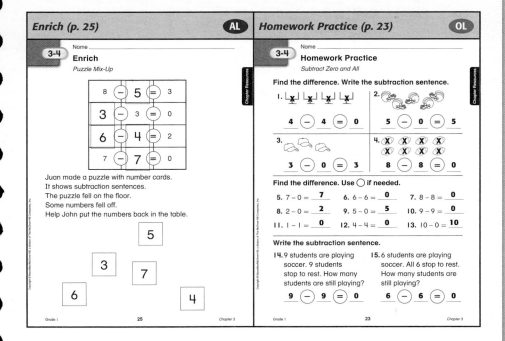

Enrich (p. 25) AL

3-4 Name ____
Enrich
Puzzle Mix-Up

8	−	5	=	3
3	−	3	=	0
6	−	4	=	2
7	−	7	=	0

Juan made a puzzle with number cards.
It shows subtraction sentences.
The puzzle fell on the floor.
Some numbers fell off.
Help John put the numbers back in the table.

5 3 7 6 4

Grade 1 25 Chapter 3

Homework Practice (p. 23) OL

3-4 Name ____
Homework Practice
Subtract Zero and All

Find the difference. Write the subtraction sentence.

1. 4 − 4 = 0
2. 5 − 0 = 5
3. 3 − 0 = 3
4. 8 − 8 = 0

Find the difference. Use ◯ if needed.

5. 7 − 0 = 7
6. 6 − 6 = 0
7. 8 − 8 = 0
8. 2 − 0 = 2
9. 5 − 0 = 5
10. 9 − 9 = 0
11. 1 − 1 = 0
12. 4 − 4 = 0
13. 10 − 0 = 10

Write the subtraction sentence.

14. 9 students are playing soccer. 9 students stop to rest. How many students are still playing? 9 − 9 = 0

15. 6 students are playing soccer. All 6 stop to rest. How many students are still playing? 6 − 6 = 0

Grade 1 23 Chapter 3

BL Alternate Teaching Strategy

If students have trouble subtracting with zero . . .

Then use one of these reteach options.

1 CRM **Daily Reteach Worksheet** (p. 21)

2 **Model the Problem** Put several two-colored counters on a table. Move your hand over the counters but do not take any. Explain that you have just subtracted zero.

3 Practice

Differentiate practice using these leveled assignments for Exercises 6–16.

Level	Assignment
BL Below/Approaching Level	Have students use two-colored counters
OL On Level	Complete the exercises independently.
AL Above/Beyond Level	Have students rework each exercise as an addition and circle those in which the answer does not change.

4 Assess

Formative Assessment

- **Douglas has 3 books. He gives 3 books to his friend. Douglas has 0 books left. Why does Douglas have 0 books?** Sample answer: All 3 books were subtracted, leaving none, or zero.

WRITING IN MATH Have students write or draw a story about eating all of something. Tell them to include a subtraction sentence.

Quick Check **Are students continuing to struggle with subtracting zero?**

If Yes → Small Group Options (p. 95B)

If No → Independent Work Options (p. 95B)

CRM Skills Practice Worksheet (p. 22)

CRM Enrich Worksheet (p. 25)

Problem-Solving Strategy
Draw a Picture

Lesson Planner _____

Objective

Use the *draw a picture* strategy to solve problems.

Resources

Materials: paper, pencils

Literature Connection: *Six Snowy Sheep* by Judith Ross Enderle and Stephanie Gordon Tessler

Teacher Technology
- TeacherWorks

- **Real-World Problem Solving Library**
  Math and Science: *What Do They Eat?*
  Use these leveled books to reinforce and extend problem-solving skills and strategies.

  Leveled for:
  - **OL** On Level
  - **ELL** Sheltered English
  - **SP** Spanish

  For additional support, see the Real-World Problem Solving Teacher Guide.

Daily Routine _____

Use these suggestions before beginning the lesson on p. 97.

5-Minute Check

(Reviews Lesson 3-4)
Solve.
1. $6 - 6 =$ _____ 0
2. $4 - 0 =$ _____ 4
3. $3 - 3 =$ _____ 0
4. $6 - 0 =$ _____ 6
5. Write the subtraction sentence. There are 6 juice boxes on the shelf. Jim and Tammy drink all 6 of the juice boxes. How many juice boxes are left? $6 - 6 = 0$

Problem of the Day

Benny and Juanita are riding home on the school bus. Their school is 10 blocks away from home. The bus has already driven 5 blocks. How many more blocks before they reach their home? Draw a picture to solve. 5 blocks; See students' work.

LINE UP When students line up for recess, lunch, or dismissal, have students in one section of the line step away from the group. Have all students count how many in that group are wearing something red. Then have the class help you write a subtraction sentence for finding the number of students in that group not wearing something red.

Differentiated Instruction

Small Group Options

Option 1 — Below/Approaching Level (BL)
LOGICAL, SOCIAL

Materials: paper, pencils, red and blue number cubes

- Have each group member roll a pair of cubes and compare each number they roll to those other group members roll.
- Ask students to decide who has the greatest number and who has the least.
- The student with the greatest number draws a picture representing that number. The student with the least number crosses out that many items in the picture.
- The group then decides what the subtraction sentence should be and writes the sentence and solution below the picture.

- Repeat the activity several times.

Option 2 — English Language Learners (ELL)
AUDITORY, VISUAL

Materials: puppet, drawing supplies
Core Vocabulary: take away, when I'm hungry, meals
Common Use Verb: eat

Hear Math This strategy connects vocabulary to the strategy of drawing a picture.

- Sing to the tune of Row, Row, Row your Boat:

  Take Take Take a-way, take away each day,

  When I'm hungry I am sure to eat 3 meals a day.

- Pantomime a puppet eating.
- Have the students draw their 3 favorite meals, singing along as they draw.
- Allow students to pantomime taking away by eating with a puppet.
- Note: you can substitute "when I'm thirsty I am sure to drink water each day," as time permits.

Independent Work Options

Option 1 — Early Finishers (OL) (AL)
LOGICAL, SPATIAL

Materials: index cards, crayons, red number cube

- Have students roll the red number cube twice and write both numbers in the corner of an index card.
- Tell them to decide which number is greater and draw that number of items on their card.
- Next, have students look at the lesser number and cross out that number of items.
- Ask students to write and solve on the back of the card a subtraction sentence that represents the picture.
- Have students repeat the activity several times to make a set of flash cards to share with the class.

Option 2 — Student Technology

Math Online > macmillanmh.com

Option 3 — Learning Station: Science (p. 83H)

Direct students to the Science Learning Station for more opportunities to explore and extend the lesson concept.

1 Introduce

Activity Choice 1 • Review

Write and read aloud the following:

Johnny collects model cars. There are 6 different model cars in a set. Johnny already has 2 of the models. How many more does he need to have a complete set?

- **What do we know?** There are 6 model cars in a set. Johnny has 2.
- **What do we want to find?** the number of cars Johnny needs to complete the set
- **What number sentence can we write to tell the story?** $6 - 2 = 4$

Activity Choice 2 • Literature

Introduce the lesson with *Six Snowy Sheep* by Judith Ross Enderle and Stephanie Gordon Tessler. For additional support, see p. TR46.

2 Teach

Have students read the problem on page 97. Guide them through the problem-solving steps.

Understand Using the questions, review what students know and what they need to find.

Plan Have them discuss their strategy.

Solve Guide students to *draw a picture* to solve the problem.

- **What picture(s) can you draw to help solve the problem?** 5 stickers
- **How can you use this picture to solve the problem?** Sample answer: Cross out the number of stickers that Arlene gave Matt and the remainder is your solution.

Check Have students look back at the problem to make sure that the answer fits the facts given.

 COMMON ERROR!

Students may put numbers in whatever order they appear in a problem. Remind them that in subtraction the larger number must always go first.

Name _____

Problem-Solving Strategy
Draw a Picture

Main Idea

I will draw a picture to solve a problem.

Arlene has 5 pages of stickers. She gave Matt 2. How many pages of stickers does she have now?

Understand

What do I need to find?
Circle the question.

Plan

How will I solve the problem?

Solve

Draw a picture.

See students' drawings.

Check

Look back.
Is my answer reasonable?
Check students' explanations.

Chapter 3   Lesson 5   ninety-seven   **97**

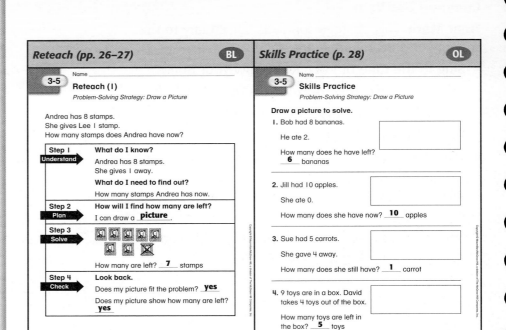

Reteach (pp. 26–27)   **BL**

3-5   Reteach (1)
Problem-Solving Strategy: Draw a Picture

Andrea has 8 stamps.
She gives Lee 1 stamp.
How many stamps does Andrea have now?

Step 1 Understand	What do I know?	Andrea has 8 stamps. She gives 1 away.
	What do I need to find out?	How many stamps Andrea has now.
Step 2 Plan	How will I find how many are left?	I can draw a **picture**.
Step 3 Solve		

How many are left? **7** stamps

Step 4 Check	Look back.

Does my picture fit the problem? **yes**
Does my picture show how many are left? **yes**

Grade 1   26   Chapter 3

Skills Practice (p. 28)   **OL**

3-5   Skills Practice
Problem-Solving Strategy: Draw a Picture

Draw a picture to solve.

1. Bob had 8 bananas.
   He ate 2.
   How many does he have left?
   6 bananas

2. Jill had 10 apples.
   She ate 0.
   How many does she have now? **10** apples

3. Sue had 5 carrots.
   She gave 4 away.
   How many does she still have? **1** carrot

4. 9 toys are in a box. David takes 4 toys out of the box.
   How many toys are left in the box? **5** toys

Grade 1   28   Chapter 3

Try It

Draw a picture to solve.

1. Andy had 6 cherries.
   He ate 3.
   How many are left?

   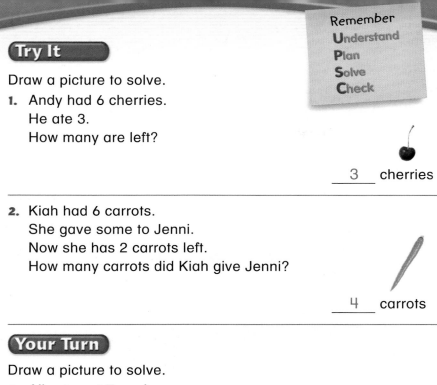

   __3__ cherries

2. Kiah had 6 carrots.
   She gave some to Jenni.
   Now she has 2 carrots left.
   How many carrots did Kiah give Jenni?

   __4__ carrots

Your Turn

Draw a picture to solve.

3. Alberto got 7 apples.
   He ate 1.
   How many does he have now?

   __6__ apples

4. There are 6 oranges in a box.
   Miles eats 2 oranges.
   How many oranges are left?

   __4__ oranges

Math at Home Activity: Give your child a simple subtraction problem and have him/her solve it by drawing a picture.

98 ninety-eight

Remember
Understand
Plan
Solve
Check

Try It Observe students as you work through Exercises 1–2 as a class.

BL Alternate Teaching Strategy

If ➤ students do not understand how to use the strategy of drawing a picture . . .

Then ➤ use one of these reteaching options.

1. [CRM] **Daily Reteach Worksheet** (pp. 26–27)

2. **Model Subtraction Stories** Give each student a handful of two-colored counters and a plastic cup. Create subtraction stories to share with the students. Each time a number is subtracted in the story, ask students to place that number of counters into the cup. Have students count the remaining counters to find what is left over.

③ Practice

Your Turn

Exercises 3–4 Remind students that they can draw symbols such as circles to represent the apples and oranges.

④ Assess

✓ Formative Assessment

Tell students the following subtraction story: *Jamal needs 5 bus tokens to get to school this week. He has 2 tokens.* How many more tokens does Jamal need?

- **How will you solve the problem?** Sample answer: Draw a picture representing the subtraction story.

- **What is the first picture you would draw?** Sample answer: the total number of bus tokens needed (5)

- **After you draw the picture(s), what is the next step toward solving the problem?** Sample answer: Cross out the number of tokens Jamal already has (2).

Quick Check ➤ **Are students continuing to struggle with drawing a picture to solve a problem?**

If Yes ➤ Small Group Options (p. 97B)
If No ➤ [CRM] Skills Practice Worksheet (p. 28)
　　　　　[CRM] Enrich Worksheet (p. 30)

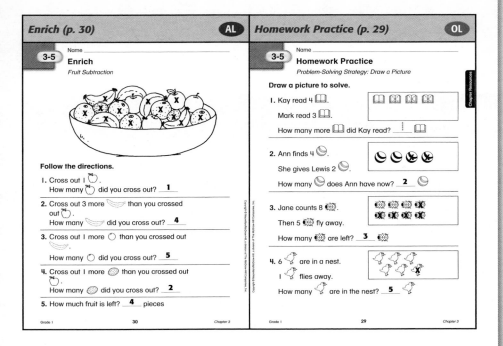

Enrich (p. 30) — AL

3-5 **Enrich**
Fruit Subtraction

Follow the directions.

1. Cross out 1 🍎.
   How many 🍎 did you cross out? __1__

2. Cross out 3 more 🍌 than you crossed out 🍎.
   How many 🍌 did you cross out? __4__

3. Cross out 1 more ○ than you crossed out 🍌.
   How many ○ did you cross out? __5__

4. Cross out 1 more ◎ than you crossed out ○.
   How many ◎ did you cross out? __2__

5. How much fruit is left? __4__ pieces

Grade 1　30　Chapter 3

Homework Practice (p. 29) — OL

3-5 **Homework Practice**
Problem-Solving Strategy: Draw a Picture

Draw a picture to solve.

1. Kay read 4 📖.
   Mark read 3 📖.
   How many more 📖 did Kay read? __1__ 📖

2. Ann finds 4 🌙.
   She gives Lewis 2 🌙.
   How many 🌙 does Ann have now? __2__ 🌙

3. Jane counts 8 🐛.
   Then 5 🐛 fly away.
   How many 🐛 are left? __3__ 🐛

4. 6 🐦 are in a nest.
   1 🐦 flies away.
   How many 🐦 are in the nest? __5__ 🐦

Grade 1　29　Chapter 3

Mid-Chapter Check

Lessons 3-1 to 3-5

Formative Assessment

Use the Mid-Chapter Check to assess students' progress in the first half of the chapter.

 Customize and create multiple versions of your Mid-Chapter Check and the test answer keys.

FOLDABLES Dinah Zike's Foldables

Use these lesson suggestions to incorporate the Foldable during the chapter.

Lesson 3-4 Label the first pocket 5-Pocket Foldable "0." Have students dictate what they learn about subtraction with "0" and record their observations on 3" x 5" index cards. Place the information cards and examples of subtraction problems with "0" in the pocket.

Lesson 3-6 Label the second pocket "4", the third pocket "5", and the fourth pocket "6." Use 3" x 5" index cards to make subtraction flashcards subtracting 4, 5, and 6 and store them in the appropriate pockets of the Foldable.

Name _____

Solve.

Fill in the missing number.

1.	Part	Part
	4	3
	Whole	
	7	

2.	Part	Part
	7	2
	Whole	
	9	

Write the subtraction sentence.

3.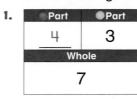

__5__ ⊖ __1__ ⊜ __4__

4.

__8__ ⊖ __8__ ⊜ __0__

5.

__3__ ⊖ __0__ ⊜ __3__

6. There are 9 owls.
3 owls fly away.
How many owls are left?

__6__ owls

7. There are 6 horses.
4 gallop away.
How many horses are still there?

__2__ horses

Data-Driven Decision Making

Based on the results of the Mid-Chapter Check, use the following resources to review concepts that continue to give students problems.

Exercises	State/Local Standards	What's the Math?	Error Analysis	Resources for Review
1–2 Lesson 3-2		Model the meaning of subtraction.	Confuses "part" and "whole."	Strategic Intervention Guide (p. 70)
3–5 Lesson 3-3		Use number sentences to solve subtraction problems. Understand symbols −, =.	Miscounts pictures. Uses symbols −, = incorrectly.	**CRM** Chapter 3 Resource Masters (Reteach Worksheets) **Math Online** Concepts in Motion Math Adventures
6–7 Lesson 3-5		Demonstrate meaning of subtraction stories.	Misreads the term "are left." Gives answer for how many flew away or galloped away. Does not use counters correctly.	

Count. Write the number.

8.  _17_

9.  _11_

Add.

10. 7 + 2 = _9_   11. 3 + 2 = _5_

12. 1 + 4 = _5_   13. 5 + 2 = _7_

14. 6 + 2 = _8_   15. 0 + 3 = _3_

Subtract.

16. 8 − 1 = _7_   17. 5 − 0 = _5_

18. 4 − 2 = _2_   19. 7 − 2 = _5_

20. 6 − 6 = _0_   21. 9 − 3 = _6_

Write the missing number.

22.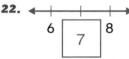
6   7   8

23.
18 19   20

24.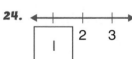
1   2   3

25.
10 11 12

100   one hundred

Formative Assessment

Spiral Review

Review Chapters 1 to 3

Objective: Review and assess mastery of skills and concepts from previous chapters.

Resources for Review

Based on student results, refer to these lessons for remediation.

- **Exercises 8–9: Lesson 1-5** (p. 27)
- **Exercises 10–15: Lesson 2-3** (p. 55)
- **Exercises 16–21: Lesson 3-3** (p. 91)
- **Exercises 22–25: Lesson 1-9** (p. 39)

Lesson Planner

Objective
Use connecting cubes to subtract from 4, 5, and 6.

Review Vocabulary
zero

Resources

Materials: small plastic bags, dominoes

Manipulatives: connecting cubes, two-colored counters

Literature Connection: *Anno's Counting Book* by Mitsumasa Anno

Alternate Lesson Use "The Hand Game" on page 190 of *Math Their Way* to provide practice subtracting with numbers 4, 5, and 6.
Use *IMPACT Mathematics: Unit A* to provide practice with using manipulatives to modeling subtracting from 4, 5, and 6.

Teacher Technology
- TeacherWorks • Math Songs Track 15 Lesson Plan

Focus on Math Background

In this lesson students focus on subtracting amounts from numbers 4, 5, and 6. Visualizing these numbers as wholes composed of smaller parts is an effective strategy for eventually committing the related subtraction facts to memory. Moreover, understanding subtraction as the inverse of addition will help children see the relationship between these two operations. For example, a child can use the fact $5 + 1 = 6$ to figure out $6 - 5$.

Daily Routine

Use these suggestions before beginning the lesson on p. 101.

5-Minute Check

(Reviews Lesson 3-5)
Draw a picture to show that after Paul ate 2 of his apples he had 3 left over. $5 - 2 = 3$

Problem of the Day

Draw a picture or use connecting cubes to model the subtraction probem. Niko has 8 pretzels in his lunch. He eats 5. How many does he have left?
3 pretzels

LINE UP Have students form lines of 4, 5, or 6. Ask different numbers of students to step out of each line. Have students describe their actions with subtraction sentences.

Review Math Vocabulary

Write the term **zero** on the board.
- Tell students that zero equals none, or nothing.
- Ask students to write an addition sentence with zero in it.
- **What happens when zero is added to a number?** The number stays the same.
- Ask students to write a subtraction sentence with zero in it.
- **What happens when zero is subtracted from a number?** The number stays the same.
- Use two-colored counters to model adding zero to or subtracting zero from a number.

Differentiated Instruction

Small Group Options

Option 1
Gifted and Talented (AL)

LOGICAL

Materials: index cards with incorrect subtraction sentences

Prepare index cards with subtraction sentences that contain an error (for example, $5 - 1 = 3$).

- Distribute the index cards to a group of students.
- Tell students that the subtraction sentences are wrong.
- Have students work together to write three different ways to correct each subtraction sentence.
- Direct students to write their corrected sentences on a separate sheet of paper.

Option 2
English Language Learners (ELL)

KINESTHETIC, VISUAL

Materials: model or picture of stop sign, yardstick or ruler
Core Vocabulary: sign, take youself away, tap
Common Use Verb: stop

See Math This strategy introduces signs and helps students understand them.

- Show a stop sign. Demonstrate that it means stopping a continuous action like walking.
- Repeat for minus sign, saying that it means "take away."
- Pantomime how to play Simon Says silently, modeling continuous action. Hold up the stop sign to signal "Simon says **stop**".
- Say "If I tap you with the minus sign, you must **take yourself away** and sit out."
- Play as time permits.

Independent Work Options

Option 1
Early Finishers (OL) (AL)

LINGUISTIC, KINESTHETIC

Materials: dominoes (with no more than 6 dots on a side)

- Ask students to take turns picking a domino and using the dots on each side in a subtraction number sentence.
- Remind students to begin their number sentence with the side that has the greater number of dots.
- Have students compare their differences. The student with the smallest difference takes all the dominoes used in the round.

Option 2
Student Technology

Math Online > macmillanmh.com

♪ Math Songs, "Take It Away" Track 15 • 🌐 Math Adventures

Option 3
Learning Station: Art (p. 83G)

Direct students to the Art Learning Station for more opportunities to explore and extend the lesson concept.

Option 4
Problem-Solving Practice

Reinforce problem-solving skills and strategies with the Problem-Solving Practice worksheet.

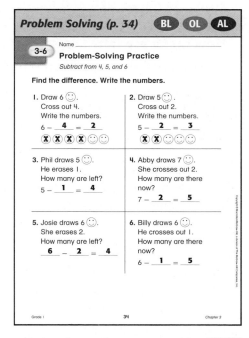

Problem Solving (p. 34) BL OL AL

Name _____

3-6 **Problem-Solving Practice**
Subtract from 4, 5, and 6

Find the difference. Write the numbers.

1. Draw 6 ☺.
   Cross out 4.
   Write the numbers.
   $6 - \underline{4} = \underline{2}$
   ✗✗✗✗☺☺

2. Draw 5 ☺.
   Cross out 2.
   Write the numbers.
   $5 - \underline{2} = \underline{3}$
   ✗✗☺☺☺

3. Phil draws 5 ☺.
   He erases 1.
   How many are left?
   $5 - \underline{1} = \underline{4}$

4. Abby draws 7 ☺.
   She crosses out 2.
   How many are there now?
   $7 - \underline{2} = \underline{5}$

5. Josie draws 6 ☺.
   She erases 2.
   How many are left?
   $\underline{6} - \underline{2} = \underline{4}$

6. Billy draws 6 ☺.
   He crosses out 1.
   How many are there now?
   $6 - \underline{1} = \underline{5}$

Grade 1   34   Chapter 3

① Introduce

Activity Choice 1 • Hands-On

Play a game of Hangman, but use a standing figure rather than a hanging figure. Call the game "Math Buddy." Use *difference* as the secret word.

- Tell students that the secret word is a word used in subtraction.
- Write an addition or a subtraction sentence on the chalkboard. If a student finds the correct answer, he or she gets to choose a letter and an opportunity to solve the puzzle. If the student answers incorrectly, draw a piece of the math person.

Activity Choice 2 • Literature

Introduce the lesson with *Anno's Counting Book* by Mitsumasa Anno. For additional support, see p. TR46.

② Teach

Give each child a small plastic bag with ten two-colored counters, a small cup, a white board, marker, and eraser. Then give the following directions:

- Place four, five, or six counters in the cup.
- Write down the total number of counters.
- Dump out the cup.
- Subtract the counters that are yellow side up. Write the minus sign and the number you subtracted.
- **How many are left?** See students' work.
- Draw an equal sign and write that number.

Get Ready Use the section at the top of p. 101 to teach the lesson concept.

Check Observe students as you work through Exercises 1–5 as a class.

Exercise 5 Assess student comprehension before assigning practice exercises.

⚠ COMMON ERROR!

Students may miscount the number of remaining cubes. Encourage students to touch the cubes one at a time and count on their fingers.

Name _____

Subtract from 4, 5, and 6

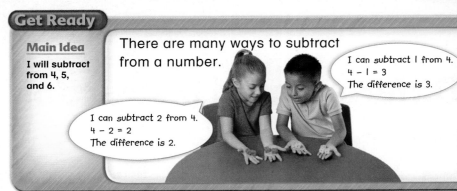

Get Ready

Main Idea
I will subtract from 4, 5, and 6.

There are many ways to subtract from a number.

I can subtract 2 from 4.
$4 - 2 = 2$
The difference is 2.

I can subtract 1 from 4.
$4 - 1 = 3$
The difference is 3.

✓ Check

Start with 4 🎲. Subtract some.
Cross out 🎲. Write the numbers.

See students' answers.

	🎲	minus	🎲	equals	difference
1.		4	−	1	=	3
2.		4	−		=	
3.		4	−		=	
4.		4	−		=	

5. Sample answer: What is left after you take some away.

5. **Talk About It** What does *difference* mean in subtraction?

Chapter 3   Lesson 6   one hundred one   101

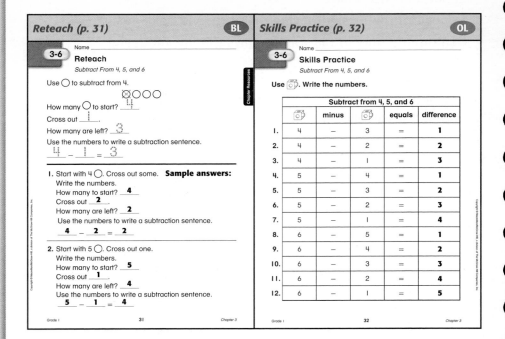

Use ⬜. Subtract some cubes.
Find the difference. Write the numbers. See students' answers.

Subtract from 5			
⬜	minus	⬜	equals	difference
6.	5	– ____	= ____
7.	5	– ____	= ____
8.	5	– ____	= ____
9.	5	– ____	= ____

Subtract from 6			
⬜	minus	⬜	equals	difference
10.	6	– ____	= ____
11.	6	– ____	= ____
12.	6	– ____	= ____
13.	6	– ____	= ____

Find the difference. You may use ⬤◯ to help you.

14. $6 - 1 = \underline{5}$ **15.** $4 - 0 = \underline{4}$ **16.** $5 - 2 = \underline{3}$

17. $5 - 5 = \underline{0}$ **18.** $4 - 2 = \underline{2}$ **19.** $6 - 0 = \underline{6}$

H.O.T. Problem

20. Make It Right
Irene wrote this
subtraction sentence.
Tell why Irene is wrong. Make it right.

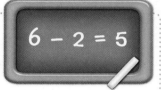

$6 - 2 = 5$

Sample answer: She subtracted incorrectly
the answer should be 4. $6 - 2 = 4$.

102   one hundred two

Math at Home Activity: Give your child 6 objects. Have him/her subtract different numbers from 4, 5, or 6 and tell the difference.

Copyright © Macmillan/McGraw-Hill, a division of The McGraw-Hill Companies, Inc.

---

③ Practice

Differentiate practice using these leveled assignments for Exercises 6–20.

Level	Assignment
BL Below/ Approaching Level	Have students check their answers with a partner and resolve any different answers.
OL On Level	Complete the exercises independently.
AL Above/Beyond Level	Have students complete the exercises without cubes.

④ Assess

✎ Formative Assessment

- **Which is always the greatest number in a subtraction sentence without zero? Why?** the first number; Sample answer: the other numbers are parts of the first number.

WRITING IN ▸ MATH Demonstrate $5 - 3 = 2$ with connecting cubes. Have children write the problem as a written sentence. "Five minus three equals two."

Quick Check   **Are students continuing to struggle with subtracting from 4, 5, and 6?**

If Yes → CRM Reteach Worksheet (p. 31)
If No → Independent Work Options (p. 101B)
   CRM Skills Practice Worksheet (p. 32)
   CRM Enrich Worksheet (p. 35)

Lesson Planner

Objective
Use connecting cubes to subtract from 7, 8, and 9.

Review Vocabulary
subtract

Resources

Materials: plastic cup, white board, small plastic bags, number cards

Manipulatives: connecting cubes, two-colored counters

Literature Connection: *Ten Black Dots* by Donald Crews

Alternate Lesson: Use "The Hand Game" on page 180 of *Math Their Way* to provide practice subtracting with numbers 7, 8, and 9.
Use *IMPACT Mathematics:* Unit A to provide practice with using manipulatives to model subtracting from 7, 8, and 9.

Teacher Technology
TeacherWorks • Math Songs Track 15 Lesson Plan

Focus on Math Background

This lesson is a continuation of the students' work subtracting amounts from single digit numbers, focusing specifically on 7, 8, and 9. As students decompose numbers, they think about relationships, such as how 7 − 3 is one more than 7 − 4, as opposed to thinking about these two numerical expressions as a pair of discrete and isolated number facts. This type of understanding yields more favorable outcomes in the future with instant recall.

Daily Routine

Use these suggestions before beginning the lesson on p. 103.

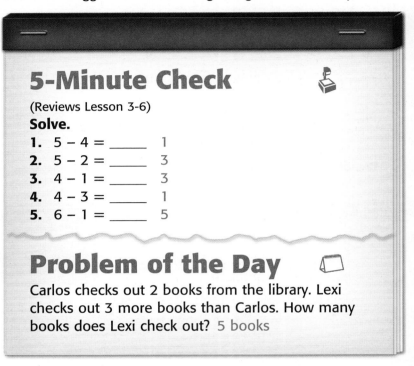

5-Minute Check

(Reviews Lesson 3-6)
Solve.

1. $5 - 4 =$ _____   1
2. $5 - 2 =$ _____   3
3. $4 - 1 =$ _____   3
4. $4 - 3 =$ _____   1
5. $6 - 1 =$ _____   5

Problem of the Day

Carlos checks out 2 books from the library. Lexi checks out 3 more books than Carlos. How many books does Lexi check out? 5 books

LINE UP   **What is 9 minus 1?** 8 Have eight students get in line. Repeat with subtraction questions using numbers less than nine until all students are in line.

Review Math Vocabulary

Write the vocabulary term **subtract** on the board.

- Hold up eight stickers for the students to see. Ask a volunteer to take away three of the stickers. Count the stickers that are left.

- Explain taking away stickers means to subtract stickers.

- Review that there were 8 stickers. _____ took away 3 stickers. There are 5 stickers left.

Visual Vocabulary Cards

Use Visual Vocabulary Card 46 to reinforce the vocabulary reviewed in this lesson. (The Define/Example/ Ask routine is printed on the back of each card.)

subtract

Differentiated Instruction

Small Group Options

Option 1 — Gifted and Talented (AL)

Materials: several index cards with subtraction stories, connecting cubes

Prepare index cards with subtraction stories for facts to 9 printed on them. For example, "José has 8 toy trucks. He gives Tyler 2 trucks. How many trucks does José have left?"

- Have one student read a story aloud to the group, while the other students model the story.
- Allow the reader to repeat the story as many times as necessary.
- After the story has been correctly answered, have the group write a subtraction sentence for the story.
- Have students rotate turns being the reader.

Option 2 — English Language Learners (ELL)

Core Vocabulary: some, the rest, partner
Common Use Verb: hide

Do Math This strategy teaches algebraic, subtraction, and listening skills.

- Have pairs sit together, one facing away from the board. Write the number 7.
- Prompt partners facing the board to take that number of counters.
- Say: "Hide some. Give the rest to your partner."
- The student who received counters must look at the board and figure out how many his/her partner has.
- Switch roles and numbers as time permits.

Independent Work Options

Option 1 — Early Finishers (OL) (AL)

Materials: plastic cup, two-colored counters, white board, dry erase marker

- Have students take turns putting seven counters in the cup.
- Ask students to shake the cup and pour out the counters.
- Have students sort the counters into color groups.
- Have students subtract the number of red counters from seven in a number sentence.
- Continue the activity with each color.

Option 2 — Student Technology

Math Online ▷ macmillanmh.com

♪ Math Songs, "Take It Away" Track 15 • Math Adventures

Option 3 — Learning Station: Health (p. 83G)

Direct students to the Health Learning Station for more opportunities to explore and extend the lesson concept.

Option 4 — Problem-Solving Practice

Reinforce problem-solving skills and strategies with the Problem-Solving Practice worksheet.

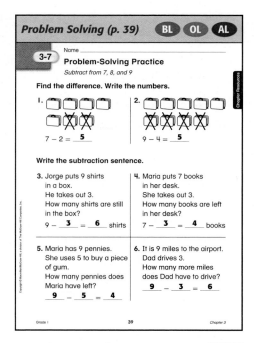

Problem Solving (p. 39) (BL) (OL) (AL)

Name ____

3-7 Problem-Solving Practice
Subtract from 7, 8, and 9

Find the difference. Write the numbers.

1. $7 - 2 = $ **5**
2. $9 - 4 = $ **5**

Write the subtraction sentence.

3. Jorge puts 9 shirts in a box. He takes out 3. How many shirts are still in the box?
$9 - $ **3** $ = $ **6** shirts

4. Maria puts 7 books in her desk. She takes out 3. How many books are left in her desk?
$7 - $ **3** $ = $ **4** books

5. Maria has 9 pennies. She uses 5 to buy a piece of gum. How many pennies does Maria have left?
9 $ - $ **5** $ = $ **4**

6. It is 9 miles to the airport. Dad drives 3. How many more miles does Dad have to drive?
9 $ - $ **3** $ = $ **6**

Grade 1   39   Chapter 3

1 Introduce

Activity Choice 1 • Hands-On

Provide each student with seven connecting cubes.

- **How many cubes in all?** 7 cubes
- Write 7 – 3 on the board. Have students use cubes to model the subtraction sentence.
- **How many cubes are left after you take away 3?** 4 cubes
- Complete the subtraction sentence on the board: 7 – 3 = 4.

Activity Choice 2 • Literature

Introduce the lesson with *Ten Black Dots* by Donald Crews. For additional support, see p. TR46.

2 Teach

Give each child a small plastic bag with 10 two-colored counters, a small cup, a white board, and eraser. Give the following directions:

- Place seven, eight, or nine counters in the cup.
- Write the total number of counters.
- Pour the counters out of the cup.
- Subtract the counters that land red-side up. Write the minus sign and the number you subtracted.
- **How many yellow counters are left?** See students' work.
- Write the equals sign and the number of counters that are left.

Get Ready Use the section at the top of p. 103 to reinforce the lesson concept.

Check Observe students as you work through Exercises 1–6 as a class.

 **Exercise 6** Assess student comprehension before assigning practice exercises.

 COMMON ERROR!

Some children understand the concept of subtraction and can commit facts to memory but have difficulty accessing the facts. It might be helpful to provide a variety of practice opportunities: board games, relays, flash cards, and computer games.

Name _____

Subtract from 7, 8, and 9

 Hands-On Activity

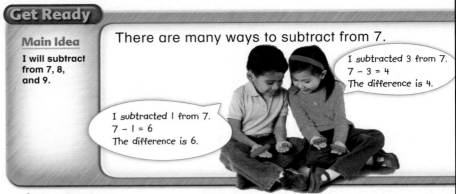

Get Ready

Main Idea

I will subtract from 7, 8, and 9.

There are many ways to subtract from 7.

I subtracted 1 from 7.
7 – 1 = 6
The difference is 6.

I subtracted 3 from 7.
7 – 3 = 4
The difference is 4.

Check

Start with 7 🎲. Subtract some cubes.
Find the difference. Write the numbers.

See students' answers.

Subtract from 7				
🎲	minus	🎲	equals	difference

1. 7 – 1 = 6
2. 7 – ___ = ___
3. 7 – ___ = ___
4. 7 – ___ = ___
5. 7 – ___ = ___

6. Sample answer: I show how many cubes in all. I break off cubes to show how many are taken away. Then I count how many are left.

6. **Talk About It** How do you use 🎲 to show subtraction?

Chapter 3   Lesson 7   one hundred three   103

Copyright © Macmillan/McGraw-Hill, a division of The McGraw-Hill Companies, Inc.

Use . Subtract some cubes.
Find the difference. Write the numbers. See students' answers.

Subtract from 8				
	minus		equals	difference
7.	8	− _____	=	_____
8.	8	− _____	=	_____
9.	8	− _____	=	_____
10.	8	− _____	=	_____
11.	8	− _____	=	_____
12.	8	− _____	=	_____
13.	8	− _____	=	_____

Subtract from 9				
	minus		equals	difference
14.	9	− _____	=	_____
15.	9	− _____	=	_____
16.	9	− _____	=	_____
17.	9	− _____	=	_____
18.	9	− _____	=	_____
19.	9	− _____	=	_____
20.	9	− _____	=	_____

Find the difference. You may use ●○ to help you.

21. $8 - 7 = \underline{1}$ **22.** $7 - 4 = \underline{3}$ **23.** $9 - 8 = \underline{1}$

24. $7 - 5 = \underline{2}$ **25.** $9 - 4 = \underline{5}$ **26.** $8 - 3 = \underline{5}$

H.O.T. Problem

27. Why is the answer in subtraction called the difference?

_ <u>Sample answer: Because it is what you have left.</u> _ _ _

104 one hundred four

Math at Home Activity: Give your child 8 objects. Then have him/her subtract different numbers from 8 and tell the difference.

Enrich (p. 40) **AL**

3-7 Name _____

Enrich
Fall into Subtraction

Follow the directions. Write two subtraction sentences that use the same numbers.

1. There are 7 🍃. Color some red. Color the rest green.
   🍃🍃🍃🍃🍃🍃🍃
   7 − _____ red = _____ green 🍃   **Answers will vary.**
   7 − _____ green = _____ red 🍃

2. There are 8 🍃. Color some blue. Color the rest yellow.
   🍃🍃🍃🍃🍃🍃🍃🍃
   8 − _____ blue = _____ yellow 🍃   **Answers will vary.**
   7 − _____ yellow = _____ blue 🍃

3. There are 9 🍃. Color some red. Color the rest brown.
   🍃🍃🍃🍃🍃🍃🍃🍃🍃
   9 − _____ red = _____ brown 🍃   **Answers will vary.**
   9 − _____ brown = _____ red 🍃

4. Count the 🍃. Color some yellow. Color the rest green.
   🍃🍃🍃🍃🍃🍃🍃🍃🍃🍃
   _____ − _____ = _____ yellow 🍃   **Answers will vary.**
   _____ − _____ = _____ red 🍃

Grade 1   40   Chapter 3

Homework Practice (p. 38) **OL**

3-7 Name _____

Homework Practice
Subtract From 7, 8, and 9

Use 🎲. Write the numbers.

Subtract from 7, 8, and 9				
🎲	minus	🎲	equals	difference
1.	7	−	5	=	2
2.	8	−	5	=	3
3.	9	−	5	=	4

Find the difference. Use ○ if needed.

4. $9 - 1 = \underline{8}$ 5. $8 - 4 = \underline{4}$ 6. $7 - 5 = \underline{2}$
7. $8 - 7 = \underline{1}$ 8. $9 - 6 = \underline{3}$ 9. $8 - 2 = \underline{6}$
10. $7 - 6 = \underline{1}$ 11. $9 - 4 = \underline{5}$ 12. $7 - 4 = \underline{3}$

Solve.

13. Rachel had 8 marbles. She lost 7 of them. How many does Rachel have now?
    _1_ marble

14. Byron had 9 toy planes. Two broke. How many toy planes are left?
    _7_ toy planes

Grade 1   38   Chapter 3

BL **Alternate Teaching Strategy**

If ▶ students have trouble subtracting from 7, 8, and 9…

Then ▶ use one of these reteach options.

1 CRM **Daily Reteach Worksheet** (p. 36)

2 **Use Number Cards** Provide students with number cards. Have them practice creating subtracting sentences with 7, 8, and 9.

③ Practice

Differentiate practice using these leveled assignments for Exercises 7–27.

Level	Assignment
BL Below/Approaching Level	Provide students with the second number of the subtraction sentence in the charts.
OL On Level	Complete the exercises independently.
AL Above/Beyond Level	Write subtraction sentences using the number zero for the charts.

④ Assess

✓ Formative Assessment

Write all the different ways to subtract from 9.
$9 - 9 = 0$; $9 - 8 = 1$; $9 - 7 = 2$; $9 - 6 = 3$;
$9 - 5 = 4$; $9 - 4 = 5$; $9 - 3 = 6$; $9 - 2 = 7$;
$9 - 1 = 8$; $9 - 0 = 9$

How did you know the numbers you could subtract from 9? The numbers must be equal to or less than 9.

WRITING IN ▶**MATH** Have students write a subtraction story using the number 8.

Quick Check | **Are students continuing to struggle with subtracting from 7, 8, and 9?**

If Yes → CRM Reteach Worksheet (p. 36)

If No → Independent Work Options (p. 103B)
   CRM Skills Practice Worksheet (p. 37)
   CRM Enrich Worksheet (p. 40)

Lesson Planner

Objective
Choose the best strategy to solve a problem.

Resources

Materials: paper, pencils

Manipulatives: connecting cubes, two-colored counters

Teacher Technology

- TeacherWorks

📖 **Real-World Problem Solving Library**
Math and Science: *What Do They Eat?*
Use these leveled books to reinforce and extend
problem-solving skills and strategies.

Leveled for:

- **OL** On Level
- **ELL** Sheltered English
- **SP** Spanish

For additional support,
see the Real-World
Problem Solving
Teacher Guide.

Daily Routine

Use these suggestions before beginning the lesson on p. 105.

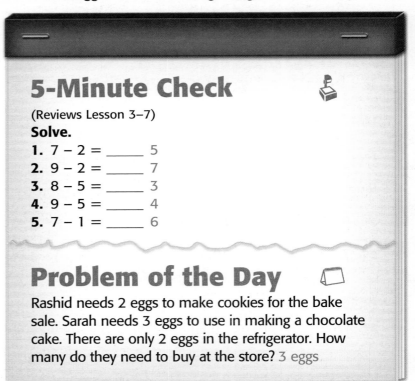

5-Minute Check

(Reviews Lesson 3–7)

Solve.

1. $7 - 2 = $ _____ 5
2. $9 - 2 = $ _____ 7
3. $8 - 5 = $ _____ 3
4. $9 - 5 = $ _____ 4
5. $7 - 1 = $ _____ 6

Problem of the Day

Rashid needs 2 eggs to make cookies for the bake
sale. Sarah needs 3 eggs to use in making a chocolate
cake. There are only 2 eggs in the refrigerator. How
many do they need to buy at the store? 3 eggs

LINE UP Ask two students to line up and then three
more. Have the class tell a number story
describing the two sets of students who lined up and how
many students lined up in all. Repeat with other groupings
to 10 until all students are in line.

Differentiated Instruction

Small Group Options

Option 1
Gifted and Talented AL
LOGICAL

Materials: paper, pencils, two sets of number cards 0–12, two-colored counters

- Have each student draw two number cards and decide how to use the numbers in a subtraction sentence.
- Explain that students should place yellow counters on a sheet of paper to show their larger number.
- Next, students should turn over some of the counters to show in red the smaller number they are subtracting.
- Students take turns showing their counters and having the group guess the numbers on their number cards.
- Group members each write and solve the subtraction sentence that describes the counters.
- Students compare their sentences and check their answers.

Option 2
English Language Learners ELL
INTERPERSONAL, SPATIAL

Materials: four sheets chart paper, markers, materials for building models
Core Vocabulary: looked at, tried, used
Common Use Verb: decided

Talk Math This strategy uses the language of problem solving and practices speaking skills.

- Divide the class into four groups. Give each group markers, chart paper and building materials.
- Present a problem they know from earlier classes.
- Ask groups to solve the problem.
- Rotate and model language as students work. Post words they seem to need to scaffold their speaking.
- Have them show their findings and present their solutions orally to the class.

Independent Work Options

Option 1
Early Finishers OL AL
LOGICAL

Materials: paper, pencil, red and blue number cubes, connecting cubes

- Have the first player roll the blue number cube and make a train with that number of cubes.
- Have the second player roll the red cube and take away from the train that number of cubes.
- Together, the two players write the subtraction sentence that tells their cube story.
- Explain that the first player keeps the cubes left in the train and the second player keeps the cubes he or she took away.
- Players trade number cubes and repeat, adding cubes to their train after each turn. When time is up, have students compare the lengths of their trains.

Option 2
Student Technology
Math Online macmillanmh.com

Option 3
Learning Station: Music (p. 83G)
Direct students to the Music Learning Station for more opportunities to explore and extend the lesson concept.

① Introduce

Activity • Review

Write and read aloud the following:
Juan's baseball team has 6 players but needs 9 to play against the opposing team. How many more players does Juan's team need?

- **What do we know?** There are 6 players. Nine are needed to play a baseball game.

- **What do we want to find?** the number of players needed

- **What number sentence can we write to tell the story?** 9 − 6 = 3

- **How many more players does Juan's team need?** 3 players

② Teach

Understand Using the questions, review what students know and what they need to find.

Plan Have them discuss their strategy. Guide students to *act it out* to solve the problem.

Solve

- **How many counters should you start with?** 5 counters

- **How many counters should you take away?** 2 counters

Check Have students look back at the problem to make sure that the answer fits the facts given.

- **What was your answer?** 3 cars

- **Does the sum of Wu's cars and Joey's cars equal 5?** yes

⚠ COMMON ERROR!

Students often try to model subtraction by making two groups of counters—one group for each number in the problem. Remind students that when subtracting, they only model the greater number with counters. The smaller number shows how many from the larger group should be removed or separated.

Name _____

Problem-Solving Investigation

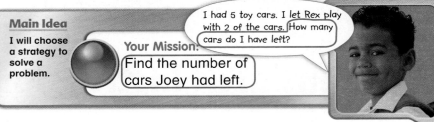

Main Idea
I will choose a strategy to solve a problem.

Your Mission: Find the number of cars Joey had left.

I had 5 toy cars. I let Rex play with 2 of the cars. How many cars do I have left?

Understand

What do I need to find?
Circle it.

Plan

How will I solve the problem?

Solve

One way is to act it out with counters.
Sample answer: I can use a counter to show each car.

3 cars

Check

Look back.

Is my answer reasonable?
Check students' explanations.

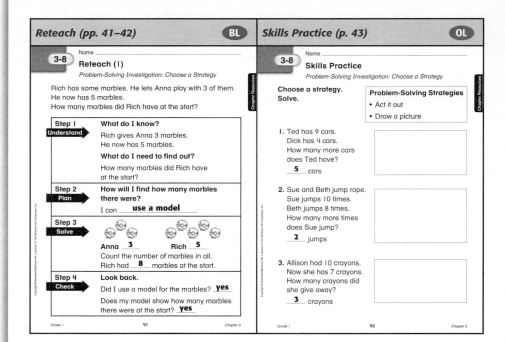

Reteach (pp. 41–42) `BL`

3-8 **Reteach (1)**
Problem-Solving Investigation: Choose a Strategy

Rich has some marbles. He lets Anna play with 3 of them. He now has 5 marbles.
How many marbles did Rich have at the start?

Step 1 Understand	**What do I know?** Rich gives Anna 3 marbles. He now has 5 marbles. **What do I need to find out?** How many marbles did Rich have at the start?
Step 2 Plan	**How will I find how many marbles there were?** I can **use a model**
Step 3 Solve	Anna **3** Rich **5** Count the number of marbles in all. Rich had **8** marbles at the start.
Step 4 Check	**Look back.** Did I use a model for the marbles? **yes** Does my model show how many marbles there were at the start? **yes**

Grade 1   41   Chapter 3

Skills Practice (p. 43) `OL`

3-8 **Skills Practice**
Problem-Solving Investigation: Choose a Strategy

Choose a strategy. Solve.

Problem-Solving Strategies
- Act it out
- Draw a picture

1. Ted has 9 cars. Dick has 4 cars. How many more cars does Ted have?
   5 cars

2. Sue and Beth jump rope. Sue jumps 10 times. Beth jumps 8 times. How many more times does Sue jump?
   2 jumps

3. Allison had 10 crayons. Now she has 7 crayons. How many crayons did she give away?
   3 crayons

Grade 1   43   Chapter 3

Problem-Solving Strategies
- Act it out
- Draw a picture
- Write a number sentence

Choose a strategy. Solve.

1. Lena had 6 books.
   She gave 2 to her sister.
   How many does Lena have left?

   __4__ books

2. Jessica caught 4 frogs.
   3 hopped away. How many
   frogs does Jessica have now?

   __1__ frogs

3. Tate has 9 paper clips.
   She gave Elena 3 paper clips.
   How many paper clips does
   Tate have now?

   __6__ paper clips

4. Marcus ate 5 crackers. Shani
   ate 9 crackers. How many more
   crackers did Shani eat than Marcus?

   __4__ crackers

106   one hundred six

Math at Home Activity: Take advantage of problem-solving opportunities during daily routines such as riding in the car, bedtime, doing laundry, putting away groceries, planning schedules, and so on.

BL **Alternate Teaching Strategy**

If ▶ students have difficulty modeling number problems . . .

Then ▶ use one of these reteach options.

1 CRM **Daily Reteach Worksheet** (pp. 41–42)

2 **Model Subtraction** Give students subtraction flash cards subtracting from numbers up to 9. Have students use connecting cubes or draw a picture to model each flash card.

③ Practice

Mixed Problem Solving

Exercises 3–4 Be sure students can read and understand the problems. Reinforce the order of steps for each problem by modeling them on the board.

④ Assess

✓ Formative Assessment

Tell students the following subtraction story: *Ana finished the 10 lessons in this chapter. Luigi was out sick. He finished 4. How many lessons behind is Luigi?*

- **How will you solve the problem?** Sample answer: Write a subtraction sentence or draw a picture in order to use subtraction.

- **What numbers are important in solving this problem?** 10 and 4

- Have students use two-colored counters to model each part of this problem.

Quick Check | **Are students continuing to struggle with modeling problems?**

If Yes → Strategy Intervention Guide (p. 70)

If No → Independent Work Options (p. 105B)

   CRM Skills Practice Worksheet (p. 43)

   CRM Enrich Worksheet (p. 45)

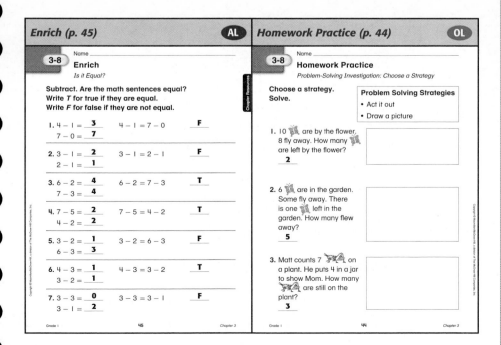

Enrich (p. 45) AL

3-8 Name _____
Enrich
Is it Equal?

Subtract. Are the math sentences equal?
Write *T* for true if they are equal.
Write *F* for false if they are not equal.

1. 4 − 1 = __3__   4 − 1 = 7 − 0   **F**
   7 − 0 = __7__

2. 3 − 1 = __2__   3 − 1 = 2 − 1   **F**
   2 − 1 = __1__

3. 6 − 2 = __4__   6 − 2 = 7 − 3   **T**
   7 − 3 = __4__

4. 7 − 5 = __2__   7 − 5 = 4 − 2   **T**
   4 − 2 = __2__

5. 3 − 2 = __1__   3 − 2 = 6 − 3   **F**
   6 − 3 = __3__

6. 4 − 3 = __1__   4 − 3 = 3 − 2   **T**
   3 − 2 = __1__

7. 3 − 3 = __0__   3 − 3 = 3 − 1   **F**
   3 − 1 = __2__

Grade 1   45   Chapter 3

Homework Practice (p. 44) OL

3-8 Name _____
Homework Practice
Problem-Solving Investigation: Choose a Strategy

Choose a strategy. Solve.

Problem Solving Strategies
- Act it out
- Draw a picture

1. 10 🦋 are by the flower.
   8 fly away. How many 🦋
   are left by the flower?
   __2__

2. 6 🦋 are in the garden.
   Some fly away. There
   is one 🦋 left in the
   garden. How many flew
   away?
   __5__

3. Matt counts 7 🐞 on
   a plant. He puts 4 in a jar
   to show Mom. How many
   🐞 are still on the
   plant?
   __3__

Grade 1   44   Chapter 3

Subtract from 10, 11, and 12

Lesson Planner

Objective

Use connecting cubes to subtract from 10, 11, and 12.

Review Vocabulary

part, whole, sum

Resources

Materials: WorkMat 1: Ten-Frame, small plastic bags

Manipulatives: two-colored counters, connecting cubes, red and blue number cubes

Literature Connection: *Ten Seeds* by Ruth Brown

Alternate Lesson: Use "The Cave" on page 192 of *Math Their Way* to provide practice subtracting with the number 10.
Use *IMPACT Mathematics:* Unit A to provide practice with using manipulatives to model subtracting from 10, 11, and 12.

Teacher Technology
TeacherWorks • Concepts in Motion • Math Tool Chest
• Math Songs Track 15 Lesson Plan

Focus on Math Background

Subtracting from 10, 11, and 12 is the focus of the lesson. Composing and decomposing to 10 with ease and efficiency is a crucial foundation for an understanding of base-ten relationships. Knowing all of the number combinations of 10 makes learning related facts with larger landmark numbers such as 100 an easy transition. For example, if students know that $10 - 6 = 4$, they can apply this fact to help them solve $100 - 60$. Students will also practice subtracting amounts from 11 and 12.

Daily Routine

Use these suggestions before beginning the lesson on p. 107.

5-Minute Check

(Reviews Lesson 3-8)
Model with connecting cubes to solve the problem.
Marcus collected 9 caterpillars in a jar. During the night 4 caterpillars crawled out! How many caterpillars did Marcus have left? $9 - 4 = 5$

Problem of the Day

It takes Anton 9 minutes to walk to Jordan's house. It only takes him 6 minutes if he rides his bicycle there. How much quicker is it if Anton rides his bike? Write a subtraction sentence to show this story. 3 minutes; $9 - 6 = 3$

LINE UP Write $12 - 3 =$ on the chalkboard. Have 12 students line up and count off. Then have 3 of those students form another line.

- **How many students are still in the first line?** 9 students
  What is the answer to the subtraction on the chalkboard? 9

Review Math Vocabulary

Write the terms **part, whole,** and **sum** on the board. Draw ten triangles on the board. Circle them.

- **How many triangles in the whole?** 10 triangles
- **Mark through three triangles with an X.**
- **How many triangles did I take away?** 3 triangles
- **How many triangles are left?** 7 triangles
- **How many triangles in all?** 10 triangles

Visual Vocabulary Cards

Use Visual Vocabulary Card 47 to reinforce the vocabulary reviewed in this lesson. (The Define/Example/ Ask routine is printed on the back of each card.)

sum

Differentiated Instruction

Small Group Options

Option 1
Below/Approaching Level (BL)   *VISUAL, SPATIAL*

Materials: egg cartons, connecting cubes

Give each group of students an egg carton and twelve connecting cubes.

- Have students place eleven connecting cubes in their egg carton, one cube to a compartment.
- Ask students subtraction problems from 11, and have students remove cubes from the egg carton to solve each problem.
- Have students put the cubes back into the egg-carton compartments after each problem.
- After asking several subtraction problems from 11, repeat the activity with subtraction problems from 10 and 12.

Option 2
English Language Learners (ELL)   *VISUAL/SPATIAL, LOGICAL*

Core Vocabulary: beans, in, ten-frame
Common Use Verb: match/matches

See Math This strategy uses visuals to help students understand a common graphic used when subtracting from ten.

- Place 10 beans on ten-frame.
- Say: "I have 10 **beans**; I take away two **beans**" (do so). How many **beans** are left?
- Write "10 − 2 = 8". Say: "This *matches* the ten-frame."
- Give 10-frames and beans to pairs.
- Write 10 − 3 = 7 and have pairs match their ten-frame to it.
- Read the problem as students point to their work.
- Repeat for 11 and 12 as time permits.

Independent Work Options

Option 1
Early Finishers (OL) (AL)   *VISUAL, SPATIAL, PAIRS*

Materials: crayons, two-colored counters

- Each student draws a picture of twelve objects and crosses out some of them.
- Direct students to exchange papers with their partners. Then have each partner write the subtraction sentence that is shown in the picture.

$12 - 3 = 9$

Option 2
Student Technology

| Math Online | macmillanmh.com |

♪ Math Songs, "Take It Away" Track 15 • Math Tool Chest • Math Adventures

Option 3
Learning Station: Science (p. 83H)

Direct students to the Science Learning Station for more opportunities to explore and extend the lesson concept.

Option 4
Problem-Solving Practice

Reinforce problem-solving skills and strategies with the Problem-Solving Practice worksheet.

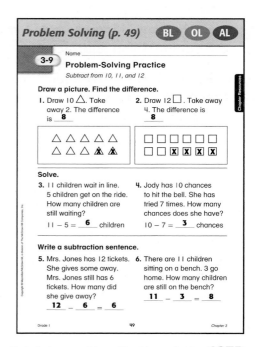

1 Introduce

Activity Choice 1 • Hands-On
Have ten students stand in a circle.

- Walk around the circle and have one student sit down by tapping that student.
- **What subtraction sentence did we show?** $10 - 1 = 9$
- Have the student stand again. Walk around, tap more than one student, and ask for the subtraction sentence.
- Continue until you have worked through all the subtraction-from-10 facts.

Activity Choice 2 • Literature

Introduce the lesson with *Ten Seeds* by Ruth Brown. For additional support, see p. TR46.

2 Teach

Give a bag of 20 two-colored counters and a ten-frame to each student. Have students use the ten-frame to subtract from 10, 11, and 12 using the yellow and red sides of the counters. Give the following directions:

- **Fill a ten-frame with counters. Add one or two more counters next to the ten-frame to make 11 or 12. Write the number of counters you used.**
- **Take away some of the counters. Write a minus sign and the number of counters you subtracted.**
- **Write an equal sign and the number you have left.**
- **Draw the number you started with. Put an X on the counters you subtracted.**

Get Ready Use p. 107 to reinforce the lesson concept.

Check Observe students as you work through Exercises 1–9 as a class.

 Exercise 9 Assess student comprehension before assigning practice exercises.

⚠ COMMON ERROR!
Students may miscount the number of connecting cubes they take away. Have students count aloud up to the "take-away" number as they take one cube at a time.

Name _____

Subtract from 10, 11, and 12

Get Ready

Main Idea
I will subtract from 10, 11, and 12.

You can take apart 10, 11, and 12 in different ways.

Here is one way to subtract from 10.

$10 - 2 = $ **8**

Here is another way to subtract from 10.

$10 - 4 = $ **6**

$11 - 4 = $ **7**

Here are two ways to subtract from 11.

$11 - 9 = $ **2**

$12 - 7 = $ **5**

Here are two ways to subtract from 12.

$12 - 3 = $ **9**

Chapter 3   Lesson 9   one hundred seven   107

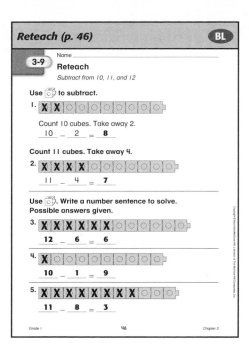

Reteach (p. 46)   BL

Name _____

3-9   **Reteach**
Subtract from 10, 11, and 12

Use ⚙ to subtract.

1. X X O O O O O O O O
Count 10 cubes. Take away 2.
10 − 2 = **8**

Count 11 cubes. Take away 4.
2. X X X X O O O O O O O
11 − 4 = **7**

Use ⚙. Write a number sentence to solve.
Possible answers given.

3. X X X X X X O O O O O O
12 − 6 = **6**

4. X O O O O O O O O O
10 − 1 = **9**

5. X X X X X X X X O O O
11 − 8 = **3**

Grade 1   46   Chapter 3

 **Check**

Draw the 🎲. Show the subtraction sentence.

1. $10 - 5 = 5$ **2.** $12 - 4 = 8$

See students' drawings.

Subtract. Write the subtraction sentence.

3.

___12___ ⊖ ___4___ ⊜ ___8___

4.

___10___ ⊖ ___6___ ⊜ ___4___

5.

___11___ ⊖ ___4___ ⊜ ___7___

Subtract.

6. $10 - 9 = \underline{\ 1\ }$ **7.** $12 - 9 = \underline{\ 3\ }$ **8.** $11 - 6 = \underline{\ 5\ }$

9. **Talk About It** What is the difference if you subtract 0 from 10, 11, or 12? 10, 11, or 12

108   one hundred eight   **GO on**

BL Alternate Teaching Strategy

If students have trouble using a ten-frame to subtract from 10 . . .

Then use one of these reteach options.

1 CRM **Daily Reteach Worksheet** (p. 46)

2 Count on Fingers Start students with both hands open. Then show students how to count up from 1 while putting down one finger at a time.

3 Have students use Math Tool Chest to help complete the problem-solving exercises.

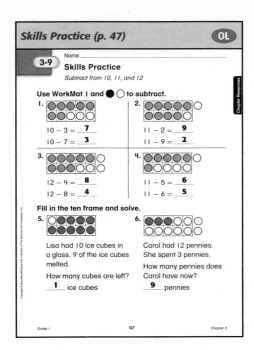

Skills Practice (p. 47) **OL**

Name _____

3-9 Skills Practice
Subtract from 10, 11, and 12

Use WorkMat 1 and ●○ to subtract.

1. $10 - 3 = \underline{7}$ $10 - 7 = \underline{3}$

2. $11 - 2 = \underline{9}$ $11 - 9 = \underline{2}$

3. $12 - 4 = \underline{8}$ $12 - 8 = \underline{4}$

4. $11 - 5 = \underline{6}$ $11 - 6 = \underline{5}$

Fill in the ten frame and solve.

5. Lisa had 10 ice cubes in a glass. 9 of the ice cubes melted. How many cubes are left? ___1___ ice cubes

6. Carol had 12 pennies. She spent 3 pennies. How many pennies does Carol have now? ___9___ pennies

Grade 1   47   Chapter 3

3 Practice

Differentiate practice using these leveled assignments for Exercises 10–25.

Level	Assignment
BL Below/ Approaching Level	Have students work in groups as you guide them through parts of the exercises.
OL On Level	Complete the exercises independently.
AL Above/Beyond Level	Have students complete the exercises without manipulatives.

Name _____

Practice

Draw the 🎲. Show the subtraction sentence.

10. $12 - 6 = 6$ See students' drawings.

11. $11 - 7 = 4$ See students' drawings.

12. $10 - 1 = 9$ See students' drawings.

Subtract. Write the subtraction sentence.

13.

$$\underline{10} \;\ominus\; \underline{7} \;=\; \underline{3}$$

14.

$$\underline{12} \;\ominus\; \underline{8} \;=\; \underline{4}$$

15.

$$\underline{12} \;\ominus\; \underline{5} \;=\; \underline{7}$$

Chapter 3   Lesson 9   one hundred nine   109

Copyright © Macmillan/McGraw-Hill, a division of The McGraw-Hill Companies, Inc.

Enrich (p. 50)   **AL**

3-9   Name _____

Enrich
Vegetable Subtraction

Color to show the subtraction sentence. Then show another way to subtract the same numbers.

1.
$10 - 6 = \underline{4}$ $10 - \underline{4} = \underline{6}$ 6 carrots are shaded.

2.
$10 - 8 = \underline{2}$ $10 - \underline{2} = \underline{8}$ 8 beans are shaded.

3.
$10 - 3 = \underline{7}$ $10 - \underline{7} = \underline{3}$ 3 pickles are shaded.

4.
$10 - 7 = \underline{3}$ $10 - \underline{3} = \underline{7}$ 7 onions are shaded.

5.
$10 - 1 = \underline{9}$ $10 - \underline{9} = \underline{1}$ 1 pea is shaded.

Grade 1   50   Chapter 3

Subtract.

16. $6 - 4 = \underline{2}$ 17. $8 - 3 = \underline{5}$

18. $12 - 9 = \underline{3}$ 19. $2 - 2 = \underline{0}$

20. $10 - 3 = \underline{7}$ 21. $5 - 4 = \underline{1}$

22. $11 - 5 = \underline{6}$ 23. $8 - 7 = \underline{1}$

Data File

There are many animals at the Birmingham Zoo in Alabama. Use the pictures. Write subtraction sentences.

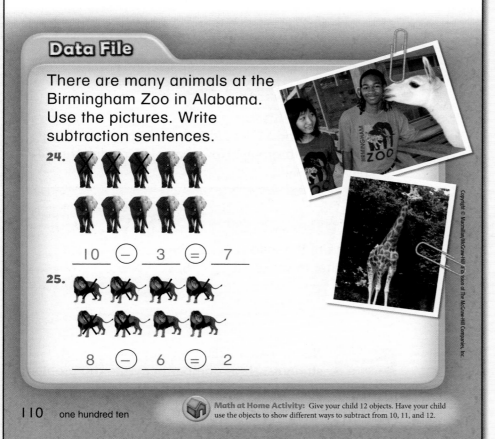

24.

$\underline{10} \ \ominus \ \underline{3} \ = \ \underline{7}$

25.

$\underline{8} \ \ominus \ \underline{6} \ = \ \underline{2}$

110 one hundred ten

Math at Home Activity: Give your child 12 objects. Have your child use the objects to show different ways to subtract from 10, 11, and 12.

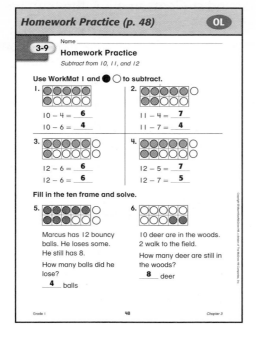

Homework Practice (p. 48) **OL**

Name _____

3-9 **Homework Practice**
Subtract from 10, 11, and 12

Use WorkMat 1 and ●○ to subtract.

1. $10 - 4 = \mathbf{6}$
   $10 - 6 = \mathbf{4}$

2. $11 - 4 = \mathbf{7}$
   $11 - 7 = \mathbf{4}$

3. $12 - 6 = \mathbf{6}$
   $12 - 6 = \mathbf{6}$

4. $12 - 5 = \mathbf{7}$
   $12 - 7 = \mathbf{5}$

Fill in the ten frame and solve.

5. Marcus has 12 bouncy balls. He loses some. He still has 8.
   How many balls did he lose?
   $\underline{4}$ balls

6. 10 deer are in the woods. 2 walk to the field.
   How many deer are still in the woods?
   $\underline{8}$ deer

Grade 1   48   Chapter 3

④ Assess

✓ Formative Assessment

Show students a group of six cubes in one color and a group of six cubes in another color.

• **Can you use these cubes to model subtraction from 10, 11, or 12? How do you know?** 12; The total number of cubes is 12.

WRITING IN ►MATH Challenge students to write as many subtraction sentences as possible that relate to 10, 11, and 12.

Quick Check **Are students continuing to struggle with subtracting from 10, 11, and 12?**

If Yes → Small Group Options (p. 107B)

If No → Independent Work Options (p. 107B)

CRM Skills Practice Worksheet (p. 47)

CRM Enrich Worksheet (p. 50)

Lesson 3-9 Subtract from 10, 11, and 12 **110**

Vertical Subtraction

Lesson Planner

Objective
Write subtraction facts in horizontal and vertical form.

Review Vocabulary
difference

Resources

Materials: dominoes, sticky notes

Manipulatives: two-colored counters

Literature Connection: *Ten Sly Piranhas* by William Wise

Alternate Lesson: Adapt "The Magic Box" on page 249 of *Math Their Way* for practice with subtraction facts in vertical and horizontal format.
Use *IMPACT Mathematics:* Unit A to provide practice with vertical subtraction.

Teacher Technology
TeacherWorks • Concepts in Motion • Math Songs Track 15 Lesson Plan

Focus on Math Background

It is important for young children to develop a solid understanding of subtraction. Subtraction and multiple subtractions are the foundation concepts for division. Students must also become familiar with both horizontal and vertical formats for subtraction. Because they are learning to read and write English from left to right, first graders are most comfortable with number sentences in a horizontal format. Helping students transfer their understanding of horizontal equations to vertical ones is an important step. The ability to decompose numbers in either direction will be helpful later in using subtraction to balance equations and for adult tasks such as using a checkbook register.

Daily Routine

Use these suggestions before beginning the lesson on p. 111.

5—Minute Check

(Reviews Lesson 3–9)
Ahmad baked 12 loaves of bread. He sold 8 loaves on Sunday morning. How many loaves did Ahmad have left? 4 loaves

Problem of the Day

Which of the following numbers can be added together to make 10: 2, 4, 6, 7? 4 and 6

LINE UP Name a subtraction fact for each pair of students. Have one partner write the problem vertically and the other write it horizontally. Partners subtract, compare answers, and then line up.

Review Math Vocabulary

Write the word **difference** on the board and remind students that it is the term we use for the answer to a subtraction problem.

- Write the subtraction sentence shown below on the board and circle the difference.
  $6 - 2 = 4$
- **What number has a circle around it?** 4
  What part of the problem is the number 4 in this subtraction sentence? the difference
- Draw an arrow from the word difference to the number 4.

Visual Vocabulary Cards
Use Visual Vocabulary Card 13 to reinforce the vocabulary reviewed in this lesson. (The Define/Example/Ask routine is printed on the back of each card.)

Differentiated Instruction

Small Group Options

Option 1
Gifted and Talented AL

LOGICAL, SOCIAL

- Tell students a subtraction riddle: *I have a number. When I subtract 3 from it, I get 2. What is my number?* 5

- Have students write the riddle as a subtraction sentence in horizontal and then in vertical form.

- Then have group members each make up another number riddle. **What number do you subtract? What number tells the difference?** See students' work.

- Have group members trade riddles and solve. Encourage groups to write all their riddles as horizontal and vertical subtraction sentences.

Option 2
English Language Learners ELL

KINESTHETIC, SOCIAL

Core Vocabulary: paper, walk, stand on
Common Use Verb: take away

Do Math This strategy teaches subtracting kinesthetically while integrating new vocabulary.

- Place 6 small squares of paper vertically on the board.

- Have 3 students stand on either side, hands down, eyes closed while music plays. When the music stops, each student covers 1 square with their hand.

- Repeat, putting an X over the bottom square while eyes are closed.

- The student who covers the X is subtracted and must take square back to their seat. Write 6 − 1 = 5 vertically.

- Repeat to zero.

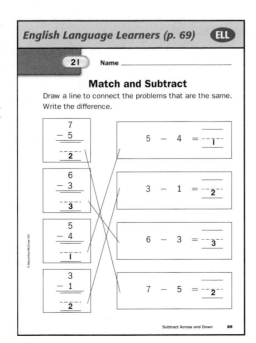

English Language Learners (p. 69) ELL

21 Name _____

Match and Subtract

Draw a line to connect the problems that are the same. Write the difference.

$$\begin{array}{r} 7 \\ -\ 5 \\ \hline 2 \end{array}$$

$$\begin{array}{r} 6 \\ -\ 3 \\ \hline 3 \end{array}$$

$$\begin{array}{r} 5 \\ -\ 4 \\ \hline 1 \end{array}$$

$$\begin{array}{r} 3 \\ -\ 1 \\ \hline 2 \end{array}$$

$5 - 4 = \underline{1}$

$3 - 1 = \underline{2}$

$6 - 3 = \underline{3}$

$7 - 5 = \underline{2}$

Subtract Across and Down 69

Independent Work Options

Option 1
Early Finishers OL AL

SOCIAL, SPATIAL

Materials: index cards

- Provide each group with twelve index cards.

- Have students write six subtraction sentences (facts to 10) on six cards. Then have them write the same subtraction sentences in vertical form on the remaining six cards.

- Have students use their cards to play a matching game. Direct them to place cards facedown on a table and take turns turning over two cards, trying to find the horizontal and vertical version of the same subtraction sentence.

Option 2
Student Technology

Math Online macmillanmh.com

♪ Math Songs, "Take It Away" Track 15

Option 3
Learning Station: Language Arts (p. 83H)

Direct students to the Language Arts Learning Station for more opportunities to explore and extend the lesson concept.

Option 4
Problem-Solving Practice

Reinforce problem-solving skills and strategies with the Leveled Problem-Solving Worksheet.

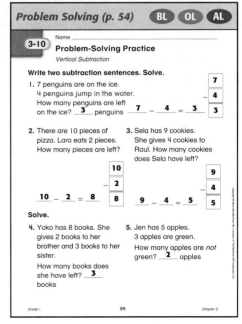

Problem Solving (p. 54) BL OL AL

Name _____

3-10 **Problem-Solving Practice**
Vertical Subtraction

Write two subtraction sentences. Solve.

1. 7 penguins are on the ice. 4 penguins jump in the water. How many penguins are left on the ice? __3__ penguins

$7 - 4 = 3$

$$\begin{array}{r} 7 \\ -\ 4 \\ \hline 3 \end{array}$$

2. There are 10 pieces of pizza. Lara eats 2 pieces. How many pieces are left?

$10 - 2 = 8$

$$\begin{array}{r} 10 \\ -\ 2 \\ \hline 8 \end{array}$$

3. Sela has 9 cookies. She gives 4 cookies to Raul. How many cookies does Sela have left?

$9 - 4 = 5$

$$\begin{array}{r} 9 \\ -\ 4 \\ \hline 5 \end{array}$$

Solve.

4. Yoko has 8 books. She gives 2 books to her brother and 3 books to her sister. How many books does she have left? __3__ books

5. Jen has 5 apples. 3 apples are green. How many apples are *not* green? __2__ apples

Grade 1 54 Chapter 3

① Introduce

Activity Choice 1 • Hands–On

- Group students in pairs, and give each pair 10 linked cubes. Set the cubes in the horizontal position on a sheet of paper or a white board.
- Ask one student in each pair to take away some. Ask the other student to write the number sentence in the same position as the cubes.
- Then have a student link the cubes and turn them so they are "up and down." Explain that *vertical* is another way to say "up and down".
- Ask one student in each pair to take away some. Ask the other student to write the number sentence in the same position as the cubes.
- **Does the number sentence change when you write it a different way?** no

Activity Choice 2 • Literature

Introduce the lesson with *Ten Sly Piranhas* by William Wise. For additional support, see p. TR47.

② Teach

- On an overhead or on the board, write: 7 − 3 =
- **What does this number sentence say?** 7 minus 3 equals **What is the answer?** 4 Ask a volunteer to demonstrate with connecting cubes.
- On an overhead or on the board, write $\begin{array}{r} 7 \\ -3 \\ \hline \end{array}$
- Touch each part of the sentence as you read it. **What is the answer?** 4
- **Does the number of counters change when you turn them a different way?** no

Get Ready Use the section at the top of p. 111 to reinforce the lesson concept.

Check Observe students as you work through Exercises 1–3 as a class.

💬 **Exercise 3** Assess student comprehension before assigning practice exercises.

⚠️ **COMMON ERROR!**

Students may not understand that the order of the first two numbers in a subtraction sentence cannot be switched as addends can. Remind students always to put the larger number at the top of a vertical subtraction sentence.

Name _____

Vertical Subtraction

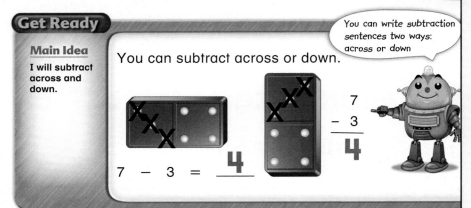

You can write subtraction sentences two ways: across or down

Get Ready

Main Idea

I will subtract across and down.

You can subtract across or down.

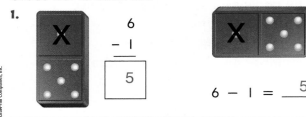

$\begin{array}{r} 7 \\ -3 \\ \hline 4 \end{array}$

7 − 3 = __4__

✓ Check

Cross out to subtract.

1.  $\begin{array}{r} 6 \\ -1 \\ \hline 5 \end{array}$

6 − 1 = __5__

2. $\begin{array}{r} 9 \\ -3 \\ \hline 6 \end{array}$

9 − 3 = __6__

3. **Talk About It** How is subtracting down like subtracting across?
Sample answer: The difference is the same.

Chapter 3   Lesson 10   one hundred eleven   111

Reteach (p. 51)   BL

3-10 **Reteach**
Vertical Subtraction

You can write the same subtraction sentence two ways. The difference is the same.

✗✗◎◎◎◎◎◎ $\begin{array}{r} 8 \\ -2 \\ \hline \end{array}$

8 − 2 = 6

$\begin{array}{r} 8 \\ -2 \\ \hline 6 \end{array}$

Cross out to subtract.

1. ✗✗◎◎◎◎◎ $\begin{array}{r} 7 \\ -2 \\ \hline 5 \end{array}$

7 − 2 = **5**

2. ✗✗✗✗✗✗◎◎ $\begin{array}{r} 8 \\ -6 \\ \hline 2 \end{array}$

8 − 6 = **2**

3. ✗✗✗◎◎◎◎◎ $\begin{array}{r} 8 \\ -3 \\ \hline 5 \end{array}$

8 − 3 = **5**

4. ✗✗✗✗✗✗◎ $\begin{array}{r} 7 \\ -6 \\ \hline 1 \end{array}$

7 − 6 = **1**

5. ✗✗✗◎◎◎ $\begin{array}{r} 6 \\ -3 \\ \hline 3 \end{array}$

6 − 3 = **3**

6. $\begin{array}{r} 8 \\ -4 \\ \hline 4 \end{array}$

8 − 4 = **4**

Grade 1   51   Chapter 3

Skills Practice (p. 52)   OL

3-10 **Skills Practice**
Vertical Subtraction

Cross out to subtract.

1. $\begin{array}{r} 9 \\ -3 \\ \hline 6 \end{array}$

9 − 3 = **6**

2. $\begin{array}{r} 6 \\ -2 \\ \hline 4 \end{array}$

6 − 2 = **4**

3. $\begin{array}{r} 6 \\ -1 \\ \hline 5 \end{array}$

6 − 1 = **5**

4. $\begin{array}{r} 8 \\ -2 \\ \hline 6 \end{array}$

8 − 2 = **6**

Write two subtraction sentences. One across ↔ and one down ↕.

5. Rory's mom buys 7 apples. Alfonso eats some of them. There are 5 left. How many did Rory eat?

$\begin{array}{r} 7 \\ -5 \\ \hline 2 \end{array}$

7 − 5 = 2

6. Mia had 9 marbles. She lost 7 of them. How many does she have now?

$\begin{array}{r} 9 \\ -7 \\ \hline 2 \end{array}$

9 − 7 = 2

Grade 1   52   Chapter 3

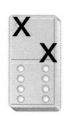

Practice

Cross out to subtract.

4.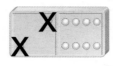

$$\begin{array}{r} 10 \\ -\ 2 \\ \hline 8 \end{array}$$

$10 - 2 = \underline{8}$

5.

$$\begin{array}{r} 4 \\ -\ 2 \\ \hline 2 \end{array}$$

$4 - 2 = \underline{2}$

6.

$$\begin{array}{r} 8 \\ -\ 5 \\ \hline 3 \end{array}$$

$8 - 5 = \underline{3}$

Problem Solving

Critical Thinking

Draw a picture to solve.

Then write a number sentence. See students' drawings

7. There are 10 crackers on the table.
Alvin ate 2.
How many are left? $\underline{10} \;\underline{\bigcirc}\; \underline{2} \;\underline{\bigcirc}\; \underline{8}$

112   one hundred twelve

Math at Home Activity: Use 12 small objects. Show subtraction by taking some objects away. Have your child write the subtraction sentence.

Enrich (p. 55)   **AL**

3-10 Name _____
Enrich
Amazing Subtraction

Solve the problems. Use the answers to go through the maze.

1. $12 - \boxed{8} = 4$ 2. $11 - 3 = \boxed{8}$
3. $\boxed{11} - 7 = 4$ 4. $12 - 5 = \boxed{7}$
5. $12 - 9 = \boxed{3}$ 6. $11 - \boxed{7} = 4$
7. $12 - 6 = \boxed{6}$ 8. $12 - \boxed{8} = 4$
9. $11 - 3 = \boxed{8}$ 10. $11 - \boxed{6} = 5$

Grade 1   55   Chapter 3

Homework Practice (p. 53)   **OL**

3-10 Name _____
Homework Practice
Vertical Subtraction

Cross out to subtract.

1. $\begin{array}{r}4\\-2\\\hline 2\end{array}$ 2. $\begin{array}{r}9\\-4\\\hline 5\end{array}$

$4 - 2 = \underline{2}$ $9 - 4 = \underline{5}$

3. $\begin{array}{r}8\\-3\\\hline 5\end{array}$ 4. $\begin{array}{r}7\\-2\\\hline 5\end{array}$

$8 - 3 = \underline{5}$ $7 - 2 = \underline{5}$

Write two subtraction sentences.
One across ↔ and one down ↕.

5. Seth had some baseball cards. He gave 2 to Jose. Then Seth had 2 cards left. How many did Seth have at the start?

$\begin{array}{r}4\\-2\\\hline 2\end{array}$

$4 - 2 = 2$

6. Eve has 6 blank sheets of paper. She draws on 3 of them. How many blank sheets does she have now?

$\begin{array}{r}6\\-3\\\hline 3\end{array}$

$6 - 3 = 3$

Grade 1   53   Chapter 3

BL Alternate Teaching Strategy

If students do not understand how subtracting across and down are alike . . .

Then use one of the following reteach options.

1 CRM **Daily Reteach Worksheet** (p. 51)

2 Domino Subtraction Have students count the total number of dots on a domino. Position the domino horizontally and cover the right half with a sticky note. Help students write a horizontal subtraction sentence, starting with the total number. Position the domino vertically with the covered dots at the bottom. Have students write the same sentence vertically. Discuss how and why the problems are the same.

③ Practice

Differentiate practice using these leveled assignments for Exercises 4–7.

Level	Assignment
BL Below/Approaching Level	Have students use connecting cubes set up vertically and horizontally.
OL On Level	Complete the exercises independently.
AL Above/Beyond Level	Write the other subtraction sentence in the same fact family.

④ Assess

Formative Assessment

Ask students why the greater number must be first horizontally and at the top vertically to subtract. **Now write a problem both ways and solve it.**

WRITING IN ►MATH Have students write about the difference between subtracting across and subtracting down. Ask them to show examples.

Quick Check **Are students continuing to struggle with subtracting across and down?**

If Yes → Strategy Intervention Guide (p. 70)

If No → Independent Work Options (p. 111B)

CRM Skills Practice Worksheet (p. 52)

CRM Enrich Worksheet (p. 55)

Problem Solving
in Social Studies

Real-World MATH

Randy's mom is a truck driver.

This book belongs to

_____

A

She drives a big truck. She delivers fruit to grocery stores.

B

Lesson Planner

Objective
Use properties and strategies to subtract.

National Standard
Students understand that most people produce and consume. As producers they make goods and services; as consumers they use goods and services.

Activate Prior Knowledge
Before you turn students' attention to the pages, discuss other jobs that require lots of travel and other ways a truck driver might use math.

- **What other jobs require a lot of travel?** Sample answers: airline pilot, flight attendant, ambassador, businessperson
- **Why else might a truck driver need to use addition and subtraction?** Sample answers: to decide how much gas is needed, to calculate distances between cities

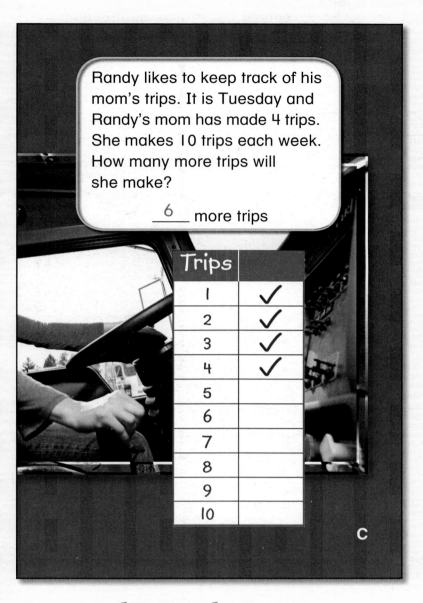

Randy likes to keep track of his mom's trips. It is Tuesday and Randy's mom has made 4 trips. She makes 10 trips each week. How many more trips will she make?

___6___ more trips

Trips	
1	✓
2	✓
3	✓
4	✓
5	
6	
7	
8	
9	
10	

C

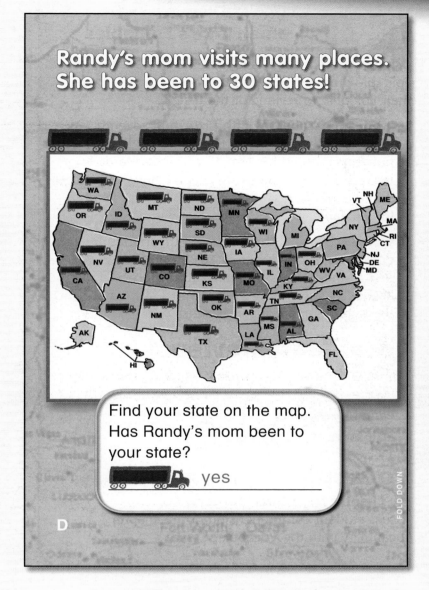

Randy's mom visits many places. She has been to 30 states!

Find your state on the map. Has Randy's mom been to your state?

yes

D

Create the Book

Guide students to create their book.

- Have them fold the page in half.
- Ask them to write their name on page A.
- Explain that page A is the front cover and page D is the back cover. If necessary, have them practice flipping through the book in order.
- Guide them in reading the information and word problems on each of the pages.

Use the Student Pages

Have students work individually or in pairs to solve the word problems on pages C and D.

Page C The chart models a subtraction problem much like students have already done with manipulatives. Make sure students understand what answer they should find.

Page D Help students find their state on the map.

WRITING IN ►MATH Have students write a problem about Randy's mother.

Extend the Activity

Have students rework the problem on page C with Randy's mom making 12 trips a week instead of 10.

FOLDABLES Dinah Zike's Foldables

Use these lesson suggestions to incorporate the Foldable during the chapter. Students can then use their Foldable to review for the test.

Lesson 3-7   Label the fifth, sixth, and seventh pockets of their 5-Pocket Foldable with the numbers 7, 8, and 9. Use 3" x 5" index cards to make subtraction flashcards subtracting 7, 8, and 9 and store them in the appropriate pockets of the Foldable.

Lesson 3-9   Label the eighth, ninth, and tenth pockets with the numbers 10, 11, and 12. Use 3" x 5" index cards to make subtraction flashcards subtracting 10, 11, and 12 and store them in the appropriate pockets.

Vocabulary Review

Review chapter vocabulary using one of the following options.

- **Visual Vocabulary Card** (46)
- **eGlossary** at macmillanmh.com

Vocabulary Test

CRM **Chapter 3 Resource Masters** (p. 60)
Assess student comprehension of the chapter vocabulary with the Vocabulary Test.

Math Online **Chapter Test**
Alternative summative assessment options are available online at macmillanmh.com.

Name _____

Vocabulary

Circle the correct answer.

1. **minus**	2. **equals**	3. **subtraction**
+ ⊖	⊜ −	(9 − 2) 9 + 2

Concepts

Fill in the missing number.

4.
●Part	●Part
I	5
Whole	
6	

5.
●Part	●Part
2	6
Whole	
8	

Write the subtraction sentence.

6.   X X X X X X X

_7_ ⊖ _7_ ⊜ _0_

7.   X X X 🍓 🍓

_5_ ⊖ _3_ ⊜ _2_

✔Chapter 3 Project

Subtraction Number Storybook

Have students discuss the results of their completed chapter project as a class. Assess their work using the Chapter Project rubric found in Chapter 3 Resource Masters, p. 65.

Subtract.

8. $8 - 1 = \underline{7}$

9. $5 - 1 = \underline{4}$

10. $4 - 2 = \underline{2}$

11. $7 - 2 = \underline{5}$

12. $10 - 5 = \underline{5}$

13. $10 - 1 = \underline{9}$

14. $6 - 6 = \underline{0}$

15. $9 - 3 = \underline{6}$

16. $10 - 8 = \underline{2}$

17. $2 - 1 = \underline{1}$

Write the subtraction sentence.

18.

$\underline{12} - \underline{6} = \underline{6}$

19.

$\underline{11} - \underline{7} = \underline{4}$

Problem Solving

20. There are 7 dogs in the park. 3 go home. How many dogs are left?

$\underline{4}$ dogs

21. Cliff ate 5 apples. Ali ate 2 apples. How many more apples did Cliff eat than Ali?

$\underline{3}$ apples

Summative Assessment

Summative Assessment

Use these alternate leveled chapter tests to differentiate assessment for the specific needs of your students.

Leveled Chapter 3 Tests			
Form	**Type**	**Level**	**CRM Pages**
1	Multiple Choice	BL	67–68
2A	Multiple Choice	OL	69–70
2B	Multiple Choice	OL	71–72
2C	Free Response	AL	73–74
2D	Free Response	AL	75–76

BL = below/approaching grade level
OL = on grade level
AL = above/beyond grade level

ExamView Assessment Suite Customize and create multiple versions of your Chapter Test and their test answer keys.

Data-Driven Decision Making

Based on the results of the Chapter Review/Test, use the following to review concepts that continue to present students with problems.

Exercises	State/Local Standards	What's the Math?	Error Analysis	Resources for Review
1–3		Understand math terms minus, subtract, subtract sentence.	Does not know terms "minus sign," "subtraction sentence," "subtract."	Strategic Intervention Guide (p. 70) CRM Chapter 3 Resource Masters (Reteach Worksheets)
4–5 18–19		Model the meaning of subtraction. Model subtraction from 11 and 12.	Miscounts pictures. Reverses numbers and subtracts incorrectly.	**Math Online** Concepts in Motion
6–7		Use number sentences to solve subtraction problems. Understand symbols -, =.	Write numbers in reverse order. Subtracts incorrectly. Does not put in all symbols.	Math Adventures
8–17		Subtract using 0. Subtract from 2, 4, 5, 6, 7, 8, 9,10.	Does not subtract accurately.	
20–21		Determine strategy to use to solve problems.	Misreads problems. Misinterprets "are left" for how many were sold, and "many more" for how many Mark ate.	

Test Practice

Formative Assessment

- Use Student Edition pp. 117–118 as practice and cumulative review. The questions are written in the same style as many state tests.
- You can also use these two pages to benchmark student progress, or as an alternative homework assignment.

Additional practice pages can be found in the Chapter 3 Resource Masters.

CRM **Chapter 3 Resource Masters**
Cumulative Test Practice
- Multiple Choice format (pp. 67–72, 77)
- Free Response format (pp. 73–76, 78)

ExamView® Assessment Suite Create practice worksheets or tests that align to your state standards.

Math Online

For additional practice, visit macmillanmh.com.

Name _____

Listen as your teacher reads each problem.
Choose the correct answer.

1.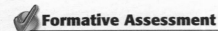

6 – 4 = ☐

- 10 ◯
- 4 ◯
- 2 ⬤
- 6 ◯

2.

4 – 4 = ☐

- 0 ⬤
- 1 ◯
- 2 ◯
- 3 ◯

3.

- 11 ◯
- 6 ◯
- 7 ⬤
- 4 ◯

4.

- 16 – 12 = 4 ◯
- 12 – 4 = 8 ⬤
- 8 + 4 = 12 ◯
- 12 + 4 = 16 ◯

5.

- + ◯
- = ⬤
- – ◯
- > ◯

6.

- 8 – 6 = 2 ◯
- 8 – 3 = 5 ⬤
- 2 + 6 = 8 ◯
- 4 + 4 = 8 ◯

Copyright © Macmillan/McGraw-Hill, a division of The McGraw-Hill Companies, Inc.

Chapter 3   one hundred seventeen 117

Test-Taking Tips

For the Teacher

- Make sure students have all the supplies they need for the test before they start.
- Make sure the students understand the directions for the test before the test day.

For the Student

- Write in your test booklet. Cross out answers that you know are wrong.
- Slow down. Take your time and make sure you mark the correct answer.

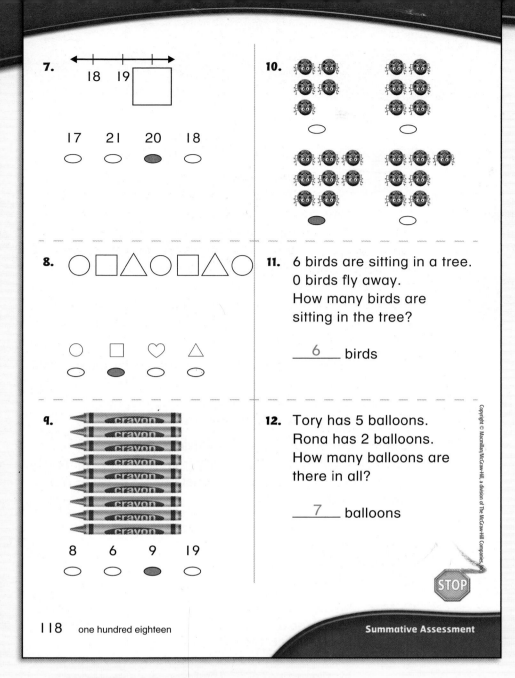

7.

18 19 [ ]

17   21   20   18
○   ○   ●   ○

8. ○□△○□△○

○   □   ♡   △
○   ●   ○   ○

9.

8   6   9   19
○   ○   ●   ○

10.

○   ○

●   ○

11. 6 birds are sitting in a tree.
0 birds fly away.
How many birds are
sitting in the tree?

_____6_____ birds

12. Tory has 5 balloons.
Rona has 2 balloons.
How many balloons are
there in all?

_____7_____ balloons

STOP

118   one hundred eighteen

Summative Assessment

Test Directions for Teachers

Read the following directions to students before they begin the test. Then read each question followed by a pause to allow students time to work on the problem and choose an answer. The first item can be worked as a class example.

- **Write your name at the top of the page.**
- **I am going to read each question to you. Listen carefully to the entire question before you choose your answer.**

Multiple Choice

1. Look at the baseballs. How many baseballs are left?
2. Find the difference.
3. Listen to the number story. 9 cats are in the sun. 2 cats go in the house. How many cats are left?
4. Listen to the number story. Dan has 12 apples in a large basket. He places 4 apples in a small basket. Which number sentence shows how many apples are left in the large basket?
5. Which sign is the equal sign?
6. Look at the beach balls. Which number sentence shows how many are left?

- **Turn the page over.**

7. What number comes after 19?
8. Look at the pattern. What comes next in the pattern?
9. Beth has 9 red crayons. What number is 9?
10. Which group has 8 ladybugs?

Short Response

11. 6 birds are sitting in a tree. 0 birds fly away. How many birds are sitting in the tree?
12. Tory has 5 balloons. Rona has 2 balloons. How many balloons are there in all?

Chapter Overview

Chapter-at-a-Glance

In Chapter 4, students will gain proficiency with data analysis as they read and make Venn diagrams, tally charts, picture graphs, and bar graphs.

Lesson	Math Objective	State/Local Standards
4-1 **Sort and Classify** (pp. 123–124)	Use a Venn diagram to sort and classify objects.	
4-2 **Picture Graphs** (pp. 125–126)	Make and read a picture graph.	
4-3 **Problem-Solving Strategy: Make a Table** (pp. 127–128)	Use the *make a table* strategy to solve problems.	
4-4 **Tally Charts** (pp. 129–130)	Make and read a tally chart.	
4-5 **Read a Bar Graph** (pp. 133–134)	Read a bar graph.	
4-6 **Make a Bar Graph** (pp. 137–140)	Make a bar graph.	
4-7 **Problem-Solving Investigation: Choose a Strategy** (pp. 141–142)	Choose the best strategy to solve a problem.	
4-8 **Certain or Impossible** (pp. 143–144)	Identify events as certain or impossible.	

Organize and Use Data

BIG Idea Graphing begins with making observations of phenomena in the environment, such as counting how many students bring their lunch to school. After collecting the data, students should be involved in sorting and organizing the information into categories that represent and quantify the entire data set. Students can then make inferences, comparisons, and conclusions about the data. Ultimately, this inquiry becomes a springboard for future analysis and empowers students to become informed decision makers about data.

Algebra Students prepare for Algebra by comparing data (largest, smallest, most often, least often). This will lay the foundation for learning equation concepts of is greater than, is less than, and is equal to. Lesson 4-4

Students prepare for Algebra by using addition and subtraction when they interpret bar graphs. This will lay the foundation for understanding equations such as $x = a + b$ and $x = a - b$. Lesson 4-5

Focal Points and Connections

G1-FP5C Measurement **and** *Data Analysis:* Children strengthen their sense of number by solving problems involving measurements and data. Measuring by laying multiple copies of a unit end to end and then counting the units by using groups of tens and ones supports children's understanding of number lines and number relationships. Representing measurements and discrete data in picture and bar graphs involves counting and comparisons that provide another meaningful connection to number relationships.

Skills Trace
Vertical Alignment

Kindergarten
In kindergarten, students learned to:
- Identify, describe, and extend simple patterns (such as circles or triangles) by referring to their shapes, sizes, or colors.
- Collect information about objects and events in their environment.
- Record results using objects, pictures, and picture graphs.

First Grade
In this chapter, students learn to:
- Sort objects and data by common attributes and describe the categories.
- Organize, represent, and compare data by category on simple graphs and charts.
- Represent and compare data by using pictures, bar graphs, tally charts, and picture graphs.
- Identify events as certain or impossible.

After this chapter, students learn to:
- Use a table to sort data relating time and events. (Chapter 7)
- Compare data using measurement with nonstandard units. (Chapter 9)

Second Grade
In second grade, students learn to:
- Collect numerical data and record, organize, display, and interpret the data on bar graphs and other representations.
- Ask and answer simple questions related to data representations.

Math Vocabulary

The following math vocabulary words for Chapter 4 are listed in the glossary of the **Student Edition.** You can find interactive definitions in 13 languages in the **eGlossary** at macmillanmh.com.

bar graph a graph that uses bars to show data (p. 133)

certain sure to happen (p. 143)

data numbers or symbols collected to show information (p. 125)

graph a way to present data collected; also a type of chart; example: a bar graph (p. 125)

impossible unable to happen (p. 143)

picture graph a graph that has different pictures to show information collected (p. 125)

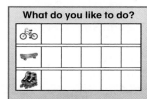

sort to group together items that have something in common (p. 123)

survey to collect data by asking people the same questions; example: This survey shows favorite sports. (p. 129)

tally chart a way to show data using tally marks (p. 129)

Visual Vocabulary Cards Use Visual Vocabulary Cards 4, 12, 19, 35, and 48 to introduce and reinforce the vocabulary in this chapter. (The Define/Example/Ask routine is printed on the back of each card.)

Backmapping and Vertical Alignment McGraw-Hill's *Math Connects* program was conceived and developed with the final results in mind: student success in Algebra 1 and beyond. The authors, using the **NCTM Focal Points and Focal Connections** as their guide, developed this brand-new series by backmapping from Algebra 1 concepts, and vertically aligning the topics so that they build upon prior skills and concepts and serve as a foundation for future topics.

Chapter Planner

	Suggested Pacing		
	Instruction	**Review and Assessment**	**TOTAL**
	8 days	2 days	**10 days**

✓ **Diagnostic Assessment**
Are You Ready? (p. 120)

	Lesson 4-1 Pacing: 1 day	**Lesson 4-2** Pacing: 1 day	**Lesson 4-3** Pacing: 1 day
Lesson/ Objective	**Sort and Classify** (pp. 123–124) **Objective:** Use a Venn diagram to sort and classify objects.	**Picture Graphs** (pp. 125–126) **Objective:** Make and read a picture graph.	**Problem-Solving Strategy Make a Table** (pp. 127–128) **Objective:** Use the *make a table* strategy to solve problems.
State/Local Standards			
Math Vocabulary	sort	graph data picture graph	
Lesson Resources	**Materials** yarn or rubber bands, crayons, copies of a blank Venn diagram, colored pencils, *Corduroy* by Don Freeman **Other Resources** CRM Leveled Worksheets (pp. 6–10) Daily Reteach • 5-Minute Check Problem of the Day	**Materials** index cards, stickers or coins, pattern block stamps **Other Resources** CRM Leveled Worksheets (pp. 11–15) Daily Reteach • 5-Minute Check Problem of the Day	**Materials** paper, pencils **Other Resources** CRM Leveled Worksheets (pp. 16–20) Daily Reteach • 5-Minute Check Problem of the Day *I Like That Too*
Technology Math Online ▶	Concepts in Motion	Math Adventures	
Reaching All Learners	Gifted and Talented, p. 123B AL English Learners, p. 123B ELL Early Finishers, p. 123B OL AL	Gifted and Talented, p. 125B AL English Learners, p. 125B ELL Early Finishers, p. 125B OL AL	Gifted and Talented, p. 127B AL English Learners, 127B ELL Early Finishers, 127B OL AL
Alternate Lessons	*Math Their Way*, pp. 61–63 *IMPACT Mathematics:* Unit E	*Math Their Way*, pp. 151 *IMPACT Mathematics:* Unit E	

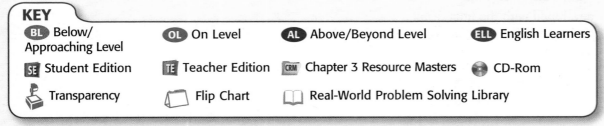

KEY

BL Below/Approaching Level   OL On Level   AL Above/Beyond Level   ELL English Learners

SE Student Edition   TE Teacher Edition   CRM Chapter 3 Resource Masters   CD-Rom

Transparency   Flip Chart   Real-World Problem Solving Library

Lesson 4-4	Pacing: 1 day	Lesson 4-5	Pacing: 1 day	Lesson 4-6	Pacing: 1 day	
Tally Charts (pp. 129–130) **Objective:** Make and read a tally chart.		**Read a Bar Graph** (pp. 133–134) **Objective:** Read a bar graph.		**Make a Bar Graph** (pp. 137–140) **Objective:** Make a bar graph.		Lesson/ Objective
						State/Local Standards
tally chart **survey**		**bar graph**				Math Vocabulary
Materials pencils, paper, overhead projector, coins,		**Materials** overhead projector, colored beads		**Materials** pencils, crayons, 1-inch grid paper **Manipulatives** red number cubes, connecting cubes		Lesson Resources
Other Resources CRM Leveled Worksheets (pp. 21–25) Daily Reteach • 5-Minute Check Problem of the Day		**Other Resources** CRM Leveled Worksheets (pp. 26–30) Daily Reteach • 5-Minute Check Problem of the Day		**Other Resources** CRM Leveled Worksheets (pp. 31–35) Daily Reteach • 5-Minute Check Problem of the Day		
		Math Adventures		Math Tool Chest, Graphs Level 1 Math Adventures Concepts in Motion		Technology Math Online
Below Level, p. 129B BL English Learners, p. 129B ELL Early Finishers, p. 129B OL AL		Below Level, p. 133B BL English Learners, p. 133B ELL Early Finishers, p. 133B OL AL		Below Level, p. 137B BL English Learners, p. 137B ELL Early Finishers, p. 137B OL AL		Reaching All Learners
IMPACT Mathematics: Unit E		*Math Their Way,* p. 154 *IMPACT Mathematics:* Unit E		*Math Their Way,* p. 156 *IMPACT Mathematics:* Unit E		Alternate Lessons
Formative Assessment • Mid-Chapter Check (p. 131) • Spiral Review (p. 132)		**Extra Practice** (p. 135) **Game Time:** Animal Race (p. 136)				

Chapter Planner

	Lesson 4-7 Pacing: 1 day	**Lesson 4-8** Pacing: 1 day
Lesson/ Objective	**Problem-Solving Investigation Choose a Strategy** (pp. 141–142) **Objective:** Choose the best strategy to solve a problem.	**Certain or Impossible** (pp. 143–144) **Objective:** Identify events as certain or impossible.
State/Local Standards		
Math Vocabulary		**certain** **impossible**
Lesson Resources	**Materials** pencils, paper **Other Resources** [CRM] Leveled Worksheets (pp. 36–40) Daily Reteach • 5-Minute Check Problem of the Day *I Like That Too*	**Materials** crayons **Manipulatives** pattern blocks, connecting cubes, color tiles **Other Resources** [CRM] Leveled Worksheets (pp. 41–45) Daily Reteach • 5-Minute Check Problem of the Day
Technology		
Reaching All Learners	Gifted and Talented, p. 141B (AL) English Learners, p. 141B (ELL) Early Finishers, p. 141B (OL) (AL)	Gifted and Talented, p. 143B (AL) English Learners, p. 143B (ELL) Early Finishers, p. 143B (OL) (AL)
Alternate Lesson		*IMPACT Mathematics:* Unit E

Problem-Solving in Science (p. 145)

✓ **Summative Assessment**
- Chapter Review/Test (pp. 147–148)
- Test Practice (p. 149–150)

Assessment Options

✓ Diagnostic Assessment

- **SE** *Option 1:* Are You Ready? (p. 120)
- *Option 2:* Online Quiz macmillanmh.com
- **CRM** *Option 3:* Alternate Diagnostic Test
- **CRM** *Option 4:* Chapter Pretest (p. 48)

✓ Formative Assessment

- **TE** Alternate Teaching Strategies (every lesson)
- **TE** Line Up (in every lesson)
- **SE** Talk About It (every lesson)
- **SE** Writing in Math (every lesson)
- **SE** Check (every lesson)
- **SE** Mid-Chapter Check (p. 131)
- **CRM** Mid-Chapter Test (p. 49)

✓ Summative Assessment

- **SE** Chapter Review/Test, (p. 147)
- **SE** Test Practice (p. 149)
- **CRM** Vocabulary Test, (p. 50)
- **CRM** Leveled Chapter Tests, (pp. 57–66)
- **CRM** Cumulative Test Practice (pp. 67–68)
- **CRM** Listening Assessment (pp. 53–54)
- **CRM** Oral Assessment (pp. 51–52)
- ExamView® Assessment Suite
- A⁺ Advance Tracker

McGraw Hill Professional Development

Targeted professional development has been articulated throughout **McGraw-Hill's** *Math Connects* program. The **McGraw-Hill Professional Development Video Library** provides short videos that support the **NCTM Focal Points and Focal Connections**. For more information, visit macmillanmh.com.

Model Lessons	Instructional Strategies

What the Research Says . . .

Sorting and classifying are essential skills underlying the ability to create categories for data collections and graphs. Juanita V. Copely (*The Young Child and Mathematics*, NAEYC, 2000) outlines these four developmental levels:

- **Level 1** Separating objects from a collection.
- **Level 2** Sorting objects by one attribute.
- **Level 3** Sorting objects in more than one way.
- **Level 4** Identifying the rule by which objects have been sorted.

Use these levels to guide and assess student progress. Most first graders should work at or toward *Level 3*.

Teacher Notes

Learning Stations
Cross-Curricular Links

 Reading

Button Graph

- Read *The Button Box* by Margarette S. Reid.
- Scoop some buttons from the jar.
- Graph them on grid paper.
- Put buttons that look the same in the same row.

Teacher Note: After graphing their selection, students return their buttons to the jar, mix them with the others, and take a new scoop of buttons to graph.

Materials:
- buttons in a jar
- grid paper
- crayons

 Language Arts

Deck of Cards

- Find ways to sort the playing cards in this deck.
- In your Math Journal, write 3 ways to sort the cards.

Teacher Note: The cards can be sorted by color, number, and suit.

Materials:
- deck of playing cards
- Math Journal
- pencil

 Health

Food Pyramid

- Cut pictures of 10 foods from magazines.
- Sort the pictures using the Food Pyramid as a guide.
- Glue the pictures in groups on a sheet of construction paper.
- Make a tally chart showing which food groups the 10 foods belong to.

Materials:
- magazines
- scissors
- glue
- pencils
- construction paper
- food pyramid

Science

small group | KINESTHETIC, VISUAL/ SPATIAL, LOGICAL

Fruit Seeds

- Count the seeds in each piece of fruit.
- Make a bar graph to show how many seeds are in each piece of fruit.
- Write a title for your bar graph.

Teacher Note: Another option is to have students estimate the number of seeds in a watermelon. Slice the watermelon and have students count the seeds in their slice. Add all results together.

	Apple					
	Peach					
	Orange					
	Cherry					

Materials:
- fruit (apple, peach, orange, olive, cherry) sliced in half
- markers
- white paper
- pencils

Social Studies

pairs | VISUAL/SPATIAL LOGICAL

Transportation

- Survey 10 students to find out how they get to school. Do they take a bus, ride in a car, walk, or ride a bike to school?
- Make a picture graph to show how students get to school.
- Write a title for your picture graph.
- How do most students get to school?

bus
car
walk
bike

Materials:
- markers
- white paper
- pencils

Calendar Time

Tally the Days

- Write the name of the current month on the calendar poster. Fill in the numbers for the days of the month.
- Make a separate list for a tally chart of the days of the week.
- Model the use of tally marks to record a number by counting the number of Mondays in the current month, recording each count as a tally mark.
- Do the same with all the other days of the week. Ask students to count the number of each day as you point to them on the calendar poster and record a tally mark for each count.
- Ask students to read from the tally chart how many of each day of the week are in the current month.

Introduce the Chapter

🌐 Real World: Which Flavor?

Introduce the chapter by taking students to the playground and telling them they will be learning about fun ways to show information.

- Using yarn, make a large Venn diagram on the playground. Label one ring *vanilla* and the other *chocolate*.

- **Which frozen yogurt flavor is your favorite— vanilla, chocolate, or swirl—a combination of vanilla and chocolate?** Have students stand inside the ring labeled with their choice of frozen yogurt.

- **Where should the students who chose fudge swirl stand?** Sample answer: In the center where the rings for vanilla and chocolate overlap.

Have students turn to page 119.

- **What would the tally chart look like if we added 2 more yellow cars?** See students' work.

Key Vocabulary Introduce key
vocabulary in the chapter using the routine below.

Define: A **picture graph** is a graph that shows information with pictures.

Example: Sometimes the weather forecast is shown in a picture graph with suns, rain clouds, or thunderbolts for each day of the week.

Ask: Where else have you seen picture graphs?

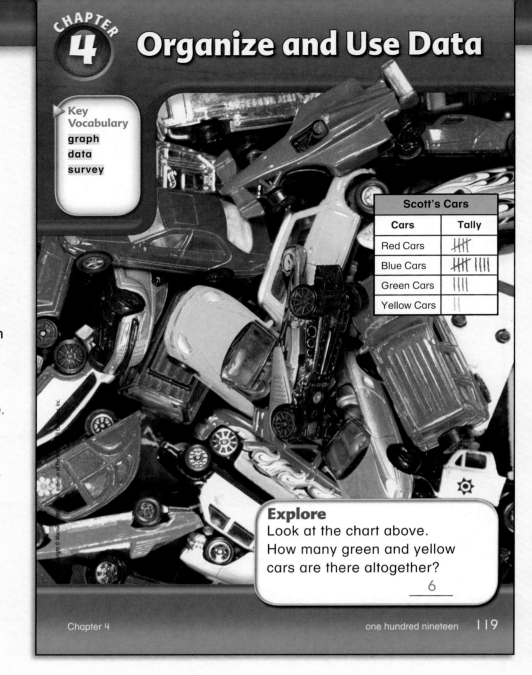

CHAPTER **4** **Organize and Use Data**

Key Vocabulary
graph
data
survey

Scott's Cars

Cars	Tally
Red Cars	卌
Blue Cars	卌 IIII
Green Cars	IIII
Yellow Cars	II

Explore
Look at the chart above.
How many green and yellow cars are there altogether?

_____6_____

Chapter 4   one hundred nineteen **119**

FOLDABLES® Study Organizer   Dinah Zike's Foldables

Guide students to create their Top Pocket Foldables to organize and use data.

① Create a Shutterfold, crease and reopen. Apply glue along the valleys of the crease lines.

② Fold the paper upwards along the horizontal axis and allow glue to adhere.

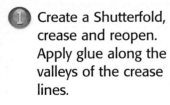

③ Fold the left and right sides of the fold inward so that they meet in the middle, using the creases from the Shutterfold as guides. Recrease and open.

④ Cut off the bottom edges of the left and right tabs stopping at the crease. Cut the resulting top tabs on each side into halves, thirds, or quarters depending on the lesson.

⑤ Worksheets and other student projects can be stored in the pocket. Students write key terms on the outer tabs and record information beneath the tabs.

When to Use It *Lessons 4-1, 4-2, 4-4, 4-5 and 4-6. (Additional instructions for using the Foldable with these lessons are found on pp. 131 and 147.)*

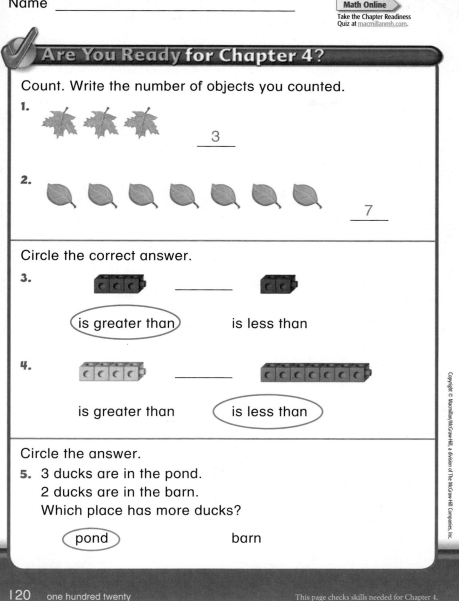

Name _____

✓ Are You Ready for Chapter 4?

Count. Write the number of objects you counted.

1.

_3_

2.

_7_

Circle the correct answer.

3.

(is greater than)   is less than

4.

is greater than   (is less than)

Circle the answer.

5. 3 ducks are in the pond.
2 ducks are in the barn.
Which place has more ducks?

(pond)   barn

120   one hundred twenty

This page checks skills needed for Chapter 4.

Diagnostic Assessment

Check for students' prerequisite skills before beginning the chapter.

- **Option 1:** *Are You Ready for Chapter 4?*
  SE Student Edition, p. 120

- **Option 2:** *Online Assessment Quiz*
  Math Online macmillanmh.com

- **Option 3:** *Diagnostic Test*
  CRM Chapter 4 Resource Master, p. 47

RTI (Response to Intervention)

Based on the results of the diagnostic assessment on p. 120, use the chart below to address individual needs before beginning the chapter.

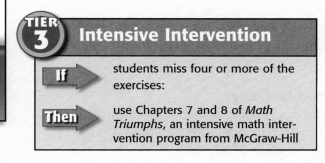

TIER 3 Intensive Intervention

If → students miss four or more of the exercises:

Then → use Chapters 7 and 8 of *Math Triumphs*, an intensive math intervention program from McGraw-Hill

TIER 2 Strategic Intervention below/approaching grade level	**TIER 1 On-Level**	**Above/Beyond-Level**
If → students miss two or three in: **Exercises 1–5**	**If** → students miss one in: **Exercises 1–5**	**If** → students miss none in: **Exercises 1–5**
Then → choose a resource:	**Then** → choose a resource:	**Then** → choose a resource:
Strategic Intervention Guide (p. 12) **CRM** Chapter 1 Resource Masters (Reteach Worksheets) **Math Online** Concepts in Motion	**TE** Learning Stations (pp. 119G–119H) **TE** Chapter Project (p. 121) **CRM** Game: *Follow the Arrow* ⊙ Math Adventures My Math Zone Chapter 3 **Math Online** Fact Dash	**TE** Learning Stations (pp. 119G–119H) **TE** Chapter Project (p. 121) ▯ Real-World Problem Solving: *I Like That Too* ⊙ Math Adventures My Math Zone Chapters 3, 4 **Math Online** Game

Before you begin Chapter 4:
- Read the Math at Home letter found on p. 121 with the class and have each student sign it.
- Send home copies of the Math at Home letter with each student.
- Use the Spanish letter on p. 122 for students with Spanish-speaking parents or guardians.

WRITING IN ►MATH

Starting the Chapter

To introduce the idea of collecting and recording data, have students write their answers to the following questions.

- **What could you do to find out what time most students in the class go to bed each night?** Sample answer: Ask everyone their bedtime.

- **How could you share the information you find with the rest of the class?** Sample answers: Draw a picture; tell everyone.

Have students draw pictures to illustrate their ideas. Provide time for students to share their ideas with the class.

Read-Aloud Anthology

For an optional reading activity to introduce this chapter's math concepts, see the Read-Aloud Anthology, on page TR27.

MATH at HOME

Dear Family,
Today my class started Chapter 4, **Organize and Use Data**. In this chapter, I will learn to make and read picture graphs, tally charts, and bar graphs. Here is an activity we can do and a list of books we can read together.

Love, _____

Activity
Have your child create a picture graph of all of the doors, windows, bathrooms, and beds in your house. Now make it a tally chart and bar graph.

Key Vocabulary
picture graph

bar graph

Math Online — Click on the eGlossary link at macmillanmh.com to find out more about these words. There are 13 languages.

Books to Read

Lemonade for Sale
by Stuart J. Murphy
Harper Collins Publishers, 1998.

Tally O'Malley
by Stuart J. Murphy
Harper Collins Publishers, 2004.

Anno's Flea Market
by Mitsumasa Anno
Putnam, 1984.

one hundred twenty-one 121

✅ Chapter 4 Project

Take a Survey

- Have students work together in small groups to design a survey.
- Each group will work together to survey peers and record the data collected in a tally chart.
- Students create a picture graph on construction paper or a bar graph on graph paper to illustrate and compare the data they collected.
- Have students present their survey, data, and graphs to the class. Provide time for students to ask questions about the different surveys and graphs and display them in the classroom or hallway.

CRM *Refer to Chapter 4 Resource Masters, p. 55 for a rubric to assess students' progress on this project.*

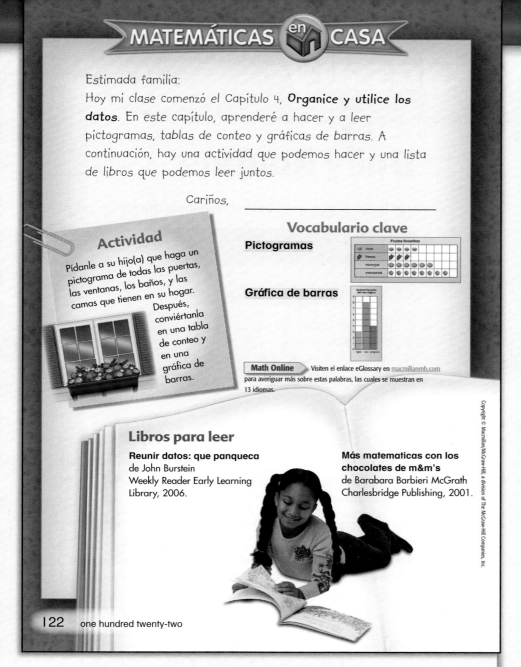

MATEMÁTICAS en CASA

Estimada familia:

Hoy mi clase comenzó el Capítulo 4, **Organice y utilice los datos**. En este capítulo, aprenderé a hacer y a leer pictogramas, tablas de conteo y gráficas de barras. A continuación, hay una actividad que podemos hacer y una lista de libros que podemos leer juntos.

Cariños, _____

Actividad

Pídanle a su hijo(a) que haga un pictograma de todas las puertas, las ventanas, los baños, y las camas que tienen en su hogar. Después, conviértanla en una tabla de conteo y en una gráfica de barras.

Vocabulario clave

Pictogramas

Gráfica de barras

> **Math Online** Visiten el enlace eGlossary en macmillanmh.com para averiguar más sobre estas palabras, las cuales se muestran en 13 idiomas.

Libros para leer

Reunir datos: que panqueca
de John Burstein
Weekly Reader Early Learning Library, 2006.

Más matematicas con los chocolates de m&m's
de Barabara Barbieri McGrath
Charlesbridge Publishing, 2001.

122 one hundred twenty-two

Chapter 4 Literature List

Lesson	Book Title
4-1	**A Pair of Socks** Stuart J. Murphy
4-2	**Ten Toads and Eleven Lizards** Cass Hollander
4-3	**Mouse Paint** Ellen Stoll Walsh
4-4	**Tally O'Malley** Stuart J. Murphy
4-5	**Lemonade for Sale** Stuart J. Murphy
4-6	**Leo the Late Bloomer** Robert Kraus
4-8	**No Fair!** Caren Holtzman
Any	**Anno's Flea Market** Mitsumaso Anno

ANNO'S FLEA MARKET
Mitsumasa Anno

ELL National ESL Standards Alignment for Chapter 4

Lesson, Page	ESL Standard	Modality	Level
4-1, p 123B	Goal 2, Standard 3, k	Logical, Visual/Spatial	Intermediate
4-2, p 125B	Goal 1, Standard 1, a	Auditory, Visual/Spatial	Beginning
4-3, p 127B	Goal 1, Standard 3, c	Visual/Spatial, Logical	Advanced
4-4, p 129B	Goal 2, Standard 1, a	Auditory, Kinesthetic	Beginning
4-5, p 133B	Goal 1, Standard 2, c	Linguistic, Auditory	Intermediate
4-6, p 137B	Goal 1, Standard 3, k	Linguistic, Social	Intermediate
4-7, p 141B	Goal 3, Standard 3, b	Logical, Kinesthetic	Advanced
4-8, p 143B	Goal 2, Standard ?, g	Linguistic	Intermediate

The National ESL Standards can be found in the Teacher Reference Handbook.

Lesson Planner

Objective
Use a Venn diagram to sort and classify objects.

Vocabulary
sort

Resources
Materials: yarn or rubber bands, crayons, copies of a blank Venn diagram, colored pencils, *Corduroy* by Don Freeman.

Literature Connection: *Pair of Socks* by Stuart J. Murphy

Alternate Lessons: Use "People Sorting" on pages 61–63 of *Math Their Way* to practice sorting and classifying. Use *IMPACT Mathematics:* Unit E to provide practice with sorting and classifying objects.

Teacher Technology
🖵 TeacherWorks • Concepts in Motion

Focus on Math Background

Sorting and Classifying Sorting and classifying are prerequisite skills for creating and adhering to categories represented on graphs. Students must be able to consider how items in a set are alike without being confused by attributes that make the objects different. A Venn diagram can help first graders do this. The section where the circles intersect provides an area where students can show common attributes. The outer sections provide a place for differences. This layout helps students see how objects can adhere to different rules. This lesson introduces the layout of a Venn diagram. Using this tool enhances a first grader's ability to sort, classify, and show likenesses and differences of data.

Daily Routine

Use these suggestions before beginning the lesson on p. 123.

5-Minute Check
(Reviews Lesson 3-10)
Subtract.

1. 11	**2.** 12	**3.** 11	**4.** 12
$-\ 5$	$-\ 8$	$-\ 3$	$-\ 7$
6	4	8	5

Problem of the Day
Sixteen children are having a tug of war. There are 8 children on one side. How many children are on the other side? 8 children

LINE UP Ask students who are six years old to line up. Then ask students who are seven years old to line up. Ask students how they were sorted. by age

▷ Building Math Vocabulary
Write the word **sort** on the board. Ask students to stand up. Ask boys to line up on one side of the classroom and girls on the other.

- **How did we sort students in this class?** gender: boys and girls
- Ask students with birthday in June to sit in their seats.
- **How are students sorted now?** birth month
- **How else could we sort students in this class?** Answers will vary. Sample answers: hair color, height, clothing, hobbies

Differentiated Instruction

Small Group Options

Option 1 **Gifted and Talented** (AL)

KINESTHETIC, LOGICAL

Materials: two-column poster, classroom items

- Select several classroom items to be inventoried. Draw pictures of each in one column on the poster.
- Have each student select an item from the poster.
- Students count the items and write the number in the second column.
- Have another student check the number by counting the same group of items. If numbers do not match, have partners count the items together.
- Optional: Students could tally the items as they count them.

✏️	26
🖍️	50
📖	30
✂️	18

Option 2 **English Language Learners** (ELL)

LOGICAL, VISUAL/SPATIAL

Materials: blocks of different colors and sizes, other classroom items

Core Vocabulary: these are/aren't, things, characteristics
Common Use Verb: am sorting by

See Math This strategy helps students understand characteristics and sorting.

- Write "**Characteristics**" on the board. Say: "A **characteristic** is a part of something."
- Underneath characteristics, write "color."
- Model sorting by color. Say, "**These** blocks **are** red. **These aren't red.** I *am sorting by* color."
- Have the students select a color and sort items into groups by colors. Model and restate language as you rotate and assess understanding.

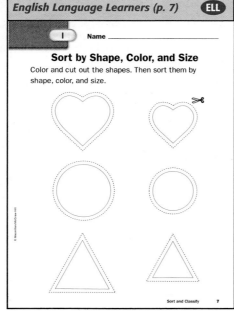

English Language Learners (p. 7) (ELL)

I | Name _____

Sort by Shape, Color, and Size
Color and cut out the shapes. Then sort them by shape, color, and size.

Sort and Classify   7

Independent Work Options

Option 1 **Early Finishers** (OL) (AL)

VISUAL/SPATIAL, LOGICAL

Materials: Venn diagram labeled *two, both,* and *red;* connecting cubes

- Have students point to the Venn diagram labels as you read them aloud.
- Give students a handful of connecting cubes. Some of the connecting cubes should be stacked into groups of two.
- Have students use the Venn diagram to sort the connecting cubes.

Option 2 **Student Technology**

Math Online ▷ macmillanmh.com

Option 3 **Learning Station: Language Arts** (p.119G)

Direct students to the Language Arts Learning Station for more opportunities to explore and extend the lesson concept.

Option 4 **Problem-Solving Practice**

Reinforce problem-solving skills and strategies with the Problem-Solving Practice worksheet.

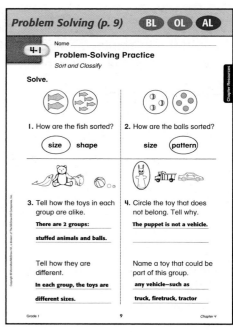

Problem Solving (p. 9) (BL) (OL) (AL)

Name _____
4-1 **Problem-Solving Practice**
Sort and Classify

Solve.

1. How are the fish sorted?
   size   (shape)

2. How are the balls sorted?
   size   (pattern)

3. Tell how the toys in each group are alike.
   There are 2 groups:
   stuffed animals and balls.
   Tell how they are different.
   In each group, the toys are different sizes.

4. Circle the toy that does not belong. Tell why.
   The puppet is not a vehicle.
   Name a toy that could be part of this group.
   any vehicle—such as truck, firetruck, tractor

Grade 1   9   Chapter 9

1 Introduce

Activity Choice 1 • Hands-On

Give each small group a red crayon, a piece of chalk, a blue crayon, a yellow pencil, a red pencil, a marker, a red counter, a red block or cube, and two large rubber bands or circles of yarn.

- Ask the students to make a group of things to write with and a group of things that are red. Students who are familiar with Venn diagrams might overlap their circles and put the red writing tools in the overlap. If a group does, ask them to explain what they did and why.

- If no group overlaps the circles, ask the students how they might use the circles to show that something belongs in both groups.

Activity Choice 2 • Literature

Introduce the lesson with *A Pair of Socks* by Stuart J. Murphy. For additional support, see p. TR47.

2 Teach

Draw a Venn diagram on the board, and label the circles *Wood*, *Metal*, and *Both*.

- Have students name classroom items that have wood, metal, or both and tell which circle the item should be in. Write the name in the proper circle.

- If an item has both wood and metal, remind students of the overlap, if necessary.

Get Ready Use the section at the top of p. 123 to reinforce the lesson concept. Guide students through the example, emphasizing that an item can belong to more than one group.

Check Observe students as you work through Exercises 1–2 as a class.

Exercise 2 Assess student comprehension before assigning practice exercises.

⚠ COMMON ERROR!

If a student does not notice that an item has both wood and metal or cannot decide how to classify it, ask: Does it have wood? Does it have metal? Where do we put things that have both wood and metal?

Name _____

Sort and Classify

Get Ready

Main Idea

I will sort and classify objects.

Vocabulary

sort

Venn diagram

You can **sort** objects using a **Venn diagram**.

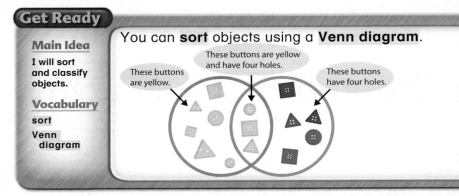

These buttons are yellow.

These buttons are yellow and have four holes.

These buttons have four holes.

✓ Check

Use pattern blocks. Sort the shapes. See students' drawings.
Draw one way you sorted.

1.

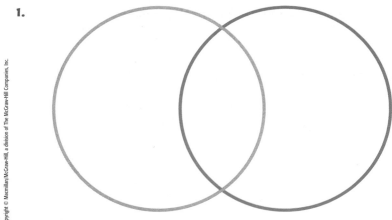

2. **Talk About It** How did you sort the shapes? Sample answer: I sorted the shapes by color.

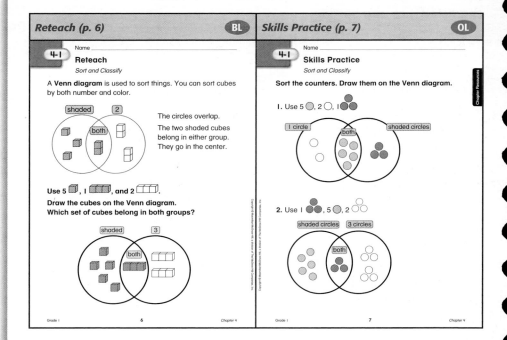

Reteach (p. 6) BL

4-1 Reteach
Sort and Classify

A **Venn diagram** is used to sort things. You can sort cubes by both number and color.

The circles overlap. The two shaded cubes belong in either group. They go in the center.

Use 5 ▱, 1 ▱▱▱, and 2 ▱▱.
Draw the cubes on the Venn diagram.
Which set of cubes belong in both groups?

Skills Practice (p. 7) OL

4-1 Skills Practice
Sort and Classify

Sort the counters. Draw them on the Venn diagram.

1. Use 5 ●, 2 ○, 1 ●●

2. Use 1 ●●, 5 ○, 2 ○○

Draw a line from each shape to where it belongs.

3.

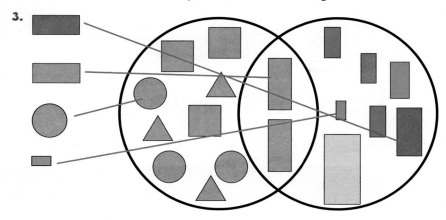

Problem Solving

4. **Application** Draw how you could sort these flowers.
See students' drawings.

Tell how you sorted.

Sample answer: Red flowers in one circle, tulips in the

other. So in the middle are red tulips.

124 one hundred twenty-four

Math at Home Activity: Have your child sort articles of clothing and explain how he or she sorted them.

Copyright © Macmillan/McGraw-Hill, a division of The McGraw-Hill Companies, Inc.

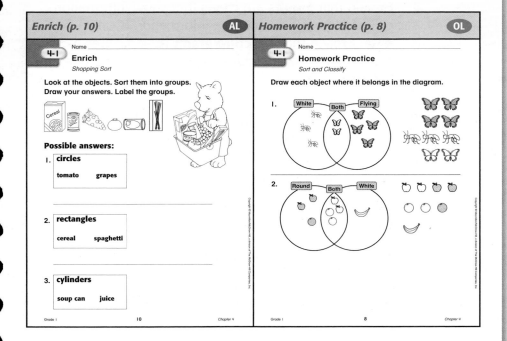

Enrich (p. 10) — **AL**

4-1 Name _____
Enrich
Shopping Sort

Look at the objects. Sort them into groups.
Draw your answers. Label the groups.

Possible answers:

1. **circles**
   tomato   grapes

2. **rectangles**
   cereal   spaghetti

3. **cylinders**
   soup can   juice

Grade 1   10   Chapter 4

Homework Practice (p. 8) — **OL**

4-1 Name _____
Homework Practice
Sort and Classify

Draw each object where it belongs in the diagram.

1. White / Both / Flying

2. Round / Both / White

Grade 1   8   Chapter 4

If students have trouble understanding how objects can adhere to two rules . . .

Then use one of these reteach options.

1 CRM **Daily Reteach Worksheet** (p. 6)

2 **Button Sort** Read aloud the book *Corduroy* by Don Freeman. Ask students to describe Corduroy's missing button. It is white and round. Hold up other buttons and have students describe them. Then have pairs of students use a Venn diagram to sort buttons. **What do the buttons in the center have in common?** See students' work.

3 Practice

Differentiate practice using these leveled assignments for Exercises 3–4.

Level	Assignment
BL Below/ Approaching Level	Guide students through the exercises. Have students use small sticky notes as manipulatives for problem solving.
OL On Level	Complete the exercises with a partner.
AL Above/Beyond Level	Complete the exercises independently.

4 Assess

Formative Assessment

What do you put in the center section of a Venn diagram? the objects that match both rules

What do you put in the other two sections of the diagram? the objects that match only one rule

WRITING IN ►MATH Write about one way that you used a Venn diagram. See students' work.

Quick Check **Are students continuing to struggle with using a Venn diagram to sort items?**

If Yes → Strategic Intervention Guide (p. 120)
If No → Independent Work Options (p. 123B)
CRM Skills Practice Worksheet (p. 7)
CRM Enrich Worksheet (p. 10)

Lesson 4-1 Sort and Classify **124**

Lesson Planner

Objective

Make and read a picture graph.

Vocabulary

graph, data, picture graph

Resources

Materials: index cards, stickers or coins, pattern block stamps

Literature Connection: *Ten Toads and Eleven Lizards* by Cass Hollander

Alternate Lessons: Adapt "Picture Graph Comparing Four Groups" on page 151 of *Math Their Way* for practice in making picture graphs.
Use *IMPACT Mathematics:* Unit E to provide practice with making and reading picture graphs.

Teacher Technology

○ TeacherWorks

Focus on Math Background

A picture graph is a useful way to show data at the primary level. Unlike bar graphs, which use same-sized block units to represent each piece of data, picture graphs use pictures. Seeing a picture of each item in the data set helps students quickly understand and interpret information. A pictograph is another way students can use pictures to represent their data. Instead of using a different picture to represent each set of data, a pictograph uses a symbol. Usually, initial graphing lessons guide students in collecting and classifying real objects, such as coins, rocks, or leaves. This lesson moves first graders one step beyond these concrete graphing experiences. Through the activities in this lesson, students begin to understand that using pictures instead of actual objects makes it easier to display, record, and examine information.

Daily Routine

Use these suggestions before beginning the lesson on p. 125.

5-Minute Check

(Reviews Lesson 4-1)
Explain two ways to sort the following:
1. crayons color and size
2. vegetables color and type
3. pattern blocks color and shape
4. pencils size and color

Problem of the Day

Isabel has 4 blue beads and 6 red beads. Olivia has 3 blue beads and 7 red beads. Do they have the same number of beads? yes How many? 10 beads

LINE UP Have students line up when you name the type of pet they have. Ask students who do not have pets to line up based on the type of pet they would like.

Building Math Vocabulary

Explain that **graphs** are charts that show information collected from a survey. The information is called **data**. Explain that a **picture graph** uses pictures to show data. Draw a picture graph similar to the one below.

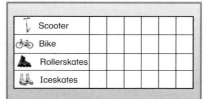

Ask students to vote for their favorite activity. Complete the graph. Discuss the results.

Visual Vocabulary Cards

Use Visual Vocabulary Cards 12, 19, and 35 to reinforce the vocabulary introduced in this lesson. (The Define/Example/Ask routine is printed on the back of each card.)

Differentiated Instruction

Small Group Options

Gifted and Talented (AL)

Materials: 1-inch grid paper, crayons, pencil

- Invite students to make a picture graph showing classmates' favorite ball games. Have each student choose four types of ball games and then survey ten people to find out which game is their favorite.

- Ask students to interpret the data in their graphs. **Which ball game got the most votes? Which ball game got the fewest votes?**

Our Favorite Ball Games

- Extend the activity by asking students to use the same data to make a pictograph.

English Language Learners (ELL)

Core Vocabulary: by car, by walking, by bus
Common Use Verb: get

Write Math This strategy activates background knowledge and applies it to graphing.

- Label "Home" on the left and "School" on the right side of the board with a line connecting them to a pocket chart titled: "Ways to **Get** to School."

- Draw a simple picture of how you get to school (a car, bus or feet). Move the picture along the line as you say: "I get to school **by car.** Place in pocket chart.

- Ask students to draw their card and repeat, placing cards into a pocket graph.

Use this worksheet to provide additional support for English Language Learners.

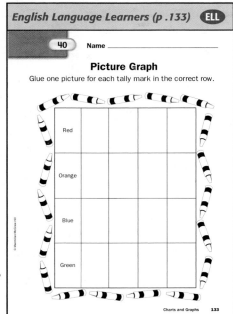

English Language Learners (p .133) **ELL**

40 Name _____

Picture Graph
Glue one picture for each tally mark in the correct row.

Red

Orange

Blue

Green

Charts and Graphs **133**

Independent Work Options

Early Finishers (OL) (AL)

Materials: connecting cubes, 1-inch grid paper, colored pencils

- Have students make a pattern with at least fifteen cubes. Ask them to use more than one color of cube.

- Instruct students to make a bar graph on 1-inch grid paper to show how many of each color they used in their pattern.

- Make sure that students record their cube pattern on the paper to show how the graph corresponds to their data.

Option 2

Student Technology

| Math Online | macmillanmh.com |

Math Adventures

Option 3

Learning Station: Social Studies (p. 119H)

Direct students to the Social Studies Learning Station for more opportunities to explore and extend the lesson concept.

Option 4

Problem-Solving Practice

Reinforce problem-solving skills and strategies with the Problem-Solving Practice worksheet.

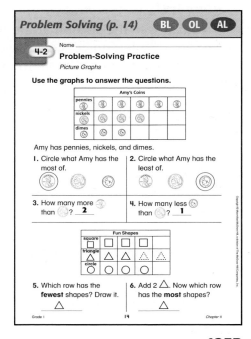

Problem Solving (p. 14) **BL** **OL** **AL**

Name _____

4-2 **Problem-Solving Practice**
Picture Graphs

Use the graphs to answer the questions.

Amy's Coins

Amy has pennies, nickels, and dimes.

1. Circle what Amy has the most of.

2. Circle what Amy has the least of.

3. How many more than ? **2**

4. How many less than ? **1**

Fun Shapes

square
triangle
circle

5. Which row has the **fewest** shapes? Draw it.

6. Add 2 △. Now which row has the **most** shapes?

Grade 1   14   Chapter 4

① Introduce

Activity Choice 1 • Hands-On

- Show students an example of a **picture graph**.
- **What is the title of the graph? What does each picture represent?** See students' work.
- Ask students questions concerning the data shown on the picture graph.
- Then display a pictograph that represents the same data as the picture graph.
- **How are these graphs alike?** Sample answers: they have the same title; they both show data
- **How are these graphs different?** Sample answer: the pictograph uses the same symbol to represent all the data. The picture graph uses a different picture to represent each set of data.

Activity Choice 2 • Literature

Introduce the lesson with *Ten Toads and Eleven Lizards* by Cass Hollander. For additional support see p. TR47.

② Teach

- Have each student draw a birthday cake on an index card. Then have students write their name and the number that tells their age.
- Create a **graph** titled *Our Birthday Graph* with a column labeled for each month of the year. Help students tape their cards in the column for their birth month.
- **Which month of the year has the most birthdays?** See students' work.

Get Ready Use the section at the top of p. 125 to reinforce the lesson concept. Guide students through the example, and help them read the picture graph.

Check Observe students as you work through Exercises 1–4 as a class.

> **Exercise 4** Assess student comprehension before assigning practice exercises.

⚠ COMMON ERROR!

When graphing data, students may fail to count or record each piece of data. Have students draw a picture to show a vote before asking the next classmate to choose a favorite drink.

Name _____

Picture Graphs

Main Idea
I will make and read a picture graph.

Vocabulary
graph
data
picture graph

A **graph** shows information or **data**.
A **picture graph** uses pictures to show data.

 Check

4. Sample answer: 10 more people might not have the same favorites.

1. Ask 10 classmates to vote for their favorite drink. Make a picture graph.

Our Favorite Drinks									
🥛 Chocolate Milk									
🥤 Orange Juice									
🥤 Grape Juice									

Use the graph to answer the questions.

2. Which drink is the favorite? See students' work.

3. Which drink is the least favorite? See students' work.

4. **Talk About It** Would the graph stay the same if you asked 10 more people? Explain.

Chapter 4   Lesson 2   one hundred twenty-five   125

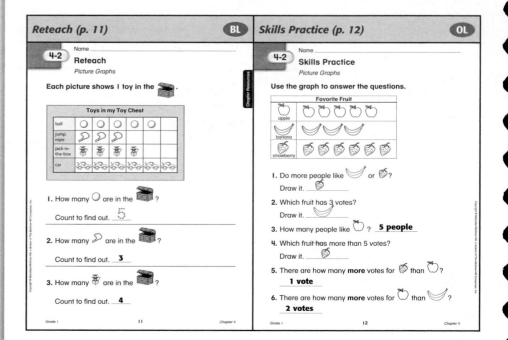

Practice

Use the graph to answer the questions.

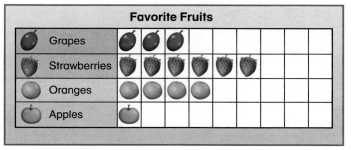

Favorite Fruits

Grapes									
Strawberries									
Oranges									
Apples									

5. How many chose 🍓 ? **6**

6. Did more choose 🍊 or 🍇 ? **oranges**

7. Did fewer choose 🍎 or 🍓 ? **apples**

8. How many more chose 🍓 than 🍇 ? **3**

9. Which fruit has one more than 🍇 ? **oranges**

Problem Solving

10. **Logical Reasoning** Finish the graph.
    3 people chose fish. 2 fewer people chose
    cats. 4 people chose dogs.

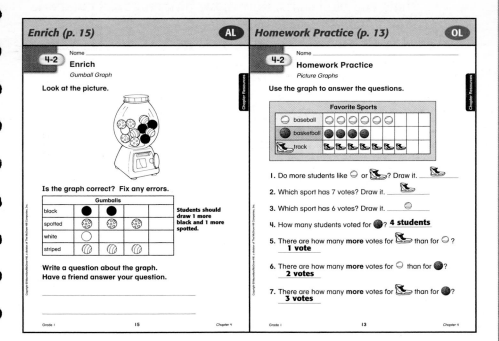

Favorite Pet

Dog						
Cat						
Fish						

Math at Home Activity: Ask your child to make a picture graph for the favorite food of family members. Have your child ask a question about the graph.

126 one hundred twenty-six

Enrich (p. 15) — AL

4-2 Enrich
Gumball Graph

Look at the picture.

Is the graph correct? Fix any errors.

Gumballs

black			
spotted			
white			
striped			

Students should draw 1 more black and 1 more spotted.

Write a question about the graph.
Have a friend answer your question.

Grade 1 — 15 — Chapter 4

Homework Practice (p. 13) — OL

4-2 Homework Practice
Picture Graphs

Use the graph to answer the questions.

Favorite Sports

baseball						
basketball						
track						

1. Do more students like 🏀 or 👟? Draw it. _____
2. Which sport has 7 votes? Draw it. _____
3. Which sport has 6 votes? Draw it. _____
4. How many students voted for 👟? **4 students**
5. There are how many **more** votes for 👟 than for 🏀 ? **1 vote**
6. There are how many **more** votes for 🏀 than for 🏀? **2 votes**
7. There are how many **more** votes for 👟 than for 🏀? **3 votes**

Grade 1 — 13 — Chapter 4

BL Alternate Teaching Strategy

If students have difficulty making or reading picture graphs . . .

Then use one of these reteach options.

1. CRM **Daily Reteach Worksheet** (p. 11)

2. **Quick Picture Graphs** To help students record results more quickly and accurately, provide stickers or coin and pattern block stamps to be used in place of drawing pictures. Have students tell you what each stamp or sticker on their graph represents.

3 Practice

Differentiate practice using these leveled assignments for Exercises 5–10.

Level	Assignment
BL Below/Approaching Level	Guide students through the exercises.
OL On Level	Complete the exercises with a partner.
AL Above/Beyond Level	Complete the exercises independently.

4 Assess

Formative Assessment

What is a picture graph? a chart that uses pictures to show information

How do you read a picture graph? by counting and comparing the number of pictures next to each type of data

WRITING IN ▶ MATH What would you make a picture graph about? See students' work.

Quick Check **Are students continuing to struggle with creating picture graphs?**

If Yes → Strategic Intervention Guide (p. 126)

If No → Independent Work Options (p. 125B)
- CRM Skills Practice Worksheet (p. 12)
- CRM Enrich Worksheet (p. 15)

Lesson 4-2 Picture Graphs **126**

Lesson Planner

Objective

Use the *make a table* strategy to solve problems.

Resources

Materials: paper, pencils

Literature Connection: *Mouse Paint* by Ellen Stoll Walsh

Teacher Technology
- TeacherWorks

📖 **Real-World Problem Solving Library**
Math and Social Studies: *I Like That Too*
Use these leveled books to reinforce and extend problem-solving skills and strategies.

Leveled for:
- **OL** On Level
- **ELL** Sheltered English
- **SP** Spanish

For additional support, see the Real-World Problem Solving Teacher Guide.

Daily Routine

Use these suggestions before beginning the lesson on p. 127.

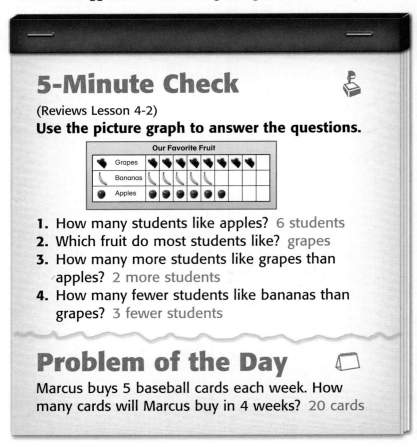

5-Minute Check

(Reviews Lesson 4-2)
Use the picture graph to answer the questions.

Our Favorite Fruit	
Grapes	🍇🍇🍇🍇🍇🍇🍇🍇
Bananas	🍌🍌🍌🍌🍌
Apples	🍎🍎🍎🍎🍎🍎

1. How many students like apples? 6 students
2. Which fruit do most students like? grapes
3. How many more students like grapes than apples? 2 more students
4. How many fewer students like bananas than grapes? 3 fewer students

Problem of the Day

Marcus buys 5 baseball cards each week. How many cards will Marcus buy in 4 weeks? 20 cards

LINE UP Have students line up in separate lines by hair color. Compare the number of students with red shirts and blue shirts. **How many different shirt colors do students in the class have?** Sample answer: 6 colors

Differentiated Instruction

Small Group Options

Option 1 — Gifted and Talented (AL) — LOGICAL, SPATIAL

Materials: paper, pencils, crayons

- Have pairs of students survey their classmates to find their favorite color.
- After students collect the data, have them record the results on a graph. Ask students to show the colors that their classmates chose at the left side of the graph.
- Suggest that students arrange the colors in order of popularity, placing the color chosen most often at the top of the graph and the color chosen least often at the bottom.
- Have students share their graph and findings with the class.

Option 2 — English Language Learners (ELL) — VISUAL/SPATIAL, LOGICAL

Core Vocabulary: matched, guesses, roll
Common Use Verb: check

Hear Math This strategy uses prediction to illustrate the guess and check strategy to make a table.

- Before rolling, have Student A write their name and what 5 numbers they think they will roll in a 2 column table. Flip the paper and Student B repeats.
- Student A rolls five times while Student B records on his partner's table. Switch and repeat.
- Say: "**Check** how many **guesses matched** your 5 **rolls**?"
- Have students circle the 2 columns with correct guesses.
- Say, "Who had 5 correct **guesses**?" Repeat for other numbers. Discuss results.

Use this worksheet to provide additional support for English Language Learners.

English Language Learners (p. 137) **ELL**

42   Name _____

What do you think?

Color the spinner to match the one you are using.
Circle a color to show your guess.

Spinner	More Likely	Less Likely
	red blue	red blue
	red blue	red blue

Probability   137

Independent Work Options

Option 1 — Early Finishers (OL) (AL) — LOGICAL

Materials: dry erase boards or white boards, markers, and erasers; paper; pencils

- Display the following example for students to read:
  Four children ran a race. Brian was in front of Kevin. Kevin was behind Cindy. Ann was in 2nd place. Who won the race? Brian
- Have students make a table to solve the problem. Then have them create their own logical-reasoning problem about a race.
- Ask students to make an answer sheet that shows their problem-solving table and the answer to the problem.
- Invite students to exchange problems with a partner and solve. Have them compare their answer to their partner's answer sheet.

Option 2 — Student Technology

Math Online macmillanmh.com

Option 3 — Learning Station: Language Arts (p.119G)

Direct students to the Language Arts Learning Station for more opportunities to explore and extend the lesson concept.

1 Introduce

Activity Choice 1 • Review

Write and read aloud the following: *There are 3 cars in the driveway. The first car is blue. The last car is behind the red car. Which car is white?*

- **What do we know?** There are 3 cars. They are blue, red, and white.
- **What do we want to find?** which car is white.
- Demonstrate how to make a table to solve the problem. Have students copy the table and use Xs to show the position of each car.
- **Which car is white?** the third, or last car

	blue	red	white
1st	X		
2nd		X	
3rd (last)			X

Activity Choice 2 • Literature

Introduce the lesson with *Mouse Paint* by Ellen Stoll Walsh. For additional support, see p. TR47.

2 Teach

Have students read the problem on page 127. Guide them through the problem-solving steps.

Understand Using the questions, review what students know and what they need to find.

Plan Have them discuss their strategy.

Solve Guide students in using make a table to solve the problem. Discuss each choice and fill in the table.

Check Have students look back at the problem to make sure that the answer fits the facts given.

- **Why is the third T-shirt the wrong shirt for Maria?** It has three words instead of four words.
- **Which T-shirt will Maria buy?** the 2nd T-shirt

> ⚠️ **COMMON ERROR!**
>
> Students may have difficulty correctly recalling the information provided in the problem. Have them go through the problem, sentence by sentence, and add the information to a picture or table.

Name _____

Problem-Solving Strategy
Make a Table

Main Idea

I will make a table to solve problems.

Kimi wants to buy a T-shirt.
She wants a picture of a bicycle on it.
She wants 4 words on it.
She wants a stripe on the sleeve.
(Which shirt should she buy?)

Understand
What do I need to find?
Circle the question.

Plan
How will I solve the problem?

Solve
Make a table. Kimi should buy the second shirt.

Shirt	Picture	Number of Words	Stripe
First	No	2	Yes
Second	Yes	4	Yes
Third	Yes	3	No
Fourth	Yes	0	Yes

Check
Look back.
Is my answer reasonable?   Check students' explanations.

Chapter 4   Lesson 3   one hundred twenty-seven   127

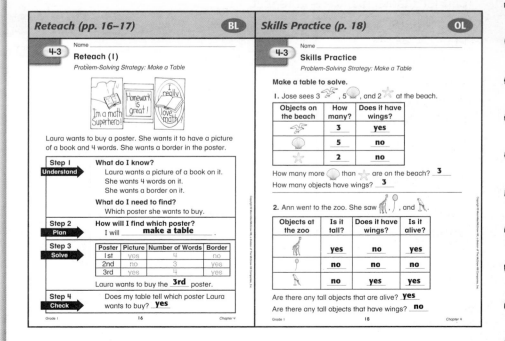

Try It

Remember
Understand
Plan
Solve
Check

1. Make a table.

Animals on the Farm	
Animal	How Many?
chicken	8
dog	1
cow	4
sheep	2

Your Turn

Use the table to answer the questions.

2. How many more cows than dogs are there? __3__

3. How many cows and sheep are there? __6__

4. What animal do you see the most? __chicken__

128   one hundred twenty-eight

 Math at Home Activity: Have your child make a table using things in the house. Items could include pets, people, or furniture.

Copyright © Macmillan/McGraw-Hill, a division of The McGraw-Hill Companies, Inc.

Try It Observe students as you work through Exercise 1 as a class.

BL Alternate Teaching Strategy

If students have trouble creating a table to solve problems . . .

Then use one of these reteach options.

1 CRM **Daily Reteach Worksheet** (pp. 16–17)

2 **Completing a Table** Ask students to fill in their tables one row at a time as you guide them with questions.

- **Does it have a picture?**
- **How many words are on it?**
- **Does it have a stripe on the sleeve?**

3 Practice

Your Turn

Exercises 2–4 Be sure students can read and understand the problems. Remind students to record what they know and decide what they are supposed to find.

4 Assess

Formative Assessment

Provide students with a picture similar to the one on page 128 that has objects that can be put into a table. Have students create a new table and fill in the data on their own.

Quick Check **Are students continuing to struggle with making a table to solve a problem?**

If Yes → CRM Reteach Worksheet (pp. 16–17)

If No → Independent Work Options (p. 127B)

     CRM Skills Practice Worksheet (p. 18)

     CRM Enrich Worksheet (p. 20)

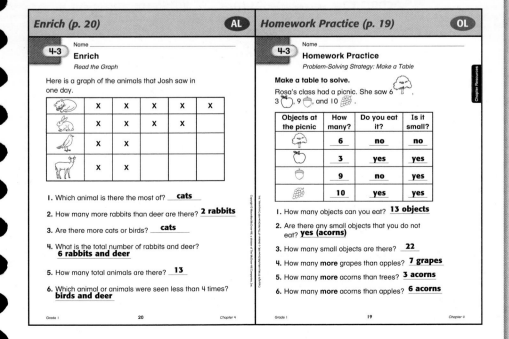

Enrich (p. 20)   **AL**

4-3 Name _____
Enrich
Read the Graph

Here is a graph of the animals that Josh saw in one day.

1. Which animal is there the most of? __cats__

2. How many more rabbits than deer are there? **2 rabbits**

3. Are there more cats or birds? __cats__

4. What is the total number of rabbits and deer?
6 rabbits and deer

5. How many total animals are there? __13__

6. Which animal or animals were seen less than 4 times?
birds and deer

Grade 1   20   Chapter 4

Homework Practice (p. 19)   **OL**

4-3 Name _____
Homework Practice
Problem-Solving Strategy: Make a Table

Make a table to solve.
Rosa's class had a picnic. She saw 6 🥦 3 🍎, 9 🌰, and 10 🍇.

Objects at the picnic	How many?	Do you eat it?	Is it small?
🥦	6	no	no
🍎	3	yes	yes
🌰	9	no	yes
🍇	10	yes	yes

1. How many objects can you eat? **13 objects**

2. Are there any small objects that you do not eat? **yes (acorns)**

3. How many small objects are there? __22__

4. How many **more** grapes than apples? **7 grapes**

5. How many **more** acorns than trees? **3 acorns**

6. How many **more** acorns than apples? **6 acorns**

Grade 1   19   Chapter 4

Lesson 4-3 Problem-Solving Strategy   **128**

Lesson Planner

Objective
Make and read a tally chart.

Vocabulary
tally chart, survey

Resources
Materials: pencils, paper, overhead projector, coins

Literature Connection: *Tally O'Malley* by Stuart J. Murphy

Alternate Lesson: Use *IMPACT Mathematics:* Unit E to provide practice with making and reading a tally chart.

Teacher Technology
 TeacherWorks

Focus on Math Background

In Lesson 4 students record data on tally charts. Through lesson activities, students will begin to see that using tally marks to represent data takes less time and space than using pictures. At first, most students will count tally marks one by one. With time, they will learn to count more efficiently. Success in counting and recording with tally marks depends in part upon a student's experience with skip counting. As students' skill in skip counting develops, so does their ability to make sense of the tally mark system. Familiarity with skip-counting helps students see a set of six tallies and think: "Five marks and one mark make six."

Favorite Vegetables		
Vegetable	Tally	Total
Carrot	|||	3
Pea	||	2
Corn	⊪⊪ ||	7

Daily Routine

Use these suggestions before beginning the lesson on p. 129.

5-Minute Check
(Reviews Lesson 4-3)
Work together to survey the class and make a table showing everyone's favorite color.

Problem of the Day
Ming needs 12 party hats for his party. He has 2 blue party hats and 5 green party hats. How many more party hats does he need? 5 more party hats

 Start a tally chart on the board. Have each student add a tally mark as he or she lines up.

Building Math Vocabulary

Write on the board the terms **tally chart** and **survey**. Explain to students that a survey is a way to get data by asking different people the same question. Point out that writing tally marks on a chart is one way to record people's answers. A tally chart can show the number of votes for something.

Our Favorite Dr. Seuss Books		
Book	Tally	Total
Hop on Pop		
Green Eggs and Ham		
Fox in Socks		
Cat in the Hat		

Have students vote for their favorite book. Discuss the survey results.

Visual Vocabulary Cards
Use Visual Vocabulary Card 48 to reinforce the vocabulary introduced in this lesson. (The Define/Example/Ask routine is printed on the back of each card.)

 tally chart

Differentiated Instruction

Small Group Options

Independent Work Options

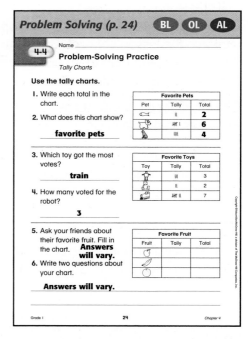

Problem Solving (p. 24) BL OL AL

① Introduce

Activity Choice 1 • Hands-On

- Ask the students to listen as you say a tongue twister, such as Peter Piper Picked a Peck of Pickled Peppers, and to make a mark on their paper each time they hear you make the sound of P.

- Display a student's **tally chart** on the overhead, and ask someone to tell you have many marks there are. Then show them how to make the same number of marks with the diagonal 5th mark and count by 5s.

Activity Choice 2 • Literature

Introduce the lesson with *Tally O'Malley* by Stuart J. Murphy. For additional support, see p. TR47.

② Teach

Make a two-column table on the board. Label one row *Fruits* and the other *Vegetables*.

- Ask one volunteer to tally *Fruits*, using the 5-tally system, and another to tally *Vegetables*, using the single tallies. Ask each student in turn, whether he or she likes apples or corn better. Repeat with other combinations such as peaches and peas, bananas and beans.

- Ask students to tell how many tally marks there are for fruits and how many for vegetables. Then ask students which system is quicker and easier to read.

Get Ready Use the section at the top of p. 129 to reinforce the lesson concept. Guide students through the example, and help them understand that tallying is another way to sort information.

Check Observe students as you work through Exercises 1–4 as a class.

> **Exercise 4** Assess student comprehension before assigning practice exercises.

COMMON ERROR!

When tallying data, students may omit data or count an item twice. Suggest that each time students make a tally on their chart, they place a counter over the item they counted.

129 **Chapter 4** Organize and Use Data

Name _____

Tally Charts

Hands-On Activity

Get Ready

Main Idea
I will make a tally chart.

Vocabulary
tally chart
survey

A **tally chart** shows a mark for each vote in a survey. A **survey** asks what people like best.

 *I took a survey. Corn is the favorite vegetable.*

Favorite Vegetables		
Vegetable	Tally	Total
Carrot	|||	3
Pea	||	2
Corn	⊬⊬ ||	7

| stands for 1. ⊬⊬ stands for 5.

✓ Check

Ask 10 friends to choose their favorite school subject. Make a tally chart. Write the totals.

Favorite Subject		
Subject	Tally	Total
Math		
Reading		
Science		

Use the tally chart. How many chose each? See students' work.

1. _____   2. _____   3. _____

---

4. **Talk About It** How are tally marks used to take surveys?
Sample answer: They keep track of information or data.

Chapter 4   Lesson 4   one hundred twenty-nine   129

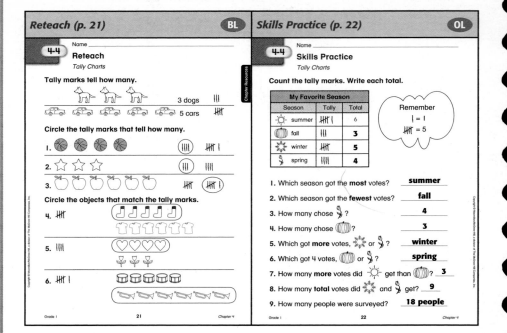

Reteach (p. 21) **BL**

4-4 Reteach
Tally Charts

Tally marks tell how many.

Skills Practice (p. 22) **OL**

4-4 Skills Practice
Tally Charts

Practice

Write each total.
Use the tally chart to answer the questions.

What is Your Favorite Color?		
Color	Tally	Total
 Red	ⵏⵏⵏ‖‖‖	8
Blue	‖‖‖	3
Purple	ⵏⵏⵏ	5
Green	‖‖	2

5. Which color is liked the most? red

6. Which color is liked the least? green

7. How many students chose red? 8

8. Do more students like purple or blue? purple

WRITING IN ▶MATH

9. What would happen if you added more color choices to your survey?

Sample answer: Some of the choices would have fewer

votes because the students liked another color more.

130   one hundred thirty

Math at Home Activity: Ask your child to make a tally chart for your family's favorite sport.

Copyright © Macmillan/McGraw-Hill, a division of The McGraw-Hill Companies, Inc.

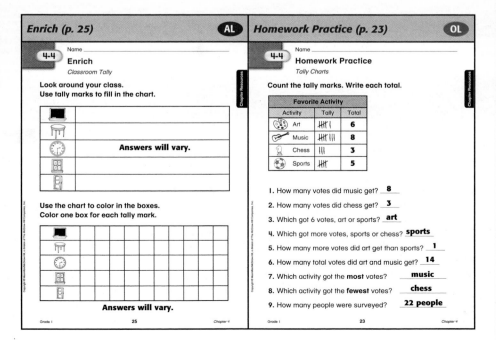

Enrich (p. 25)   AL

4-4 Name _____
Enrich
Classroom Tally

**Look around your class.
Use tally marks to fill in the chart.**

🖥	
🪑	
🕐	Answers will vary.

**Use the chart to color in the boxes.
Color one box for each tally mark.**

🖥						
🪑						
🕐						

Answers will vary.

Grade 1   25   Chapter 4

Homework Practice (p. 23)   OL

4-4 Name _____
Homework Practice
Tally Charts

Count the tally marks. Write each total.

Favorite Activity		
Activity	Tally	Total
🎨 Art	ⵏⵏⵏ‖	6
🎵 Music	ⵏⵏⵏ‖‖‖	8
♟ Chess	‖‖‖	3
⚽ Sports	ⵏⵏⵏ	5

1. How many votes did music get? __8__
2. How many votes did chess get? __3__
3. Which got 6 votes, art or sports? __art__
4. Which got more votes, sports or chess? __sports__
5. How many more votes did art get than sports? __1__
6. How many total votes did art and music get? __14__
7. Which activity got the **most** votes? __music__
8. Which activity got the **fewest** votes? __chess__
9. How many people were surveyed? __22 people__

Grade 1   23   Chapter 4

BL Alternate Teaching Strategy

If students have difficulty counting and representing the fifth slash in a set of five tally marks . . .

Then use one of these reteach options.

1 CRM **Daily Reteach Worksheet** (p. 21)

2 **Tally Mark Finger Play** Teach a finger play to relate the 5-mark that crosses four tallies to students folding a thumb over the other four fingers on their hand:
One, two, three, four,
(Raise one finger as you say each number)
Now there are five! (Lift thumb.)
Shut the door. (Fold thumb over the four fingers.)

❸ Practice

Differentiate practice using these leveled assignments for Exercises 5–9.

Level	Assignment
BL Below/Approaching Level	Guide students through the exercises, using craft sticks as manipulatives
OL On Level	Complete the exercises independently, using manipulatives as needed.
AL Above/Beyond Level	Complete the exercises without manipulatives.

❹ Assess

Formative Assessment

Give students a handful of coins and ask them to create a tally sheet to show the number of coins.

WRITING IN ▶MATH Have students write about how grouping tally marks in bundles of five makes it faster to read a tally chart. It is easier to count larger amounts by fives than by ones.

Quick Check   Are students continuing to struggle with creating a tally sheet?

If Yes ➝ Small Group Options (p. 129B)
If No ➝ Independent Work Options (p. 129B)
CRM Skills Practice Worksheet (p. 22)
CRM Enrich Worksheet (p. 25)

 **Mid-Chapter Check**

Lessons 4-1 to 4-4

Formative Assessment

Use the Mid-Chapter Check to assess student's progress in the first half of the chapter.

ExamView Assessment Suite Customize and create multiple versions of your Mid-Chapter Check and the test answer keys.

FOLDABLES Dinah Zike's Foldables

If students have not completed their Foldables, guide them to create and fill in the appropriate information using the instructions on page 119.

You may choose to use the Foldable to help students review the concepts presented in this chapter and as a tool for studying for the Mid-Chapter Check.

Name _____

Draw a line from each dog to where it belongs.

1.

Write each total.
Use the tally chart to answer the questions.

2. Which sport is liked the least?

3. How many students chose soccer? __8__ people

4. How many more like basketball than baseball? __2__ people

Favorite Sport		
Sport	Tally	Total
	⦀ ⦀⦀	8
	⦀	5
	⦀⦀⦀	3

Solve.

5. I took a survey of favorite colors.
   The choices were green, purple, and blue.
   Most people liked blue.
   More people liked purple than green.
   Which was the least favorite color? ____green____

Chapter 4   one hundred thirty-one   131

Data-Driven Decision Making

Based on the results of the Mid-Chapter Check, use the following resources to review concepts that continue to give students problems.

Exercises	State/Local Standards	What's the Math?	Error Analysis	Resources for Review
1 Lesson 4-1		Sort objects and data by common attributes.	Does not understand what each circle describes. Draws line to wrong circle location. Does not draw all lines.	Strategic Intervention Guide (p. 118) CRM Chapter 4 Resource Masters (Reteach Worksheets) **Math Online** Concepts in Motion Math Adventures
2–4 Lesson 4-4		Represent and compare data. Represent data by using tally charts.	Does not fill in numbers in chart. Does not understand word "least." Switches words "baseball" and "basketball."	
5 Lesson 4-3		Sort and represent data by using pictures, graphs or charts.	Does not understand word "survey." Does not understand word "least." Does not record choices correctly.	

Spiral Review Chapters 1-4

Add or subtract.

6. $4 - 1 =$ ___3___   7. $2 + 2 =$ ___4___   8. $10 - 4 =$ ___6___

9. $8 + 1 =$ ___9___   10. $8 - 8 =$ ___0___   11. $7 + 3 =$ ___10___

Use the graph to answer the questions.

Each picture stands for 1 student.

12. How many students chose ? ___1___

13. How many more chose than ? ___5___

14. Circle which snack has three more than ?

15. Circle which snack was chosen the most?

Formative Assessment

Spiral Review

Reviews Chapters 1 to 4

Objective: Review and assess mastery of skills and concepts from previous chapters.

Resources for Review

Based on student results, refer to these lessons for remediation.

- **Exercises 6–11: Lessons 2-3, 3-3** (p. 55, 91)
- **Exercises 12–15: Lesson 4-2** (p. 125)

Lesson Planner

Objective
Read a bar graph.

Vocabulary
bar graph

Resources
Materials: overhead projector, colored beads

Literature Connection: *Lemonade for Sale* by Stuart J. Murphy

Alternate Lessons: Adapt "Symbolic Graphs Comparing Four Groups" on page 154 of *Math Their Way* for practice with bar graphs.
Use *IMPACT Mathematics:* Unit E to provide practice with reading a bar graph.

Teacher Technology
⊙ TeacherWorks

Focus on Math Background

Bar graphs are used to quantify and compare sets of data. The lengths of the bars show how many more or fewer data are in different categories. This makes it easy for students to see a size-to-quantity relationship. This lesson familiarizes students with the layout and the features of bar graphs. Students will learn to read horizontal and vertical graphs. Unlike conventional bar graphs, the bar graphs in Lesson 5 are partitioned into squares, which each represent one unit of data. Students will learn to count these squares in order to quantify each category. They also will learn to check their counting against the number scale marked on the graph.

Daily Routine

Use these suggestions before beginning the lesson on p. 133.

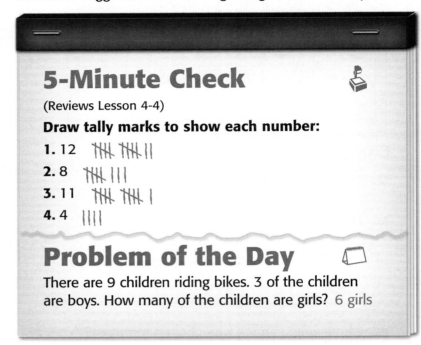

5-Minute Check

(Reviews Lesson 4-4)

Draw tally marks to show each number:

1. 12   𝍱 𝍱 ||
2. 8   𝍱 |||
3. 11   𝍱 𝍱 |
4. 4 ||||

Problem of the Day

There are 9 children riding bikes. 3 of the children are boys. How many of the children are girls? 6 girls

LINE UP Give each student one of three colors of cubes. Have students line up in three lines by color. Which line has the most students? the least?

Building Math Vocabulary

Write the term **bar graph** on the board. Explain that a bar graph uses bars to show data. Display three sets of cubes—9 red, 8 blue, and 10 yellow. Spread the blue set apart to make it appear larger. Ask students to predict which set has the most cubes. Have volunteers count the cubes to check the predictions. Next, connect the cubes in each set. Place the bars next to each other.

- **Which has the most cubes?** yellow
- **How can I make the red bar equal to the yellow bar?** Add 1 red cube or remove 1 yellow cube.

Visual Vocabulary Cards

Use Visual Vocabulary Card 4 to reinforce the vocabulary introduced in this lesson. (The Define/Example/Ask routine is printed on the back of each card.)

bar graph

Differentiated Instruction

Small Group Options

Option 1 — Below Level (BL)

Materials: completed bar graph, counters

- Show small groups a completed bar graph.
- Ask students questions about the data in the graph. Have students use counters to model the answers.
- Guide students in using their counters to compare numbers in the bar graph.
- Have students talk about how their counters model the facts found in the bar graph.

Option 2 — English Language Learners (ELL)

Materials: color blocks, graph with one row
Core Vocabulary: What color, best, we
Common Use Verb: like/don't like

Hear Math This strategy allows students to hear and vocalize their likes and dislikes as they learn to graph.

- Show students a bucket with color blocks.
- Say: **"What color do you like best?** . . . I *like* blue."
  (Note: pass the bucket to all students before you pick your favorite.)
- Repeat with each student, having each student select a block.
- Listen to student's answer and model answer if necessary ("I *like* ___.")
- Help the students use the manipulatives to build a graph.
- Ask the class, "What color do **we** *like* best? **We** *like* ___."
  Model ways to use the vocabulary to talk about the graph.
- Repeat for least ("I don't *like* ___.") if time permits.

Independent Work Options

Option 1 — Early Finishers (OL) (AL)

Materials: clipboards, paper, pencils, markers

- Have students develop a question to ask ten or fifteen friends for a survey.
- Challenge students to create a layout for a bar graph to show their results.
- Remind students to include a title for their bar graph.

"What type of pet do you have at home?"

Option 2 — Student Technology

Math Online macmillanmh.com

Math Adventures

Option 3 — Learning Station: Science (p. 119H)

Direct students to the Science Learning Station for more opportunities to explore and extend the lesson concept.

Option 4 — Problem-Solving Practice

Reinforce problem-solving skills and strategies with the Problem-Solving Practice worksheet.

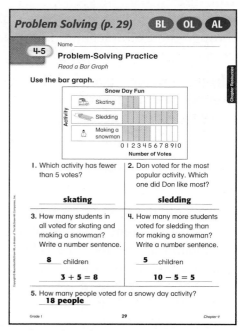

Problem Solving (p. 29) BL OL AL

4-5 Problem-Solving Practice
Read a Bar Graph

Use the bar graph.

Snow Day Fun

1. Which activity has fewer than 5 votes?
   skating
2. Don voted for the most popular activity. Which one did Don like most?
   sledding
3. How many students in all voted for skating and making a snowman? Write a number sentence.
   8 children
   3 + 5 = 8
4. How many more students voted for sledding than for making a snowman? Write a number sentence.
   5 children
   10 − 5 = 5
5. How many people voted for a snowy day activity?
   18 people

1 Introduce

Activity Choice 1 • Hands-On

Display on an overhead projector a **bar graph** for graphing the colors of colored beads in a package. Have volunteers sort the beads by color. Record the data on the bar graph.

- **Which color were most beads? Which color were the fewest number of beads? Did any colors appear the same number of times?** See students' work.

- **How many more/fewer yellow beads were there than red ones?** See students' work.

Activity Choice 2 • Literature

Introduce the lesson with *Lemonade for Sale* by Stuart J. Murphy For additional support, see p. TR48.

2 Teach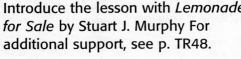

Have students suggest five activities they enjoy. Use the activities as category labels on a large bar graph. Have students vote for their favorite activity. Record the data and discuss the results.

- **Which activity received the most votes? Which activity received the least votes?** See students' work.

- **How many more votes did it get than the least favorite activity?** See students' work.

- **How is a bar graph like a tally chart?** Both compare data.

Get Ready Use the section at the top of p. 133 to reinforce the lesson concept. Guide students through the example, and help them read the bar graph.

Check Observe students as you work through Exercises 1–5 as a class.

> **Exercise 5** Assess student comprehension before assigning practice exercises.

COMMON ERROR!

Students may count the zero line of a graph as *one*. Show them a picture of a ladder and explain that the zero line is like the ground under the ladder. The line above or after the first box is the line to count as *one*, like the first step above the ground.

Name _____

Read a Bar Graph

Hands-On Activity

Get Ready

Main Idea
I will read a bar graph.

Vocabulary
bar graph

A **bar graph** shows information or data. The bars tell how many. Look where each bar ends. Read the number.

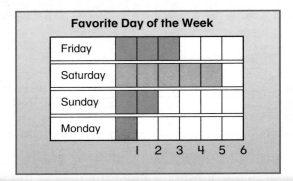

Favorite Day of the Week

✓ Check

Use the graph. Answer the questions.

1. How many students chose Sunday? __2__

2. How many students chose Friday or Saturday? __8__

3. Which day was the favorite? __Saturday__

4. Which day was the least favorite? __Monday__

5. **Talk About It** Why is this graph called a bar graph? Sample answer: The colored boxes make bars to show totals.

Chapter 4   Lesson 5   one hundred thirty-three   133

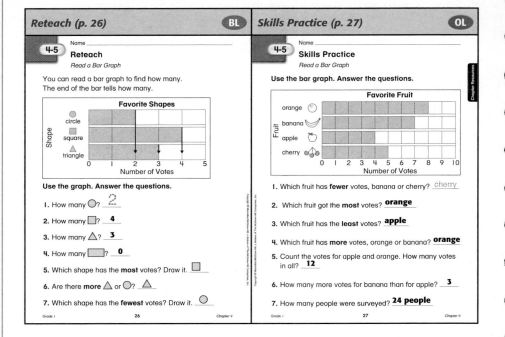

Reteach (p. 26) BL

4-5 **Reteach**
Read a Bar Graph

You can read a bar graph to find how many. The end of the bar tells how many.

Favorite Shapes

Use the graph. Answer the questions.

1. How many ○? __2__
2. How many ■? __4__
3. How many △? __3__
4. How many ▭? __0__
5. Which shape has the **most** votes? Draw it. ■
6. Are there **more** △ or ○? △
7. Which shape has the **fewest** votes? Draw it. ○

Grade 1   26   Chapter 4

Skills Practice (p. 27) OL

4-5 **Skills Practice**
Read a Bar Graph

Use the bar graph. Answer the questions.

Favorite Fruit

1. Which fruit has **fewer** votes, banana or cherry? cherry
2. Which fruit got the **most** votes? **orange**
3. Which fruit has the **least** votes? **apple**
4. Which fruit has **more** votes, orange or banana? **orange**
5. Count the votes for apple and orange. How many votes in all? __12__
6. How many more votes for banana than for apple? __3__
7. How many people were surveyed? **24 people**

Grade 1   27   Chapter 4

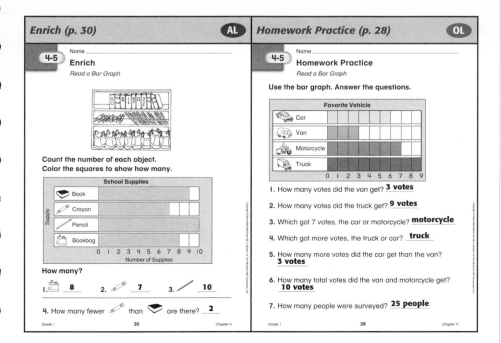

Practice

Use the graph. Answer the questions.

Favorite Zoo Animal

6. How many chose the tiger or penguin? **7**

7. Did more choose the penguin or the panda? **panda**

8. How many fewer votes did the tiger get than the panda? **5**

9. Which animal was chosen *less than* 4 times? **tiger**

10. Which animal was chosen *more than* 4 times? **panda**

Tiger Panda Penguin

Data File

Shallow holes filled with seawater are called tide pools. If you visit South Carolina, you may see these on the beach. Many kinds of animals live in tide pools. Use the graph to tell how many of each.

	Crabs									
Sea Stars									
Sea Urchins									

11. How many crabs? **2**
12. How many sea stars? **5**

134 one hundred thirty-four

Math at Home Activity: Create a bar graph showing your family's favorite foods. Ask your child questions about this bar graph.

Enrich (p. 30) — AL

4-5 Enrich
Read a Bar Graph

Count the number of each object.
Color the squares to show how many.

School Supplies

Supply: Book, Crayon, Pencil, Bookbag
0 1 2 3 4 5 6 7 8 9 10
Number of Supplies

How many?
1. (bookbag) **8** 2. (crayon) **7** 3. (pencil) **10**

4. How many fewer (pencil) than (book) are there? **2**

Grade 1 — 30 — Chapter 4

Homework Practice (p. 28) — OL

4-5 Homework Practice
Read a Bar Graph

Use the bar graph. Answer the questions.

Favorite Vehicle

Car, Van, Motorcycle, Truck
0 1 2 3 4 5 6 7 8 9

1. How many votes did the van get? **3 votes**
2. How many votes did the truck get? **9 votes**
3. Which got 7 votes, the car or motorcycle? **motorcycle**
4. Which got more votes, the truck or car? **truck**
5. How many more votes did the car get than the van? **3 votes**
6. How many total votes did the van and motorcycle get? **10 votes**
7. How many people were surveyed? **25 people**

Grade 1 — 28 — Chapter 4

BL **Alternate Teaching Strategy**

If students have trouble reading a bar graph . . .

Then use one of these reteach options.

1. **CRM Daily Reteach Worksheet** (p. 26)

2. **Handprint Graph** Have students sort themselves based on right-handedness and left-handedness. Have them make handprints on square pieces of paper, using red paint for right-handed and blue paint for left-handed. Have students arrange squares in a horizontal columns by color. Create a two-column graph to display data.

③ Practice

Differentiate practice using these leveled assignments for Exercises 6–12.

Level	Assignment
BL Below/Approaching Level	Guide students through the exercises.
OL On Level	Complete the exercises with a partner.
AL Above/Beyond Level	Complete the exercises independently.

Have students complete Exercises 11–12 independently. Ask them to think about the data and write two questions using the data from the bar graph.

④ Assess

Formative Assessment

Display a bar graph that shows students' favorite animals. **Which animal is most popular? Which animal is least popular?** See students' work.

WRITING IN ▸MATH Ask students to write about why bar graphs make it easier to compare data. Sample answer: It is easy to see how many more or less there are by looking at bars on a graph.

Quick Check Are students continuing to struggle with making and reading bar graphs?

If Yes → Small Group Options (p. 133B)
If No → Independent Work Options (p. 133B)
   CRM Skills Practice Worksheet (p. 27)
   CRM Enrich Worksheet (p. 30)

Reviews Lessons 4-1 to 4-5

Objective: Review and assess mastery of previous lessons' skills and concepts.

- Review with students how to read a bar graph.
- Explain that this bar graph shows the favorite color choices of students.
- Students may wish to use counters to help them analyze data from the bar graph.

Practice with Technology

Math Online Have students visit macmillanmh.com for additional practice with online activities, games, and quizzes.

Name _____

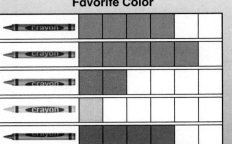

Favorite Color

Use the graph. Answer the questions.

1. How many students chose 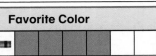? __2__

2. Did more choose ⬛ or ⬛?

3. Did fewer choose ⬛ or ⬛?

4. How many more chose ⬛ than ⬛? __3__

5. Which color has one less than ⬛?

6. Which two colors do the same number of people like? Circle two colors.

Color one balloon to show each student's favorite color.

Game Time

Animal Race
Using Data

This game can be played individually or in a group of 4.

- Spin the ◓.
- Determine which animal gets the point for the spin.
- Place a ● on the game board for that animal.
- The first animal to finish wins the race!

You Will Need

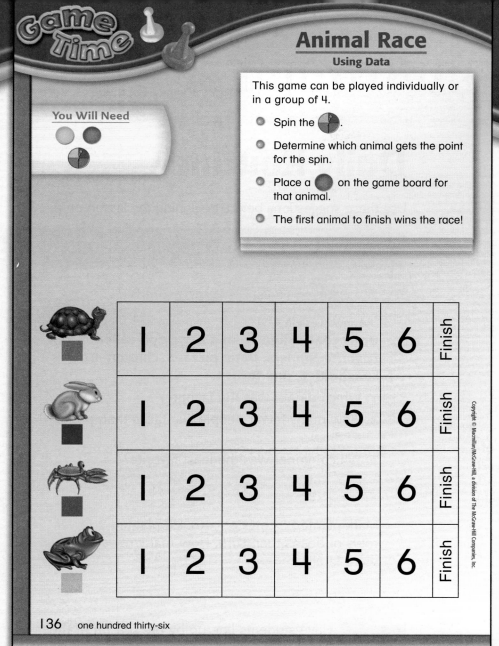

🐢	1	2	3	4	5	6	Finish
🐰	1	2	3	4	5	6	Finish
🦀	1	2	3	4	5	6	Finish
🐸	1	2	3	4	5	6	Finish

Differentiated Practice

Use these leveling suggestions to differentiate the game for all learners.

Level	Assignment
BL Below/Approaching Level	To make it easier for students to identify which animal matches each color on the spinner, allow them to draw a circle around each animal, using a crayon of the color assigned to it.
OL On Level	Have students play the game with the rules as written.
AL Above/Beyond Level	Before players move their counters forward, they must add the number in the new space to the previous number to continue. For example, if a counter is on number 2 and is about to move to number 3, the player must add 2 + 3 and give the sum before moving his or her counter forward.

Animal Race

Math Concept:
Modeling Subtraction

Manipulatives: two-color counters, four-color spinner

Introduce the game on page 136 to students to play as a class, in small groups, or at a learning workstation to review concepts introduced in this chapter.

Instructions

- Note: This game can be played individually or in a group of 4. If 4 students play, each chooses an animal as his or hers.
- Assign a color on the spinner to each animal. (Example: turtle – red, rabbit – blue, crab – green, frog – yellow)
- Players take turns spinning the spinner.
- The player whose animal matches the color to which the spinner points moves his or her counter forward one space.
- The first player to Finish wins the race!

Extend the Game

Have students create a new game board using different animals and more spaces.

Make a Bar Graph

Lesson Planner

Objective
Make a bar graph.

Review Vocabulary
data

Resources
Materials: pencils, crayons, 1-inch grid paper

Manipulatives: number cubes, connecting cubes

Literature Connection: *Leo the Late Bloomer* by Robert Kraus

Alternate Lessons: Adapt "Other Graphs" on page 156 of *Math Their Way* for practice using a bar graph to answer questions.
Use *IMPACT Mathematics:* Unit E to provide practice with making a bar graph.

Teacher Technology
TeacherWorks • Concepts in Motion

Focus on Math Background

Unlike the previous lessons, in which students sorted and showed data through a variety of representations, this lesson focuses on helping students interpret information already organized and displayed on graphs. The analysis skills presented in this lesson focus on helping students answer questions about data represented on bar graphs, with specific emphasis on making quantitative comparisons. Students will need to determine how many more and how many fewer data there are and use formal mathematical language, such as "Which data occur most/least often?"

Daily Routine

Use these suggestions before beginning the lesson on p. 137.

5-Minute Check

(Reviews Lesson 4-5)

Draw conclusions from a bar graph called *Favorite Dinners*. Data: pizza–5, chicken–8, spaghetti–6, and taco–1.

1. Which dinner was the favorite? chicken

2. How many fewer people like tacos than pizza?
   4 people

3. Which dinner was the least favorite? taco

Problem of the Day

Mark planted 5 rows of corn. He planted 2 fewer rows of beans than corn. How many rows did he plant in all? 8 rows

 Have students line up by the season of their birthday month.

Review Math Vocabulary

Review the term **data** and write it on the board. Explain that data is another word for information. When students vote for their favorite sandwich or their favorite color, for example, their votes are data that can be gathered. This information can be tallied to find out which sandwich or color is the most favorite or least favorite. Remind students that they have been reading and using data from picture graphs, tally charts, and bar graphs.

Visual Vocabulary Cards

Use Visual Vocabulary Card 12 to reinforce the vocabulary reviewed in this lesson. (The Define/Example/Ask routine is printed on the back of each card.)

Differentiated Instruction

Small Group Options

Option 1

Below Level **BL**

KINESTHETIC, LINGUISTIC

Materials: connecting cubes

- Invite students to use connecting cubes to model story problems.
- *Melissa has 6 purple toy cars. She has 3 fewer yellow toy cars than purple. She has 2 more green toy cars than yellow.*
- Direct students to model the 6 purple cars with their cubes. Then have them model the yellow and green cars.
- Have students tell you the color they are modeling and how many are in that group. 3 yellow; 5 green **How many purple and yellow cars in all?** 9 cars Have students make a bar graph to show their answer.

Option 2

English Language Learners **ELL**

LOGICAL, VISUAL/SPATIAL, SOCIAL

Core Vocabulary: sort by shape, diamond, heart
Common Use Verb: practice

Talk Math This strategy shelters speaking practice.

- Show a bar graph with heart and diamond shapes. Say the names as you disassemble the graph.
- Sit with students in a circle; placing cards in front of them.
- Have students simultaneously pick up a card, say the name of the shape and pass it to the person to their right.
- Repeat with all students working as fast as they can (without throwing cards).
- When students are comfortable speaking, introduce colors and numbers from previous graphs and add to your set.
- Continue practice as time permits.

Use this worksheet to provide additional support for English Language Learners.

English Language Learners (p .135) **ELL**

41 Name _____

Chart and Graph

Draw tally marks to show how many students like each shape.
Count the tally marks and record the total.

Shape	Tally	Total
★		
♥		
●		

Color the squares to show how many students like each shape.

Our Favorite Shapes

Number of Votes

Bars and Graphs **135**

Independent Work Options

Option 1

Early Finishers **OL** **AL**

VISUAL/SPATIAL, INTERPERSONAL

Materials: daily lunch count, 1-inch grid paper, crayons

- Have students make a bar graph on grid paper to show how many students ordered a hot lunch and how many students brought their lunch that day.

- Have students write two to three questions about the data on their graph.

Option 2

Student Technology

Math Online ⟩ macmillanmh.com

Math Adventures

Option 3

Learning Station: Reading (p. 119G)

Direct students to the Reading Learning Station for opportunities to explore and extend the lesson concept.

Option 4

Problem-Solving Practice

Reinforce problem-solving skills and strategies with the Problem-Solving Practice worksheet.

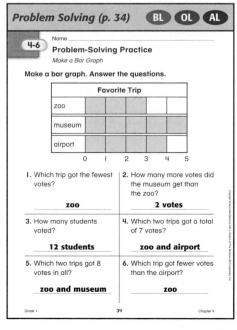

Problem Solving (p. 34) **BL** **OL** **AL**

4-6 Name _____
Problem-Solving Practice
Make a Bar Graph

Make a bar graph. Answer the questions.

Favorite Trip

| | 0 | 1 | 2 | 3 | 4 | 5 |
zoo
museum
airport

1. Which trip got the fewest votes?

zoo

2. How many more votes did the museum get than the zoo?

2 votes

3. How many students voted?

12 students

4. Which two trips got a total of 7 votes?

zoo and airport

5. Which two trips got 8 votes in all?

zoo and museum

6. Which trip got fewer votes than the airport?

zoo

Grade 1   34   Chapter 4

1 Introduce

Activity Choice 1 • Hands-On

Have students make a bar graph on grid paper and label the rows with the numerals 0–5. Make a bar graph for students to use as a model.

- Have students roll their number cubes twelve times. After each roll, they can record the number on the cube on their bar graphs.
- **Which number came up most often?** See students' work.

Activity Choice 2 • Literature

Introduce the lesson with *Leo the Late Bloomer* by Robert Kraus. For additional support, see p. TR48.

2 Teach

Have students write their name, one letter per square, on a strip of 1-inch grid paper. After their name, have students write the number of letters. Display the strips on chart paper to create a horizontal bar graph. Draw conclusions by answering the following questions:

- **Which number of letters appears most often?** See students' work.
- **Which name has the most letters? the fewest?** See students' work.
- **How many more letters are there in *Jennifer* than *José*?** four more letters

Get Ready Use the section at the top of page 137 to reinforce the lesson concept. Guide students through the example, and help them see that they can use the information from a tally to create a bar graph.

Check Observe students as you work through Exercises 1–4 as a class.

Exercise 4 Assess student comprehension before assigning practice exercises.

! COMMON ERROR!

When asked comparison questions such as "How many more chose apples than oranges?" students may state the total number of apples. Restating the question may help. "How can you make the number of apples equal to the number of oranges?"

Name _____

Make a Bar Graph

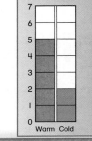
Hands-On Activity

Get Ready

Main Idea
I will make a bar graph.

You can use a tally chart to make a bar graph. Tyler asked his friends what kind of weather they liked the best.

Favorite Weather		
Weather	Tally	Total
Warm	卌	5
Cold	||	2

Favorite Weather (bar graph, Warm and Cold, scale 0–7)

Check

Favorite Sandwich		
Sandwich	Tally	Total
Peanut Butter	卌 |||	8
Turkey	|||	3
Ham	卌	5
Cheese	||	2

Favorite Sandwich (bar graph, Peanut Butter, Turkey, Ham, Cheese, scale 0–9)

Fill in the totals. Color the graph. Answer the questions.

1. How many chose turkey?
   __3__ students
2. How many more chose peanut butter than ham? __3__ students
3. Did more choose cheese or turkey? ___turkey___

4. **Talk About It** How are tally charts and bar graphs alike?
   Sample answer: They both show data.

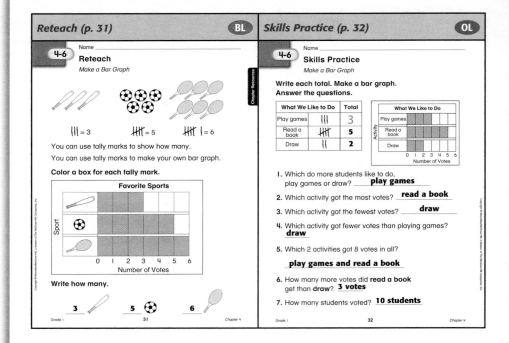

Reteach (p. 31) BL

4-6 Reteach
Make a Bar Graph

||| = 3   卌 = 5   卌 | = 6

You can use tally marks to show how many.
You can use tally marks to make your own bar graph.

Color a box for each tally mark.

Favorite Sports (bar graph, Sport, scale 0–6)

Write how many.

__3__ (bat)   __5__ (soccer ball)   __6__ (racket)

Grade 1   31   Chapter 4

Skills Practice (p. 32) OL

4-6 Skills Practice
Make a Bar Graph

Write each total. Make a bar graph. Answer the questions.

What We Like to Do	Total
Play games	3
Read a book	5
Draw	2

What We Like to Do (bar graph, Number of Votes 0–6)

1. Which do more students like to do, play games or draw? **play games**
2. Which activity got the most votes? **read a book**
3. Which activity got the fewest votes? **draw**
4. Which activity got fewer votes than playing games? **draw**
5. Which 2 activities got 8 votes in all? **play games and read a book**
6. How many more votes did **read a book** get than **draw**? **3 votes**
7. How many students voted? **10 students**

Grade 1   32   Chapter 4

5. Ask 10 friends what their favorite playground activity is. Make a tally chart to show your data.

Playground Activity		
Activity	Votes	Total
Jump Rope		
Slide		
Basketball		

See students' work.

Make a tally for each vote.

6. Use the tally chart to make a bar graph. Then answer the questions.

Playground Activity									
Jump Rope									
Slide									
Basketball									

See students work.

7. How many voted for basketball? _____ students

8. Did more students vote for the jump rope or the slide? _____

9. What playground activity has the most votes? _____

7.–9. Students' responses will vary according to the data collected.

138   one hundred thirty-eight

Math at Home Activity: Have your child create a bar graph that shows your family's favorite color.

Enrich (p. 35) **AL**

4-6   Name _____
Enrich
Make a Bar Graph

Complete the graphs. Solve. Draw your answers.

1. Ana and her friends like fruit. Mike likes 🍌 and 🍎. Ana likes 🍐 and 🍌. Sue likes 🍎 and 🍌. Which do they like best?
student drawing of a banana

Favorite Fruit

2. Scott and his friends like sports. Jane likes ⚾ and 🏀. Ray likes 🏈 and ⚾. Scott likes 🏀 and ⚾. Which do they like best?
student drawing of a baseball

Favorite Sport

3. Mel and her friends like school. Todd likes 📖 and 🎨. Mel likes 📖 and 🎵. Dan likes 🎨 and 🎵. Which do they like best?
student drawing of a book

Favorite Subject

Grade 1   35   Chapter 4

Homework Practice (p. 33) **OL**

4-6   Name _____
Homework Practice
Make a Bar Graph

1. Ask 10 friends what their favorite vegetable is. Make a tally chart to show your data.

Favorite Vegetable		
Vegetable	Tally Marks	Total
Broccoli		
Carrot		
Lettuce		

2. Use the tally chart to make a bar graph below.

Make a bar graph. Answer the questions.

Favorite Vegetable	
Broccoli	
Carrot	
Lettuce	

0 1 2 3 4 5 6 7 8 9 10

3. Which vegetable got the least votes? **Answers will vary.**

4. Which vegetable got the most votes? **Answers will vary.**

Grade 1   33   Chapter 4

BL Alternate Teaching Strategy

If ▶ students have trouble making a bar graph . . .

Then ▶ use one of these reteach options.

1 CRM **Daily Reteach Worksheet** (p. 31)

2 Connecting Cubes Allow students to use connecting cubes to represent the data. Have students match a cube to each square on the bar graph. They can connect the cubes to replicate the bars on the graph. Encourage students to use their connecting cubes to answer questions about the data.

③ Practice

Differentiate practice using these leveled assignments for Exercises 5–9.

Level	Assignment
BL Below/Approaching Level	Guide students through the exercises.
OL On Level	Complete the exercises with a partner.
AL Above/Beyond Level	Complete the exercises independently.

④ Assess

✓ Formative Assessment

Provide a collection of connecting cubes. Ask students to make a bar graph showing how many cubes there are of each color.

WRITING IN ▶MATH In their Math Journals, have students make a bar graph to show how many people live in their house. Use the categories *adults, male children, female children.* Then have students write a sentence that tells which category represents the most people in their house. See students' work.

Quick Check **Are students continuing to struggle with making bar graphs?**

If Yes → Small Group Options (p. 137B)

If No → Independent Work Options (p. 137B)

CRM Skills Practice Worksheet (p. 32)

CRM Enrich Worksheet (p. 35)

Tech Link

Math Objective

Use technology to label and read bar graphs. Record observations using technology.

Resources

Math Tool Chest *(accessible in three ways)*

> **Math Online** macmillanmh.com

- StudentWorks Plus
- Math Tool Chest

Getting Started

- The activities and exercises on pp. 139–140 use the Level 1, Graphing Tool in Math Tool Chest. They may be completed as a class, in pairs, or individually.
- As a class, read and then work through the information and instructions on the top of p. 139.
- Guide students as they work through Exercises 1–2.

Using Math Tool Chest

Graphs The graphing tool in the Math Tool Chest program allows students to quickly create graphs.

- Students can experiment by creating many different bar and picture graphs to learn more about graphing.
- To label their graphs, students click in a box and then enter the label. To create the bars, students click on a color and then stamp out the appropriate number of squares.
- They can erase any square from the graph by clicking on the eraser key and then clicking on any squares to be erased.

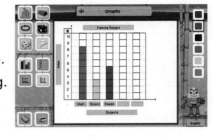

Name _____

> **Practice** with Technology

Make a Bar Graph • Computer

Click on ▮▮.

Click on Level I ▮▮.

- Stamp out 8 squares for Math.
- Stamp out 3 squares for Science.
- Stamp out 5 squares for Reading.

10. Which subject is liked the most? _____Math_____

11. How many more liked Math than Science? _____5_____ students

---

Click on ▮▮.

Click on Level I ▮▮.

- Stamp out 7 squares for oranges.
- Stamp out 5 squares for grapes.
- Stamp out 2 squares for strawberries.

12. Which fruit has the fewest votes? _strawberries_

13. How many more votes for oranges than strawberries?

_____5_____ votes

Graphs Button Bar

The Graphs Button Bar offers four buttons that perform functions specific to the Graphs tool.

Bar Graph When students first open the Graphs tool, a bar graph displays. If students are working on a picture graph, they can click on ▮▮ to show their data in bar graph format.

Picture Graph To convert a bar graph to a picture graph, have students click on ⁝⁝.

Horizontal View When students first open the Graphs tool, the graph displays vertically. If students click on ☰, the graph switches to display horizontally.

Vertical View Students can click on ▥ to convert the graph back into the vertical display.

Click on .

Click on Level 1 .

Complete the graph. Label the graph.

- Stamp out 3 squares for cats.
- Stamp out 4 squares for fish.
- Stamp out 6 squares for dogs.

14. How many have a fish? __4 classmates__

15. Which group has fewer animals, cats or dogs? __cats__

16. Which group has the most animals? __dogs__

H.O.T. Problem

17. Thinking Math Which bar on the graph is the tallest? Explain why that bar is the tallest.

__Dogs, because the most people have a dog as a pet.__

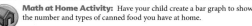

140   one hundred forty

Math at Home Activity: Have your child create a bar graph to show the number and types of canned food you have at home.

Practice

Alone or in pairs, have students complete Exercises 1–5 as you observe their work.

Thinking Math

Exercise 8 Assess student comprehension using the H.O.T. Problem question.

Extending the Link

- The students can use four different graph formats to represent their data.
- On the left side of the screen, have students click on .
- Encourage students to switch their bar graph from a vertical to a horizontal layout.
- **What is different about the graph?** The bars go from side to side instead of up and down.
- **What is the same about the graph?** The bars are still the same length.
- If time permits, allow students to create another graph. Have them make a survey to collect data.
- The students can use a tally chart to keep track of the survey answers.
- Have students use their tally charts to make a bar graph. Remind the students to label the graph appropriately.

Lesson Planner

Objective

Choose the best strategy to solve a problem.

Resources

Materials: pencils, paper

Teacher Technology

⊙ TeacherWorks

📖 **Real-World Problem Solving Library**
Math and Social Studies: *I Like That Too*
Use these leveled books to reinforce and extend
problem-solving skills and strategies.

Leveled for:

OL On Level
ELL Sheltered English
SP Spanish

For additional support,
see the Real-World
Problem Solving
Teacher Guide.

Daily Routine

Use these suggestions before beginning the lesson on p. 141.

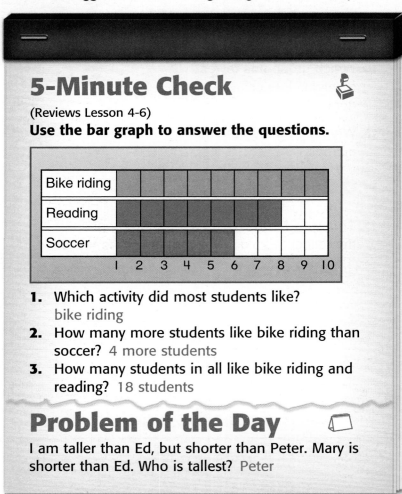

5-Minute Check

(Reviews Lesson 4-6)
Use the bar graph to answer the questions.

	1	2	3	4	5	6	7	8	9	10
Bike riding										
Reading										
Soccer										

1. Which activity did most students like?
   bike riding
2. How many more students like bike riding than
   soccer? 4 more students
3. How many students in all like bike riding and
   reading? 18 students

Problem of the Day

I am taller than Ed, but shorter than Peter. Mary is
shorter than Ed. Who is tallest? Peter

LINE UP Have students line up by favorite season.
Which season do most students like best?
Which season do the fewest students like best?

Differentiated Instruction

Small Group Options

Option 1

Gifted and Talented (AL)

LOGICAL

Materials: paper, pencil

- Have students survey classmates to find out how many like cats best and how many like dogs the best.
- After the student collects the information, the student should write a number sentence describing the information.
- The students will need to write the number sentence of how many more like one animal than the other animal and then write the answer to that number sentence.

Option 2

LOGICAL, KINESTHETIC

English Language Learners (ELL)

Core Vocabulary: thank you, could you tell me, please
Common Use Verb: excuse (me)

Talk Math This strategy integrates acquired language with polite language to teach students how to get data.

- Review graphs. Discuss what the data means and why graphing is helpful.
- Write "What is your favorite color?" on the board and introduce polite questions as a way to obtain data. Say: "Asking questions is one way to get information for a graph. When you ask questions, use polite words." Post and model the words.
- Have groups choose a strategy and get the data from their classmates by asking the question and using target phrases.
- Rotate, prompt and restate as necessary.

Independent Work Options

Option 1

Early Finishers (OL) (AL)

LOGICAL

Materials: paper, pencil

- Display examples of problems and solutions for each of the following problem-solving strategies: *use logical reasoning, draw a picture, and write a number sentence.*
- Invite students to write three problems of their own and use a different strategy to solve each one.

Option 2

Student Technology

Math Online macmillanmh.com

Option 3

Learning Station: Science (p. 119H)

Direct students to the Science Learning Station for more opportunities to explore and extend the lesson concept.

1 Introduce

Activity • Review

Write and read aloud the following:

A horse has 4 hooves, or feet. Each hoof needs a horseshoe. How many horseshoes are needed for 3 horses?

- **What do we know?** A horse has 4 hooves. Each hoof needs a horseshoe.
- **What do we want to find?** how many horseshoes are needed for 3 horses
- Discuss which problem-solving strategy would be appropriate here: *guess and check, draw a picture,* or *write a number sentence.*
- Guide students to draw a picture. Have students draw three horses with four legs each and then count the feet to find the answer.
- **How many horseshoes are needed?**
  12 horseshoes

2 Teach

Have students read the problems on page 141. Guide them through the problem-solving steps.

Understand Using the questions, review what students know and what they need to find.

Plan Have them discuss their strategy.

Solve Guide students to write a number sentence to solve the problem.

- **Are you using addition or subtraction to solve?** subtraction

Check Have students look back at the problem to make sure that the answer fits the facts given.

- Have students use addition to check their answer.

⚠ COMMON ERROR!

Students may have difficulty choosing the most efficient strategy to solve a problem. Use various strategies to solve the same problem and discuss why one strategy works better than the others.

Name _____

Problem-Solving Investigation

My 1st grade class collected 11 cans. A 2nd grade class collected 5 cans. How many more cans did we collect?

Main Idea

I will choose a strategy to solve problems.

Your Mission: Find how many more cans 1st grade collected than 2nd grade.

Understand

What do I need to find?
Circle it.

Plan

How will I solve the problem?

Solve

One way is to write a number sentence.

$$11 - 5 = 6$$

Check

Look back.
Is my answer reasonable?

Check students' explanations.

Chapter 4   Lesson 7   one hundred forty-one   141

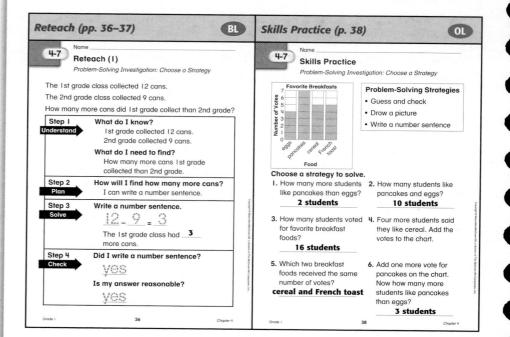

Reteach (pp. 36–37) `BL`

4-7 Name _____
Reteach (I)
Problem-Solving Investigation: Choose a Strategy

The 1st grade class collected 12 cans.
The 2nd grade class collected 9 cans.
How many more cans did 1st grade collect than 2nd grade?

Step 1 Understand	**What do I know?** 1st grade collected 12 cans. 2nd grade collected 9 cans. **What do I need to find?** How many more cans 1st grade collected than 2nd grade.
Step 2 Plan	**How will I find how many more cans?** I can write a number sentence.
Step 3 Solve	**Write a number sentence.** 12 - 9 = 3 The 1st grade class had __3__ more cans.
Step 4 Check	**Did I write a number sentence?** yes **Is my answer reasonable?** yes

Grade 1   36   Chapter 4

Skills Practice (p. 38) `OL`

4-7 Name _____
Skills Practice
Problem-Solving Investigation: Choose a Strategy

Favorite Breakfasts (bar graph)

Problem-Solving Strategies
- Guess and check
- Draw a picture
- Write a number sentence

Choose a strategy to solve.

1. How many more students like pancakes than eggs?
   2 students

2. How many students like pancakes and eggs?
   10 students

3. How many students voted for favorite breakfast foods?
   16 students

4. Four more students said they like cereal. Add the votes to the chart.

5. Which two breakfast foods received the same number of votes?
   cereal and French toast

6. Add one more vote for pancakes on the chart. Now how many more students like pancakes than eggs?
   3 students

Grade 1   38   Chapter 4

Mixed Problem Solving

Problem-Solving Strategies
- Write a number sentence
- Make a table
- Draw a picture

Choose a strategy. Solve.

1. A chicken has two legs.
How many legs would 4 chickens have?

_____8_____ legs

2. A cat has four legs.
How many legs would 3 cats have?

_____12_____ legs

3. There are 3 plates on the table.
Each plate has 2 rolls.
How many rolls are there in all?

_____6_____ rolls

4. There are 3 maple trees.
There are 5 oak trees.
There are 8 redwood trees.
How many oak and maple trees are there altogether?

_____8_____ trees

142   one hundred forty-two

Math at Home Activity: Take advantage of problem-solving opportunities during daily routines such as riding in the car, bedtime, doing laundry, putting away groceries, planning schedules, and so on.

BL **Alternate Teaching Strategy**

If students have trouble choosing the most appropriate problem-solving strategy . . .

Then use one of these reteach options.

1 **CRM** **Daily Reteach Worksheet** (pp. 36–37)

2 **Choose a Strategy** Ask students to try different strategies for solving the same problem.
- **Which strategy worked best for you?**
  See students' work.

③ Practice

Mixed Problem Solving

Exercises 1–4 Be sure students can read and understand the problems. Remind students to think about what they know and what they need to find out. Have them think about which strategy will best help them find out what they need to know.

④ Assess

✓ Formative Assessment

To check for understanding, ask students to explain their thought process.
- **Which strategy did you choose for Exercise 4?**
  See students' work.
- **Why did you choose this strategy?**
  See students' work.

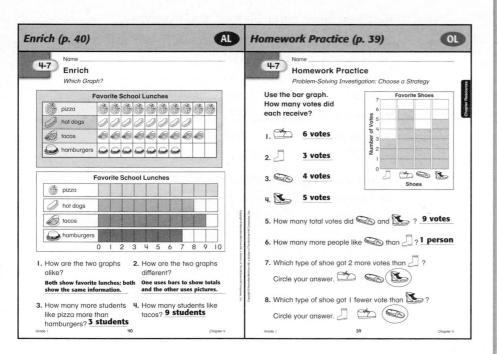

Quick Check **Are students continuing to struggle with choosing problem-solving strategies?**

If Yes → **CRM** Reteach Worksheet (pp. 36–37)

If No → Independent Work Options (p. 141B)
CRM Skills Practice Worksheet (p. 38)
CRM Enrich Worksheet (p. 40)

Lesson Planner

Objective
Identify events as certain or impossible.

Vocabulary
certain, **impossible**

Resources

Materials: crayons
Manipulatives: pattern blocks, connecting cubes, color tiles
Literature Connection: *No Fair!* by Caren Holtzman
Alternate Lesson: Use *IMPACT Mathematics:* Unit E to provide practice with identifying events as certain or impossible.
Teacher Technology
　　TeacherWorks

Daily Routine

Use these suggestions before beginning the lesson on p. 143.

5-Minute Check
(Reviews Lesson 4-7)

Choose a strategy and solve the problem.
Ben has two more sisters than he has brothers. There are nine children in Ben's family. How many brothers does Ben have? Guess and Check;
3 brothers

Problem of the Day

Ann had a box of 16 crayons. Yesterday she lost three of her crayons and has not found them. Today six more crayons are missing from the box. How many crayons does Ann have? 7 crayons

LINE UP Have students with blue clothing line up. Have students with red clothing line up. Repeat with different colors until all students have lined up.

▷ Building Math Vocabulary

- Place six blue color tiles on the overhead.
- Write the vocabulary words **certain** and **impossible** on the board. Explain that *certain* means that something will happen for sure. *Impossible* means that an event cannot happen.
- **What are my chances of picking a blue tile? Certain or impossible?** certain **Why?** Sample answer: There are only blue tiles to choose from.
- **What are my chances of picking a red tile? Certain or impossible?** impossible **Why?** Sample answer: There are no red tiles to choose from.

Differentiated Instruction

Small Group Options

Option 1
Gifted and Talented (AL)
LOGICAL

Materials: bag with three different buttons

- Have students predict how many of each color there will be if you choose a button twenty times. Have students record their prediction.

- Ask students to justify their predictions. Encourage students to use words such as *certain, impossible, likely,* and *unlikely.*

- Have students choose a button from the bag twenty times without looking, and then replace the button after making each choice. Record each choice.

- After making twenty choices, count the times each color was chosen and compare with their original prediction.

Option 2
English Language Learners (ELL)
LINGUISTIC

Materials: colored blocks, bag
Core Vocabulary: pull out, blocks, what color
Common Use Verb: are/are not

See Math This strategy helps students understand impossibility and certainty.

- Show all the colors of blocks (separated by color).

- Label their color names.

- Put 4 blue blocks in the bag. Vocalize your actions by saying: "These are blue blocks."

- Shake the bad. Ask: "What color will I pull out of the bag?"

- Accept responses. Repeat, asking if you will pull out red blocks. Restate responses and repeat as time permits.

Independent Work Options

Option 1
Early Finishers (AL) (OL)
VISUAL/SPATIAL, KINESTHETIC, SOCIAL

Materials: connecting cubes, clear plastic bag.

- Have students take turns putting different colored cubes in a bag and asking each other whether it is certain or impossible that they will pick a particular colored cube.

- To extend the activity, explain that when something is *likely* that means it will probably happen. Explain that when something is *unlikely*, it probably will not happen. Have students ask each other whether it is likely or unlikely that they will pick a particular colored cube.

Option 2
Student Technology
Math Online macmillanmh.com

Option 3
Learning Stations: Language Arts (p. 119G)

Direct students to the Language Arts Learning Station for more opportunities to explore the lesson concept.

Option 4
Problem-Solving Practice

Reinforce problem-solving skills and strategies with the Problem-Solving Practice worksheet.

English Language Learners (p. 137) **ELL**

42 Name _____

What do you think?
Color the spinner to match the one you are using.
Circle a color to show your guess.

Spinner	More Likely	Less Likely
	red blue	red blue
	red blue	red blue

Probability **137**

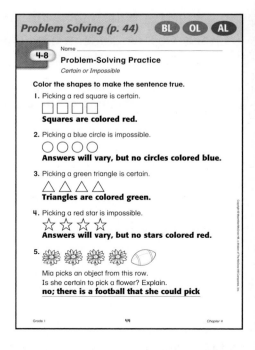

Problem Solving (p. 44) **BL** **OL** **AL**

4-8 Name _____
Problem-Solving Practice
Certain or Impossible

Color the shapes to make the sentence true.

1. Picking a red square is certain.
□ □ □ □
Squares are colored red.

2. Picking a blue circle is impossible.
○ ○ ○ ○
Answers will vary, but no circles colored blue.

3. Picking a green triangle is certain.
△ △ △ △
Triangles are colored green.

4. Picking a red star is impossible.
☆ ☆ ☆ ☆
Answers will vary, but no stars colored red.

5.
Mia picks an object from this row.
Is she certain to pick a flower? Explain.
no; there is a football that she could pick

Grade 1   44   Chapter 4

① Introduce

Activity Choice 1 • Hands-On

- Have student pairs put one red crayon, one blue crayon, and one yellow crayon in a bag.
- **Is it certain or impossible that you will choose a green crayon?** impossible
- Have student pairs put two red crayons in a bag.
- **Is it certain or impossible that you will choose a red crayon?** certain

Activity Choice 2 • Literature

Introduce the lesson with *No Fair!* by Caren Holtzman. For additional support, see p. TR48.

② Teach

- Have students sort the pattern blocks by shape.
- Then put three triangles in the bag.
- **Is it certain or impossible to choose a square?** impossible
- **Is it certain or impossible to choose a triangle?** certain
- Repeat the activity with various combinations.
- Once students have a strong understanding of *certain* and *impossible*, introduce the terms *likely* and *unlikely*.
- Explain how to identify what makes an event more likely to happen.

Get Ready Use the section at the top of student p. 143 to teach the lesson concept.

Check Observe students as you work through Exercises 1–5 as a class.

> **Exercise 5** Assess student comprehension before assigning practice exercises.

⚠ COMMON ERROR!

Some students may confuse the vocabulary, *certain* and *impossible*. To reinforce the correct meaning of the words in discussion and questioning, follow the words with a synonym or defining phrase: *Is it certain—will it happen for sure? Would it be impossible—is there no way it could happen?*

Name _____

Certain or Impossible

Get Ready

Main Idea
I will identify events as certain or impossible.

Vocabulary
certain
impossible

Look at the bowl of cubes.
Choosing a 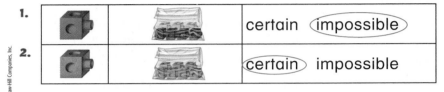 is **certain**.
Choosing a is **impossible**.

✓ Check

5. Impossible. If no red tiles are in the bag, then it is impossible to choose one.

Circle the word to tell if choosing the cube is *certain* or *impossible*.

1.		certain ⟨impossible⟩
2.		⟨certain⟩ impossible

Color to make each sentence true.

All cubes are colored red.

3. Choosing a is certain.

No cubes are colored yellow.

4. Choosing a is impossible.

5. **Talk About It** If a bag had and in it, would it be certain or impossible to choose a ? Explain.

Chapter 4   Lesson 8   one hundred forty-three   143

Reteach (p. 41) **BL**

4-8 Reteach
Certain or Impossible

Greg had 6 blue marbles. He put them in a bag.

Greg's mom pulls a marble out of the bag. Greg is **certain** it is a blue marble.

Greg knows it cannot be a red marble. It is **impossible**.

Look at the tally chart. Circle your answers.

Number of Marbles in a Bag	
⬤ Black Marble	ҤҤ I
◯ White Marble	II

1. You pick an object out of the bag. It is a marble. ⟨certain⟩ impossible

2. You pick 4 white marbles out of the bag. certain ⟨impossible⟩

3. You pick an object out of the bag. It is a gray marble. certain ⟨impossible⟩

Grade 1   41   Chapter 4

Skills Practice (p. 42) **OL**

4-8 Skills Practice
Certain or Impossible

Helen cuts out some shapes. She puts them in a bag.

Shapes in Helen's Bag					
☐ square					
◯ circle					
☆ star					
	0	1	2	3	4	5

Look at the bar graph. Circle your answers.

1. You can pick a square from the bag. certain ⟨impossible⟩

2. You can pick a star from the bag. ⟨certain⟩ impossible

3. You can pick a circle from the bag. certain ⟨impossible⟩

Grade 1   42   Chapter 4

Practice

Circle the word to tell if choosing the cube is *certain* or *impossible*.

#				
6.			(certain)	impossible
7.			certain	(impossible)
8.			(certain)	impossible

Color to make each sentence true.

9. Choosing a is certain.

   All cubes are colored green.

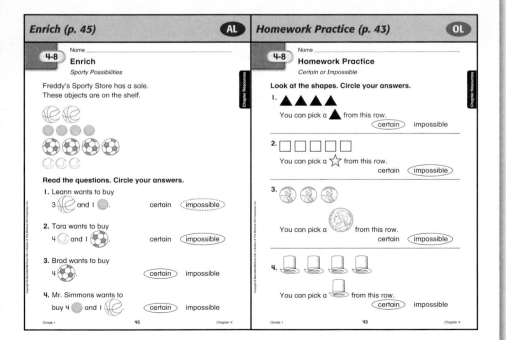

10. Choosing a is impossible.

   No cubes are colored purple.

H.O.T. Problem

11. **Thinking Math** Felix put 4 and 4 in a bag. Is it certain he will choose a ? Explain.

No, it's possible to choose a yellow or a green cube.

Math at Home Activity: Place 4 red pieces of paper and 5 green pieces of paper in a bowl. Ask your child if it is certain or impossible to draw out a blue piece of paper. Have your child explain his or her answer.

144 one hundred forty-four

Enrich (p. 45) **AL**

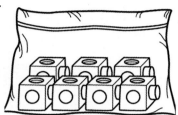

4-8 Name _____

Enrich

Sporty Possibilities

Freddy's Sporty Store has a sale. These objects are on the shelf.

Read the questions. Circle your answers.

1. Leann wants to buy 3 and 1 .   certain (impossible)

2. Tara wants to buy 4 and 1 .   certain (impossible)

3. Brad wants to buy 4 .   (certain) impossible

4. Mr. Simmons wants to buy 4 and 1 .   (certain) impossible

Grade 1 — 45 — Chapter 4

Homework Practice (p. 43) **OL**

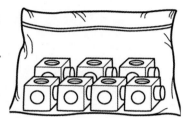

4-8 Name _____

Homework Practice

Certain or Impossible

Look at the shapes. Circle your answers.

1. ▲▲▲▲
   You can pick a ▲ from this row.
   (certain) impossible

2. ☐☐☐☐☐
   You can pick a ☆ from this row.
   certain (impossible)

3.
   You can pick a from this row.
   certain (impossible)

4.
   You can pick a from this row.
   (certain) impossible

Grade 1 — 43 — Chapter 4

Alternate Teaching Strategy

If students have difficulty identifying events as certain or impossible . . .

Then use one of the following reteach options.

1. **CRM** **Daily Reteach Worksheet** (p. 41)

2. **Use Connecting Cubes** Give students a set of orange connecting cubes. Invite them to select a yellow connecting cube from the set. Students should determine that it is impossible to choose a yellow cube. Then give students yellow connecting cubes and ask them to choose a yellow cube. Students should determine that it is certain that they will choose a yellow cube.

③ Practice

Differentiate practice using these leveled assignments for Exercises 6–11.

Level	Assignment
BL Below/Approaching Level	Guide students through the exercises. Use connecting cubes for support.
OL On Level	Complete exercises with connecting cubes for support.
AL Above/Beyond Level	Complete exercises independently.

④ Assess

Formative Assessment

Model putting red and yellow tiles in a bag. **Is it certain or impossible to choose a green tile? Explain.** Sample answer: It is impossible to choose a green tile because there are no green tiles in the bag.

WRITING IN ►MATH Have students write their own problem that is similar to Exercise 10. Sample answer: Students should draw a bag with red tiles and write, "Pulling a blue tile is impossible."

Quick Check Are students continuing to struggle with identifying an event as certain or impossible?

If Yes → **CRM** Reteach Worksheet (p. 41)

If No → Independent Work Options (p. 143B)

   CRM Skills Practice Worksheet (p. 42)

   CRM Enrich Worksheet (p. 45)

Problem Solving in Science

Real-World MATH

Summer is a time for fun. You can swim, fish, hike, and see all kinds of animals.

This book belongs to

_____

A

You can swim in the summer if it is warm enough.

B

How would you find the temperature of the water?

use a thermometer

Lesson Planner

Objectives

Introduce tools and use a bar graph to solve problems in science.

National Standard

Students should develop understanding about scientific inquiry.

Vocabulary

scale, thermometer, binoculars

Activate Prior Knowledge

Before you turn students' attention to the pages, discuss tools that are used in science.

- **What kind of tool would help you measure temperature?** a thermometer
- **What kind of tool would help you weigh something?** a scale or balance
- **What kind of tool would help you see things that are far away?** binoculars or telescope
- If possible, show students a thermometer, a scale, and binoculars.

What tool would you use to find out how much each fish weighs?

a scale

On which day were the most fish caught?

Thursday

5 fish					
4 fish					
3 fish					
2 fish					
1 fish					
0 fish	Monday	Tuesday	Wednesday	Thursday	Friday

C

You can go on a hike and look at animals.

What is the boy using to see the animals?

binoculars

FOLD DOWN

D

Create the Book

Guide students to create their book.

- Have them fold the page in half.
- Ask them to write their name on page A.
- Explain that page A is the front cover and page D is the back cover. If necessary, have them practice flipping through the book in order.
- Guide them in reading the information and word problems on each of the pages.

Extend the Activity

Have students work in small groups to use a scale to measure the weight of different classroom objects or to use a thermometer to measure the temperature of a cup of water.

Use the Student Pages

Have students work individually or in pairs to solve the word problems on pages B–D.

Page B Students may have difficulty understanding the measurement of temperature. Suggest that students think about the tool people use to take their own temperature. Explain that different temperatures can be measured, such as body temperature, air temperature, or water temperature.

Page C requires that students have an understanding of bar graphs. If necessary, review how to read a bar graph.

WRITING IN ▶ MATH Have students write a question about comparing the data in the bar graph on page C.

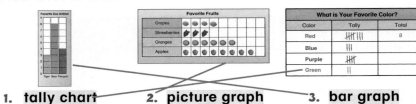

Chapter Review/Test

Vocabulary

Draw lines to match.

1. **tally chart**   2. **picture graph**   3. **bar graph**

Concepts

Use the graph to answer the questions.

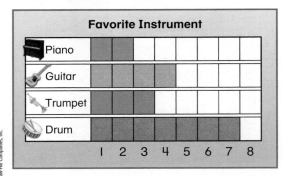

Favorite Instrument

4. How many students chose ? ___4___ students

5. Which instrument has four more than ?

6. How many more students chose
   than ? ___1___

FOLDABLES Dinah Zike's Foldables

If students have not completed their Foldables, guide them to create and fill in the appropriate information using the instructions on pp. 119 and 131.

You may choose to use the Foldable to help students review the concepts presented in this chapter and as a tool for studying for the Chapter Review/Test.

Vocabulary Review

Review chapter vocabulary using one of the following options.

- **Visual Vocabulary Cards** (4, 12, 19, 35, and 48)
- **eGlossary** at macmillanmh.com

Vocabulary Test

CRM Chapter 4 Resource Masters (p. 50)
Assess student comprehension of the chapter vocabulary with the Vocabulary Test.

Math Online Chapter Test
Alternative summative assessment options are available online at macmillanmh.com.

Chapter 4 Project

Take a Survey

Alone, in pairs, or in small groups, have students discuss the results of their completed chapter project with the class. Assess their work using the Chapter Project rubric found in Chapter 4 Resource Masters on page 55.

Alicia asked her classmates what their favorite sea animal was.
2 chose whales.
6 chose dolphins.
9 chose sharks.

7. Make a tally chart of the data.

Favorite Sea Animal		
Animal	Tally	Total
Whales		2
Dolphins		6
Sharks		9

8. Use the tally chart to make a bar graph of the data.

Whales	
Dolphins	
Sharks	

9. Did more students choose whales or dolphins? <u>dolphins</u>

Problem Solving

10. Mandy put 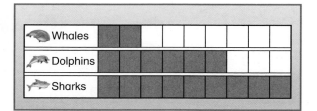 and in a bag. Is it certain or impossible she will choose a ? Explain.

<u>Impossible, Mandy did not put any yellow cubes in</u>
<u>the bag.</u>

Copyright © Macmillan/McGraw-Hill, a division of The McGraw-Hill Companies, Inc.

148   one hundred forty-eight

Summative Assessment

Summative Assessment

Use these alternate leveled chapter tests to differentiate assessment for the specific needs of your students.

Leveled Chapter 4 Tests			
Form	Type	Level	CRM Pages
1	Multiple Choice	BL	57–58
2A	Multiple Choice	OL	59–60
2B	Multiple Choice	OL	61–62
2C	Multiple Choice	AL	63–64
2D	Free Response	AL	65–66

BL = below/approaching grade level
OL = on grade level
AL = above/beyond grade level

ExamView®
Assessment Suite   Customize and create multiple versions of your Chapter Test and their test answer keys.

Data-Driven Decision Making

Based on the results of the Chapter Review/Test, use the following to review concepts that continue to present students with problems.

Exercises	State/Local Standards	What's the Math?	Error Analysis	Resources for Review
1–6		Identify a tally chart, picture graph, and bar graph. Represent and compare data using graphs and charts.	Draws lines to wrong chart or graph. Does not recognize tally chart, picture graph, bar graph. Does not understand "four more than," "how many more students chose."	Strategic Intervention Guide (p. 118) CRM Chapter 4 Resource Masters (Reteach Worksheets) **Math Online** Concepts in Motion Math Adventures
7		Organize and represent data in a tally chart and bar graph.	Does not understand how to make "tally chart."	
8, 9		Sort and represent data by using a bar graph. Use a bar graph to answer questions.	Does not know how to make a bar graph. Misreads numbers from bar graph.	

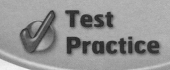

Test Practice

Formative Assessment

- Use Student Edition pp. 149–150 as practice and cumulative review. The questions are written in the same style as many state tests.

- You can use these two pages to benchmark student progress, or as an alternative homework assignment.

Additional practice pages can be found in the Chapter 4 Resource Masters.

CRM Chapter 4 Resource Masters
Cumulative Test Practice

- Multiple Choice format (pp. 57–62, 67)

- Free Response format (pp. 63–66, 68)

ExamView®
Assessment Suite — Create practice worksheets or tests that align to your state standards.

Math Online — For additional practice visit macmillanmh.com.

Name _____

Listen as your teacher reads each problem.
Choose the correct answer.

1. $2 + 4 = 6$

$2 + 6 = 8$ ○ $4 + 2 = 6$ ●

$4 + 6 = 10$ ○ $2 + 3 = 5$ ○

3.

Favorite Snack		
Snack	Tally	Total
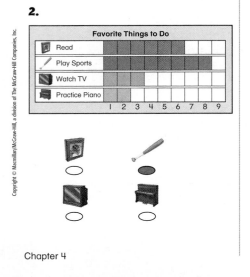	|||	3
	||||	4
	||	2
	|	1

○   ●   ○   ○

2.

Favorite Things to Do	
Read	
Play Sports	
Watch TV	
Practice Piano	
1 2 3 4 5 6 7 8 9	

○   ○
○   ○

4.

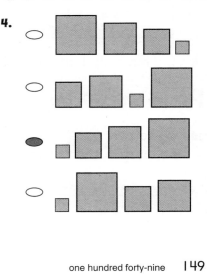

○
○
●
○

Chapter 4   one hundred forty-nine **149**

Test-Taking Tips

For the Teacher

- Explain that different types of test questions will take different amounts of time to complete.

- Before starting a test, check for student understanding of the test questions.

For the Student

- Tell students that different types of test questions will take different amounts of time to complete.

- Encourage students to make a good guess for an answer if time is running out and they are stuck on a question.

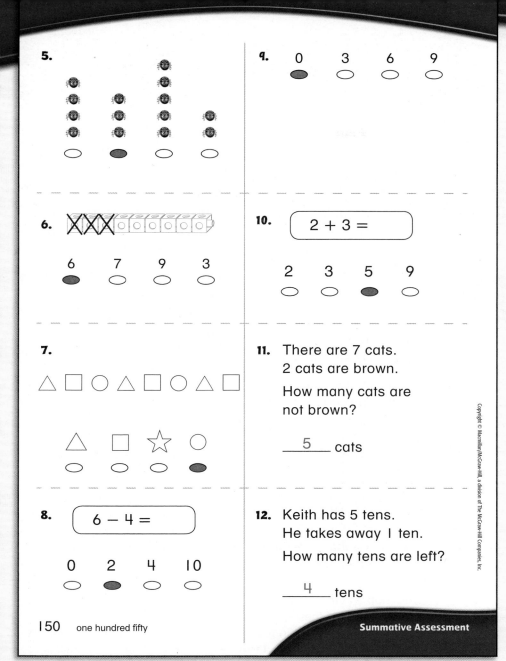

5.

6.

6   7   9   3

7.

8.   6 − 4 =

0   2   4   10

9.   0   3   6   9

10.   2 + 3 =

2   3   5   9

11. There are 7 cats.
2 cats are brown.

How many cats are
not brown?

_____5_____ cats

12. Keith has 5 tens.
He takes away 1 ten.

How many tens are left?

_____4_____ tens

Summative Assessment

Test Directions for Teachers

Read the following directions to students before they begin the test. Then read each question followed by a pause to allow students time to work on the problem and choose an answer. The first test item can be worked as a class example.

- **Write your name at the top of the page.**
- **I am going to read each question to you. Listen carefully to the entire question before you choose an answer.**

Multiple Choice

1. Which is a related addition fact?
2. Look at the graph. It shows the activities and number of votes that children like to do. Find the activity that got the most votes. Mark the picture that shows the most favorite activity.
3. Look at the tally chart. It shows favorite snacks. Find the snack that has two votes. Mark the picture that shows two votes.
4. Look at groups of shapes. Find the group that shows the shapes grouped by size from smallest to largest.

- **Turn the page over.**

5. Which group has three ladybugs?
6. Look at the connecting cubes. How many are left?
7. Look at the pattern. What comes next in the pattern?
8. What is the difference?
9. Katie had 3 balloons. All 3 float away. How many balloons does Katie have left?
10. What is the sum?

Short Response

11. There are 7 cats. 2 cats are brown. How many cats are not brown?
12. Keith has 5 tens. He takes away 1 ten. How many tens are left?

Chapter Overview

Chapter-at-a-Glance

In Chapter 5, students learn basic math facts to 12 through strategy instruction, hands-on activities, and practice activities.

Lesson	Math Objective	State/Local Standards
5-1 **Add in Any Order** (pp. 155–156)	Identify related addition facts with sums to 12.	
5-2 **Count On 1, 2, or 3** (pp. 157–158)	Count on from the greater number to find the sum.	
5-3 **Problem-Solving Strategy: Act It Out** (pp. 161–162)	Use the *act it out* strategy to solve problems.	
5-4 **Add 1, 2, or 3** (pp. 163–164)	Practice adding by counting on from the greater number.	
5-5 **Use a Number Line to Add** (pp. 165–166)	Use a number line to add.	
5-6 **Doubles** (pp. 169–170)	Use doubles facts to add.	
5-7 **Doubles Plus 1** (pp. 171–172)	Identify and use doubles plus 1 facts to add.	
5-8 **Problem-Solving Investigation: Choose a Strategy** (pp. 173–174)	Choose the best strategy to solve a problem.	

Develop Addition Strategies

BIG Idea The memorization of addition facts can be simplified for students through the use of several simple strategies introduced in this chapter. These strategies include: counting on, using a number line, and utilizing doubles facts.

In addition, students are also introduced to the Commutative Property and how it relates to addition.

Algebra Readiness Students prepare for Algebra through practice in solving addition equations written vertically and horizontally. Lesson 5-1

Students use manipulatives to count on to find the sum of addition problems. This use of manipulatives helps prepare students to work with equations. Lesson 5-3

Focal Points and Connections

G1-FP2 *Number and Operations:* **Developing an understanding of whole number relationships, including grouping in tens and ones**

Children compare and order whole numbers (at least to 100) to develop an understanding of and solve problems involving the relative sizes of these numbers. They think of whole numbers between 10 and 100 in terms of groups of tens and ones (especially recognizing the numbers 11 to 19 as 1 group of ten and particular numbers of ones). They understand the sequential order of the counting numbers and their relative magnitudes and represent numbers on a number line.

G1-FP6C *Algebra:* Through identifying, describing, and applying number patterns and properties in developing strategies for basic facts, children learn about other properties of numbers and operations, such as odd and even (e.g., "Even numbers of objects can be paired, with none left over"), and 0 as the identity element for addition.

Skills Trace
Vertical Alignment

Kindergarten
In kindergarten, students learned to:
- Understand simple addition stories.
- Use objects to determine the answers to addition problems.

First Grade
During this chapter, students learn to:
- Know addition facts and commit them to memory.
- Use a number line to show the meaning of addition.
- Use manipulatives to model addition.
- Use addition strategies such as counting on and identifying and using doubles facts.

After this chapter, students learn to:
- Use the inverse relationship between addition and subtraction to solve problems. (Chapter 10)
- Represent equivalent forms of the same number through the use of physical models, diagrams, and number expressions (to 20). (Chapter 10)

Second Grade
In second grade, students learn to:
- Use the Commutative and Associative Properties to simplify mental calculations and check results.
- Find the sum of two whole numbers (two-digit and three-digit).
- Use estimation strategies in computation and problem solving that involve numbers that use the ones, tens, hundreds, and thousands places.

Back-Mapping and Vertical Alignment McGraw-Hill's *Math Connects* program was conceived and developed with the final results in mind: student success in Algebra 1 and beyond. The authors, using the **NCTM Focal Points and Focal Connections** as their guide, developed this brand-new series by backmapping from Algebra 1 concepts, and vertically aligning the topics so that they build upon prior skills and concepts and serve as a foundation for future topics.

▷ Math Vocabulary

The following math vocabulary words for Chapter 5 are listed in the glossary of the *Student Edition.* You can find interactive definitions in 13 languages in the *eGlossary* at macmillanmh.com.

addend any numbers or quantities being added together; example: in the problem 2 + 3 = 5, both 2 and 3 are addends (p. 155)

count on start at a number on a number line and count up to the next number (p. 157)

doubles two addends that are the same number; example: 7 + 7 = 14 (p. 169)

doubles plus 1 two addends in which one number is one larger than the other; example: 6 + 7 = 13 (p. 171)

Visual Vocabulary Cards Use Visual Vocabulary Card 2 to introduce and reinforce the vocabulary in this chapter. (The Define/Example/Ask routine is printed on the back of each card.)

addend

Chapter Planner

Suggested Pacing		
Instruction	**Review and Assessment**	**TOTAL**
8 days	2 days	**10 days**

Diagnostic Assessment
Are You Ready? (p. 152)

	Lesson 5-1 Pacing: 1 day	**Lesson 5-2** Pacing: 1 day	**Lesson 5-3** Pacing: 1 day
Lesson/ Objective	**Add in Any Order** (pp. 155–156) **Objective:** Identify related addition facts with sums to 12.	**Count On 1, 2, or 3** (pp. 157–158) **Objective:** Count on from the greater number to find the sum.	**Problem-Solving Strategy Act It Out** (pp. 161–162) **Objective:** Use the *act it out* strategy to solve problems.
State/Local Standards			
Math Vocabulary	addend	count on	
Lesson Resources	**Materials** WorkMat 1: Ten-Frame, dominoes **Manipulatives** blue and red connecting cubes, two-colored counters **Other Resources** CRM Leveled Worksheets (pp. 6–10) Daily Reteach • 5-Minute Check Problem of the Day	**Materials** dominoes **Manipulatives** connecting cubes **Other Resources** CRM Leveled Worksheets (pp. 11–15) Daily Reteach • 5-Minute Check Problem of the Day	**Materials** bird stickers, sports cards or playing cards **Manipulatives** connecting cubes **Other Resources** CRM Leveled Worksheets (pp. 16–20) Daily Reteach • 5-Minute Check Problem of the Day *Finding the Way*
Technology *Math Online*	♪ Math Song Track 11	♪ Math Song Track 11 🌐 Math Adventures	
Reaching All Learners	Gifted and Talented, p. 155B **AL** English Learners, p. 155B **ELL** Early Finishers, p. 155B **OL** **AL**	Gifted and Talented, p. 157B **AL** English Learners, p. 157B **ELL** Early Finishers, p. 157B **OL** **AL**	Gifted and Talented, p. 161B **AL** English Learners, p. 161B **ELL** Early Finishers, p. 161B **OL** **AL**
Alternate Lessons	*Math Their Way*, p. 196 *IMPACT Mathematics*: Unit B	*Math Their Way*, p. 104 *IMPACT Mathematics*: Unit B	

Extra Practice (p. 159)
Game Time: All Mixed Up (p. 160)

KEY
BL Below/ Approaching Level   **OL** On Level   **AL** Above/Beyond Level   **ELL** English Learners
SE Student Edition   **TE** Teacher Edition   **CRM** Chapter 3 Resource Masters   💿 CD-Rom
Transparency   Flip Chart   Real-World Problem Solving Library

	Lesson 5-4 Pacing: 1 day	**Lesson 5-5** Pacing: 1 day	**Lesson 5-6** Pacing: 1 day	
Lesson/ Objective	**Add 1, 2, or 3** (pp. 163–164) **Objective:** Practice adding by counting on from the greater number.	**Use a Number Line to Add** (pp. 165–166) **Objective:** Use a number line to add.	**Doubles** (pp. 169–170) **Objective:** Use doubles facts to add.	
State/Local Standards				
Math Vocabulary			doubles	
Lesson Resources	**Materials** cup **Manipulatives** connecting cubes, two-colored counters, number cubes **Other Resources** CRM Leveled Worksheets (pp. 21–25) Daily Reteach • 5-Minute Check Problem of the Day	**Materials** number cards (1–10), masking tape WorkMat 4: Number Lines **Manipulatives** two-colored counters **Other Resources** CRM Leveled Worksheets (pp. 26–30) Daily Reteach • 5-Minute Check Problem of the Day	**Materials** 1-inch grid paper, pennies **Manipulatives** connecting cubes **Other Resources** CRM Leveled Worksheets (pp. 31–35) Daily Reteach • 5-Minute Check Problem of the Day	
Technology / Math Online	Math Song Track 11 Math Tool Chest, Counters Level 1 Math Adventures	Math Song Track 11 Concepts in Motion	Math Song Track 11 Math Adventures	
Reaching All Learners	Below Level, p. 163B BL English Learners, p. 163B ELL Early Finishers, p. 163B OL AL	Gifted and Talented, p. 165B AL English Learners, p. 165B ELL Early Finishers, p. 165B OL AL	Below Level, p. 169B BL English Learners, p. 169B ELL Early Finishers, p. 169B OL AL	
Alternate Lessons	*Math Their Way,* pp. 197–198	*IMPACT Mathematics*: Unit B	*IMPACT Mathematics*: Unit B	

Formative Assessment
• Mid-Chapter Check (p. 167)
• Spiral Review (p. 168)

	Lesson 5-7 Pacing: 1 day	**Lesson 5-8** Pacing: 1 day
Lesson/ Objective	**Doubles Plus 1** (pp. 171–172) **Objective:** Identify and use doubles plus 1 facts to add.	**Problem-Solving Investigation** **Choose a Strategy** (pp. 173–174) **Objective:** Choose the best strategy to solve a problem.
State/Local Standards		
Math Vocabulary	doubles plus 1	
Lesson Resources	**Materials** WorkMat 1: Ten-Frame **Manipulatives** connecting cubes, two-colored counters **Other Resources** CRM Leveled Worksheets (pp. 36–40) Daily Reteach • 5-Minute Check Problem of the Day	**Manipulatives** connecting cubes **Other Resources** CRM Leveled Worksheets (pp. 41–45) Daily Reteach • 5-Minute Check Problem of the Day *Finding the Way*
Technology Math Online	♪ Math Song Track 11 Math Adventures Concepts in Motion	
Reaching All Learners	Below Level, p. 171B BL English Learners, p. 171B ELL Early Finishers, p. 171B OL AL	Below Level, p. 173B BL English Learners, p. 173B ELL Early Finishers, p. 173B OL AL
Alternate Lessons		

Problem Solving in Social Studies (p. 175)

Summative Assessment
- Chapter Review/Test (p. 177)
- Test Practice (p. 179)

Assessment Options

✓ Diagnostic Assessment

SE *Option 1:* Are You Ready? (p. 151)

Option 2: Online Quiz macmillanmh.com

CRM *Option 3:* Alternate Diagnostic Test (p. 47)

CRM *Option 4:* Chapter Pretest (p. 48)

✓ Formative Assessment

TE Alternate Teaching Strategies (every lesson)

SE Talk About It (every lesson)

SE Writing in Math (every lesson)

SE Check (every lesson)

TE Line Up (every lesson)

SE Mid-Chapter Check (p. 167)

CRM Mid-Chapter Test (p. 49)

✓ Summative Assessment

SE Chapter/Review Test (p. 177)

SE Test Practice (p. 179)

CRM Vocabulary Test (p. 50)

CRM Leveled Chapter Tests (pp. 57–66)

CRM Cumulative Test Practice (pp. 67–68)

CRM Listening Assessment (pp. 53–54)

CRM Oral Assessment (pp. 51–52)

💿 Exam*View*® Assessment Suite

A⁺ Advance Tracker

McGraw Hill Professional Development

Targeted professional development has been articulated throughout **McGraw-Hill's** *Math Connects* program. The **McGraw-Hill Professional Development Video Library** provides short videos that support the **NCTM Focal Points and Focal Connections**. For more information, visit macmillanmh.com.

| Model Lessons | Instructional Strategies |

Assessment Tips

Students need to commit to memory the basic facts of addition but not before they understand the meaning of addition.

- Either individually or in a small group, read a word problem to the student(s). Ex: "Sally had 6 markers. Tom gave her 5 more markers. How many markers does Sally have now?"
- Encourage the students to use counters to solve the problem.
- Students should verbally tell you how they are solving the problem.
- Tape record their responses to review and assess later.

Teacher Notes

Learning Stations
Cross-Curricular Links

Reading

Addition Concentration

- Get 3 cards. Write an addition story on each card.
- Get 3 more cards. Write the addition number sentence for each story.
- Find a partner. Mix your story cards together. Lay them facedown.
- Mix your number sentence cards. Place them face up.
- Take turns turning over a story card. Read the story. Find the number sentence that matches it.

Teacher Note: Provide picture books or other materials to help give students ideas for addition stories.

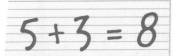

$5 + 3 = 8$

I have 5 blue cars.
I have 3 red cars.

Materials:
- index cards
- crayons
- markers

Art

👥 **pairs** | **VISUAL/ SPATIAL**

Create an Addition Fact Game

- Design a game board. Glue squares of colored paper next to each other to make a path.
- Write **Start** at the beginning of the path and **Finish** at the end.
- On index cards write addition facts such as $2 + 3 = \_$. Write 10 different facts.
- Play your game with a partner. Put the cards facedown. Take turns picking a card and telling the sum. The sum tells the number of spaces to move your counter.

Teacher Note: Provide other board games as examples.

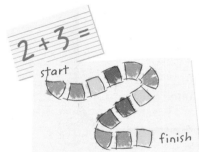

$2 + 3 =$

start

finish

Materials:
- 2 in. × 2 in. squares of colored construction paper
- index cards
- 11 in. × 17 in. construction paper or poster board
- glue
- markers
- two-colored counters

Language Arts

👤 **individual** | **VISUAL/ SPATIAL**

Make an Addition Book

- Write "My Addition Book" and your name on the cover of your book.
- On the first page, write the addition fact $3 + 7 = \_$.
- On the second page, draw three of your favorite animal.
- On the third page, draw a plus sign.
- On the fourth page, draw seven of your favorite animal.
- On the fifth page, draw an equals sign.
- On the sixth page, draw ten of your favorite animal and write the complete addition fact below. $3 + 7 = 10$.
- Make another book using a different addition fact.

My Addition Book

By Adam

Materials:
- 2 sheets of $8\frac{1}{2}$ in. × 11 in. construction paper folded and stapled to make a book
- markers
- crayons

Science

individual | **VISUAL/ SPATIAL**

Bugs, Bugs, and More Bugs!
- Fold your paper in half. Fold it again to make 4 boxes for pictures.
- In each box, draw a place where you can see bugs.
- "Hide" bug stickers in each picture. You can draw bugs if you do not have stickers.
- Find a partner. Take turns finding the number of bugs in each picture.

Teacher Note: Be sure students place more than one bug in each picture.

Materials:
- $8\frac{1}{2}$ in. × 11 in. construction paper
- crayons
- markers
- bug stickers

Health

small group | **KINESTHETIC**

Score!
- Play with a partner.
- Crumple up 10 pieces of scrap paper into balls.
- Stand a few feet away from the basket. Take turns tossing the balls into the basket.
- Count how many baskets you make. That is your score.
- Add your score to your partner's score to see how many baskets you made together. Write down the addition sentence.

Materials:
- scrap paper
- basket

Calendar Time

Weekend Days
- Write the name of the current month on the calendar poster. Ask students to help you fill in the numbers for the days of the month.
- Circle today's date and have students count the number of days from today to the next Saturday. Then have them say the dates for each different day of the week.
- Ask students how many Saturdays there are in this month. Ask them how many Sundays are in this month. Have students add the number of Saturdays and Sundays to find the total number of weekend days.
- Ask students to write a number sentence to show what numbers they added together to find the sum of the number of weekend days. Share number sentences.
- Discuss how the number sentences are alike and different.

Introduce the Chapter

Find the Total

Share with students that in this chapter they are going to develop addition strategies. Explain that they will learn new ways to solve addition problems that will make it easy to learn and recall the facts quickly.

- Have pairs of students take turns using counters to make two groups. Ask pairs to find the total number of counters in the groups.
- **How did you find the total number of counters?** Sample answer: We counted each group and added them together.

Have students turn to p. 151.

- Ask students to use the image to answer the Explore question.
- Have students draw a picture of the spider. **What number sentence shows the total number of legs?** $4 + 4 = 8$

Key Vocabulary
Introduce key vocabulary in the chapter using the routine below.

Define: **Doubles** are two addends that are the same number.
Example: The number sentence $2 + 2 = 4$ is a doubles sentence. The addends are both 2.
Ask: Can you write a doubles sentence with a different number?

CHAPTER 5

Develop Addition Strategies

Key Vocabulary
addend
count on
doubles
doubles plus one

Explore
How many legs are there in all?
Sample answer:
___4___ + ___4___ = ___8___

Chapter 5   one hundred fifty-one **151**

 **Dinah Zike's Foldables**

Guide students to create their Bound Book Foldable for developing addition strategies.

① Take two pieces of poster board and separately fold them like a hamburger. Place the posters on top of each other, leaving about a half inch between the mountaintops.

② Mark both folds one inch from the outer edges.

③ On one of the folded posters, cut from the top and bottom edge to the marked spot on both sides.

④ On the second folded poster, start at one of the marked spots and cut the fold between the two marks.

⑤ Take the cut poster from Step 3 and fold it like a burrito. Place the burrito through the other sheet and then open the burrito. Fold the bound pages in half to form an eight-page book.

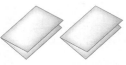  

When to Use It *Lessons 5-1, 5-2, 5-4, 5-5, 5-6, and 5-7. (Additional instructions for using the Foldable with these lessons are found on pp. 167 and 177.)*

Name _____

Math Online
Take the Chapter Readiness
Quiz at macmillanmh.com

Are You Ready for Chapter 5?

1. Circle the symbol that means to **add**.

(+)   −   =

2. Circle the symbol that means **equals**.

+   −   (=)

Add.

3. $\begin{array}{r} 4 \\ + 0 \\ \hline 4 \end{array}$	**4.** $\begin{array}{r} 2 \\ + 2 \\ \hline 4 \end{array}$	**5.** $\begin{array}{r} 7 \\ + 1 \\ \hline 8 \end{array}$
6. $\begin{array}{r} 6 \\ + 3 \\ \hline 9 \end{array}$	**7.** $\begin{array}{r} 4 \\ + 1 \\ \hline 5 \end{array}$	**8.** $\begin{array}{r} 3 \\ + 4 \\ \hline 7 \end{array}$
9. $\begin{array}{r} 5 \\ + 2 \\ \hline 7 \end{array}$	**10.** $\begin{array}{r} 8 \\ + 1 \\ \hline 9 \end{array}$	**11.** $\begin{array}{r} 9 \\ + 1 \\ \hline 10 \end{array}$

Use the pictures to write a number sentence.

12.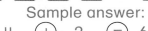

Sample answer:

__4__ (+) __2__ (=) __6__   or 6 − 2 = 4

152   one hundred fifty-two

This page checks skills needed for Chapter 5.

Copyright © Macmillan/McGraw-Hill, a division of The McGraw-Hill Companies, Inc.

Diagnostic Assessment

Check for students' prerequisite skills before beginning the chapter.

- **Option 1:** *Are You Ready for Chapter 5?*
  📖 Student Edition, p. 152

- **Option 2:** *Online Assessment*
  Math Online macmillanmh.com

- **Option 3:** *Diagnostic Test*
  CRM Chapter 5 Resource Masters, p. 47

RTI (Response to Intervention)

Apply the Results Based on the results of the diagnostic assessment on student p. 152, use the chart below to address individual needs before beginning the chapter.

TIER 3 Intensive Intervention

If → students miss eight or more of the exercises:

Then → use Chapters 1 and 3 of *Math Triumphs*, an intensive math intervention program from McGraw-Hill

TIER 2 Strategic Intervention
below grade level

If → students miss four to seven in: **Exercises 1–12**

Then → choose a resource:

Strategic Intervention Guide (p. 62)

CRM Chapter 5 Resource Masters (Reteach Worksheets)

Math Online Concepts in Motion

TIER 1 On-Level

If → students miss two or three: **Exercises 1–12**

Then → choose a resource:

TE Learning Stations (pp. 151G–151H)

TE Chapter Project (p. 153)

CRM Game: *Match to Add*

Math Adventures

My Math Zone Chapter 4

Math Online Fact Dash

Above-Level

If → students miss one or less in: **Exercises 1–12**

Then → choose a resource:

TE Learning Stations (pp. 151G–151H)

TE Chapter Project (p. 153)

📖 Real-World Problem Solving: *Finding the Way*

Math Adventures

My Math Zone Chapter 4, 5

Math Online Game

Chapter 5 Diagnostic Assessment   **152**

MATH at HOME

Before you begin Chapter 5:

- Read the Math at Home letter found on p. 153 with the class and have each student sign it.
- Send home copies of the Math at Home letter with each student.
- Use the Spanish letter on p. 154 for students with Spanish-speaking parents or guardians.

WRITING IN ▶ MATH

Starting the Chapter

Ask students to write about the different ways they use addition in their daily lives and the kinds of things they add. For example, they might add snacks or toys.

Have a class discussion about why knowing how to add is useful and necessary in their lives. Then ask students to write about why they want to be able to add well.

Read-Aloud Anthology

For an optional reading activity to introduce this chapter's math concepts, see the Read-Aloud Anthology on p. TR30.

MATH at HOME

Dear Family,

Today my class started Chapter 5, **Develop Addition Strategies**. In this chapter, I will learn to use different strategies for addition. Here is an activity we can do and a list of books we can read together.

Love, _____

Activity

Call out a number between 1 and 3. Have your child do double that number of jumping jacks and count aloud.

Key Vocabulary

count on counting up 1, 2, or 3 numbers
$$5 + 2 = 7$$

doubles two addends that are the same number
$$7 + 7 = 14$$
addends

Math Online Click on the eGlossary link at macmillanmh.com to find out more about these words. There are 13 languages.

Books to Read

Splash
by Ann Jonas
Harper Trophy Publishing, 1997.

Animals on Board
by Stuart J. Murphy
Harper Trophy
Publishing, 1998.

Monster Math
by Grace Maccarone
Voyager Books, 2002.

one hundred fifty-three 153

✔ Chapter 5 Project

My Addition Number Story Book

- Have students create addition number story books.
- Ask students to write addition number stories throughout the chapter.
- Each story should include a drawing and number sentence to illustrate the story.
- Students design and create a cover for their book with the title *My Addition Number Story Book.*
- Staple or bind each student's book together.
- Ask students to share their book and one addition number story with the class. Students may also share their books with a Kindergarten class to introduce them to addition.

CRM *Refer to Chapter 5 Resource Masters, p. 55 for a rubric to assess students' progress on this project.*

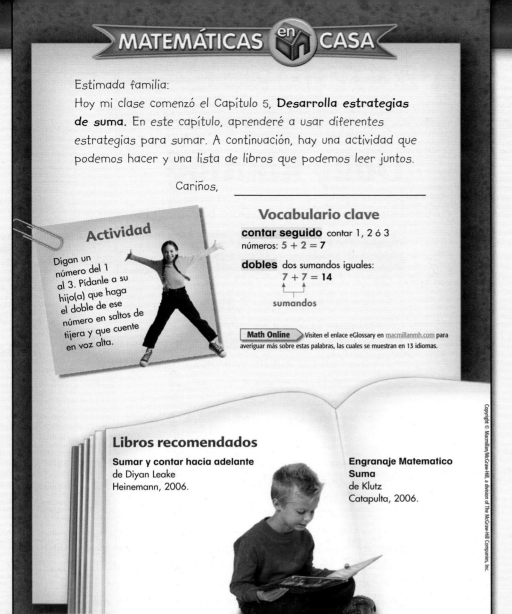

MATEMÁTICAS en CASA

Estimada familia:

Hoy mi clase comenzó el Capítulo 5, **Desarrolla estrategias de suma.** En este capítulo, aprenderé a usar diferentes estrategias para sumar. A continuación, hay una actividad que podemos hacer y una lista de libros que podemos leer juntos.

Cariños, _____

Actividad

Digan un número del 1 al 3. Pídanle a su hijo(a) que haga el doble de ese número en saltos de tijera y que cuente en voz alta.

Vocabulario clave

contar seguido contar 1, 2 ó 3 números: $5 + 2 = 7$

dobles dos sumandos iguales:
$$7 + 7 = 14$$
sumandos

Math Online Visiten el enlace eGlossary en macmillanmh.com para averiguar más sobre estas palabras, las cuales se muestran en 13 idiomas.

Libros recomendados

Sumar y contar hacia adelante
de Diyan Leake
Heinemann, 2006.

Engranaje Matematico Suma
de Klutz
Catapulta, 2006.

154 one hundred fifty-four

Chapter 5 Literature List

Lesson	Book Title
5-1	**Domino Addition** Lynette Long
5-2	**Fish Eyes: A Book You Can Count On** Lois Ehlert
5-3	**12 Ways to Get to 11** Eve Merriam
5-4	**Animals on Board** Stuart J. Murphy
5-5	**Little Quack** Lauren Thompson
5-6	**Double Trouble** Rose Greydanus
5-7	**Plant Fruits & Seeds** David M. Schwartz
Any	**Splash** Ann Jonas
Any	**Monster Math** Grace Maccarone

ELL National ESL Standards Alignment for Chapter 1

Lesson, Page	ESL Standard	Modality	Level
5-1, p 155B	Goal 2, Standard 1, k	Visual/Spatial	Intermediate
5-2, p 157B	Goal 2, Standard 3, a	Visual/Spatial	Intermediate
5-3, p 161B	Goal 2, Standard 2, c	Logical	Advanced
5-4, p 163B	Goal 1, Standard 2, a	Visual, Auditory	Beginning
5-5, p 165B	Goal 1, Standard 3, c	Auditory, Kinesthetic	Intermediate
5-6, p 137B	Goal 1, Standard 3, k	Kinesthetic	Intermediate
5-7, p 141B	Goal 2, Standard 1, b	Logical, Spatial	Intermediate
5-8, p 143B	Goal 2, Standard 2, g	Intrapersonal	Advanced

The National ESL Standards can be found in the Teacher Reference Handbook.

Lesson Planner

Objective
Identify related addition facts with sums to 12.

Vocabulary
addend

Resources
Materials: WorkMat 1: Ten-Frame, dominoes

Manipulatives: blue and red connecting cubes, two-colored counters

Literature Connection: *Domino Addition* by Lynette Long

Alternate Lessons: Adapt "Say It Fast" on p. 196 of *Math Their Way* for practice adding numbers in any order. Use *IMPACT Mathematics: Unit B* to provide practice with related addition facts.

Teacher Technology
- TeacherWorks • Math Songs Track 11 Lesson Plan

Focus on Math Background

Students become comfortable with the commutative property of addition when they add in any order through hands-on work with math manipulatives. The multiple experiences composing numbers and the multiple representations that can be used (counters, connecting cubes, pictures, and numbers) all contribute to student confidence in seeing number equalities.

Dr. Liping Ma did extensive research on the importance of a strong foundation in composing (and decomposing) numbers as the basis for success with mathematical computation algorithms and solving algebraic equations.

Daily Routine

Use these suggestions before beginning the lesson on p. 155.

5-Minute Check
(Reviews Lesson 4-8)

Raoul put 3 green cubes and 1 yellow cube in a bag. Is it certain he will pick a yellow cube? No, he could choose a green cube or yellow cube.

Problem of the Day

Jenny uses 9 beads to make a necklace. The pattern of beads is purple, pink, yellow. How many pink beads will she use? 3 pink beads

LINE UP Have students hold up fingers on both hands to make 8. Ask students who used three fingers on their right hand to get in line, three fingers on their left hand to get in line, and then four fingers on either hand to get in line.

▷ Building Math Vocabulary
- Write the vocabulary word **addend** on the board and read the word to students.
- **Addends are the numbers that are added together in an addition problem.**
- Write the problem $3 + 6 = 9$ on the chalkboard and circle or underline the numbers 3 and 6. **In this problem, 3 and 6 are the *addends*.**
- Display flash cards or write addition problems on the chalkboard. Have students tell which numbers in each problem are addends.

Visual Vocabulary Cards
Use Visual Vocabulary Card 2 to reinforce the vocabulary introduced in this lesson. (The Define/Example/Ask routine is printed on the back of each card.)

Differentiated Instruction

Small Group Options

Option 1 — Gifted and Talented (AL)

KINESTHETIC, SOCIAL

Materials: white board, dry erase marker, red number cube

- Students work in groups of three to practice adding with three addends. Explain that the first numbers are added first and then that sum is added to the third number.
- Each student takes a turn rolling the number cube and writing on the white board the number he or she rolled.
- Students take turns writing a number sentence with the three addends on the white board.
- Each number sentence on the white board must have the addends written in a different order.
- Number sentences may be written horizontally or vertically.
- Students compare the sums of their three number sentences.

Erase the board after three problems have been written correctly and repeat.

$$3, 1, 4$$
$$3 + 1 + 4 = 8$$
$$1 + 3 + 4 = 8$$
$$4 + 3 + 1 = 8$$

Option 2 — English Language Learners (ELL)

VISUAL, SPATIAL

Materials: overhead pattern blocks

Vocabulary: in order, How have they changed? order

Common Use Verb: change

Math This strategy allows students to visualize order changes.

- Place shapes on overhead, from left to right.
- "**These are in order**" and number them from left to right. Say: "**Change** the **order.**"
- Using *another* set of blocks, place them, from left to right, underneath the first set.
- "**How have they changed?**" Accept answers and say: "The **order** has **changed.**"
- [illegible]
- Extend the activity by having students act out sorting and ordering themselves.

Independent Work Options

Option 1 — Early Finishers (OL) (AL)

KINESTHETIC, SOCIAL

Materials: dominoes

- One partner picks up a domino and says the number sentence he or she can make with the dots, or addends.
- The other partner uses the same domino to say the number sentence with addends in reverse order.

Option 2 — Student Technology

Math Online > macmillanmh.com

🎵 Math Songs, "The Addition Boogie" Track 11

Option 3 — Learning Station: Health (p. 151H)

Direct students to the Health Learning Station for more opportunities to explore and extend the lesson concept.

Option 4 — Problem-Solving Practice

Reinforce problem-solving skills and strategies with the Problem-Solving Practice worksheet.

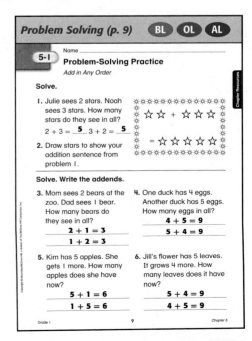

Problem Solving (p. 9) BL OL AL

5-1 Name _____
Problem-Solving Practice
Add in Any Order

Solve.

1. Julie sees 2 stars. Noah sees 3 stars. How many stars do they see in all?
$2 + 3 = \underline{5}$ $3 + 2 = \underline{5}$

2. Draw stars to show your addition sentence from problem 1.
$= ☆☆☆☆☆$

Solve. Write the addends.

3. Mom sees 2 bears at the zoo. Dad sees 1 bear. How many bears do they see in all?
$2 + 1 = 3$
$1 + 2 = 3$

4. One duck has 4 eggs. Another duck has 5 eggs. How many eggs in all?
$4 + 5 = 9$
$5 + 4 = 9$

5. Kim has 5 apples. She gets 1 more. How many apples does she have now?
$5 + 1 = 6$
$1 + 5 = 6$

6. Jill's flower has 5 leaves. It grows 4 more. How many leaves does it have now?
$5 + 4 = 9$
$4 + 5 = 9$

Grade 1   9   Chapter 5

1 Introduce

Activity Choice 1 • Hands-On
Display a ten-frame and mix up ten two-colored counters to fill the ten-frame.
- Have students tell the addition sentence in two ways. Repeat this process and record addition sentences.

Activity Choice 2 • Literature
Introduce the lesson with *Domino Addition* by Lynette Long. For additional support, see p. TR48.

2 Teach

Show students a set of five red connecting cubes and a set of two blue connecting cubes. Connect the cubes with the five red on top of the two blue.
- **What are the two addends?** 5 and 2
- **What number sentence do the cubes show?** $5 + 2 = 7$
- Move the blue connecting cubes on top of the red cubes. **What number sentence do the cubes show now?** $2 + 5 = 7$
- **How are the number sentences different?** The addends are in a different order. **Did the sum change when we added in a different order?** No
- Explain to students that the commutative property of addition allows addends to be added in any order without changing the sum.

Get Ready Use the section at the top of student p. 155 to reinforce the lesson concept. Guide students through the example, and let students use physical counters if necessary.

Check Observe students as you work through Exercises 1–5 as a class.

Exercise 5 Assess student comprehension before assigning practice exercises.

⚠ COMMON ERROR!

Exercises 6–13 Students may have two different sums for problems with the same addends when they are written in a different order. Encourage students to work slowly and check their work to make sure the sum for each problem is correct. Have counters available for students to use so they can check their work.

155 **Chapter 5** Develop Addition Strategies

Name _____

Add in Any Order

Get Ready

Main Idea
I will add in any order.

Vocabulary
addend

Addends are the numbers you add. You can change the order of the addends and get the same sum.

$3 + 6 = 6 + 3$

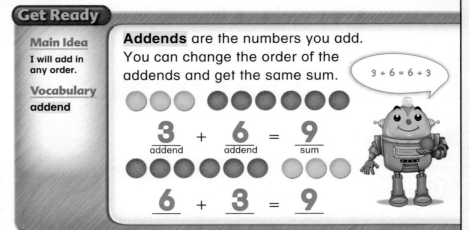

$$\underset{\text{addend}}{3} + \underset{\text{addend}}{6} = \underset{\text{sum}}{9}$$

$$\underline{6} + \underline{3} = \underline{9}$$

✓ Check

Write the addends. Use ⚪⚪. Then add.

1.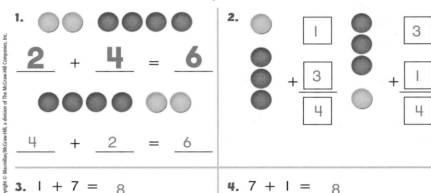

$$\underline{2} + \underline{4} = \underline{6}$$

$$\underline{4} + \underline{2} = \underline{6}$$

2.

$$+ \boxed{3} \over \boxed{4}$$

$$+ \boxed{1} \over \boxed{4}$$

with boxes: | 1 | 3 |

3. $1 + 7 = \underline{8}$

4. $7 + 1 = \underline{8}$

5. **Talk About It** Tell how you can show that $1 + 9$ is the same as $9 + 1$. 9 counters and 1 counter and count them. The sum is also 10.

Chapter 5   Lesson 1   one hundred fifty-five   **155**

Reteach (p. 6)   **BL**

Name _____
5-1 **Reteach**
Add in Any Order

The domino has 7 dots.
Turn the domino around.
It still has 7 dots.
The addends are the same.

$3 + 4 = 7$
$4 + 3 = 7$

Find the sum. Turn the 🁢 around.
Write the addends. Add.

1.
$3 + 2 = \underline{5}$ $2 + 3 = \underline{5}$

2.
$1 + 4 = \underline{5}$ $4 + 1 = \underline{5}$

3.
$5 + 4 = \underline{9}$ $4 + 5 = \underline{9}$

4.
$5 + 2 = \underline{7}$ $2 + 5 = \underline{7}$

Grade 1   6   Chapter 5

Skills Practice (p. 7)

Name _____
5-1 **Skills Practice**
Add in Any Order

Write the addends. Add. You can use ⚪⚪

1. ●●●○○○○○○○
   ○○○○○○●●●
   $3 + \underline{}$
   addend
   $\underline{5} +$
   addend
   $= 6$

2. ●●○○○○○
   ○○○○●●
   $2 + $
   4
   $= 6$

3. ●●●●●●●○
   ○●●●●●●●●
   $7 +$
   1
   $= 8$

4. $6 + 3 = \underline{9}$
   $3 + 6 = \underline{9}$

5. $1 + 5 \over 6$

6. There are 4 lions in the zoo. 5 more come. How many lions are in the zoo?
   $4 + 5 = 9$
   $5 + 4 = 9$

7. The ... come. the ...es are in H... th...
   | 5 |
   | 2 |
   | 7 |

Grade 1   7   Chapter 5

4-3 Skills Practice

Problem-Solving Strategy: Make a Table

Make a table to solve.

Jose sees 3 , 5 , and 2 ⭐ at the beach.

Objects on the beach	How many?	Does it have wings?
🐦	3	Y
🐚	5	N
⭐	2	N

How many more 🐚 than ⭐ are on the beach? __3__

How many objects have wings? __1__

$\dfrac{5}{-2}{3}$

---

2. Ann went to the zoo. She saw 🦒, 🎈, and 🦜.

Objects at the zoo	Is it tall?	Does it have wings?	Is it alive?
🦒	Y	N	Y
🎈	N	N	N
🦜	N	Y	Y

Are there any tall objects that are alive? __Y__

Are there any tall objects that have wings? __No__

Homework Practice

Problem-Solving Strategy: Make a Table

Make a table to solve.

Rosa's class had a picnic. She saw 6 🌳, 3 🍎, 9 🌰, and 10 🍇.

Objects at the picnic	How many?	Do you eat it?	Is it small?
🌳	6	N	N
🍎	3	Y	Y
🌰	9	N	Y
🍇	10	Y	Y

1. How many objects can you eat? ___2___

2. Are there any small objects that you do not eat? ___yes___

3. How many small objects are there? ___3___

4. How many **more** grapes than apples? ___7___

5. How many **more** acorns than trees? ___3___

6. How many **more** acorns than apples? ___6___

$$\begin{array}{r} 10 \\ -3 \\ \hline 7 \end{array}$$

$$\begin{array}{r} 9 \\ -4 \\ \hline 9 \end{array}$$

$$\begin{array}{r} 6 \\ -3 \end{array}$$

Write the addends.
Use ⚫⚪. Then add.

Remember
If you change the order of the addends, you get the same sum.

6. ⚫⚫ ⚫⚫⚫

$$\underline{2} + \underline{3} = \underline{5}$$

⚫⚫⚫ ⚪⚪

$$\underline{3} + \underline{2} = \underline{5}$$

7.

$$+ \boxed{3} \quad + \boxed{4}$$
$$\boxed{4} \quad \boxed{3}$$
$$\boxed{7} \quad \boxed{7}$$

8. $2 + 6 = \underline{8}$

9. $6 + 2 = \underline{8}$

10. $2 + 5 = \underline{7}$

11. $5 + 2 = \underline{7}$

12.
$$\begin{array}{r} 1 \\ + 3 \\ \hline 4 \end{array}$$

13.
$$\begin{array}{r} 3 \\ + 1 \\ \hline 4 \end{array}$$

H.O.T. Problem

14. Thinking Math

Can you subtract in any order? __No__

Use ⚫⚪.

Explain. Check students' work.

156 one hundred fifty-six

Math at Home Activity: Show your child 4 plates and 2 cups. Have him/her write two addition sentences about them.

Enrich (p. 10) **AL**

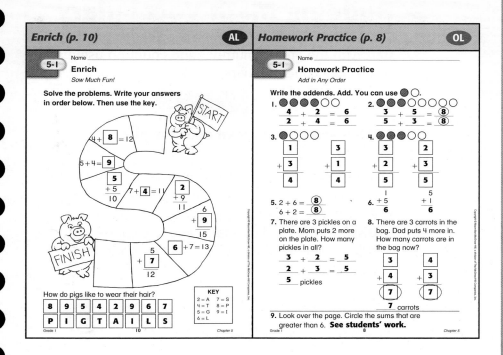

Homework Practice (p. 8) **OL**

If students have trouble understanding that the order of addends in an addition problem does not change the sum . . .

Then use one of these reteach options.

1 CRM **Daily Reteach Worksheet** (p. 6)

2 Domino Turnaround Have students each choose a domino and write the number sentence they can make with the dots. Next, have them turn the domino and write the new number sentence.

- **Which property of addition allows addends to be added in any order without changing the sum?** commutative property

3 Practice

Differentiate practice using these leveled assignments for Exercises 6–14.

Level	Assignment
BL Below/Approaching Level	Guide students in using two-colored counters to solve each problem.
OL On Level	Complete the exercises independently with two-colored counters.
AL Above/Beyond Level	Complete the exercises independently without counters.

4 Assess

Formative Assessment

Show students $2 + 9 = 11$ and $9 + 2 = 11$. **Why is the sum the same?** You are adding the same amounts but in a different order.

WRITING IN ▶ MATH What is the related addition fact for $4 + 2 = 6$? Write a number story using that fact. $2 + 4 = 6$; Sample answer: I had 2 dogs. One of the dogs had 4 puppies. Now I have 6 dogs.

Quick Check **Are students continuing to struggle with adding in any order?**

If Yes → CRM Reteach Worksheet (p. 6)

If No → Independent Work Options (p. 155B)
CRM Skills Practice Worksheet (p. 7)
CRM Enrich Worksheet (p. 10)

Lesson Planner

Objective

Count on from the greater number to find the sum.

Vocabulary

count on

Resources

Materials: dominoes

Manipulatives: connecting cubes

Literature Connection: *Fish Eyes: A Book You Can Count On* by Lois Ehlert

Alternate Lessons: Adapt "Cover Up" on p. 104 of *Math Their Way* for practice with counting on.
Use *IMPACT Mathematics:* Unit B to provide practice with the counting on strategy.

Teacher Technology

🔘 TeacherWorks • Math Songs Track 11 Lesson Plan

Focus on Math Background

The counting on (1, 2, or 3) strategy is especially helpful in becoming efficient with basic facts computation. Students need to be able to conserve a number for this strategy. Many young children tend to recount the "larger" number prior to counting on. The essential task is to make sure students recognize the greater addend, can conserve that number (hold that number in their thoughts), and then count on to determine the sum.

The counting on strategy addresses many of the basic facts students need to be proficient with.

Daily Routine

Use these suggestions before beginning the lesson on p. 157.

5-Minute Check

(Reviews Lesson 5-1)

Solve.

1. $5 + 3 =$ _____ $3 + 5 =$ _____

2. $2 + 9 =$ _____ $9 + 2 =$ _____

3. $4 + 1 =$ _____ $1 + 4 =$ _____

8, 8; 11, 11; 5, 5

What is different about each set of problems?
The addends are the same, but in a different order.

Problem of the Day

Five children were playing on the playground. Then 3 children left. How many children stayed on the playground? 2 children

LINE UP Hold up an addition flash card. Have students at one table or in one row say the fact and sum. Then have them reverse the addends, say the new fact and sum, and line up. Repeat until all students are in line.

▷ Building Math Vocabulary

Share with students that when they **count on**, they start with the greater number and count on using connecting cubes or manipulatives.

4 +

- **What addition problem does the picture show?** $4 + 2 = 6$
- Model counting on. Say "4" as you point to the number and "5, 6" as you point to the cubes.
- Repeat and have students count on with you. Display other addition facts and use connecting cubes to guide students in counting on to find each sum.

Differentiated Instruction

Small Group Options

Option 1 — Gifted and Talented (AL)
LOGICAL, SOCIAL

Materials: number lines (61–100), workmats, number cube

- Students work with a partner to make and solve addition problems.
- One partner calls out a number between 61 and 90.
- The other partner rolls the number cube and makes a number sentence by adding the number on the cube to the first number.
- To find the sum of the addition problem, partners find the first number on the number line and then count on.
- Students continue taking turns naming the first addend and rolling the number cube to get a second addend. Have them work together to find each sum.

Option 2 — English Language Learners (ELL)
VISUAL, SPATIAL

Core Vocabulary: hidden, how many more, count on from
Common Use Verb: can/can't see

Hear Math This strategy visually illustrates addition in a pre-algebraic form and negation with modal verbs.

- Show 5 beans on the overhead. Say: "How many *can* you *see*?"
- Cover them with a cup. Say: "How many *can't* you *see*?" Show 5 fingers. Say: "5."
- Put 2 beans outside the cup where they are visible. Say: "**How many more can you see?**"
- Say: "There are five hidden. I *can* count on from 5."
- Point and say: "5 **hidden**, and I *can see* 2 more. 5, 6, 7. I have 7 altogether."
- Repeat as time permits.

Use this worksheet to provide additional support for English Language Learners.

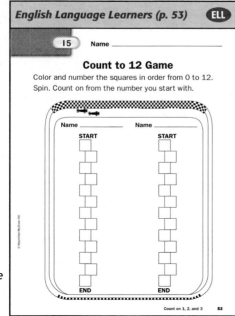

English Language Learners (p. 53) **ELL**

15   Name _____

Count to 12 Game
Color and number the squares in order from 0 to 12. Spin. Count on from the number you start with.

Name _____   Name _____
START   START

END   END

Count on 1, 2, and 3   **53**

Independent Work Options

Option 1 — Early Finishers (OL) (AL)
KINESTHETIC, SOCIAL

Materials: dominoes, connecting cubes

- One partner picks up a domino and says the addition fact he or she can make with the dots, or addends, on the domino.
- The other partner models the problem with connecting cubes and counts on from the greater number to find the sum of the addition problem.

Option 2 — Student Technology

Math Online ＞ macmillanmh.com

♪ Math Songs, "The Addition Boogie" Track 11 • Math Adventures

Option 3 — Learning Station: Art (p. 151G)

Direct students to the Art Learning Station for more opportunities to explore and extend the lesson concept.

Option 4 — Problem-Solving Practice

Reinforce problem-solving skills and strategies with the Problem-Solving Practice worksheet.

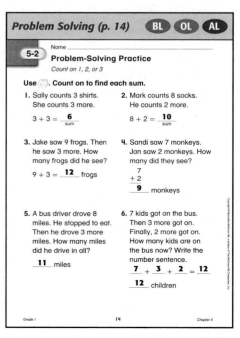

Problem Solving (p. 14) **BL** **OL** **AL**

Name _____
5-2   **Problem-Solving Practice**
Count on 1, 2, or 3

Use 🔢. Count on to find each sum.

1. Sally counts 3 shirts. She counts 3 more.
$3 + 3 = \underline{6}$ sum

2. Mark counts 8 socks. He counts 2 more.
$8 + 2 = \underline{10}$ sum

3. Jake saw 9 frogs. Then he saw 3 more. How many frogs did he see?
$9 + 3 = \underline{12}$ frogs

4. Sandi saw 7 monkeys. Jan saw 2 monkeys. How many did they see?
$\begin{array}{r} 7 \\ + 2 \\ \hline 9 \end{array}$ monkeys

5. A bus driver drove 8 miles. He stopped to eat. Then he drove 3 more miles. How many miles did he drive in all?
$\underline{11}$ miles

6. 7 kids got on the bus. Then 3 more got on. Finally, 2 more got on. How many kids are on the bus now? Write the number sentence.
$\underline{7} + \underline{3} + \underline{2} = \underline{12}$
$\underline{12}$ children

Grade 1   14   Chapter 5

5-2

1 Introduce

Activity Choice 1 • Hands-On

- Call five students to stand in a row at the front of the room. Ask a volunteer to count the students.
- Call three more students to the front of the room. Ask a volunteer to start with five and show how to **count on** to find out how many people there are.
- Repeat with additional combinations.

Activity Choice 2 • Literature

Introduce the lesson with *Fish Eyes: A Book You Can Count On* by Lois Ehlert. For additional support, see p. TR48.

2 Teach

Write $3 + 6 =$ ___ on the board and have students model the problem with connecting cubes.

- **Which number is less?** 3 **greater?** 6
- Have students add these numbers. **Which number should you start from?** 6
- **How many cubes will you count on?** 3 cubes
- **Why is it easier to begin with the greater number?** You do not have to count on as many numbers.
- Have students start at 6 and count on 3 cubes. Touch each cube as you count: 7, 8, 9. **What is the sum?** 9
- Continue to practice counting on with cubes for more addition facts.

Get Ready Use the section at the top of student p. 157 to reinforce the lesson concept. Guide students in counting on to add.

Check Observe students as you work through Exercises 1–5 as a class.

Exercise 5 Assess student comprehension before assigning practice exercises.

 COMMON ERROR!

Some students recount the entire group, starting with one. Although this is not "wrong," it is immature, and students should practice stating the greater number and counting on from that point.

Name _____

Count On 1, 2, or 3

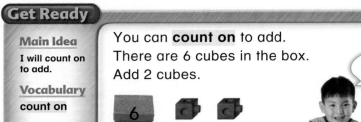

Get Ready

Main Idea
I will count on to add.

Vocabulary
count on

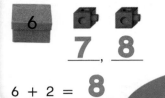

You can **count on** to add.
There are 6 cubes in the box.
Add 2 cubes.

Start with 6.
Count on 2: 7, 8.
6 + 2 = 8

6   **7**, **8**

6 + 2 = **8**

✓ Check

Use 🎲. Start with the greater number.
Count on to add.

1. 5
6, **7**, **8**
5 + 3 = **8**

2. 8
9, 10, 11
3 + 8 = **11**

3. 6
7, 8, 9
3 + 6 = **9**

4. 7
8, 9
7 + 2 = **9**

5. **Talk About It** Why should you start with the greater number when you count on? Sample answer: You have less to count on.

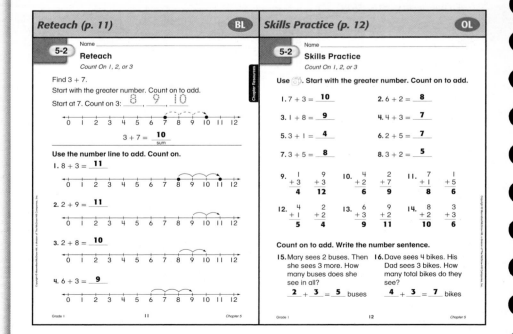

Reteach (p. 11) **BL**

5-2 Name _____
Reteach
Count On 1, 2, or 3

Find 3 + 7.
Start with the greater number. Count on to add.
Start at 7. Count on 3: 8, 9, 10

3 + 7 = **10**
sum

Use the number line to add. Count on.
1. 8 + 3 = **11**
2. 2 + 9 = **11**
3. 2 + 8 = **10**
4. 6 + 3 = **9**

Grade 1   11   Chapter 5

Skills Practice (p. 12) **OL**

5-2 Name _____
Skills Practice
Count On 1, 2, or 3

Use 🎲. Start with the greater number. Count on to add.
1. 7 + 3 = **10**   2. 6 + 2 = **8**
3. 1 + 8 = **9**   4. 4 + 3 = **7**
5. 3 + 1 = **4**   6. 2 + 5 = **7**
7. 3 + 5 = **8**   8. 3 + 2 = **5**

9. 1 +3 **4**   9 +3 **12**   10. 4 +2 **6**   2 +7 **9**   11. 7 +1 **8**   1 +5 **6**

12. 4 +1 **5**   2 +2 **4**   13. 6 +3 **9**   9 +2 **11**   14. 8 +2 **10**   3 +3 **6**

Count on to add. Write the number sentence.
15. Mary sees 2 buses. Then she sees 3 more. How many buses does she see in all?
2 + **3** = **5** buses

16. Dave sees 4 bikes. His Dad sees 3 bikes. How many total bikes do they see?
4 + **3** = **7** bikes

Grade 1   12   Chapter 5

Use . Start with the greater number.
Count on to add.

6. $9 + 3 = \underline{12}$ **7.** $3 + 8 = \underline{11}$ **8.** $1 + 8 = \underline{9}$

9. $3 + 7 = \underline{10}$ **10.** $2 + 9 = \underline{11}$ **11.** $2 + 3 = \underline{5}$

12. $9 + 1 = \underline{10}$ **13.** $1 + 7 = \underline{8}$ **14.** $8 + 3 = \underline{11}$

15.
$$\begin{array}{r} 8 \\ +\ 2 \\ \hline 10 \end{array}$$

16.
$$\begin{array}{r} 1 \\ +\ 4 \\ \hline 5 \end{array}$$

17.
$$\begin{array}{r} 5 \\ +\ 2 \\ \hline 7 \end{array}$$

18.
$$\begin{array}{r} 3 \\ +\ 9 \\ \hline 12 \end{array}$$

19.
$$\begin{array}{r} 1 \\ +\ 2 \\ \hline 3 \end{array}$$

20.
$$\begin{array}{r} 4 \\ +\ 3 \\ \hline 7 \end{array}$$

WRITING IN ▶ MATH

21. Explain how you count on to find $3 + 7$.

Sample answer: start with

7...count on 8 ,9 ,10

158   one hundred fifty-eight

Math at Home Activity: Have your child explain how he/she would find the sum of 6 and 2.

BL Alternate Teaching Strategy

If ▶ students have difficulty counting on . . .

Then ▶ use one of these reteach options.

1 CRM **Daily Reteach Worksheet** (p. 11)

2 Display a domino with three dots on one side and five dots on the other.
- **Will we start counting from 3 or 5?** 5
- **Which side has more dots?** the side with 5
- Count on together while pointing to each dot: 6, 7, 8.
- **What is the sum of the dots?** 8

3 Practice

Differentiate practice using these leveled assignments for Exercises 6–21.

Level	Assignment
BL Below/ Approaching Level	Read each problem and help students identify the greatest addend. Students count on using connecting cubes
OL On Level	Complete the exercises independently using connecting cubes.
AL Above/Beyond Level	Complete the exercises independently without connecting cubes.

4 Assess

Formative Assessment

How do you use connecting cubes and counting on to add 6 + 2? What is the sum? Say "6" and then count on as you point to each of the 2 connecting cubes. The number you say as you count the last cube is the sum. The sum is 8.

WRITING IN ▶ MATH Have students explain why it is important to know more than one way to solve an addition problem. Sample answer: I could use one strategy to solve the problem and another to check my answer.

Quick Check **Are students continuing to struggle with counting on?**

If Yes ▶ Strategic Intervention Guide (p. 96)

If No ▶ Independent Work Options (p. 155B)

CRM Skills Practice Worksheet (p. 12)

CRM Enrich Worksheet (p. 15)

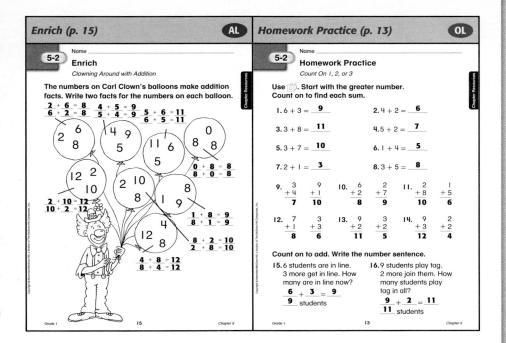

Extra Practice

Reviews Lessons 5-1 to 5-2

Objective: Review and assess mastery of previous lessons' skills and concepts.

- Review with students strategies for solving addition math facts.
- Remind students that they can add in any order and that addition problems with the same addends have the same sum.
- Students may need to use counters or a number line to find the sums.

Practice with Technology

Math Online Have students visit macmillanmh.com for additional practice with online activities, games, and quizzes.

Name _____

Count on to add.

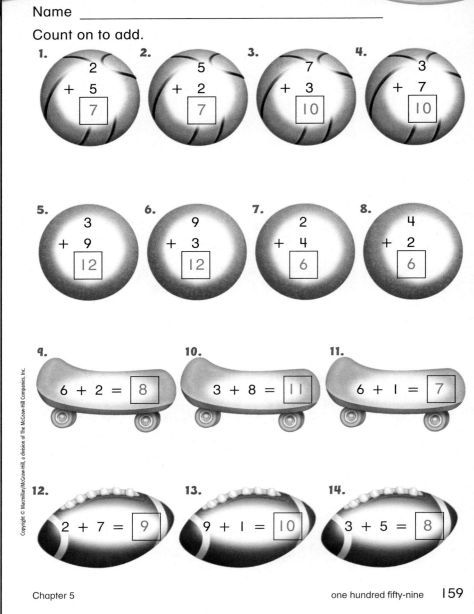

1. $2 + 5 = 7$
2. $5 + 2 = 7$
3. $7 + 3 = 10$
4. $3 + 7 = 10$

5. $3 + 9 = 12$
6. $9 + 3 = 12$
7. $2 + 4 = 6$
8. $4 + 2 = 6$

9. $6 + 2 = 8$
10. $3 + 8 = 11$
11. $6 + 1 = 7$

12. $2 + 7 = 9$
13. $9 + 1 = 10$
14. $3 + 5 = 8$

Chapter 5   one hundred fifty-nine 159

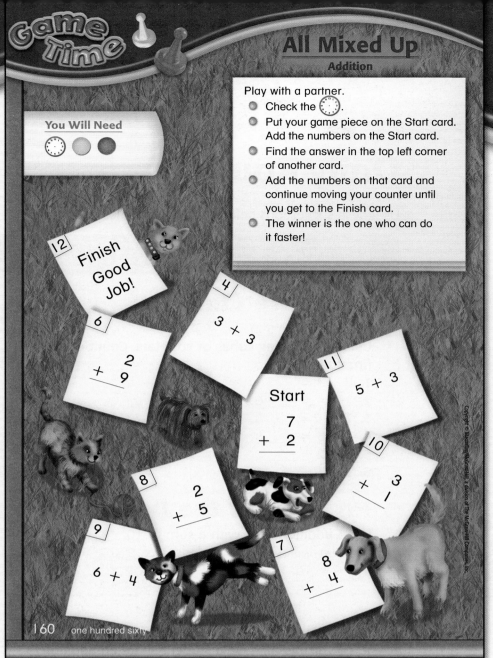

All Mixed Up
Addition

You Will Need

Play with a partner.
- Check the ⏱.
- Put your game piece on the Start card. Add the numbers on the Start card.
- Find the answer in the top left corner of another card.
- Add the numbers on that card and continue moving your counter until you get to the Finish card.
- The winner is the one who can do it faster!

Finish Good Job!

12

6
  2
+ 9

4
3 + 3

11
5 + 3

Start
7
+ 2

10
  3
+ 1

8
  2
+ 5

9
6 + 4

7
  8
+ 4

160 one hundred sixty

All Mixed Up

Math Concept:
Addition Math Facts

Materials: WorkMat 4: Number Line (1–20)
Manipulatives: two-colored counters, connecting cubes

Introduce the game on page 160 to students to play as a class, in small groups, or at a learning workstation to review concepts introduced in this chapter.

Instructions

- Each player picks a red or yellow counter as a game piece.
- Put the game pieces on the Start card in the center of the game board.
- Each player adds the numbers on the Start card and writes the sum.
- Each player finds the sum at the top of another card and moves his or her game piece to that card.
- Have students time each other to see who can finish in the least amount of time, or have students race by playing the game at the same time.
- Notify students that they may need to start over if they find the wrong sum because only the correct answers will lead to the Finish card.

Extend the Game

Have students design and create their own game board using both addition and subtraction facts.

Differentiated Practice

Use these leveling suggestions to differentiate the game for all the learners.

Level	Assignment
BL Below/Approaching Level	Have students use connecting cubes or a number line (1–20) to help them find the sum.
OL On Level	Have students play the game with the rules as written.
AL Above/Beyond Level	After students find the sum of each addition fact card, they must say another fact with the same sum.

Problem-Solving Strategy
Act It Out

Lesson Planner

Objective

Use the *act it out* strategy to solve problems.

Resources

Materials: bird stickers, sports cards or playing cards

Manipulatives: connecting cubes

Literature Connection: *12 Ways to Get 11* by Eve Merriam

Teacher Technology
- 🖲 TeacherWorks

📖 **Real-World Problem Solving Library**
Math and Social Studies: *Finding the Way*
Use these leveled books to reinforce and extend problem-solving skills and strategies.

Leveled for:
- **OL** On Level
- **ELL** Sheltered English
- **SP** Spanish

For additional support, see the Real-World Problem Solving Teacher Guide.

Daily Routine

Use these suggestions before beginning the lesson on p. 161.

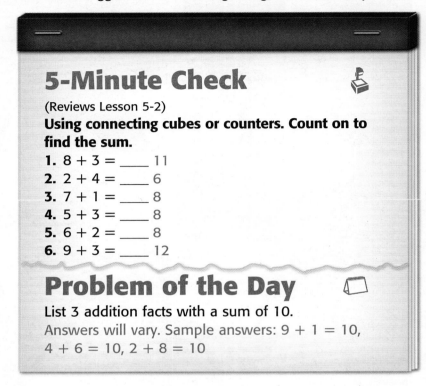

5-Minute Check 🖨

(Reviews Lesson 5-2)

Using connecting cubes or counters. Count on to find the sum.

1. $8 + 3 =$ _____ 11
2. $2 + 4 =$ _____ 6
3. $7 + 1 =$ _____ 8
4. $5 + 3 =$ _____ 8
5. $6 + 2 =$ _____ 8
6. $9 + 3 =$ _____ 12

Problem of the Day 📖

List 3 addition facts with a sum of 10.
Answers will vary. Sample answers: $9 + 1 = 10$, $4 + 6 = 10$, $2 + 8 = 10$

LINE UP When students line up for recess, lunch, or dismissal, have a student share an addition math fact. Ask another student to say the same fact with the addends in reverse order. Continue until all students are lined up. Sample answer: $3 + 6 = 9$ and $6 + 3 = 9$

Differentiated Instruction

Small Group Options

Option 1 Gifted and Talented (AL) LOGICAL

Materials: drawing paper, crayons, pencils, sentence strips

- Help the group choose an item that they can all draw—footballs, cats, apples, and so on.

- Have each student choose a secret number from 1 to 12 and draw the item that number of times.

- Ask students to find a partner and write on a sentence strip an addition sentence using the numbers of the items shown on their papers.

- Invite pairs to display their number sentence on a pocket chart. Then students find new partners and repeat the activity.

- Challenge the group to find out how many different addition sentences they can make.

Option 2 English Language Learners (ELL) LOGICAL

Core Vocabulary: solve the problem, shows, model
Common Use Verb: build

Do Math This strategy allows students to integrate their mathematical understanding with acquired language.

- Divide the class into four groups. Say: "Each group has different materials to **build** a **model** that shows how they **solved the problem**."

- Present the same problem to each group. Give each group different things to build the model they used to solve the problem. (One group gets paper strips, the second group will use craft sticks and glue, another group gets pipe cleaners and buttons, a third group gets connecting cubes and rubber bands.)

- Have students act out their findings and discuss how using models to act out problems helps solve them.

Independent Work Options

Option 1 Early Finishers (OL) (AL) LOGICAL

Materials: dominoes

- Tell students that they will make up a number story for the two sets of dots on a domino. Share the following example for a domino with three dots and two dots: *I picked up 3 balls on the playground. My friend picked up 2 more balls than I did. How many balls did my friend pick up?* 5 balls

- Have students take turns telling number stories and using dominoes or other manipulatives to solve the stories they hear.

Option 2 Student Technology

Math Online macmillanmh.com

Option 3 Learning Station: Reading (p. 151G)

Direct students to the Reading Learning Station for more opportunities to explore and extend the lesson concept.

① Introduce

Activity Choice 1 • Review

Write and read aloud the following problem:
Three students are in line. Seven more join. How many students are in line?

- **What addition strategy can you use to solve this problem?** counting on, adding in any order
- **How would you count on?** Start at 7 and count on 3 more.
- **What two math facts would you make if you added in any order?** 7 + 3, 3 + 7
- **What is the total number of students in line?** 10 students
- **Do you get the same total using either strategy?** yes

Activity Choice 2 • Literature

Introduce the lesson with Eve Merriam's *12 Ways to Get to 11*. For additional support, see p. TR49.

② Teach

Understand Using the questions, review what students know and what they need to find.

Plan Have them discuss their strategy.

Solve Guide students to *act it out* to solve the problem.

- **Should you add or subtract to find how many cans Tess collected?** add
- **If you use connecting cubes for cans, how many cubes will you show for Max?** 6 cubes
- **How many cubes will you show for Tess at the start?** 6 cubes
- **How many more cubes will you use to show the additional cans Tess collected?** 4 cubes
- **How many cans did Tess collect?** 10 cans

Check Have students look back at the problem to make sure that the answers fit the facts given.

 COMMON ERROR!

Students may not understand why they should use six cubes and four cubes for Marcy. Model using groups of cubes when reading the problem aloud to these students.

Name _____

Problem-Solving Strategy
Act It Out

Main Idea
I will use models to act out and solve problems.

> Max collected 6 cans. Tess collected 4 more cans than Max. How many cans did Tess collect?

Understand
What do I need to find? Circle the question.

Plan
How will I solve the problem?

Solve
Act it out with models. Sample answer: I will use a cube for each can. I will show 6 cubes for Max's cans and four more cubes for Tess's cans. I will count all the cubes to find how many cans Tess collected. __10__ cans.

Check
Look back.
Is my answer reasonable?   Check students' explanations.

Chapter 5   Lesson 3   one hundred sixty-one   161

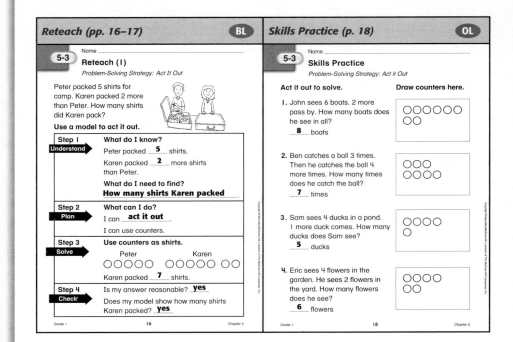

Try It

Act it out to solve.

1. Lu saw 5 birds in a tree.
6 more birds joined them.
How many birds are in the tree now?

$\underline{11}$ birds

2. Ron has 9 baseball cards.
His brother gives him 3 more.
How many cards does Ron
have altogether?

$\underline{12}$ cards

Your Turn

Act it out to solve.

3. Brad drew 7 butterflies.
Renee drew 3 butterflies more
than Brad.
How many butterflies did
Renee draw?

$\underline{10}$ butterflies

4. Tiffany brought 6 books to school.
Lola brought 2 more books
than Tiffany. How many books did
Lola bring to school?

$\underline{8}$ books

162 one hundred sixty-two

 Math at Home Activity: Give your child an addition problem and have him/her solve by acting it out.

Remember
Understand
Plan
Solve
Check

Try It: Observe students as you work through Exercises 1–2 as a class.

BL Alternate Teaching Strategy

If students have trouble using a model in Exercises 1–2 . . .

Then use one of these reteach options.

1 CRM **Daily Reteach Worksheet** (pp. 16–17)

2 Make It Real! Provide bird stickers and sports cards or playing cards for students to use in modeling Exercises 1 and 2.

- As you read each problem, have students use the corresponding objects to represent each group you mention.
- Solve the problems together by counting the total number of objects.
- Have students replace each object with a counter. Then count again and compare results.

③ Practice

Your Turn

Exercises 3–4 Be sure students can read and understand the problems. Help them use counters or cubes to model the problems as necessary. Remind students that they are joining two groups to find how many in all.

④ Assess

Formative Assessment

Tell students the following addition story:
There are 4 dogs playing at the park. Five more join. How many dogs in all? 9 dogs

- **How will you solve the problem?** add
- **What numbers will you use?** 4 and 5

Quick Check | **Are students continuing to struggle with using models to solve problems?**

If Yes → CRM Reteach Worksheet (pp. 16–17)
If No → Independent Work Options (p. 161B)
CRM Skills Practice Worksheet (p. 18)
CRM Enrich Worksheet (p. 20)

Enrich (p. 20) · AL

5-3 Name ___
Enrich
Draw 12

Draw counters to show sums of 12.
Write an addition sentence for your model.

○○○○
○○○○○○○○ $\underline{4} + \underline{8} = 12$

Answers will vary.

___ + ___ = 12

___ + ___ = 12

___ + ___ = 12

Grade 1   **20**   Chapter 5

Homework Practice (p. 19) · OL

5-3 Name ___
Homework Practice
Problem-Solving Strategy: Act it Out

Act it out to solve. | Draw counters here.

1. Bonnie has 3 books. She buys 1 more. How many books does she have in all?
$\underline{4}$ books

○○○
○

2. Chris has 4 red pens. She has 5 blue pens. How many pens does she have?
$\underline{9}$ pens

○○○○
○○○○○

3. Rosa has 4 big brushes and 3 little brushes. How many brushes does she have?
$\underline{7}$ brushes

○○○○
○○○

4. Bill has 5 green crayons and 5 red crayons. How many crayons does he have in all?
$\underline{10}$ crayons

○○○○○
○○○○○

Grade 1   19   Chapter 5

Lesson Planner _____

Objective

Practice adding by counting on from the greater number.

Review Vocabulary

greater than

Resources

Materials: cup

Manipulatives: connecting cubes, two-colored counters, number cubes

Literature Connection: *Animals on Board* by Stuart J. Murphy

Alternate Lesson: Adapt "Presto-Change-O" on pp. 197 and 198 of *Math Their Way* for practice increasing sums up to 12.

Teacher Technology

💿 TeacherWorks • Math Songs Track 11 Lesson Plan

🖱 **Math Tool Chest**

Focus on Math Background

Using a linear model (the number line) to explain counting on (1, 2, or 3) strategy is the easiest model for most children to "see" and will be introduced in Lesson 6.

Other models that include the use of manipulatives and illustrations must also be presented for there to be true understanding of the strategy.

Daily Routine _____

Use these suggestions before beginning the lesson on p. 163.

5-Minute Check

(Reviews Lesson 5-3)

Draw dominoes with the dots described below. Count on to find each sum.

1. 3 dots/5 dots 8   **3.** 6 dots/2 dots 8
2. 1 dot/8 dots 9   **4.** 4 dots/1 dot 5

Problem of the Day

Show three ways to make 8.

Sample answers: $8 + 0 = 8$, $7 + 1 = 8$, $4 + 4 = 8$

LINE UP Name a number from 0 to 9 and ask how many more are needed to make 10. The student who answers correctly lines up. Continue until all students are in line.

Review Math Vocabulary

Write **greater than** on the board and read the term aloud.

- Review with students that *greater than* is used to identify which of two addends is greater than the other.
- Remind students that they must decide which number is greater than the other when counting on.
- **In the problem 3 + 6, which number is greater than the other?** 6 is greater than 3.
- **In the problem 9 + 2, which number is greater than the other?** 9 is greater than 2.

Visual Vocabulary Cards

Use Visual Vocabulary Card 23 to reinforce the vocabulary reviewed in this lesson. (The Define/Example/Ask routine is printed on the back of each card.)

is greater than

Differentiated Instruction

Small Group Options

Below Level BL
SOCIAL, VISUAL/SPATIAL

Materials: crayons

- Have students choose an addition fact. **What picture can you draw to show this fact? How will you show each addend?** See students' work.

- Invite students to share their drawings with the class. **How did you find the sum?** Sample answer: I counted on, using my pictures to add.

- Explain that a strategy is a way to find an answer. **What other addition strategies can you use to find the sum?** Sample answers: You can count on 1, 2, or 3; use a related addition fact; add in any order; use manipulatives or counters.

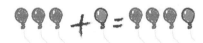

Option 2 **English Language Learners** ELL
VISUAL, AUDITORY

Materials: beans, marker for overhead
Core Vocabulary: quicker, when, count on
Common Use Verb: start on

Hear Math This strategy uses music to teach students how to count on. Sing the following to the tune of *Are You Sleeping*?

Start on greater, *start on* greater, yes you can, yes you can. **When** you *start on* greater, you can **count on quicker,** Now **count on,** now **count on.**

As you get to the last line, **clap on** *now* and put out your thumb and finger like you are counting. Continue with the beat of the last line, clap and say a number (5) and then **count on** (6, 7).

Use this worksheet to provide additional support for English Language Learners.

English Language Learners (p. 55) ELL

16   Name _____

Greater Than or Less Than
Color some shapes blue.
Color the rest of the shapes red.
Use counters to model each problem. Find the sum.
Circle the sums greater than 10.
Answers will vary. Sample answers shown below.

$4 + 7 = 11$

$6 + 6 = 12$

$5 + 4 = 9$

$8 + 2 = 10$

Make 11 and 12   55

Independent Work Options

Option 1 **Early Finishers** OL AL
LINGUISTIC, SOCIAL

Materials: index cards or flash cards with addends 1, 2, or 3

- Provide flash cards for all addition facts that include addends of 1, 2, or 3. Have partners place the cards facedown on a table.

- Have students take turns matching related addition facts. A player who matches a pair then estimates whether the sum is more than or less than 10. The other partner counts on to check the estimate.

Start with 4. Count on 2.

$4 + 2 = 6$ $2 + 4 = 6$

Option 2 **Student Technology**

Math Online > macmillanmh.com

♪ Math Songs, "The Addition Boogie" Track 11 • Math Tool Chest • Math Adventures

Option 3 **Learning Station: Language Arts** (p. 151G)

Direct students to the Language Arts Learning Station for more opportunities to explore and extend the lesson concept.

Option 4 **Problem-Solving Practice**

Reinforce problem-solving skills and strategies with the Problem-Solving Practice worksheet.

Problem Solving (p. 24) BL OL AL

Name _____
5-4   **Problem Solving Practice**
Add 1, 2, or 3

Circle the greater number. Count on to add.

1. 3 birds fly to a nest. 4 more birds fly to it. How many birds are in the nest?
$3 + 4 = 7$
7 birds

2. 4 acorns are in a tree. 2 more are on the grass. How many total acorns are there?
$4 + 2 = 6$
6 acorns

3. A butterfly is on a flower. 3 more are on the grass. How many butterflies are there?
$1 + 3 = 4$
4 butterflies

4. 6 bees are in a hive. 6 more fly in. How many bees are in the hive now?
$6 + 6 = 12$
12 bees

5. Joe catches 2 fish. Mom catches 5 fish. Dad catches 4 fish. How many fish do they catch?
$2 + 5 + 4$
$= 11$ fish

6. Kevin and Lisa each see 2 bugs. Lo sees 4 bugs. How many total bugs do they see?
$2 + 2 + 4$
$= 8$ bugs

Grade 1   24   Chapter 5

1 Introduce

Activity Choice 1 • Hands-On

Give each student a cup and 20 two-colored counters.

- Take a number card from a deck with the numbers 1 through 9. Tell the students to place that number of counters into the cup.
- Ask a volunteer to choose a number from 1 through 3. Ask the students to count on that number of counters into the cup.
- Have students record their "total" and then count all the counters to check that they have used the strategy correctly.

Activity Choice 2 • Literature

Introduce the lesson with *Animals on Board* by Stuart J. Murphy. For additional support, see p. TR49.

2 Teach

Show students one train of three red cubes and another of one yellow cube.

- **Which has the greater number?** the red train
- Find the sum. Start with 3 and then add the yellow cube. Add as a class: 4.
- **Why did we begin with the three red cubes?** 3 is the greater number, and we only had to count on 1 instead of starting with 1 and counting on 3.
- Remind students that adding 1 is just finding the next number.
- Repeat by adding more yellow cubes.

Get Ready Use the section at the top of student p. 163 to reinforce the lesson concept. Guide students in counting on from the greater number.

Check Observe students as you work through Exercises 1–7 as a class.

Exercise 7 Assess student comprehension before assigning practice exercises.

⚠ COMMON ERROR!

When using manipulatives to solve these addition problems, some students may skip over one and get an inaccurate count. Suggest that they touch and push away each manipulative as they count it.

Name _____

Add 1, 2, or 3

Get Ready

Main Idea
I will add 1, 2, or 3.

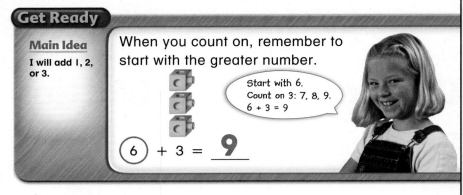

When you count on, remember to start with the greater number.

Start with 6.
Count on 3: 7, 8, 9.
6 + 3 = 9

⑥ + 3 = __9__

✓ Check

Use 🎲. Circle the greater number.
Then count on to add.

1. 3 + ⑨ = **12**

2. 1 + ⑧ = __9__

3. 2 + ⑤ = __7__

4. ④ + 1 = __5__

5. 2 + ⑥ = __8__

6. ⑨ + 2 = __11__

7. **Talk About It** Explain how to add 3 to any number.
Sample answer: Think of the other number then count up 3

Chapter 5   Lesson 4   one hundred sixty-three   163

Reteach (p. 21) BL

5-4 Reteach
Add 1, 2, or 3

You can add by counting on.
Circle and start with the greater number.

3 + ⑤ = 8

Use ● ○. Circle the greater number.
Then count on to add.

1. ⑨ + 3 = **12**   2. ⑤ + 2 = **7**

3. 1 + ④ = **5**   4. ⑧ + 3 = **11**

5. 2 + ⑦ = **9**   6. 3 + ⑤ = **8**

7. 1 ●
   +⑤
   6

8. ⑧
   + 2 ●●
   10

9. ⑥
   + 1 ●
   7

10. 3 ●●●
    +⑦
    10

11. 2 ●●
    +⑨
    11

12. ⑥
    + 3 ●●●
    9

Grade 1   21   Chapter 5

Skills Practice (p. 22) OL

5-4 Skills Practice
Add 1, 2, or 3

Circle the greater number. Then count on to add.

1. 2 + ③ = **5**   2. ⑤ + 2 = **7**

3. 4 + ⑨ = **13**   4. ⑥ + 3 = **9**

5. ⑤ + 1 = **6**   6. 3 + ⑤ = **8**

7. 3 + ⑧ = **11**   8. 1 + ③ = **4**

9. ④
   + 3
   7

10. 3
    +⑥
    9

11. ⑨
    + 2
    11

12. ⑧
    + 2
    10

13. 2
    +⑥
    8

14. ⑤
    + 1
    6

Start with the greater number. Count on to find each sum. Write the number sentence.

15. Jose kicked the ball 2 times. Then he kicked the ball 5 more times. How many times did he kick the ball?
2 + **5** = **7** times

16. Lara runs 3 laps. She takes a break. Then she runs 2 more laps. How many total laps does she run?
3 + **2** = **5** laps

Grade 1   22   Chapter 5

Circle the greater number.
Then count on to add.

8. 1 + ⑤ = _6_	9. 2 + ⑨ = _11_	10. 3 + ④ = _7_
11. ⑥ + 2 = _8_	12. ⑧ + 1 = _9_	13. ⑧ + 3 = _11_
14. ⑦ + 2 = _9_	15. 1 + ⑨ = _10_	16. 3 + ⑨ = _12_

17.
```
  ⑤
+ 3
───
  8
```

18.
```
  2
+ ⑧
───
 10
```

19.
```
  1
+ ④
───
  5
```

Data File

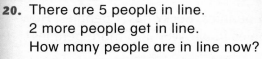

It is fun to go to Six Flags in Chicago.
It is a big park with rides and many
things to see and do.

20. There are 5 people in line.
2 more people get in line.
How many people are in line now? _7_

21. 8 people are waiting in line.
3 more people get in line.
How many people are in the line in all? _11_

 Math at Home Activity: Say a number between 1 and 9. Ask
your child to add 1, 2, and 3 to that number.

BL **Alternate Teaching Strategy**

If > students do not understand which
number to count on from . . .

Then > use one of these reteach options.

1 CRM **Daily Reteach Worksheet** (p. 21)

2 Use a number cube to roll two numbers. Ask
students to make a cube train for each
number. Point out that the longer train shows
the greater number and they should always
count on from that number.

3 Have students use Math Tool Chest to help
complete the problem-solving exercises.

③ Practice

Differentiate practice using these leveled
assignments for Exercises 8–21.

Level	Assignment
BL Below/Approaching Level	Read the problems aloud to students and have them use connecting cubes to identify the greater addend and count on to add.
OL On Level	Complete the exercises independently using connecting cubes.
AL Above/Beyond Level	Complete the exercises independently without connecting cubes.

④ Assess

Formative Assessment

Show students 5 + 2 = ___. **What is the sum?** 7
How did you find the sum? Sample answers:
memorized it; modeling; drawing

WRITING IN ►**MATH**

Explain how to add 1, 2, and 3 to a kindergartner.
Sample answer: Start with the greater number.
Then count 1, 2, or 3 to find the sum.

Quick Check **Are students continuing to struggle with adding 1, 2, or 3?**

If Yes → Small Group Options (p. 163B)
Strategic Intervention Guide (p. 96)

If No → Independent Work Options (p. 163B)
CRM Skills Practice Worksheet (p. 22)
CRM Enrich Worksheet (p. 25)

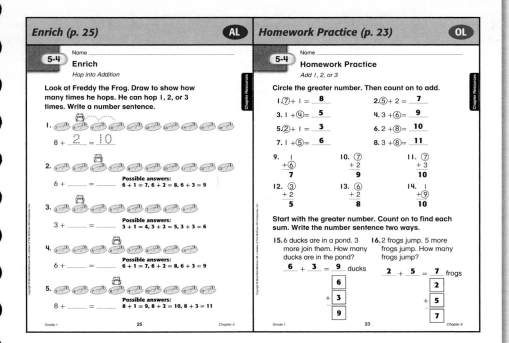

Enrich (p. 25) **AL**

5-4 Name ____
Enrich
Hop into Addition

Look at Freddy the Frog. Draw to show how
many times he hops. He can hop 1, 2, or 3
times. Write a number sentence.

1. 8 + _2_ = 10

2. 6 + ____ =
Possible answers:
6 + 1 = 7, 6 + 2 = 8, 6 + 3 = 9

3. 3 + ____ =
Possible answers:
3 + 1 = 4, 3 + 2 = 5, 3 + 3 = 6

4. 6 + ____ =
Possible answers:
6 + 1 = 7, 6 + 2 = 8, 6 + 3 = 9

5. 8 + ____ =
Possible answers:
8 + 1 = 9, 8 + 2 = 10, 8 + 3 = 11

Grade 1   25   Chapter 5

Homework Practice (p. 23) **OL**

5-4 Name ____
Homework Practice
Add 1, 2, or 3

Circle the greater number. Then count on to add.

1. ⑦ + 1 = _8_   2. ⑤ + 2 = _7_
3. 1 + ④ = _5_   4. 3 + ⑥ = _9_
5. ②+ 1 = _3_   6. 2 + ⑧ = _10_
7. 1 + ⑤ = _6_   8. 3 + ⑧ = _11_

9.
```
  1
+⑥
──
  7
```
10.
```
 ⑦
+ 2
──
  9
```
11.
```
 ⑦
+ 3
──
 10
```
12.
```
 ③
+ 2
──
  5
```
13.
```
 ⑥
+ 2
──
  8
```
14.
```
  1
+⑨
──
 10
```

Start with the greater number. Count on to find each
sum. Write the number sentence two ways.

15. 6 ducks are in a pond. 3
more join them. How many
ducks are in the pond?

_6_ + _3_ = _9_ ducks

```
 6
+3
──
 9
```

16. 2 frogs jump. 5 more
frogs jump. How many
frogs jump?

_2_ + _5_ = _7_ frogs

```
 2
+5
──
 7
```

Grade 1   23   Chapter 5

Lesson Planner

Objective
Use a number line to add.

Review Vocabulary
number line

Resources
Materials: number cards (1–10), masking tape, WorkMat 4: Number Lines

Manipulatives: two-colored counters

Literature Connection: *Little Quack* by Lauren Thompson

Alternate Lesson: Use *IMPACT Mathematics:* Unit B to provide practice with using a number line to add.

Teacher Technology
 TeacherWorks • Concepts in Motion • Math Songs Track 11 Lesson Plan

Focus on Math Background

Young children come to school with the concept of "more." This lesson focuses on "more" as an increase of number or quantity. It is important to relate the concepts of quantification and increasing to symbolic recording with numbers and addition number sentences.

As in the previous lesson, using a number line to count on is an easy way for students to "see" the concept and learn basic math facts. Number lines can be used as pictorial models to add, subtract, and skip count.

Number lines can also be transformed into line plots which is one way for students to represent data.

Daily Routine

Use these suggestions before beginning the lesson on p. 165.

5-Minute Check

(Reviews Lesson 5-4)

Solve by adding.

1. $3 + 5 = \_\_$ **2.** $7 + 1 = \_\_$ **3.** $4 + 1 = \_\_$
4. $9 + 2 = \_\_$ **5.** $1 + 11 = \_\_$ **6.** $3 + 4 = \_\_$
8, 8, 5, 11, 12, 7

Problem of the Day

Kim has 6 pennies. Becky has 4 pennies. How many pennies in all? Who has more pennies? 10 pennies; Kim has more pennies.

LINE UP Draw a number line from 0 through 10. Have each student roll either a red or blue number cube. Call students up by the number they rolled. Before getting in line, have each student draw an X above their number on the number line. Explain that they used the number line to make a line plot. A line plot is another way to show data.

Review Math Vocabulary

Review with students that a **number line** is a line with numbers arranged in order on it. Model how to point to a starting number and count on as your finger "jumps" from number to number.

- **What are some ways to use a number line?** Sample answers: to count; to help you add or subtract; to compare numbers
- **Which direction do you move on the number line to count on?** to the right

Visual Vocabulary Cards

Use Visual Vocabulary Card 30 to reinforce the vocabulary reviewed in this lesson. (The Define/Example/Ask routine is printed on the back of each card.)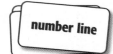

number line

Differentiated Instruction

Small Group Options

Option 1 **Gifted and Talented** AL LINGUISTIC, SPATIAL

Materials: number line, white board, dry erase marker, drawing paper, crayons, red number cube

- Explain the following steps in a game: One student rolls the number cube three times. A second student writes the numbers as three addends in a number sentence on a white board. A third student uses a number line to find the sum.

- Have students pass the materials around the circle and continue the steps until everyone has had a turn at each job.

- Ask students to choose one set of three addends to use in writing a number story. Have students include with their story a picture and the corresponding number sentence.

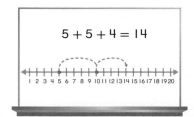

$5 + 5 + 4 = 14$

Option 2 **English Language Learners** ELL AUDITORY, KINESTHETIC

Materials: masking tape, numbers cards 1 to 10, number cube
Core Vocabulary: Where are you?, step, I'm on __.
Common Use Verb: walk forward

Write Math This strategy helps students increase understanding of adding by acting out number sentences.

- Make a number line with tape on the floor; label with number cards.

- Have a student stand on 0, facing 10.

- Say: "You're on zero." Roll cube. Say: "*Walk __ steps forward*."

- Ask: "**Where are you**"?

- Prompt the answer, "**I'm on 2**."

- Repeat until past 10.

- Have a student write a number sentence as the student moves forward.

- Variation: Pairs of students 'race' using two number lines and taking turns walking forward.

Independent Work Options

Option 1 **Early Finishers** OL AL LINGUISTIC, SOCIAL

Materials: two sets of number cards for 0–9, number lines

- Have students put the cards facedown on a table.

- Players each choose two cards and use a number line to find the sum of the numbers. Players write their number sentences and compare them.

- The player with the greater sum keeps all four cards.

Option 2 **Student Technology**

Math Online ⟩ macmillanmh.com

♪ Math Songs, "The Addition Boogie" Track 11

Option 3 **Learning Station: Art** (p. 151G)

Direct students to the Art Learning Station for more opportunities to explore and extend the lesson concept.

Option 4 **Problem-Solving Practice**

Reinforce problem-solving skills and strategies with the Problem-Solving Practice worksheet.

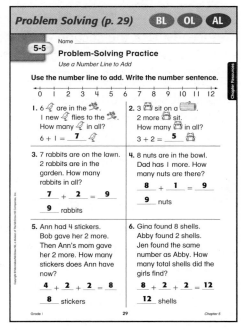

Problem Solving (p. 29) BL OL AL

1 Introduce

Activity Choice 1 • Hands-On

Use masking tape and number cards 1–10 to make a walk-on number line on the floor.

- Ask a volunteer to stand next to the number 6. **Now hop 2 more spaces.**
- Have all students count on "7, 8" as the student hops. Point out that 6 + 2 = 8.
- Repeat with other volunteers, using other facts to 10.

Activity Choice 2 • Literature

Introduce the lesson with *Little Quack* by Lauren Thompson. For additional support, see p. TR49.

2 Teach

Have students look at WorkMat 4: Number Line (1–20).

- **Start at 4. How many jumps to 7?** 3 jumps
- **Start at 2. How many jumps to 6?** 4 jumps
- **Use the number line to add 3 + 7 = __. Which addend is greater?** 7 **How many will you count on from 7?** 3 **What is the sum?** 10
- **Why is it best to count on from 7?** It is faster to start with the greater number (7) and count on only 3 than to start with 3 and count on 7.
- **How does a number line help you find the sum of two numbers?** Sample answer: You can start at the greater number and point to the numbers as you count on or add.

Get Ready Use the section at the top of student p. 165 to reinforce the lesson concept. Guide students in counting on using a number line.

Check Observe students as you work through Exercises 1–9 as a class.

> **Exercise 9** Assess student comprehension before assigning practice exercises.

COMMON ERROR!

When adding on a number line, students may begin counting on the starting number. Point out that they are to count the "jumps," so they should not begin counting until their finger has made the first jump.

Name _____

Use a Number Line to Add

Main Idea

I will use a number line to add.

You can use a number line to add. Start with the greater number and count on.

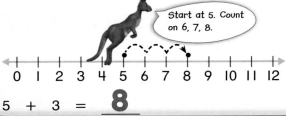
Start at 5. Count on 6, 7, 8.

$$0\ 1\ 2\ 3\ 4\ 5\ 6\ 7\ 8\ 9\ 10\ 11\ 12$$

$$5 + 3 = \underline{8}$$

Check 9. Sample answer: It shows the numbers in order and helps you count on.

Use the number line. Add.

$$0\ 1\ 2\ 3\ 4\ 5\ 6\ 7\ 8\ 9\ 10\ 11\ 12$$

1. $2 + 6 = \underline{8}$ | 2. $8 + 2 = \underline{10}$

3. $1 + 4 = \underline{5}$ | 4. $3 + 6 = \underline{9}$

5. $\begin{array}{r} 7 \\ + 3 \\ \hline 10 \end{array}$ 6. $\begin{array}{r} 6 \\ + 1 \\ \hline 7 \end{array}$ 7. $\begin{array}{r} 8 \\ + 3 \\ \hline 11 \end{array}$ 8. $\begin{array}{r} 1 \\ + 9 \\ \hline 10 \end{array}$

9. **Talk About It** How does a number line help you add?

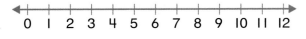

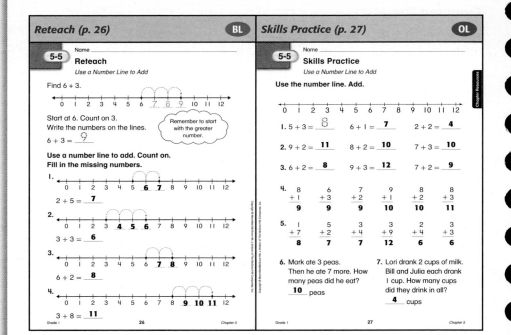

Reteach (p. 26) BL

5-5 **Reteach**
Use a Number Line to Add

Find 6 + 3.

$$0\ 1\ 2\ 3\ 4\ 5\ 6\ 7\ 8\ 9\ 10\ 11\ 12$$

Start at 6. Count on 3.
Write the numbers on the lines.   Remember to start with the greater number.
$6 + 3 = \underline{9}$

Use a number line to add. Count on.
Fill in the missing numbers.

1.
$$0\ 1\ 2\ 3\ 4\ 5\ 6\ 7\ 8\ 9\ 10\ 11\ 12$$
$2 + 5 = \underline{7}$

2.
$$0\ 1\ 2\ 3\ 4\ 5\ 6\ 7\ 8\ 9\ 10\ 11\ 12$$
$3 + 3 = \underline{6}$

3.
$$0\ 1\ 2\ 3\ 4\ 5\ 6\ 7\ 8\ 9\ 10\ 11\ 12$$
$6 + 2 = \underline{8}$

4.
$$0\ 1\ 2\ 3\ 4\ 5\ 6\ 7\ 8\ 9\ 10\ 11\ 12$$
$3 + 8 = \underline{11}$

Grade 1   26   Chapter 5

Skills Practice (p. 27) OL

5-5 **Skills Practice**
Use a Number Line to Add

Use the number line. Add.

$$0\ 1\ 2\ 3\ 4\ 5\ 6\ 7\ 8\ 9\ 10\ 11\ 12$$

1. $5 + 3 = \underline{8}$ $6 + 1 = \underline{7}$ $2 + 2 = \underline{4}$

2. $9 + 2 = \underline{11}$ $8 + 2 = \underline{10}$ $7 + 3 = \underline{10}$

3. $6 + 2 = \underline{8}$ $9 + 3 = \underline{12}$ $7 + 2 = \underline{9}$

4. $\begin{array}{r} 8 \\ +1 \\ \hline 9 \end{array}$ $\begin{array}{r} 6 \\ +3 \\ \hline 9 \end{array}$ $\begin{array}{r} 7 \\ +2 \\ \hline 9 \end{array}$ $\begin{array}{r} 9 \\ +1 \\ \hline 10 \end{array}$ $\begin{array}{r} 8 \\ +2 \\ \hline 10 \end{array}$ $\begin{array}{r} 8 \\ +3 \\ \hline 11 \end{array}$

5. $\begin{array}{r} 1 \\ +7 \\ \hline 8 \end{array}$ $\begin{array}{r} 5 \\ +2 \\ \hline 7 \end{array}$ $\begin{array}{r} 3 \\ +4 \\ \hline 7 \end{array}$ $\begin{array}{r} 3 \\ +9 \\ \hline 12 \end{array}$ $\begin{array}{r} 2 \\ +4 \\ \hline 6 \end{array}$ $\begin{array}{r} 3 \\ +3 \\ \hline 6 \end{array}$

6. Mark ate 3 peas. Then he ate 7 more. How many peas did he eat? $\underline{10}$ peas

7. Lori drank 2 cups of milk. Bill and Julia each drank 1 cup. How many cups did they drink in all? $\underline{4}$ cups

Grade 1   27   Chapter 5

Use the number line. Add.

```
◄─┼──┼──┼──┼──┼──┼──┼──┼──┼──┼──┼──┼──►
  0  1  2  3  4  5  6  7  8  9  10 11 12
```

10.	11.	12.	13.
1 + 4 5	2 + 7 9	9 + 3 12	5 + 2 7

14.	15.	16.	17.
2 + 6 8	1 + 7 8	4 + 2 6	6 + 3 9

18. 2 + 3 = __5__ 19. 3 + 5 = __8__ 20. 2 + 9 = __11__

21. 1 + 8 = __9__ 22. 4 + 3 = __7__ 23. 3 + 8 = __11__

Problem Solving

24. Number Sense

Amelio has 7 soccer balls.
He gave 3 to his brother.
Then he bought 2 new ones.
How many soccer balls
does Amelio have now?

__6__ soccer balls

166 one hundred sixty-six

Math at Home Activity: Ask your child to use the number line to show 5 + 7.

Lessons 5-1 to 5-5

 Formative Assessment

Use the Mid-Chapter Check to assess student's progress in the first half of the chapter.

ExamView Assessment Suite Customize and create multiple versions of your Mid-Chapter Check and the test answer keys.

FOLDABLES Dinah Zike's Foldables

Use these lesson suggestions to incorporate the Foldable during the chapter.

Lesson 5-1 Use the second page of the addition journal to illustrate how addition can be performed in any order.

Lesson 5-2 On the third page of the addition journal, draw as "counting on". Add to a number by counting on 1, 2, or 3.

Lesson 5-4 On the fourth page of the addition journal, add 1, 2, or 3 with sums to 12.

Lesson 5-5 Glue or draw a number line to the fifth page of the journal and use it to add with sums up to 12.

Lesson 5-6 Show the addition of doubles with sums to 12 on the sixth page of the addition journal.

Name _____

Add. Use 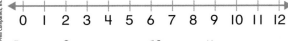.

1. $1 + 9 = \underline{10}$ **2.** $9 + 1 = \underline{10}$

Start with the greater number.
Count on to add.

3. $9 + 3 = \underline{12}$ **4.** $3 + 8 = \underline{11}$ **5.** $1 + 3 = \underline{4}$

Circle the greater number.
Then count on to add.

6.   ⑥
    $+\ \ 3$
    $\boxed{9}$

7.   1
    $+\ ⑦$
    $\boxed{8}$

8.   2
    $+\ ③$
    $\boxed{5}$

Use the number line. Add.

0 1 2 3 4 5 6 7 8 9 10 11 12

9.   3
    $+\ \ 8$
    11

10.   4
    $+\ \ 1$
    5

11.   7
    $+\ \ 3$
    10

12. Craig has 7 fish. He bought 2 more fish. How many fish does Craig have now?

_____9_____ fish

13. Theo caught 5 butterflies. Ines caught 2 more butterflies than Theo. How many butterflies did Ines catch?

_____7_____ butterflies

Chapter 5   one hundred sixty-seven   167

Copyright © Macmillan/McGraw-Hill, a division of The McGraw-Hill Companies, Inc.

Data-Driven Decision Making

Based on the results of the Mid-Chapter Check, use the following resources to review concepts that continue to give students problems.

Exercises	State/Local Standards	What's the Math?	Error Analysis	Resources for Review
1–2 Lesson 5-1		Models the meaning of addition.	Adds incorrectly. Writes incorrect numbers.	Strategic Intervention Guide (p. 62) CRM Chapter 5 Resource Masters (Reteach Worksheets)
3–8 Lesson 5-2 Lesson 5-4		Show the meaning of addition by "counting on."	Does not understand "greater." Does not circle "greater" number. Adds incorrectly.	**Math Online** Concepts in Motion Math Adventures
9–11 Lesson 5-5		Use a number line to add.	Adds all numbers together. Does incorrect adding and subtracting.	

Spiral Review   Chapters 1–5

Use the graph. Answer the questions.

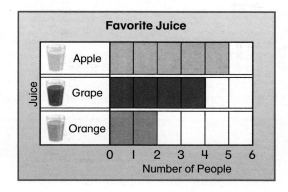

Favorite Juice

14. How many people chose apple juice? ___5___ people

15. How many more people like apple juice than orange juice? ___3___ people

16. Which juice was chosen more than 4 times? _apple juice_

17. Fernando plays soccer. He scored 4 goals in his first game. He scored 3 goals in his second game. How many goals did he score in all?

    ___7___ goals

18. Which shape is missing?

    The missing shape is a ___green triangle___.

Copyright © Macmillan/McGraw-Hill, a division of The McGraw-Hill Companies, Inc.

Formative Assessment

Spiral Review

Reviews Chapters 1 to 5

Objective: Review and assess mastery of skills and concepts from previous chapters.

Resources for Review

Based on student results, refer to these lessons for remediation.

- **Exercises 14–16: Lesson 4-5** (p. 133)
- **Exercise 17: Lesson 2-1** (p. 51)
- **Exercise 18: Lesson 1-1** (p. 17)

Doubles

Lesson Planner

Objective
Use doubles facts to add.

Vocabulary
doubles

Resources
Materials: 1-inch grid paper, pennies

Manipulatives: connecting cubes

Literature Connection: *Double Trouble* by Rose Greydanus

Alternate Lesson: Use *IMPACT Mathematics:* Unit B to provide practice with using doubles facts to add.

Teacher Technology
- TeacherWorks • Math Songs Track 11 Lesson Plan

Focus on Math Background

Doubling a quantity of food, materials, or a number—instead of one book, get two—is a concept built on "just one more." The idea of having "twice" the amount or number is often very engaging for young children, and they love to see how something "grows" by doubling the item or items.

Some students are ready to see skip counting by twos as a doubling pattern, but others will need to build the pattern with concrete objects or manipulatives. Understanding doubles is an efficient addition strategy and the concept also helps with subtraction, multiplication, and dividing by two.

Daily Routine

Use these suggestions before beginning the lesson on p. 169.

5-Minute Check
(Reviews Lesson 5-5)

Use a number line to solve.

1. $3 + 6 =$ __ **2.** $10 + 3 =$ __ **3.** $2 + 6 =$ __
4. $1 + 9 =$ __ **5.** $5 + 3 =$ __ 9, 13, 8, 10, 8

Problem of the Day

The zoo has 12 flamingos that live in the west lagoon. Six of the flamingos fly to the east lagoon to nest. How many flamingos are left? 6 flamingos

LINE UP Have students count to find which student is number 5 in line. Help them count on to find who is number 7. Repeat with other numbers. Have students tell how many they count on each time.

Building Math Vocabulary

- Write the vocabulary word **doubles** on the chalkboard and explain that a double is an addition problem that has identical addends.

- Review with students that an **addend** is a number being added to another number. **In the problem $4 + 6 = 10$, what numbers are the addends?** 4 and 6

- Write $2 + 2 = 4$ and $4 - 2 =$ __ on the chalkboard. **This is a doubles fact. What do you notice about the addends?** They are the same. Point out that knowing $2 + 2 = 4$ can help students solve $4 - 2$. **What is $4 - 2$?** 2 **How are $2 + 2 = 4$ and $4 - 2 = 2$ related?** They use the same numbers.

- **What is another doubles fact you know?** Sample answer: $3 + 3 = 6$, $5 + 5 = 10$

Differentiated Instruction

Small Group Options

Option 1
KINESTHETIC, SPATIAL

Below/Approaching Level (BL)

Materials: blue and yellow connecting cubes

Make one pile of six yellow cubes and one pile of six blue cubes.

- Have students take a handful of cubes from one pile. **How many cubes do you have?** See students' work. Have them count to see how many cubes they have. Have them take the same number of cubes from the other pile.

- **What doubles fact can you write?** See students' work. Have students write a number sentence to show the doubles fact.

$$4 + 4 = 8$$

- Repeat with other amounts of cubes.

Option 2
KINESTHETIC

English Language Learners (ELL)

Materials: dominos in a bag
Core Vocabulary: doubles, no troubles, domino
Common Use Verb: rumble

Do Math This strategy uses background knowledge to recognize doubles facts.

- Draw doubles on the board. Say: "**doubles** mean **no troubles** because they are **helpful** in math."

- Demonstrate making a rumbling sound with fists on the desk. Say: "This sound is called "**rumble**." It usually means rain, a storm, or **trouble**.

- Model game. Students **rumble** desks as you pull dominos, saying: "no double" when non-doubles are pulled. For doubles, students put hands flat on the desk and say: "**doubles, no troubles!**"

- Extend vocalization as students master language by having them call out the whole double fact.

Independent Work Options

Option 1
LOGICAL, SPATIAL

Early Finishers (OL) (AL)

Materials: number cards (1–6), white board, dry erase marker, orange and green connecting cubes

- Partners take turns drawing a number card.

- Both students build a cube train for the number drawn.

- Students combine their cube trains and write the addition sentence that tells what they did.

- Students remove one color of cubes from the train and write the subtraction sentence that tells what they did.

Option 2

Student Technology

Math Online > macmillanmh.com

♪ Math Songs, "The Addition Boogie" Track 11 • Math Adventures

Option 3

Learning Station: Science (p. 151H)

Direct students to the Science Learning Station for more opportunities to explore and extend the lesson concept.

Option 4

Problem-Solving Practice

Reinforce problem-solving skills and strategies with the Problem-Solving Practice worksheet.

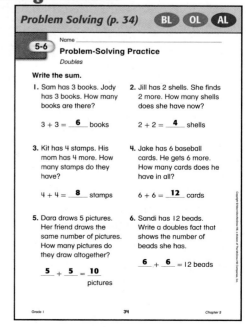

Problem Solving (p. 34) BL OL AL

Name _____

5-6 **Problem-Solving Practice**
Doubles

Write the sum.

1. Sam has 3 books. Jody has 3 books. How many books are there?

   $3 + 3 = \underline{6}$ books

2. Jill has 2 shells. She finds 2 more. How many shells does she have now?

   $2 + 2 = \underline{4}$ shells

3. Kit has 4 stamps. His mom has 4 more. How many stamps do they have?

   $4 + 4 = \underline{8}$ stamps

4. Jake has 6 baseball cards. He gets 6 more. How many cards does he have in all?

   $6 + 6 = \underline{12}$ cards

5. Dara draws 5 pictures. Her friend draws the same number of pictures. How many pictures do they draw altogether?

   $\underline{5} + \underline{5} = \underline{10}$ pictures

6. Sandi has 12 beads. Write a doubles fact that shows the number of beads she has.

   $\underline{6} + \underline{6} = 12$ beads

Grade 1   34   Chapter 5

① Introduce

Activity Choice 1 • Hands-On

- Ask two boys and two girls to stand. **What number sentence can you make to add boys and girls?** 2 + 2 = 4

- Next have five boys and five girls stand. **What number sentence can you make to add boys and girls?** 5 + 5 = 10

- Ask the five boys to sit. **What number sentence can you make to tell about the boys sitting down?** 10 − 5 = 5

- Repeat this activity with other numbers. Ask students to tell the **doubles** fact and related subtraction fact.

Activity Choice 2 • Literature

Introduce the lesson with *Double Trouble* by Rose Greydanus. For additional support, see p. TR49.

② Teach

- Write 3 + 3 = 6 on the chalkboard.
- **Why is this a doubles fact?** The addends are the same.
- **What is the related subtraction fact?** 6 − 3 = 3
- **How are the number sentences the same?** They use the same numbers.
- **How are they different?** One is an addition fact and one is a subtraction fact.

Get Ready Use the section at the top of student p. 169 to reinforce the lesson concept. Reinforce the concept that doubles are two of the same number.

Check Observe students as you work through Exercises 1–9 as a class.

 Exercise 9 Assess student comprehension before assigning practice exercises.

⚠ COMMON ERROR!

Students who favor the counting on strategy may have difficulty adding numbers greater than three. Encourage students to use manipulatives such as counters or connecting cubes, until they are more familiar with addends greater than three.

Name _____

Doubles

Get Ready

Main Idea
I will add using doubles.

Vocabulary
doubles

You can use a **doubles fact** to find the sum. Both addends are the same in a doubles fact.

__5__ + __5__ = __10__

5 + 5 is a doubles fact.

✓ **Check**

9. Sample answer: No, because the addends are not the same when the sum is 7.

Complete the addition sentence. Use 🎲.

1.   __3__ + __3__ = __6__

2.   __6__ + __6__ = __12__

Write the sum. Circle the doubles facts.

3. (6 + 6) = __12__   4. 4 + 6 = __10__   5. 7 + 4 = __11__

6. 9
  + 2
  ____
  |11|

7. (5)
  + (5)
  ____
  |10|

8. 3
  + 2
  ____
  |5|

9. **Talk About It** Can you use doubles to make a sum of 7? Explain.

Chapter 5 Lesson 6   one hundred sixty-nine 169

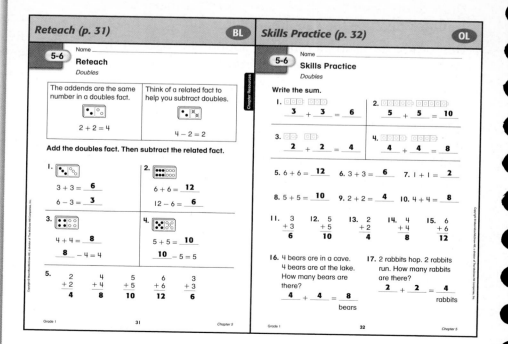

Reteach (p. 31) BL

5-6 **Reteach**
Doubles

The addends are the same number in a doubles fact.	Think of a related fact to help you subtract doubles.
2 + 2 = 4	4 − 2 = 2

Add the doubles fact. Then subtract the related fact.

1. 3 + 3 = **6**   6 − 3 = **3**
2. 6 + 6 = **12**   12 − 6 = **6**
3. 4 + 4 = **8**   8 − 4 = 4
4. 5 + 5 = **10**   10 − 5 = 5

5. 2   4   5   6   3
  +2 +4 +5 +6 +3
  __ __ __ __ __
   4   8 10 12   6

Skills Practice (p. 32) OL

5-6 **Skills Practice**
Doubles

Write the sum.

1. __3__ + __3__ = 6   2. __5__ + __5__ = 10
3. __2__ + __2__ = 4   4. __4__ + __4__ = 8

5. 6 + 6 = **12**   6. 3 + 3 = **6**   7. 1 + 1 = **2**
8. 5 + 5 = **10**   9. 2 + 2 = **4**   10. 4 + 4 = **8**

11. 3   12. 5   13. 2   14. 4   15. 6
  +3   +5   +2   +4   +6
  __   __   __   __   __
   6   10   4   8   12

16. 4 bears are in a cave. 4 bears are at the lake. How many bears are there?
4 + **4** = **8** bears

17. 2 rabbits hop. 2 rabbits run. How many rabbits are there?
2 + **2** = **4** rabbits

Practice

Complete the addition sentence. Use .

10.

<u> 2 </u> + <u> 2 </u> = <u> 4 </u>

11.

<u> 1 </u> + <u> 1 </u> = <u> 2 </u>

12.

<u> 4 </u> + <u> 4 </u> = <u> 8 </u>

13.

<u> 5 </u> + <u> 5 </u> = <u> 10 </u>

Write the sum. Circle the doubles facts.

14. ⑥
　　+ ⑥
　　[12]

15.　 3
　　+ 6
　　[9]

16.　 9
　　+ 0
　　[9]

17. ③
　　+ ③
　　[6]

18. 8 + 3 = <u>11</u>

19. 1 + 5 = <u>6</u>

20. 6 + 4 = <u>10</u>

21. 3 + 9 = <u>12</u>

H.O.T. Problems

Algebra Fill in the numbers to make a doubles fact.

22. 3 + <u>3</u> = 6

23. 4 + <u>4</u> = 8

24. <u>5</u> + 5 = 10

25. <u>6</u> + 6 = 12

170　one hundred seventy

 Math at Home Activity: Have your child identify things that show doubles. Fingers on both hands, toes on both feet, or windows in a car.

Copyright © Macmillan/McGraw-Hill, a division of The McGraw-Hill Companies, Inc.

BL **Alternate Teaching Strategy**

If students have trouble understanding the concept of a doubles fact . . .

Then use one of these reteach options.

1 CRM **Daily Reteach Worksheet** (p. 31)

2 **Double Your Money** Give partners twelve pennies and a strip of 1-inch grid paper with two rows and six boxes in each row. Have one partner put five pennies in the top row of the grid. Ask the other partner to put the same number in the bottom row. **How many pennies in all?** 10 pennies **What addition number sentence can you write for these sets of pennies?** 5 + 5 = 10

❸ Practice

Differentiate practice using these leveled assignments for Exercises 10–25.

Level	Assignment
BL Below/Approaching Level	Complete the exercises using connecting cubes to add, with teacher support as needed.
OL On Level	Complete the exercises independently, using a number line to add.
AL Above/Beyond Level	Complete the exercises without connecting cubes.

❹ Assess

✓ Formative Assessment

Ask students to write two of their own complete addition sentence using doubles.

WRITING IN ►MATH Have students write about things they know come in doubles. Sample answers: shoes, socks, eyes, twins, feet, bicycle wheels.

Quick Check **Are students continuing to struggle with doubles facts?**

If Yes → Small Group Options (p. 169B)

　　　Strategic Intervention Guide (p. 88)

If No → Independent Work Options (p. 169B)

　　CRM Skills Practice Worksheet (p. 32)

　　CRM Enrich Worksheet (p. 35)

Enrich (p. 35) **AL**

Name _____

5-6 **Enrich**
Beary Fun Doubles Facts

Solve the problems.
Color the doubles facts brown.
Color the other facts blue.

3 + 7 = **10** bl
2 + 5 = **7** bl
7 + 7 = **14** br
5 + 4 = **9** bl
6 + 4 = **10** bl
4 + 4 = **8** br
8 + 8 = **16** br
2 + 2 = **4** br
6 + 6 = **12** br
8 + 3 = **11** bl
9 + 2 = **11** bl
5 + 5 = **10** br
3 + 3 = **6** br
4 + 8 = **12** bl
2 + 9 = **11** bl

Grade 1　　35　　Chapter 5

Homework Practice (p. 33) **OL**

Name _____

5-6 **Homework Practice**
Doubles

Write the sum.

1. **6** + **6** = **12**　　2. **1** + **1** = **2**

3. **4** + **4** = **8**　　4. **5** + **5** = **10**

5. 2 + 2 = **4**　 6. 4 + 4 = **8**　 7. 3 + 3 = **6**

8.　1
　+1
　2

9.　5
　+5
　10

10.　2
　+2
　4

11.　6
　+6
　12

12.　3
　+3
　6

13.　3
　+9
　12

14.　8
　+2
　10

15.　7
　+3
　10

16.　6
　+3
　9

17.　3
　+8
　11

18. May has 2 marbles. Her dad gives her 2 more. How many marbles does May have now?

2 + **2** = **4**
marbles

19. 3 children play tag. 3 more play hide-and-seek. How many children are playing?

3 + **3** = **6**
children

Grade 1　　33　　Chapter 5

Lesson 5-6 Doubles　**170**

Lesson Planner

Objective
Identify and use doubles plus 1 facts to add.

Vocabulary
doubles plus 1

Resources
Materials: WorkMat 1: Ten-Frame

Manipulatives: two-colored counters, connecting cubes

Literature Connection: *Plant Fruits & Seeds* by David M. Schwartz

Teacher Technology
  TeacherWorks • Concepts in Motion • Math Songs Track 11 Lesson Plan

Focus on Math Background

Doubles plus one introduces the concept of even numbers plus one to make an odd sum. Understanding the concept of division with a remainder at an introductory level also follows this concept. Students begin to see the patterns involved with doubling and using the counting on 1 strategy as a way to know some of the basic facts such as $6 + 7$. Students see $6 + 7$ as $6 + 6$, a doubles fact, plus 1.

All the basic addition facts to 20 can be learned using counting on 1, 2, or 3, doubles, and doubles plus 1 strategies. It is important for students to understand the concepts of the strategies as well as to be able to implement them when memorization fails.

Daily Routine

Use these suggestions before beginning the lesson on p. 171.

5-Minute Check

(Reviews Lesson 5-6)

Solve.

1. $3 + 3 = 6$	**4.** $5 + 5 = 10$
2. $2 + 2 = 4$	**5.** $4 + 4 = 8$
3. $1 + 1 = 2$	**6.** $6 + 6 = 12$

7. What is the same about all these problems? They are all doubles facts.

Problem of the Day

There are 12 boys on Randy's basketball team. The team has 2 coaches at every practice. Today 4 boys from the team are sick. Counting Randy's coaches, how many people are at practice today? 10 people

LINE UP Have two or three students stand. Hold up a flash card for a doubles or doubles plus 1 fact. Have the students say the sum and then line up. Continue until all students are in line.

▷ Building Math Vocabulary

- Write **doubles plus 1** on the chalkboard and have students tell what they know about each part of the term.
- Explain that an example of a doubles plus 1 fact is $2 + 3 = 5$. Point out that this fact has one addend (3) that is 1 more than the other addend (2). Give other examples and help students relate each example to one of the doubles facts.
- **How can knowing doubles facts help you solve doubles plus 1 facts?** They have nearly the same sum. For a doubles plus 1 fact, just add 1 to the sum of the related double.

Differentiated Instruction

Small Group Options

Option 1

Below Level BL

LINGUISTIC, SOCIAL

Materials: red and yellow counters

- Give students three yellow counters and three red counters.
- **What doubles fact can you make?** $3 + 3 = 6$
- Give students one more yellow counter. **What is your new number sentence?** $3 + 4 = 7$
- **How did the addend change?** It got larger by 1.
- **How did the sum change?** It got larger by 1.
- Continue making other doubles and doubles plus 1 facts and have students identify the changes that occur in forming each doubles plus 1 fact.

Option 2

English Language Learners ELL

LOGICAL, SPATIAL

Core Vocabulary: make even rows, even, extra
Common Use Verb: can/can't

Do Math This strategy allows students to act out their math understanding while introducing new vocabulary.

- Show 4 counters. Ask: "***Can*** I **make even rows**?"
- Make an array. Say: "Yes, **I** *can*. I have **even rows**."
- Say, "This is a doubles fact".
- Repeat with an odd number. Use the same question, then say: "No, **I** **can't**. I have **extra**."
- Give students a handful of counters. Say: "**Make even rows.**"
- Observe and ask students if they could make a doubles fact. Restate answers to scaffold their language.

Independent Work Options

Option 1

Early Finishers OL AL

KINESTHETIC, SOCIAL, SMALL GROUP

Materials: index cards, markers

- Ask each group to write on separate index cards all of the addition doubles facts and the related doubles plus 1 facts.
- Have students lay the cards facedown. Players take turns turning over two cards at a time.
- If the cards show a doubles addition fact and the matching doubles plus 1 fact, the player calls, "It is a match!" The player keeps the pair and takes another turn.

Option 2

Student Technology

Math Online macmillanmh.com

♪ Math Songs, "The Addition Boogie" Track 11 • 🌐 Math Adventures

Option 3

Learning Station: Art (p. 151G)

Direct students to the Art Learning Station for more opportunities to explore and extend the lesson concept.

Option 4

Problem-Solving Practice

Reinforce problem-solving skills and strategies with the Problem-Solving Practice worksheet.

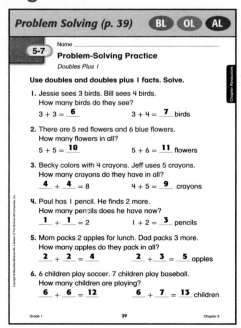

Problem Solving (p. 39) BL OL AL

Name _____

5-7 **Problem-Solving Practice**
Doubles Plus 1

Use doubles and doubles plus 1 facts. Solve.

1. Jessie sees 3 birds. Bill sees 4 birds. How many birds do they see?
$3 + 3 = \underline{6}$ $3 + 4 = \underline{7}$ birds

2. There are 5 red flowers and 6 blue flowers. How many flowers in all?
$5 + 5 = \underline{10}$ $5 + 6 = \underline{11}$ flowers

3. Becky colors with 4 crayons. Jeff uses 5 crayons. How many crayons do they have in all?
$\underline{4} + \underline{4} = 8$ $4 + 5 = \underline{9}$ crayons

4. Paul has 1 pencil. He finds 2 more. How many pencils does he have now?
$\underline{1} + \underline{1} = 2$ $1 + 2 = \underline{3}$ pencils

5. Mom packs 2 apples for lunch. Dad packs 3 more. How many apples do they pack in all?
$\underline{2} + \underline{2} = \underline{4}$ $\underline{2} + \underline{3} = \underline{5}$ apples

6. 6 children play soccer. 7 children play baseball. How many children are playing?
$\underline{6} + \underline{6} = \underline{12}$ $\underline{6} + \underline{7} = \underline{13}$ children

Grade 1   39   Chapter 5

① Introduce

Activity Choice 1 • Hands-On

- On the chalkboard, draw a domino with five dots on each side and another with five dots on the left side and six dots on the right. **What is the number sentence for each domino?** 5 + 5 = 10; 5 + 6 = 11

- **How is the second number sentence similar to and different from the first sentence?** One addend is the same and the other is 1 greater.

Activity Choice 2 • Literature

Introduce the lesson with *Plant Fruits & Seeds* by David M. Schwartz. For additional support, see p. TR49.

② Teach

- Write 4 + 4 on the chalkboard.
- Use counters and a ten-frame model this fact for students.
- Add one more counter. **What is the new number sentence?** 4 + 5 = 9
- **How is 4 + 5 different from a doubles fact?** It has one addend (5) that is greater by 1.
- **When the addend gets bigger by 1, what happens to the sum?** It gets bigger by 1, too.
- **Why is 4 + 5 called a doubles plus 1 fact?** It is a doubles fact with 1 added to one of the addends.
- Help students identify other doubles plus 1 facts using counters and a ten-frame. 1 + 2 = 3, 3 + 4 = 7, 5 + 6 = 11, 6 + 7 = 13

Get Ready Use the section at the top of student p. 171 to reinforce the lesson concept.

Check Observe students as you work through Exercises 1–4 as a class.

💬 **Exercise 4** Assess student comprehension before assigning practice exercises.

⚠️ **COMMON ERROR!**

Some students will recognize a near double problem but have difficulty keeping two ideas running in their heads at the same time. It might be helpful for them to write the double equation above the near double equation until the doubles become automatic.

Name _____

Doubles Plus 1

 Hands-On Activity

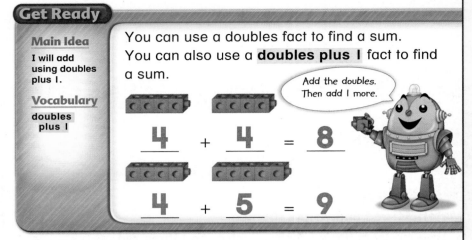

Get Ready

Main Idea
I will add using doubles plus 1.

Vocabulary
doubles plus 1

You can use a doubles fact to find a sum. You can also use a **doubles plus 1** fact to find a sum.

Add the doubles. Then add 1 more.

4 + 4 = 8

4 + 5 = 9

✓ Check

Write the addition sentence. Use 🎲.

1.
3 + 3 = 6   3 + 4 = 7

Find each sum. Use 🎲.

2. 5 + 5 = 10   3. 1 + 1 = 2

5 + 6 = 11   1 + 2 = 3

6 + 5 = 11   2 + 1 = 3

4. **Talk About It** How does knowing 4 + 4 help you find 4 + 5? Sample answer: 4 + 4 is 8, so 4 + 5 is 8 plus 1 more; 9

Chapter 5   Lesson 7   one hundred seventy-one   **171**

Reteach (p. 36) BL

5-7 **Reteach**
Doubles Plus 1

You can use doubles to find other sums.

Find the sum for the doubles fact.   Then add 1 to the sum.

3 + 3 = 6   3 + 4 = 7

Circle the doubles. Add.

1.
2 + 2 = 4
2 + 3 = 5

2.
5 + 5 = 10
5 + 6 = 11

3.
4 + 4 = 8
4 + 5 = 9

4.
3 + 3 = 6
3 + 4 = 7

5.
6 + 6 = 12
6 + 7 = 13

6.
1 + 1 = 2
1 + 2 = 3

Grade 1   36   Chapter 5

Skills Practice (p. 37) OL

5-7 **Skills Practice**
Doubles Plus 1

Find each sum. Use 🎲.

1. 3 + 3 = 6   2. 4 + 3 = 7

3. 2 + 2 = 4   4. 3 + 2 = 5

5. 4 + 4 = 8   6. 4 + 5 = 9

7. 1 + 1 = 2   8. 1 + 2 = 3

9. 6   10. 7   11. 1
  + 6   + 6   + 1
  ___   ___   ___
   12   13   2

12. 1   13. 5   14. 5
  + 2   + 5   + 6
  ___   ___   ___
    3   10   11

Use a doubles plus 1 fact to solve.

15. Nathan has 3 sticks. Jack has 4 sticks. How many total sticks do they have?

3 + 3 = 6 will help 3 + 4 = 7 sticks

16. Meg drew 5 triangles. Ann drew 6 triangles. How many triangles did they draw?

5 + 5 = 10 will help 5 + 6 = 11 triangles

Grade 1   37   Chapter 5

Find each sum. Use .

5.	3	6.	4	7.	1
	+ 2		+ 4		+ 1
	5		8		2

8.	2	9.	5	10.	3
	+ 3		+ 5		+ 4
	5		10		7

11.	6	12.	4	13.	5
	+ 6		+ 3		+ 6
	12		7		11

14. $1 + 2 = \underline{3}$ 15. $4 + 5 = \underline{9}$ 16. $6 + 5 = \underline{11}$

17. $3 + 3 = \underline{6}$ 18. $2 + 2 = \underline{4}$ 19. $5 + 4 = \underline{9}$

Problem Solving

Number Sense Solve. What doubles fact can help you?

20. Tyra sees 5 beetles.
Sara sees 6 beetles.
How many beetles do they see in all?

$5 + 6 = \underline{11}$ beetles

$\underline{5} + \underline{5} = \underline{10}$ will help

172 one hundred seventy-two

Math at Home Activity: Give your child an addition problem such as $4 + 5$; $3 + 4$; or $5 + 6$. Have your child give you the doubles fact that will help him/her find the sum.

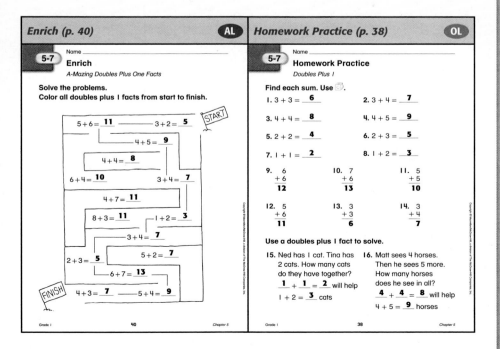

BL Alternate Teaching Strategy

If students have trouble understanding how to identify a doubles-plus-1 fact . . .

Then use one of these reteach options.

1 **CRM Daily Reteach Worksheet** (p. 36)

2 **Doubles Plus 1 Trains** Give each pair of students connecting cubes in two colors. Ask one partner to make a train of three cubes for each color and put the trains together. **What is your number sentence?** $3 + 3 = 6$
Have the other partner add one more cube to the train. **What is the new number sentence?** $3 + 4 = 7$ Continue with other doubles and doubles plus 1 facts.

③ Practice

Differentiate practice using these leveled assignments for Exercises 5–20.

Level	Assignment
BL Below/Approaching Level	Read each problem aloud and have students use connecting cubes to add.
OL On Level	Complete the exercises independently, using connecting cubes to add.
AL Above/Beyond Level	Complete the exercises independently without using connecting cubes.

④ Assess

Formative Assessment

Have students name three doubles facts and show how to make a doubles plus 1 fact from each. Check that they found the correct sum as well.

WRITING IN ▶MATH Write a letter to a friend about why it is helpful to know doubles plus 1 facts.

Quick Check **Are students continuing to struggle with doubles-plus-1 facts?**

If Yes → Small Group Options (p. 171B)
If No → Independent Work Options (p. 171B)
CRM Skills Practice Worksheet (p. 37)
CRM Enrich Worksheet (p. 40)

Lesson Planner _____

Objective

Choose the best strategy to solve a problem.

Resources

Manipulatives: connecting cubes

Teacher Technology
- 💿 TeacherWorks

📖 **Real-World Problem Solving Library**
Math and Social Studies: *Finding the Way*
Use these leveled books to reinforce and extend
problem-solving skills and strategies.

Leveled for:
- **OL** On Level
- **ELL** Sheltered English
- **SP** Spanish

For additional support, see the
Real-World Problem Solving
Teacher Guide.

Daily Routine _____

Use these suggestions before beginning the lesson on p. 173.

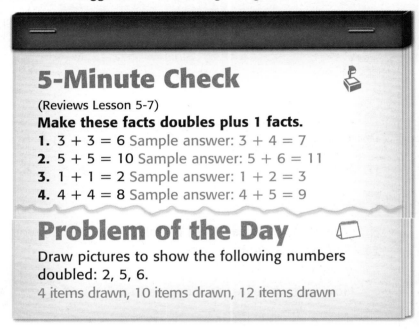

5-Minute Check

(Reviews Lesson 5-7)
Make these facts doubles plus 1 facts.
1. $3 + 3 = 6$ Sample answer: $3 + 4 = 7$
2. $5 + 5 = 10$ Sample answer: $5 + 6 = 11$
3. $1 + 1 = 2$ Sample answer: $1 + 2 = 3$
4. $4 + 4 = 8$ Sample answer: $4 + 5 = 9$

Problem of the Day

Draw pictures to show the following numbers
doubled: 2, 5, 6.
4 items drawn, 10 items drawn, 12 items drawn

LINE UP When students line up for recess, lunch, or
dismissal, have them share an example of
something they have that they would like to double and
how many they would have after doubling. Sample
answer: I have 2 dogs. I want to double them to have
4 dogs.

Differentiated Instruction

Small Group Options

Option 1
Below Level BL

LOGICAL, SPATIAL

Materials: a jar, paper, pencils, connecting cubes

- Display a jar containing a total of twelve connecting cubes. Include cubes of two different colors. Have students guess how many of each color there are and record their estimates.
- Invite students to empty the jar, connect the like colors, and compare their estimations to the actual numbers.
- Ask students to write an addition sentence that represents the number of cubes of each color with a sum that represents the total number of cubes from the jar.

Option 2
English Language Learners ELL

INTRAPERSONAL

Core Vocabulary: used, thought about, grouped
Common Use Verb: tried

Write Math This strategy provides students with more practice writing number sentences.

- Present a solution for an unknown addition problem. If students need more scaffolding, write something like ___ + ___ = 12.
- Have students work in groups to write and model a possible problem to go with the solution. Give each group different materials to work with (for example, 12 paper strips, rubber bands, paper clips, or buttons). Prompt counting on, doubles or other strategies as needed.
- Allow each group to demonstrate or show their problem. Discuss the various ways groups created the problem to match the solution as time permits.

Independent Work Options

Option 1
Early Finishers OL AL

LOGICAL, LINGUISTIC

Materials: red number cubes

- Students roll the number cube two times. The numbers rolled become addends for a number story.
- Have students work with their group to write a simple number story for the addends they roll.
- Invite each group to share their number story with another group. Have members of the second group solve the number story using any strategy they find useful.
- Allow time for groups to share the number story they solved, the strategy they used, and how they used it to find the answer.

Option 2
Student Technology

Math Online macmillanmh.com

Option 3
Learning Station: Science (p. 151H)

Direct students to the Science Learning Station for more opportunities to explore and extend the lesson concept.

1 Introduce

Activity • Review

Hold up trains of five red connecting cubes and five blue connecting cubes. Join the trains as students watch.

- **What is the number sentence?** 5 + 5 = 10
- Separate the trains and add one more red cube to the red train. Join the trains again.
- **What kind of fact do we have now?** doubles plus 1
- **What is the number sentence?** 5 + 6 = 11
- Have students work with a partner. One partner uses cubes to show a doubles fact and the other partner makes it a doubles plus 1 fact.
- Ask students to show their cubes to the class and tell the sum of each fact.

2 Teach

Have students read the problem on page 173. Guide them through the problem-solving steps.

Understand Using the questions, review what students know and what they need to find.

Plan Have them discuss their strategy.

Solve Help students *act it out* to solve the problem.

- **How many feathers does Amy have?** 9 feathers
- Have students use counters to model nine feathers.
- **How many feathers does Bill have?** 7 feathers
- Have students use counters to model seven feathers.
- **How many more feathers does Bill need?** 2 feathers

Check Have students look back at the problem to make sure that the answers fit the facts given.

! COMMON ERROR!

Students may add 7 + 9 while acting out the problem. Make sure students understand that they want to find the difference between the number of feathers Amy has versus the number of feathers Bill has.

Name _____

Problem-Solving Investigation

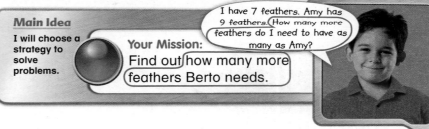

Main Idea
I will choose a strategy to solve problems.

Your Mission: Find out how many more feathers Berto needs.

I have 7 feathers. Amy has 9 feathers. How many more feathers do I need to have as many as Amy?

Understand

What do I need to find?
Circle it.

Plan

How will I solve the problem?

Solve

One way is to act it out. Sample answer: I will use a counter for each feather. I will show 7 counters for Berto's feathers and 9 counters for Amy's feathers. I will count how many more 9 counters is than 7 counters. That is how many more feathers Amy has than Berto.

2 feathers

Check

Look back.
Is my answer reasonable?

Check students' explanations.

Chapter 5   Lesson 8   one hundred seventy-three   173

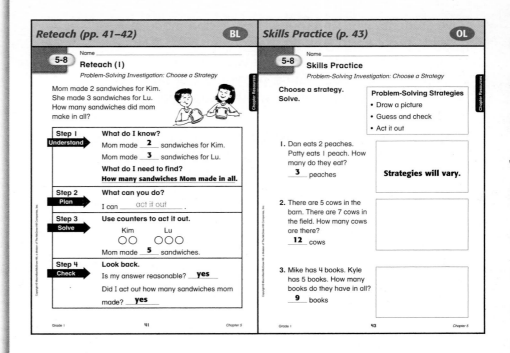

Reteach (pp. 41–42) BL

Name _____
5-8 **Reteach (1)**
Problem-Solving Investigation: Choose a Strategy

Mom made 2 sandwiches for Kim. She made 3 sandwiches for Lu. How many sandwiches did mom make in all?

Step 1 Understand	What do I know? Mom made __2__ sandwiches for Kim. Mom made __3__ sandwiches for Lu. What do I need to find? How many sandwiches Mom made in all.
Step 2 Plan	What can you do? I can ___act it out___.
Step 3 Solve	Use counters to act it out. Kim Lu OO OOO Mom made __5__ sandwiches.
Step 4 Check	Look back. Is my answer reasonable? __yes__ Did I act out how many sandwiches mom made? __yes__

Grade 1   41   Chapter 5

Skills Practice (p. 43) OL

Name _____
5-8 **Skills Practice**
Problem-Solving Investigation: Choose a Strategy

Choose a strategy. Solve.

Problem-Solving Strategies
- Draw a picture
- Guess and check
- Act it out

1. Dan eats 2 peaches. Patty eats 1 peach. How many do they eat?
__3__ peaches

Strategies will vary.

2. There are 5 cows in the barn. There are 7 cows in the field. How many cows are there?
__12__ cows

3. Mike has 4 books. Kyle has 5 books. How many books do they have in all?
__9__ books

Grade 1   43   Chapter 5

Mixed Problem Solving

Choose a strategy. Solve.

Problem-Solving Strategies
- Act it out
- Draw a picture
- Guess and check

1. Lucas picked 2 apples.
   Jordan picked 10 apples.
   How many apples
   did they pick in all?

   __12__ apples

2. Jan has 3 necklaces.
   Kim has 3 necklaces.
   How many do they have altogether?

   __6__ necklaces

3. The monkey ate 5 peanuts.
   The elephant ate 7 peanuts.
   How many total peanuts were eaten?

   __12__ peanuts

4. The clown sells toy animals in boxes of
   2, 4, and 6. Nela's mom bought 2 boxes
   with 10 animals in all.
   Which two boxes did she buy?

   __4__ and __6__

174 one hundred seventy-four

Copyright © Macmillan/McGraw-Hill, a division of The McGraw-Hill Companies, Inc.

BL **Alternate Teaching Strategy**

If students have trouble acting it out in Exercises 1–2 . . .

Then use one of these reteach options.

1 **CRM** **Daily Reteach Worksheet** (pp. 41–42)

2 **Act Out a Problem** Read aloud the problems to students.

- Discuss how students could act out each problem to find the solution.
- Provide students with props or manipulatives to help them act out a problem or guess and check.
- Have students share and discuss strategies and solutions for each problem.

③ Practice

Mixed Problem Solving

Exercises 1–4 Be sure students can read and understand all the problems. Have manipulatives available for students to use. Remind them of the different problem-solving strategies they can try.

④ Assess

Formative Assessment

Ask students which strategy they would use to solve the following problem and why:

There were 5 peanuts in the bowl. There were 6 almonds on the table. How many nuts?

Sample answer: I would guess and check. I know that 5 + 5 = 10 and one more would make 11. I could check using a number line or counters.

Quick Check **Are students continuing to have difficulty choosing a problem-solving strategy?**

If Yes → Small Group Options (p. 173B)

If No → Independent Work Options (p. 173B)

CRM Skills Practice Worksheet (p. 43)

CRM Enrich Worksheet (p. 45)

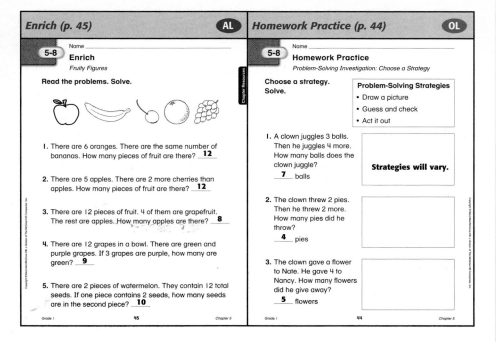

Enrich (p. 45) **AL**

5-8 Name ___
Enrich
Fruity Figures

Read the problems. Solve.

1. There are 6 oranges. There are the same number of bananas. How many pieces of fruit are there? __12__

2. There are 5 apples. There are 2 more cherries than apples. How many pieces of fruit are there? __12__

3. There are 12 pieces of fruit. 4 of them are grapefruit. The rest are apples. How many apples are there? __8__

4. There are 12 grapes in a bowl. There are green and purple grapes. If 3 grapes are purple, how many are green? __9__

5. There are 2 pieces of watermelon. They contain 12 total seeds. If one piece contains 2 seeds, how many seeds are in the second piece? __10__

Grade 1   45   Chapter 5

Homework Practice (p. 44) **OL**

5-8 Name ___
Homework Practice
Problem-Solving Investigation: Choose a Strategy

Choose a strategy. Solve.

Problem-Solving Strategies
- Draw a picture
- Guess and check
- Act it out

1. A clown juggles 3 balls. Then he juggles 4 more. How many balls does the clown juggle?
   __7__ balls

Strategies will vary.

2. The clown threw 2 pies. Then he threw 2 more. How many pies did he throw?
   __4__ pies

3. The clown gave a flower to Nate. He gave 4 to Nancy. How many flowers did he give away?
   __5__ flowers

Grade 1   44   Chapter 5

Problem Solving
in Social Studies

Real-World MATH

Manuel's favorite plant is a cactus. Have you ever seen a cactus?

This book belongs to

_____

A

Cacti grow in the desert where there is little water. Cacti have sharp leaves called spines. They have thick stems that store water.

B

Lesson Planner

Objective
Write an addition number sentence to solve problems in science.

National Standard

Students should develop an understanding of organisms and evnironment.

Vocabulary
number sentence

Activate Prior Knowledge

Before you turn students' attention to the pages, discuss the features of a cactus plant. Explain that more than one cactus are called *cacti*. Use *foot* and *feet* as a comparison.

- **Have you ever seen a cactus before? Where?** Sample answer: Yes, I saw a cactus as a plant in someone's home.

- **What does a cactus look like?** Sample answer: Mostly green with spines. If students do not mention it, explain that cacti are spiny. The needles can prick people and animals and help protect the plant.

- Tell students that a cactus has a waxy coating that keeps it from losing water and helps it live in the hot, dry desert.

- **How are cacti different from most other plants?** They have a waxy coating to help them survive in the desert. They can live where it is very hot and they do not need much water. They do not have regular leaves like other plants. Most have spines.

Cacti can be different sizes. Manuel likes big cacti. Which is your favorite?

C

Did you know that some cacti have flowers?

How many flowers do you see in all?

__4__ + __2__ = __6__

D

FOLD DOWN

Create the Book

Guide students to create their book.

- Have them fold the page in half.
- Ask them to write their name on page A.
- Explain that page A is the front cover and page D is the back cover. If necessary, have them practice flipping through the book in order.
- Guide them in reading the information and word problems on each of the pages.

Use the Student Pages

Have students work individually or in pairs to solve the word problem on page D.

Page D Point out that students will use the number of flowers in each picture as addends in the number sentence. Ask students to find the sum for the number sentence and then check their work. Provide counters for students who need them.

WRITING IN ►**MATH** Have students write an addition number story about flowers.

FOLDABLES® Dinah Zike's Foldables

Use this lesson suggestion to incorporate the Foldable during the chapter. Students can then use their Foldable to review for the test.

Lesson 5-7 Show the addition of doubles plus one on the last page of the addition journal.

Vocabulary Review

Review chapter vocabulary using one of the following options.

- **Visual Vocabulary Card (2)**
- **eGlossary** at macmillanmh.com

Vocabulary Test

CRM Chapter 5 Resource Masters (p. 50)
Assess student comprehension of the chapter vocabulary with the Vocabulary Test.

Math Online Chapter Test

Alternative summative assessment options are available online at macmillanmh.com.

Name _____

Vocabulary

Circle the right answer.

1. doubles	2. addend	3. doubles plus 1
$(3+3)$ $4+1$	$(5+\underline{3}=8)$ $5+3=\underline{8}$	$6+6$ $(6+7)$

Concepts

Count on to find the sum.

4.
$$\begin{array}{r} 3 \\ + 7 \\ \hline \boxed{10} \end{array}$$

5.
$$\begin{array}{r} 1 \\ + 9 \\ \hline \boxed{10} \end{array}$$

6.
$$\begin{array}{r} 8 \\ + 3 \\ \hline \boxed{11} \end{array}$$

Circle the greater number.
Then count on to add.

7. $2 + \underline{(5)} = \underline{7}$ 8. $\underline{(9)} + 2 = \underline{11}$ 9. $1 + \underline{(8)} = \underline{9}$

Add.

10.
$$\begin{array}{r} 4 \\ + 4 \\ \hline \boxed{8} \end{array}$$

11.
$$\begin{array}{r} 8 \\ + 2 \\ \hline \boxed{10} \end{array}$$

12.
$$\begin{array}{r} 5 \\ + 6 \\ \hline \boxed{11} \end{array}$$

13.
$$\begin{array}{r} 3 \\ + 6 \\ \hline \boxed{9} \end{array}$$

14.
$$\begin{array}{r} 8 \\ + 3 \\ \hline \boxed{11} \end{array}$$

15.
$$\begin{array}{r} 6 \\ + 6 \\ \hline \boxed{12} \end{array}$$

16.
$$\begin{array}{r} 6 \\ + 7 \\ \hline \boxed{13} \end{array}$$

17.
$$\begin{array}{r} 5 \\ + 5 \\ \hline \boxed{10} \end{array}$$

✓ Chapter 5 Project

My Addition Number Story Book

Alone, in pairs, or in small groups, have students discuss the results of their completed chapter project with the class. Assess their work using the Chapter Project rubric found in Chapter 5 Resource Masters on p. 55.

Write the sum. Circle the doubles facts.

18. (5 + 5) = 10   **19.** 3 + 4 = 7   **20.** 8 + 0 = 8

21. 9 + 3 = 12   **22.** (3 + 3) = 6   **23.** (6 + 6) = 12

Find each sum. Use .

24. 4 + 4 = 8   5 + 4 = 9   4 + 5 = 9

25. 3 + 3 = 6   3 + 4 = 7   4 + 3 = 7

26.
5	5	6	3
+ 5	+ 6	+ 5	+ 2
10	11	11	5

Problem Solving

Solve.

27. Lea drank 2 glasses of water before lunch. She drank 3 glasses of water after lunch. How many glasses of water did she drink today?

___5___ glasses of water

28. Jamal has 3 rocks to show his class. Katy has the same number of rocks. How many rocks do they have in all?

___6___ rocks

Copyright © Macmillan/McGraw-Hill, a division of The McGraw-Hill Companies, Inc.

178 one hundred seventy-eight

Summative Assessment

Summative Assessment

Use these alternate leveled chapter tests to differentiate assessment for the specific needs of your students.

Leveled Chapter 5 Tests			
Form	Type	Level	CRM Pages
1	Multiple Choice	BL	57–58
2A	Multiple Choice	OL	59–60
2B	Multiple Choice	OL	61–62
2C	Free Response	AL	63–64
2D	Free Response	AL	65–66

BL = below/approaching grade level
OL = on grade level
AL = above/beyond grade level

ExamView
Assessment Suite   Customize and create multiple versions of your chapter test and their test answer keys.

Data-Driven Decision Making

Based on the results of the Chapter Review/Test, use the following to review concepts that continue to present students with problems.

Exercises	State/Local Standards	What's the Math?	Error Analysis	Resources for Review
1–3		Understand vocabulary, "doubles," "addend," "doubles plus 1."	Does not understand "doubles," "addend," and "doubles plus 1."	Strategic Intervention Guide (p. 62) CRM Chapter 5 Resource Masters (Reteach Worksheets)
4–9		Show the meaning of addition. Use the counting strategy. Identify the greater number.	Writes wrong number. Adds incorrectly. Circles wrong number.	**Math Online** Concepts in Motion Math Adventures
10–17		Know the meaning of the symbols +, –, and =.	Does not do the addition. Adds incorrectly.	
18–26		Know doubles and doubles plus 1 facts. Use manipulatives to model addition.	Adds incorrectly. Circles incorrect facts.	

Test Practice

Formative Assessment

- Use Student Edition pp. 179–180 as practice and cumulative review. The questions are written in the same style as many state tests.

- You can use these two pages to benchmark student progress, or as an alternative homework assignment.

Additional practice pages can be found in the Chapter 5 Resource Masters.

 Chapter 5 Resource Masters
Cumulative Test Practice

- **Multiple Choice format** (pp. 57–62, 67)

- **Free Response format** (pp. 63–66, 68)

ExamView
Assessment Suite Create practice worksheets or tests that align to state standards.

Math Online For additional standards practice, visit macmillanmh.com.

Name _____

Listen as your teacher reads the problem.
Choose the correct answer.

1.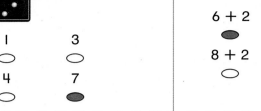

| 1 ○ | 3 ○ |
| 4 ○ | 7 ⬤ |

2.   3 + 2 = _____

| 3 ○ | 4 ○ | 5 ⬤ | 6 ○ |

3.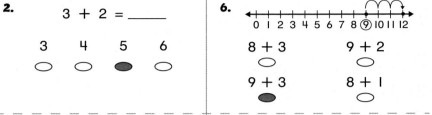

| 3 ○ | 6 ○ | 7 ○ | 8 ⬤ |

4.   1 + 6 = _____

| 2 ○ | 5 ○ | 6 ○ | 7 ⬤ |

5.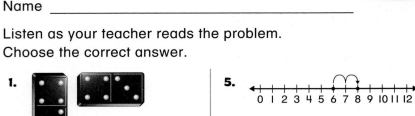

| 6 + 2 ⬤ | 6 + 3 ○ |
| 8 + 2 ○ | 4 + 2 ○ |

6.

| 8 + 3 ○ | 9 + 2 ○ |
| 9 + 3 ⬤ | 8 + 1 ○ |

7.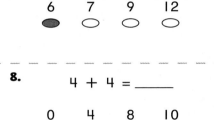

| 6 ⬤ | 7 ○ | 9 ○ | 12 ○ |

8.   4 + 4 = _____

| 0 ○ | 4 ○ | 8 ⬤ | 10 ○ |

Chapter 5   one hundred seventy-nine **179**

Copyright © Macmillan/McGraw-Hill, a division of The McGraw-Hill Companies, Inc.

Test Taking Tips

For the Teacher

- Before starting a test, look at examples of how the questions are to be completed.

For the Student

- Encourage students to make a good guess for an answer if time is running out and they are stuck on a question.

- Encourage students to use as much of the test time as they need.

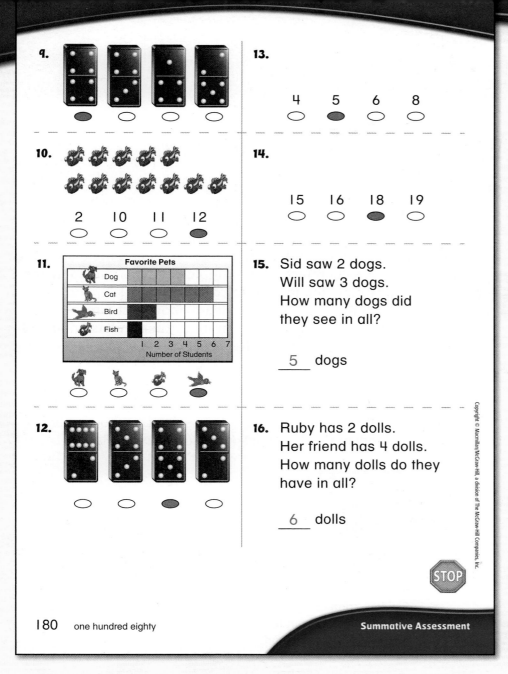

9.

13.

4   5   6   8

10.

2   10   11   12

14.

15   16   18   19

11.

Favorite Pets

Dog	
Cat	
Bird	
Fish	

1 2 3 4 5 6 7
Number of Students

15. Sid saw 2 dogs.
Will saw 3 dogs.
How many dogs did
they see in all?

_5_ dogs

12.

16. Ruby has 2 dolls.
Her friend has 4 dolls.
How many dolls do they
have in all?

_6_ dolls

STOP

180   one hundred eighty

Summative Assessment

Test Directions for Teachers

Read the following directions to students before they begin the test. Then read each question followed by a pause to allow students time to work on the problem and choose an answer. The first test item can be worked as a class example.

- **Write your name at the top of the page.**
- **I am going to read each question to you. Listen carefully to the entire question before you choose an answer.**

Multiple Choice

1. Look at the pair of dominoes. You can add across to find the sum. You can also add down to find the sum. What is the sum?
2. What is the sum?
3. Look at the number line. What is the sum?
4. What is the sum?
5. Look at the number line. Which problem does the number line show?
6. Look at the number line. Which problem does the number line show?
7. Look at eggs in the carton. What number makes a doubles fact? $6 + \_\_\_ = 12$
8. What is the sum?
- **Turn the page over.**
9. Look at the dominoes. Which domino shows $4 + 4$?
10. Listen to the number story. Cody has 5 fish. Max has 7. How many fish do they have together?
11. Look at the bar graph. It shows favorite pets. Which pet got 2 votes?
12. Look at the dominoes. Which shows a sum of 9?
13. Luke has 5 marbles. Which number is 5?
14. What number comes just after 17?

Short Response

15. Sid saw 2 dogs. Will saw 3 dogs. How many dogs did they see in all?
16. Ruby has 2 dolls. Her friend has 4 dolls. How many dolls do they have in all?

Chapter Overview

Chapter-at-a-Glance

In Chapter 6, the emphasis is on solving subtraction problems, writing subtraction sentences and fact families, and using strategies and skills to solve problems.

Lesson	Math Objective	State/Local Standards
6-1 Count Back 1, 2, or 3 (pp. 185–186)	Count back by 1, 2, or 3 to subtract.	
6-2 Problem-Solving Strategy: Write a Number Sentence (pp. 187–188)	Use the *write a number sentence* strategy to solve problems.	
6-3 Use a Number Line to Subtract (pp. 189–190)	Use a number line to subtract differences to 12.	
6-4 Problem-Solving Investigation: Choose a Strategy (pp. 193–194)	Choose the best strategy to solve a problem.	
6-5 Use Doubles to Subtract (pp. 195–196)	Use doubles facts to subtract.	
6-6 Relate Addition to Subtraction (pp. 197–198)	Relate addition and subtraction facts to solve problems.	
6-7 Fact Families (pp. 199–200)	Write fact families to 12.	

Develop Subtraction Strategies

BIG Idea Because of the inverse relationship of addition and subtraction, many of the addition strategies learned in the previous chapter can be reversed to aid in the computation and memorization of subtraction facts. For example, students can apply the concept of counting on to count back by 1, 2, and 3. In this chapter, students also learn about fact families which serve as a foundation for further understanding of number operations as they progress to the upper elementary grades.

Algebra Readiness In Lesson 6-6, students prepare for Algebra by further developing their understanding of how to use operation symbols + and −, and by showing how the addition and subtraction of doubles are related.

Focal Points and Connections

G1-FP2 *Number and Operations:* **Developing an understanding of whole number relationships, including grouping in tens and ones**

Children compare and order whole numbers (at least to 100) to develop an understanding of and solve problems involving the relative sizes of these numbers. They think of whole numbers between 10 and 100 in terms of groups of tens and ones (especially recognizing the numbers 11 to 19 as 1 group of ten and particular numbers of ones). They understand the sequential order of the counting numbers and their relative magnitudes and represent numbers on a number line.

G1-FP6C *Algebra:* Through identifying, describing, and applying number patterns and properties in developing strategies for basic facts, children learn about other properties of numbers and operations, such as odd and even (e.g., "Even numbers of objects can be paired, with none left over"), and 0 as the identity element for addition.

Skills Trace
Vertical Alignment

Kindergarten

In kindergarten, students learned to:

- Model subtraction as taking away from or separating sets of objects.
- Use concrete objects to solve subtraction problems.
- Use concrete objects to show different ways to take away from 8 and 9.

First Grade

During this chapter, students learn to:

- Relate addition to subtraction.
- Use a number line to subtract.
- Use strategies and skills to solve problems.

After this chapter, students learn to:

- Tell time to the hour and half hour. (Chapter 7)
- Use different strategies to solve differences to 20. (Chapter 10)

Second Grade

In second grade, students learn to:

- Subtract a 1-digit number from a 2-digit number.
- Multiply twos and fives.
- Compare fractions.

Backmapping and Vertical Alignment
McGraw-Hill's *Math Connects* program was conceived and developed with the final results in mind: student success in Algebra 1 and beyond. The authors, using the **NCTM Focal Points and Focal Connections** as their guide, developed this brand-new series by backmapping from Algebra 1 concepts, and vertically aligning the topics so that they build upon prior skills and concepts and serve as a foundation for future topics.

Math Vocabulary

The following math vocabulary words for Chapter 6 are listed in the glossary of the **Student Edition.** You can find interactive definitions in 13 languages in the **eGlossary** at macmillanmh.com.

count back
(p. 185)

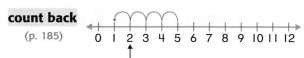

fact family addition and subtraction sentences that use the same numbers; example:

6 + 7 = 13	13 − 7 = 6
7 + 6 = 13	13 − 6 = 7 (p. 199)

Visual Vocabulary Cards Use Visual Vocabulary Card 18 to reinforce the vocabulary in this chapter. (The Define/Example/Ask routine is printed on the back of each card.)

Chapter Planner

Suggested Pacing		
Instruction	**Review and Assessment**	**TOTAL**
7 days	2 days	**9 days**

Diagnostic Assessment
Are You Ready? (p. 182)

	Lesson 6-1 Pacing: 1 day	**Lesson 6-2** Pacing: 1 day	**Lesson 6-3** Pacing: 1 day
Lesson/ Objective	**Count Back 1, 2, or 3** (pp. 185–186) **Objective:** Count back by 1, 2, or 3 to subtract.	**Problem-Solving Strategy** **Write a Number Sentence** (pp. 187–188) **Objective:** Use the *write a number sentence* strategy to solve problems.	**Use a Number Line to Subtract** (pp. 189–190) **Objective:** Use a number line to subtract differences to 12.
State/Local Standards			
Math Vocabulary	count back		
Lesson Resources	**Materials** walk-on number line **Manipulatives** connecting cubes **Other Resources** CRM Leveled Worksheets (pp. 6–10) Daily Reteach • 5-Minute Check Problem of the Day	**Materials** sticky notes **Manipulatives** two-colored counters **Other Resources** CRM Leveled Worksheets (pp. 11–15) Daily Reteach • 5-Minute Check Problem of the Day *Rock Collections*	**Materials** walk-on number line, number cards (1–20) **Manipulatives** number cube **Other Resources** CRM Leveled Worksheets (pp. 16–20) Daily Reteach • 5-Minute Check Problem of the Day
Technology [Math Online]	♪ Math Song Track 15 Math Tool Chest, Counter Level 1 Concepts in Motion		♪ Math Song Track 10 Concepts in Motion
Reaching All Learners	Gifted and Talented, p. 185B **AL** English Learners, p. 185B **ELL** Early Finishers, p. 185B **OL** **AL**	Below Level, p. 187B **BL** English Learners, p. 187B **ELL** Early Finishers, p. 187B **OL** **AL**	Below Level, p. 189B **BL** English Learners, p. 189B **ELL** Early Finishers, p. 189B **OL** **AL**
Alternate Lessons	*Math Their Way*, p. 109 *IMPACT Mathematics*: Unit B		*IMPACT Mathematics*: Unit B

Formative Assessment
• Mid-Chapter Check (p. 191)
• Spiral Review (p. 192)

KEY
BL Below/ Approaching Level   **OL** On Level   **AL** Above/Beyond Level   **ELL** English Learners
SE Student Edition   **TE** Teacher Edition   **CRM** Chapter 3 Resource Masters   CD-Rom
Transparency   Flip Chart   Real-World Problem Solving Library

	Lesson 6-4 Pacing: 1 day	Lesson 6-5 Pacing: 1 day	Lesson 6-6 Pacing: 1 day	
Lesson/ Objective	**Problem-Solving Investigation Choose a Strategy** (pp. 193–194) **Objective:** Choose the best strategy to solve a problem.	**Use Doubles to Subtract** (pp. 195–196) **Objective:** Use doubles facts to subtract.	**Relate Addition to Subtraction** (pp. 197–198) **Objective:** Relate addition and subtraction facts to solve problems.	
State/Local Standards				
Math Vocabulary				
Lesson Resources		**Materials** WorkMat 1: Ten-Frame **Manipulatives** two-colored counters	**Materials** number cards, symbol cards $(+, -, =)$ **Manipulatives** connecting cubes, number cubes	
	Other Resources CRM Leveled Worksheets (pp. 21–25) Daily Reteach • 5-Minute Check Problem of the Day *Rock Collections*	**Other Resources** CRM Leveled Worksheets (pp. 26–30) Daily Reteach • 5-Minute Check Problem of the Day	**Other Resources** CRM Leveled Worksheets (pp. 31–35) Daily Reteach • 5-Minute Check Problem of the Day	
Technology		♪ Math Song Track 15 Math Adventures	♪ Math Song Track 15 Math Online	
Reaching All Learners	Below Level, p. 193B BL English Learners, p. 193B ELL Early Finishers, p. 193B OL AL	Gifted and Talented, p. 195B AL English Learners, p. 195B ELL Early Finishers, p. 195B OL AL	Gifted and Talented, 197B AL English Learners, p. 197B ELL Early Finishers, 197B OL AL	
Alternate Lessons		*IMPACT Mathematics*: Unit A	*Math Their Way*, pp. 183–184 *IMPACT Mathematics*: Unit B	

Chapter Planner

Lesson 6-7
Pacing: 1 day

Lesson/ Objective	**Fact Families** (pp. 199–200) **Objective:** Write fact families to 12.
State/Local Standards	
Math Vocabulary	**fact family**
Lesson Resources	**Manipulatives** connecting cubes, number cubes **Other Resources** [CRM] Leveled Worksheets (pp. 36–40) 🖬 Daily Reteach • 5-Minute Check 🗂 Problem of the Day
Technology	♪ Math Song Track 12
Reaching All Learners	Gifted and Talented, p. 199B **AL** English Learners, p. 199B **ELL** Early Finishers, p. 199B **OL** **AL**
Alternate Lessons	*Math Their Way*, p. 174 *IMPACT Mathematics*: Unit A

Extra Practice (p. 201)
Problem-Solving in Science (p. 203)

✓ **Summative Assessment**
• Chapter Review/Test (p. 205)
• Test Practice (p. 207)

Assessment Options

✓ Diagnostic Assessment
- [SE] *Option 1:* Are You Ready? (p. 182)
  Option 2: Online Quiz macmillanmh.com
- [CRM] *Option 3:* Diagnostic Test (p. 42)
- [CRM] *Option 4:* Chapter Pretest (p. 43)

✓ Formative Assessment
- [TE] Alternate Teaching Strategies (every lesson)
- [TE] Line Up (every lesson)
- [SE] Talk About It (every lesson)
- [SE] Writing in Math (every lesson)
- [SE] Check What You Know (every lesson)
- [SE] Mid-Chapter Check (p. 191)
- [CRM] Mid-Chapter Test (p. 44)

✓ Summative Assessment
- [SE] Chapter Review/Test (pp. 205–206)
- [SE] Test Practice (pp. 207–208)
- [CRM] Vocabulary Test (p. 45)
- [CRM] Leveled Chapter Tests (pp. 52–61)
- [CRM] Cumulative Test Practice (p. 62–63)
- [CRM] Listening Assessment (p. 48–49)
- [CRM] Oral Assessment (p. 46–47)
- 💿 Exam*View*® Assessment Suite
- ⚙ Advance Tracker

Mc Graw Hill **Professional Development**

Targeted professional development has been articulated throughout **McGraw-Hill's** *Math Connects* program. The **McGraw-Hill Professional Development Video Library** provides short videos that support the **NCTM Focal Points and Focal Connections**. For more information, visit macmillanmh.com.

Model Lessons	Instructional Strategies

Teacher Notes

CHAPTER 6

Learning Stations
Cross-Curricular Links

Reading

group | KINESTHETIC

Listen, Jump, Count!

- Read *Chicka Chicka 1 2 3* with your group. Take turns. Read one page and then pass the book.
- Each time you hear "Chicka, Chicka, 1, 2, 3," jump up and repeat the words. Raise one hand high and put up one, two, and then three fingers.

Teacher Note: If some readers are not ready to read aloud, assign one person in the group to be the "leader," who reads every page while the rest of the group listens and participates.

Materials:
- *Chicka Chicka 1 2 3* by Bill Martin Jr., Michael Sampson, and Lois Ehlert

Art

individual | SPATIAL

Fact Family Dominoes

- Write the number sentences for one fact family. Use addends from 0 through 6.
- Make a domino for your fact family. Fold the black paper in half. Stick dots on each side of the fold to show the fact family.
- Use your domino to tell a classmate about the sentences in your fact family.

Materials:
- black construction paper
- dot stickers

Language Arts

pair | LOGICAL

Write Math Riddles

- Read this riddle: *I am a number. When you subtract 4 from 12, I am the number left. Which number am I?*
- Write the riddle as a subtraction sentence and solve. $12 - 4 = 8$
- Make up a new riddle. Write a subtraction sentence and choose one number to be the secret number.
- Write the riddle. Start with *I am a number*. Then write a clue the secret number would say. End with *Which number am I?*
- Trade riddles with your partner and solve.

Materials:
- paper
- pencil

$$12 - 4 = 8$$

Science

Science Survey

- On a blank sheet of paper, write the numbers 1 through 12.
- Look through magazines for pictures of plants and animals to cut out. Paste each picture next to a number until you have 12.
- Now count how many plants you have. Circle them in green. Count how many animals you have. Circle them in red.
- Write a subtraction sentence to show how many plants you have.

Teacher Note: If magazines are not available, have children randomly draw plants and animals.

Materials:
- paper
- pencil
- magazines

 ## Health

"Good for You" Math Stories

- Place the number cards facedown in the middle the circle.
- Take turns choosing a number card. Make up a subtraction story that starts with that number. In your story, use fruits, vegetables, or other foods your body needs.
- Write the subtraction sentence. Have everyone in the circle use counters to find the answer.
- Put back your number card and mix up the cards for the next player.
- Continue until all players have had a turn.

Materials:
- number cards 5–12
- white board
- dry erase marker
- counters

Calendar Time

What Day Is It?

- Have students look at the classroom calendar. **What is today's date? How many days of the month have passed?** Check students' explanations.
- Invite students to think of similar questions to ask about the calendar. To prompt ideas, point to the current date and the past or coming weekend. **What question could you ask about these dates?** Sample answers: How many days until the weekend? How many days since the last weekend?
- Have the class use the information to generate a list of number sentences related to the questions.

Introduce the Chapter

 Real World: How Many?

Share with students that they are going to study strategies that will aid them in subtraction.

- Have nine volunteers bring their chairs to the front of the class. Direct students to stand behind their chair. Write the number 9 on the chalkboard.
- Ask two of the volunteers to sit. Write the subtraction sign and the number 2. **How many students remain standing?** 7 students
- Then have the 2 students stand again while the other 7 sit. **What is the number sentence related to this story?** $9 - 7 = 2$
- Discuss fact families and explain that knowing fact families makes it easier to memorize addition and subtraction facts.

Have students turn to p. 181.
- If 2 more fish jump to the other bowl, how many fish will be left in the first bowl? 9 fish

Key Vocabulary

Introduce the key vocabulary in the chapter using the routine below.

Define: A **fact family** is an addition or subtraction sentence that uses the same numbers.
Example: The fact family for 6, 7, and 13 is $6 + 7 = 13$, $7 + 6 = 13$, $13 - 7 = 6$, and $13 - 6 = 7$.
Ask: What is the fact family for 3, 2, and 5?

CHAPTER 6 Develop Subtraction Strategies

Key Vocabulary
count back
fact family

Explore
12 fish were in a bowl.
Then 1 fish jumped to another bowl.
How many fish are left in the first bowl? ___11___ fish

Chapter 6   one hundred eighty-one   181

 **Dinah Zike's Foldables**

Guide students to create their Bound Book Foldable for subtraction strategies.

1. Take two sheets of 8 1/2 x 11 paper and separately fold them like a hamburger. Place the papers on top of each other, leaving one sixteenth of an inch between the mountain tops.

2. Mark both folds one inch from the outer edges.

3. On one of the folded sheets, cut from the top and bottom edge to the marked spot on both sides.

4. On the second folded sheet, start at one of the marked spots and cut the fold between the two marks.

5. Take the cut sheet from step 3 and fold it like a burrito. Place the burrito through the other sheet and then open the burrito. Fold the bound pages in half to form an eight-page book.

Develop Subtraction Strategies Journal

When to Use It *Lessons 6-1, 6-2, 6-3, 6-5 and 6-6. (Additional instructions for using the Foldable with these lessons are found on pp. 191 and 205.)*

Name _____

✓ Are You Ready for Chapter 6?

1. Circle the minus sign.   **2.** Circle the equal sign.

+   ⊖   =   +   −   ⊜

Find the difference.

3. $\begin{array}{r} 6 \\ - \ 0 \\ \hline 6 \end{array}$	**4.** $\begin{array}{r} 4 \\ - \ 2 \\ \hline 2 \end{array}$	**5.** $\begin{array}{r} 9 \\ - \ 8 \\ \hline 1 \end{array}$
6. $\begin{array}{r} 4 \\ - \ 3 \\ \hline 1 \end{array}$	**7.** $\begin{array}{r} 6 \\ - \ 1 \\ \hline 5 \end{array}$	**8.** $\begin{array}{r} 9 \\ - \ 4 \\ \hline 5 \end{array}$
9. $\begin{array}{r} 5 \\ - \ 4 \\ \hline 1 \end{array}$	**10.** $\begin{array}{r} 3 \\ - \ 2 \\ \hline 1 \end{array}$	**11.** $\begin{array}{r} 2 \\ - \ 1 \\ \hline 1 \end{array}$

12. Cross out 4 carrots. Use the pictures to write a number sentence.

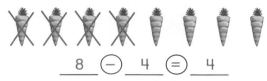

$\underline{\ 8\ }\ \ominus\ \underline{\ 4\ }\ \circleddash\ \underline{\ 4\ }$

182   one hundred eighty-two   This page checks skills needed for Chapter 6.

Diagnostic Assessment

Check for students' prerequisite skills before beginning the chapter.

- **Option 1:** *Are You Ready for Chapter 6?*
  - SE Student Edition, p. 182

- **Option 2:** *Online Assessment*
  - **Math Online** macmillanmh.com

- **Option 3:** *Diagnostic Test*
  - CRM Chapter 6 Resource Masters, p. 42

RTI (Response to Intervention)

Apply the Results Based on the results of the diagnostic assessment on page 182, use the chart below to address individual needs before beginning the chapter.

TIER 3 Intensive Intervention

If students miss eight or more of the exercises:

Then use Chapters 2 and 3 of *Math Triumphs*, an intensive math intervention program from McGraw-Hill

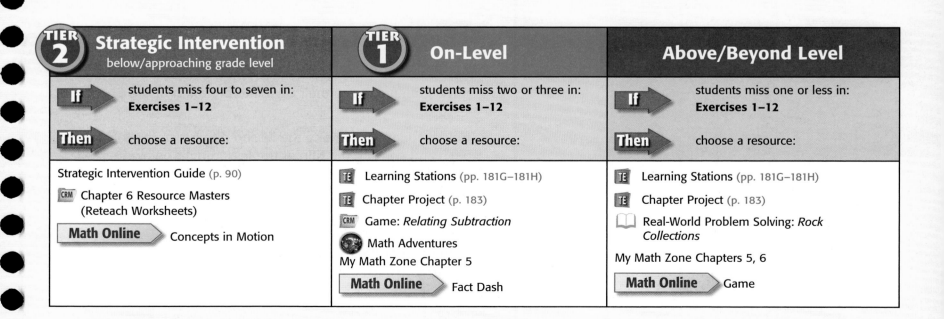

TIER 2 Strategic Intervention
below/approaching grade level

If students miss four to seven in: **Exercises 1–12**

Then choose a resource:

Strategic Intervention Guide (p. 90)

CRM Chapter 6 Resource Masters (Reteach Worksheets)

Math Online Concepts in Motion

TIER 1 On-Level

If students miss two or three in: **Exercises 1–12**

Then choose a resource:

TE Learning Stations (pp. 181G–181H)

TE Chapter Project (p. 183)

CRM Game: *Relating Subtraction*

Math Adventures
My Math Zone Chapter 5

Math Online Fact Dash

Above/Beyond Level

If students miss one or less in: **Exercises 1–12**

Then choose a resource:

TE Learning Stations (pp. 181G–181H)

TE Chapter Project (p. 183)

Real-World Problem Solving: *Rock Collections*

My Math Zone Chapters 5, 6

Math Online Game

Before you begin Chapter 6:
- Read the Math at Home letter found on p. 183 with the class and have each student sign it.
- Send home copies of the Math at Home letter with each student.
- Use the Spanish letter on p. 184 for students with Spanish-speaking parents or guardians.

Starting the Chapter
Roll the blue number cube two times and write the numbers down on a sheet of paper. Instruct students to write a simple story about the two numbers. Encourage students to draw a picture relating to the sentence they have just written.

Read-Aloud Anthology
For an optional reading activity to introduce this chapter's Math Concepts, see the Read-Aloud Anthology on p. TR30.

MATH at HOME

Dear Family,
Today my class started Chapter 6, **Develop Subtraction Strategies**. In this chapter, I will learn to use different strategies for subtraction. Here is an activity we can do and a list of books we can read together.

Love, _____

Activity
Write numbers 1-12 on index cards. Keep the number 12 separate and turn the rest upside down. Pick a card. Decide what additional number you need to make a sum of 12. Take turns turning cards over until you find it. Create a subtraction sentence.

Key Vocabulary
count back counting back 1, 2, or 3 numbers: Example: 5 – 3. Start at 5 and count back 4, 3, **2**.

fact family addition and subtraction sentences that use the same numbers

Math Online Click on the eGlossary link at macmillanmh.com to find out more about these words. There are 13 languages.

Books to Read
Elevator Magic
by Stuart J. Murphy
Harper Trophy
Publishing, 1997.

The Shopping Basket
by John Burningham
Candlewick Press, 1997.

Five Little Monkeys Sitting in a Tree
by Eileen Christelow
Clarion Books, 1999.

one hundred eighty-three   183

Chapter 6 Project

My Story of Chapter 6
- Have students create their own interpretation of the Chapter 6 lessons.
- Guide students in writing the lesson number at the top of each page and copying the title of the lesson right below that number.
- Have students write or create something on that page that represents the subject matter of the lesson. It could be an illustration, a number sentence, or a diagram.
- At the end of the chapter, invite partners to exchange books and review each other's work.

CRM *Refer to Chapter 6 Resource Masters p. 50 for a rubric to assess students' progress on this project.*

Estimada familia:

Hoy mi clase comenzó el Capítulo 6, **Desarrolle la sustracción las estrategias**. En este capítulo, aprenderé a usar diferentes estrategias para restar. A continuación, hay una actividad que podemos hacer y una lista de libros que podemos leer juntos.

Cariños, _____

Actividad

Escriban en tarjetas los números del 1 al 12. Mantengan separado el número 12 y coloquen el resto boca abajo. Seleccionen una tarjeta y decidan qué número se necesita para que sume 12. Túrnense para voltear las tarjetas hasta encontrar la respuesta. Inventen un enunciado de resta.

Vocabulario clave

contar al revés contar al revés 1, 2 ó 3 números: Ejemplo: 5 – 3. Comienza con 5 y cuenta al revés 4, 3, **2**

familia de operaciones problemas de suma y resta que usan los mismos números

Math Online Visiten el enlace eGlossary en macmillanmh.com para averiguar más sobre estas palabras, las cuales se muestran en 13 idiomas.

Libros para leer

Restar y quitar
de Diyan Leake
Heinemann, 2006.

Puedo restar
de Gerry Price
Nueva Guia, 2002.

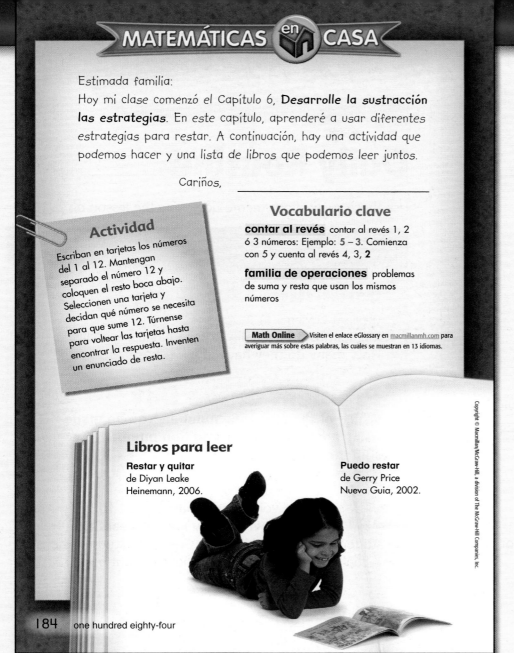

184 one hundred eighty-four

Chapter 6 Literature List

Lesson	Book Title
6-1	**Ten Sly Piranhas** William Wise
6-2	**Ten Sly Piranhas** William Wise
6-3	**12 Ways to Get to 11** Eve Merriam
6-5	**More Bugs? Less Bugs?** Don L. Curry
6-6	**A Bag Full of Pups** Dick Gackenbach
6-7	**Math Fables** Greg Tang
Any	**Elevator Magic** Stuart J. Murphy
Any	**The Shopping Basket** John Burningham
Any	**Five Little Monkeys Sitting in a Tree** Eileen Christelow

ELL National ESL Standards Alignment for Chapter 6

Lesson, Page	ESL Standard	Modality	Level
6-1, p 185B	Goal 2, Standard 2, e	Auditory, Visual/Spatial	Beginning
6-2, p 187B	Goal 2, Standard 2, i	Visual/Interpersonal	Intermediate
6-3, p 189B	Goal 2, Standard 3, h	Auditory, Kinesthetic	Intermediate
6-4, p 193B	Goal 1, Standard 3, d	Auditory	Beginning
6-5, p 195B	Goal 1, Standard 2, d	Linguistic, Social	Intermediate
6-6, p 197B	Goal 1, Standard 3, k	Visual, Auditory	Intermediate
6-7, p 199B	Goal 2, Standard 2, a	Visual/Spatial	Intermediate

The National ESL Standards can be found in the Teacher Reference Handbook.

Count Back 1, 2, or 3

Lesson Planner

Objective

Count back by 1, 2, or 3 to subtract.

Vocabulary

count back

Resources

Materials: walk-on number line

Manipulatives: connecting cubes

Literature Connection: *Ten Sly Piranhas* by William Wise

Alternate Lessons: Adapt "Stand Up, Sit Down" on page 109 of *Math Their Way* for practice in counting backward.

Use *IMPACT Mathematics:* Unit B, to provide practice using the counting back strategy.

Teacher Technology

🌐 TeacherWorks • Concepts in Motion • ⬤ Math Tool Chest • ♪ Math Songs Track 15 Lesson Plan

Focus on Math Background

The counting back (1, 2, or 3) strategy is a valuable tool for developing efficiency in subtraction computations. The strategy addresses many of the basic facts students need to master to be successful in subtracting.

The concept of working backward can be developed in a variety of situations. An example of counting back in a language listening situation is to have students recall in reverse order the last three things they did in the class schedule.

Young children must learn that in subtraction, unlike in addition, there is a "starting" number and that it is always the greater number. Recognizing these conventions is central to understanding the meaning of subtraction.

Daily Routine

Use these suggestions before beginning the lesson on p. 185.

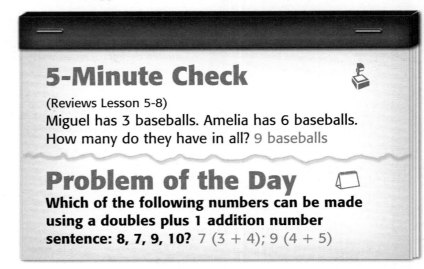

5-Minute Check 🖾

(Reviews Lesson 5-8)
Miguel has 3 baseballs. Amelia has 6 baseballs. How many do they have in all? 9 baseballs

Problem of the Day 📖

Which of the following numbers can be made using a doubles plus 1 addition number sentence: 8, 7, 9, 10? 7 (3 + 4); 9 (4 + 5)

LINE UP Say to a volunteer, **Count back 2 from your age and tell how old you were 2 years ago.** Have the student answer and line up. Give each student the same challenge, varying the number to count back.

▷ Building Math Vocabulary

Write **count back** on the chalkboard and explain that counting back on the number line is one way to subtract.

- Ask students to use their 12-inch ruler as a number line.
- Have students place their finger on 9 and count, or jump, back 2. What number does your finger land on? 7
- **How is this like subtracting 2 from 9?** You are using the same numbers 2, 7, and 9.

Differentiated Instruction

Small Group Options

Option 1 — Gifted and Talented **AL**

Materials: rulers or 0–12 number lines

- **Model ways to solve this riddle:** *I am the number 7. What is one way to find me on a number line?* Sample answer: Count back 3 from 10.
- **What number sentence matches the riddle?** Sample answer: $10 - 3 = 7$
- Challenge students to write their own counting-back riddles.
- Have partners trade and solve each other's riddles. Ask them to write a subtraction sentence for each riddle they solve.

Option 2 — English Language Learners **ELL**

AUDITORY, VISUAL/SPATIAL

Core Vocabulary: in a line, lunch, going to

Common Use Verb: count back

Write Math This strategy teaches students how to count back.

- Call 8 students to stand in line. Count heads.
- Say: "3 students are going to lunch. How many are left?" 5
- Model Counting back 3. Have students write the problem.
- Repeat as time permits.

Use this worksheet to provide additional support for English Language Learners.

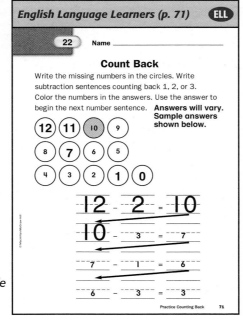

Independent Work Options

Option 1 — Early Finishers **OL** **AL**

Materials: ruler, red number cube, number cards 6–12

- Have one partner select a number card.
- Have the other partner roll the red number cube. Then partners decide how to count back to subtract. Strategies will vary. Possible strategy: Use the ruler as a number line.
- Partners write subtraction sentences to model their counting back.

Option 2 — Student Technology

Math Online  macmillanmh.com

♪ Math Songs, "Take It Away" Track 15 • 🖐 Math Tool Chest • 🌐 Math Adventures

Option 3 — Learning Station: Reading (p. 181G)

Direct students to the Reading Learning Station for more opportunities to explore and extend the lesson concept.

Option 4 — Problem-Solving Practice

Reinforce problem-solving skills and strategies with the Problem-Solving Practice worksheet.

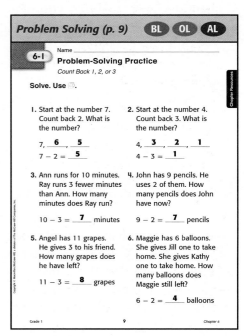

1 Introduce

Activity Choice 1 • Hands-On

- Use a finger play, such as "10 Little Monkeys," to help the students **count back** by taking away one.
- Hold up 10 fingers and say the first verse: *Ten little monkeys sleeping on the bed. One rolled off and the other ones said, "Nine little monkeys sleeping on the bed."*
- Repeat back through 1.

Activity Choice 2 • Literature

Introduce the lesson with *Ten Sly Piranhas* by William Wise. For additional support, see p. TR50.

2 Teach

Model subtraction by counting back with connecting cubes. Have students connect twelve cubes.

- **How many cubes are left after you count back 3 cubes?** 9 cubes
- **What is the number sentence?** 12 − 3 = 9
- **How many cubes are left if you count back 2 more cubes?** 7 cubes
- **What is this number sentence?** 9 − 2 = 7

Get Ready Use the section at the top of student p. 185 to reinforce the lesson concept. Have students focus on the big number they start with. "I am on 6, and I am going to get rid of 2. Throw one away and I have 5. Throw two away and I have 4."

Check Observe students as you work through Exercises 1–10 as a class.

> **Exercise 10** Assess student comprehension before assigning practice exercises.

! COMMON ERROR!

When writing the subtraction number sentences involving counting back, students may forget to write the greater number first. Remind them that the number where they start counting back is also the number they must write to "start" the problem.

185 **Chapter 6** Develop Subtraction Strategies

Name _____

Count Back 1, 2, or 3

Get Ready

Main Idea
I will count back to subtract.

Vocabulary
count back

You can **count back** to subtract.

6 − 2 = **4**

Start with 6.   Count back 2.

6   6, **5**, **4**

✓ Check

Count back to subtract. Use  to help.

1. 8 − 3 = **5**

    8   8, **7**, **6**, **5**

2. 7 − 1 = **6**

   7, **6**

3. 4 − 2 = **2**

   4, **3**, **2**

4. 5 − 1 = **4**

5. 6 − 3 = **3**

6. 8 − 2 = **6**

7. 5 − 2 = **3**

8. 7 − 3 = **4**

9. 7 − 2 = **5**

10. **Talk About It** Why do you count back when subtracting?
Sample answer: Because you are taking away, so the number is smaller.

Chapter 6   Lesson 1   one hundred eighty-five   **185**

Reteach (p. 6) — BL

6-1 Name _____
Reteach
Count Back 1, 2, or 3

Counting back is one way to subtract.
Start with the first number.
Count back the second number.
Find 7 − 2.   7, **6**, **5**
Start at 7. Count back 2.   7 − 2 = **5**

Count back to subtract. Use to help you.

1. 5, **4**, **3**
    Start at **5**
    Count back **2**.
    5 − 2 = **3**

2. 8, **7**, **6**, **5**
    Start at **8**
    Count back **3**.
    8 − 3 = **5**

3. 6, **5**, **4**, **3**, **2**
    Start at **6**
    Count back **4**.
    6 − 4 = **2**

4. 9, **8**, **7**
    Start at **9**
    Count back **2**.
    9 − 2 = **7**

Grade 1   6   Chapter 6

Skills Practice (p. 7) — OL

6-1 Name _____
Skills Practice
Count Back 1, 2, or 3

Count back to subtract. Use to help.

1. 5, **4**, **3**
    5 − 2 = **3**

2. 7, **6**, **5**, **4**
    7 − 3 = **4**

3. 4 − 3 = **1**   4. 5 − 1 = **4**
5. 9 − 2 = **7**   6. 10 − 3 = **7**

Write the number sentence. Count back to solve. Use .

7. There are 12 cars on the bridge.
   3 drive away. How many cars are left?
   12 − **3** = **9** cars

8. 7 apples are in the tree. 3 fall off.
   How many apples are in the tree now?
   7 − **3** = **4** apples

Grade 1   7   Chapter 6

Count back to subtract. Use to help.

11. $6 - 3 = \underline{3}$

6   6, $\underline{5}$, $\underline{4}$, $\underline{3}$

12. $11 - 2 = \underline{9}$ **13.** $8 - 3 = \underline{5}$ **14.** $12 - 3 = \underline{9}$

15. $5 - 3 = \underline{2}$ **16.** $3 - 2 = \underline{1}$ **17.** $10 - 3 = \underline{7}$

18. $9 - 3 = \underline{6}$ **19.** $4 - 1 = \underline{3}$ **20.** $9 - 1 = \underline{8}$

21. $4 - 3 = \underline{1}$ **22.** $6 - 1 = \underline{5}$ **23.** $11 - 3 = \underline{8}$

24. $\begin{array}{r} 10 \\ - 1 \\ \hline \boxed{9} \end{array}$ **25.** $\begin{array}{r} 10 \\ - 2 \\ \hline \boxed{8} \end{array}$ **26.** $\begin{array}{r} 9 \\ - 2 \\ \hline \boxed{7} \end{array}$ **27.** $\begin{array}{r} 8 \\ - 1 \\ \hline \boxed{7} \end{array}$

Problem Solving

28. Number Sense There are 11 boats at the dock. 3 boats leave. How many boats are still at the dock?

$\underline{11} \ominus \underline{3} \ominus \underline{8}$

186   one hundred eighty-six

Math at Home Activity: Write $12 - 3 = \underline{\ \ }$. Have your child use counting back to subtract.

6-1 Name _____
Enrich
Tow Truck Trouble

The tow truck has gone too far down the street. Count back to the car. Finish the subtraction sentence.

1. _____ 4 — 5 — 6 — 7 — 8 — 9 — _____

$8 - \boxed{2} = \boxed{6}$

2. _____ 7 — 8 — 9 —10 —11 —12

$10 - \boxed{3} = \boxed{7}$

3. _____ 1 — 2 — 3 — 4 — 5 — 6 _____

$6 - \boxed{1} = \boxed{5}$

4. _____ 6 — 7 — 8 — 9 —10 _____

$9 - \boxed{3} = \boxed{6}$

5. _____ 3 — 4 — 5 — 6 — 7 _____

$6 - \boxed{2} = \boxed{4}$

6. _____ 7 — 8 — 9 —10 —11 —12

$11 - \boxed{3} = \boxed{8}$

Grade 1   10   Chapter 6

6-1 Name _____
Homework Practice
Count Back 1, 2, or 3

Count back to subtract. Use to help.

1. 7, $\underline{6}$ **2.** 9, $\underline{8}$, $\underline{7}$, 6
$7 - 1 = \underline{6}$ $9 - 3 = \underline{6}$

3. 4, $\underline{3}$, $\underline{2}$, 1   **4.** 6, $\underline{5}$, 4
$4 - 3 = \underline{1}$ $6 - 2 = \underline{4}$

5. $11 - 3 = \underline{8}$ **6.** $8 - 1 = \underline{7}$

7. $5 - 2 = \underline{3}$ **8.** $8 - 3 = \underline{5}$

9. $11 - 2 = \underline{9}$ **10.** $10 - 3 = \underline{7}$

11. $7 - 3 = \underline{4}$ **12.** $9 - 2 = \underline{7}$

13. $8 - 2 = \underline{6}$ **14.** $7 - 2 = \underline{5}$

Write the number sentence. Count back to solve. Use .

15. Jeff has a lemonade stand. He has 9 cups to sell. He sells 3. How many more does he have left?
$9 \ominus 3 \oplus \underline{\ \ }$ cups

16. Sharon plays a guitar with 6 strings. Two strings break. How many strings are left?
$6 \ominus 2 \oplus \underline{4}$ strings

Grade 1   8   Chapter 6

If students have difficulty counting back 1, 2, or 3 to subtract . . .

Then use one of the following reteach options.

1 **CRM** **Daily Reteach Worksheet** (p. 6)

2 Have students create a fun number line of their own that runs from 1 to 5. Provide a cut out of a hopping frog for students to practice counting ("hopping") back.

3 Have students use Math Tool Chest to help complete the problem-solving exercises.

3 Practice

Differentiate practice using these leveled assignments for Exercises 11–28.

Level	Assignment
BL Below/ Approaching Level	Guide students in using connecting cubes and number lines to set up and solve problems.
OL On Level	Complete the exercises independently.
AL Above/Beyond Level	Complete the exercises without the use of manipulatives.

4 Assess

Formative Assessment

Ask students to count back with the connecting cubes to model the following problems:
$9 - 3 = 6$
$5 - 2 = 3$
$7 - 3 = 4$

WRITING IN ▶**MATH** Draw 4 dominoes and write the subtraction sentences associated with each.

Quick Check Are students continuing to struggle with counting back to subtract?

If Yes → Strategic Intervention Guide (p. 90)

If No → Independent Work Options (p. 185B)

   CRM Skills Practice Worksheet (p. 7)

   CRM Enrich Worksheet (p. 10)

Problem-Solving Strategy
Write a Number Sentence

Lesson Planner _____

Objective

Use the *write a number sentence* strategy to solve problems.

Resources

Materials: sticky notes
Manipulatives: two-colored counters
Literature Connection: *Ten Sly Piranhas* by William Wise
Teacher Technology

 TeacherWorks

📖 **Real-World Problem Solving Library**
Math and Science: *Rock Collections*
Use these leveled books to reinforce and extend problem-solving skills and strategies.

Leveled for:
- **OL** On Level
- **ELL** Sheltered English
- **SP** Spanish

For additional support, see the Real-World Problem Solving Teacher Guide

Daily Routine _____

Use these suggestions before beginning the lesson on p. 187.

5-Minute Check

(Reviews Lesson 6-1)
1. Start with 8, count back 2. What number do you have? 6
2. Start with 10, count back 3. What number do you have? 7
3. Start with 8, count back 3. What number do you have? 5
4. Start with 12, count back 2. What number do you have? 10

Problem of the Day

Teresa, Clare, and Juan are cleaning the chalkboard. Clare finishes her section and sits. How many students are now cleaning the chalkboard? Write a subtraction sentence. Two students are cleaning the chalkboard. $3 - 1 = 2$

LINE UP When students line up, have each one choose and hold up a number or symbol card to create subtraction sentences. The first chooses a number, the second a plus (+) or minus (−) symbol, the third a smaller number, the fourth an equals (=) sign, and the fifth finds the correct number to finish the subtraction sentence. Continue until all students are in line.

Differentiated Instruction

Small Group Options

Option 1 — Below/Approaching Level BL

LOGICAL, SOCIAL

Materials: dominoes, paper, pencils

- One group member places five dominoes facedown on the table.
- Another member turns over the dominoes one at a time.
- Students write the subtraction sentence that each domino can represent. Remind them that their subtraction sentences should start with the total number of dots on the domino.
- Encourage students to discuss how they created each subtraction sentence.

Option 2 — English Language Learners ELL

VISUAL, INTERPERSONAL

Materials: paper squares, construction paper with a plus sign in the center, pencils, red stamp pad and glue
Core Vocabulary: ladybugs, pad (finger and stamp), press
Common Use Verb: print

See Math This strategy introduces words with two meanings and new vocabulary while allowing students to practice subtraction.

- Demonstrate pressing the pad of your finger into a stamp pad and printing it on clean paper. Draw the head, two antennae, spots and legs.
- Give them two cards and allow them to print some ladybugs.
- Have students glue their bug cards on either side of the + sign. Pass out the remaining squares. Have them write an = sign on one and the total on the other.
- Move cards to the left side of ladybugs. Repeat with other side. Emphasize both sentences meaning the same thing.

Independent Work Options

Option 1 — Early Finishers OL AL

VISUAL/SPATIAL, SOCIAL

Materials: paper, crayons

- Have partners write and illustrate a subtraction story using facts to 12.
- Tell them to write the subtraction sentence at the top of their paper with the story and illustration below.
- Display students' work and encourage classmates to read and check the stories and number sentences.

Option 2 — Student Technology

Math Online > macmillanmh.com

Option 3 — Learning Station: Science (p. 181H)

Direct students to the Science Learning Station for more opportunities to explore and extend the lesson concept.

1 Introduce

Activity Choice 1 • Review

Write 5 + 3 = 8 and cover the 3 with a sticky note. Have students use two-colored counters to model.

- **How many counters in all?** 8 counters Ask a student to set eight red counters in a line.
- **How many do we know are in one of the groups?** 5 Have a student turn over five red counters to show the yellow side. **How many red counters do we have now?** 3 counters
- Remove the sticky note to confirm the answer.

Activity Choice 2 • Literature

Introduce the lesson with *Ten Sly Piranhas* by William Wise. For additional support, see p. TR50.

2 Teach

Have students read the problem on page 187. Guide them through the problem-solving steps.

Understand Using the questions, review what students know and what they need to find.

Plan Have them discuss their strategy.

Solve Guide students to *write a number sentence* to solve the problem.

- **What numbers will be part of your sentence?** 8 and 5
- **What does the minus sign mean?** take away
- **What happens when you take away 5 from 8?** You are left with 3.

Check Have students look back at the problem to make sure that the answer fits the facts given.

- **Is the final answer greater or less than 8?** less than

COMMON ERROR!

Students may represent subtraction facts by making one group representing the beginning number and an additional group representing the number to take away. Remind them that the objects to be taken away should be objects from the original group that get covered, crossed out, or separated from the rest.

Name _____

Problem-Solving Strategy
Write a Number Sentence

Main Idea

I will write a number sentence to solve the problem.

There are 8 children on the playground.
5 children go home.
How many children are left?

Understand
What do I know?
Underline what you know.
What do I need to find?
Circle the question.

Plan
How will I solve the problem?

Solve
Write a number sentence.

$$8 - 5 = 3$$

___3___ children are left

Check
Look back.
Is my answer reasonable?

Copyright © Macmillan/McGraw-Hill, a division of The McGraw-Hill Companies, Inc.

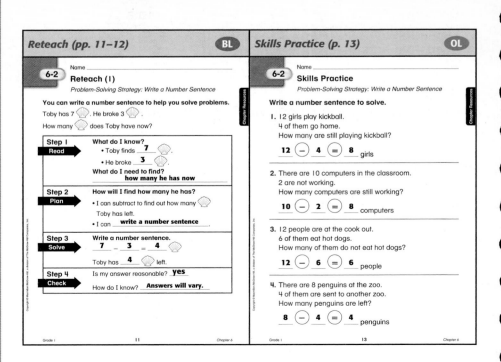

Reteach (pp. 11–12) **BL**

6-2 Name _____
Reteach (1)
Problem-Solving Strategy: Write a Number Sentence

You can write a number sentence to help you solve problems.
Toby has 7 🐚. He broke 3 🐚.
How many 🐚 does Toby have now?

Step 1 Read	What do I know? • Toby finds __7__ 🐚. • He broke __3__ 🐚. What do I need to find? how many he has now
Step 2 Plan	How will I find how many he has? • I can subtract to find out how many 🐚 Toby has left. • I can __write a number sentence__
Step 3 Solve	Write a number sentence. __7__ – __3__ = __4__ 🐚 Toby has __4__ 🐚 left.
Step 4 Check	Is my answer reasonable? __yes__ How do I know? __Answers will vary.__

Grade 1   11   Chapter 6

Skills Practice (p. 13) **OL**

6-2 Name _____
Skills Practice
Problem-Solving Strategy: Write a Number Sentence

Write a number sentence to solve.

1. 12 girls play kickball.
4 of them go home.
How many are still playing kickball?

__12__ – __4__ = __8__ girls

2. There are 10 computers in the classroom.
2 are not working.
How many computers are still working?

__10__ – __2__ = __8__ computers

3. 12 people are at the cook out.
6 of them eat hot dogs.
How many of them do not eat hot dogs?

__12__ – __6__ = __6__ people

4. There are 8 penguins at the zoo.
4 of them are sent to another zoo.
How many penguins are left?

__8__ – __4__ = __4__ penguins

Grade 1   13   Chapter 6

Try It

Solve.

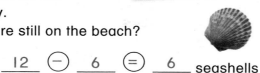

Remember
Understand
Plan
Solve
Check

1. There were 12 seashells on the beach. 6 washed away.
How many seashells are still on the beach?

<u>12</u> ⊖ <u>6</u> ⊜ <u>6</u> seashells

2. There were 8 dogs taking a nap.
5 left to chase a cat.
How many dogs are still taking a nap?

<u>8</u> ⊖ <u>5</u> ⊜ <u>3</u> dogs

Your Turn

Solve.

3. There were 11 horses eating hay.
4 left to get a drink.
How many horses were left eating hay?

<u>11</u> ⊖ <u>4</u> ⊜ <u>7</u> horses

4. I have 10 baby chicks.
I gave my brother 5 of them.
How many baby chicks do I have now?

<u>10</u> ⊖ <u>5</u> ⊜ <u>5</u> chicks

188 one hundred eighty-eight

Math at Home Activity: Give your child a subtraction problem about things around the house. Have him/her write a number sentence to solve the problem.

Copyright © Macmillan/McGraw-Hill, a division of The McGraw-Hill Companies, Inc.

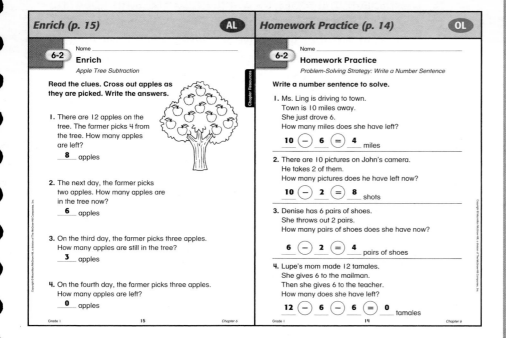

Enrich (p. 15) **AL**

Name _____
6-2 **Enrich**
Apple Tree Subtraction

Read the clues. Cross out apples as they are picked. Write the answers.

1. There are 12 apples on the tree. The farmer picks 4 from the tree. How many apples are left?

    8 apples

2. The next day, the farmer picks two apples. How many apples are in the tree now?

    6 apples

3. On the third day, the farmer picks three apples. How many apples are still in the tree?

    3 apples

4. On the fourth day, the farmer picks three apples. How many apples are left?

    0 apples

Grade 1   15   Chapter 6

Homework Practice (p. 14) **OL**

Name _____
6-2 **Homework Practice**
Problem-Solving Strategy: Write a Number Sentence

Write a number sentence to solve.

1. Ms. Ling is driving to town. Town is 10 miles away. She just drove 6. How many miles does she have left?

    10 ⊖ **6** ⊜ **4** miles

2. There are 10 pictures on John's camera. He takes 2 of them. How many pictures does he have left now?

    10 ⊖ **2** ⊜ **8** shots

3. Denise has 6 pairs of shoes. She throws out 2 pairs. How many pairs of shoes does she have now?

    6 ⊖ **2** ⊜ **4** pairs of shoes

4. Lupe's mom made 12 tamales. She gives 6 to the mailman. Then she gives 6 to the teacher. How many does she have left?

    12 ⊖ **6** ⊖ **6** ⊜ **0** tamales

Grade 1   14   Chapter 6

Try It Observe students as you work through Exercises 1–2 as a class.

BL **Alternate Teaching Strategy**

> **If** students have trouble writing a subtraction sentence . . .

> **Then** use one of the following reteach options.

1 **CRM** **Daily Reteach Worksheet** (pp. 11–12)

2 Have students draw an illustration to represent the number sentence. Have them draw the total number of children and then cross out or cover with sticky notes those who leave the playground.

③ Practice

Your Turn

Exercise 3–4 Be sure students can read and understand the problems. Use counters to model if necessary. Remind students that they are subtracting.

④ Assess

Formative Assessment

- **How do you know whether to add or subtract?**
  Add when putting together or making more in a group; subtract when comparing to find a difference, taking away, or making less.

- Have students write an addition or a subtraction fact. Ask students to write a number story that describes the fact. See students' work.

Quick Check **Are students continuing to struggle with writing number sentences?**

If Yes → Small Group Options (p. 187B)
Strategic Intervention Guide (p. 90)

If No → Independent Work Options (p. 187B)
CRM Skills Practice Worksheet (p. 13)
CRM Enrich Worksheet (p. 15)

Lesson Planner

Objective
Use a number line to subtract differences to 12.

Review Vocabulary
number line, subtract

Resources
Materials: walk-on number line, number cards (1–20)

Manipulatives: number cube

Literature Connection: *12 Ways to Get to 11* by Eve Merriam

Alternate Lesson: Use *IMPACT Mathematics:* Unit B to provide practice using number lines to subtract.

Teacher Technology
⊙ TeacherWorks • Concepts in Motion • ♪ Math Songs Track 10 Lesson Plan

Focus on Math Background

Subtracting on a Number Line Subtracting on a horizontal or vertical number line gives students a strong linear model that will later facilitate the understanding of positive and negative integers in the intermediate grades.

The number line is a universal tool used to represent intervals in graphs, the coordinate graphing system, and in measuring linear measurements as well as temperature.

Representing Data on a Number Line or Line Plot A number line can be used to show data in the form of a line plot. Line plots are generally used to find the frequency of certian events. Before understanding the concept of a line plot, students must know how to draw and use a number line.

Daily Routine

Use these suggestions before beginning the lesson on p. 189.

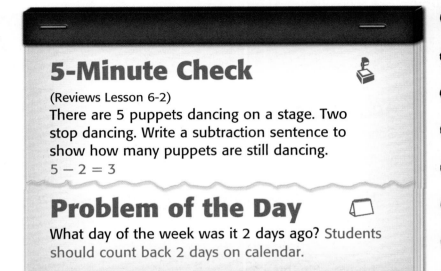

5-Minute Check
(Reviews Lesson 6-2)
There are 5 puppets dancing on a stage. Two stop dancing. Write a subtraction sentence to show how many puppets are still dancing.
$5 - 2 = 3$

Problem of the Day
What day of the week was it 2 days ago? Students should count back 2 days on calendar.

LINE UP As a "ticket" to get in line, ask each student to write a number between 1 and 10 and then write its double. Have students show their ticket, tell you a subtraction fact that uses only those two numbers, and then line up.

Review Math Vocabulary
Write **subtract** and **number line** on the chalkboard. Explain that students will learn to use a number line to subtract larger numbers.
- On number line, have students place their finger on a number greater than 5 and then write it as the first number in a subtraction sentence.
- Display a number card from 1 to 5. Have students write the number as the number to subtract in their sentence.
- Model counting back on the number line. Then ask students to do the same to complete their number sentence.

Visual Vocabulary Cards
Use Visual Vocabulary Cards 30 and 46 to reinforce the vocabulary reviewed in this lesson. (The Define /Example/Ask routine is printed on the back of each card.)

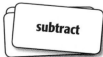

subtract

Differentiated Instruction

Small Group Options

Option 1
Below/Approaching Level BL

Materials: index cards

- Ask students to make a number card with a number between 10 and 20 for each member of the group.
- Place number cards 10 and 20 on the chalkboard ledge to show a starting and ending place for a number line.
- Then have group members hold their cards and arrange themselves in order from least to greatest number on the number line.
- Invite students to take turns placing their card on the chalkboard ledge while they move forward to look at the whole number line. Have each checker tell whether he or she thinks the numbers are ordered correctly.

Option 2
English Language Learners ELL

Materials: masking tape, number cards 1 to 10; number cube
Core Vocabulary: backward, forward, facing
Common Use Verb: walk

Hear Math This strategy helps students distinguish the difference in directional words by connecting what they hear to movement.

- Make a number line on the floor with numbers 0 to 10.
- Have one student stand at 10, facing away from number 0. Write: "10."
- Roll a number cube. If you get 2, for example, tell the student: "Walk 2 steps backward down the number line." Write: "-2."
- Ask: "What number are you on?" Write: "8" completing the number sentence.
- Repeat as time permits.

Independent Work Options

Option 1
Early Finishers OL AL

Materials: WorkMat 4: Number Lines

- Invite partners to write counting-back riddles that require using a number line. For example: I am the number 12. What is one way to find me on a number line? Sample answer: Count back 2 from 14.
- Partners can exchange riddles and use a number line to help them solve each riddle.
- Have students write subtraction sentences for each riddle they solve. $14 - 2 = 12$

Option 2
Student Technology

Math Online macmillanmh.com

Option 3
Learning Station: Language Arts (p. 181G)

Direct students to the Language Arts Learning Station for more opportunities to explore the lesson concept.

Option 4
Problem-Solving Practice

Reinforce problem-solving skills and strategies with the Problem-Solving Practice worksheet.

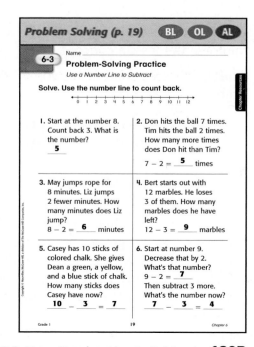

1 Introduce

Activity Choice 1 • Hands-On

- Number and tape together sheets of paper or plastic placemats to create a large 0–20 walk-on number line.
- Have a volunteer stand at seven and take five steps back. Count back with the students.
- **What subtraction sentence shows what happened?** 7 − 5 = 2
- Repeat with other numbers and volunteers.

Activity Choice 2 • Literature

Introduce the lesson with *12 Ways to Get to 11* by Eve Merriam. For additional support, see p. TR50.

2 Teach

- On a number line from 1 to 12, use finger jumps to model subtracting 3, 4, 5, or 6 from a greater number.
- Ask students to count each space you "jump" over.
- As each difference is found, record the subtraction number sentence.
- Repeat, having students assist in counting back and recording the number sentences.
- As a class, create a line plot that shows each difference found.
- Ask students to use the line plot to find which difference was found the most.

Get Ready Use the section at the top of p. 189 to reinforce the lesson concept.

Check Observe students as you work through Exercise 1–5 as a class.

Exercise 5 Assess student comprehension before assigning practice exercises.

! COMMON ERROR!

Subtracting with a number line confuses some students. They might think: "I am on 10. I take away 2. I get rid of two numbers—9 and 8. That leaves 7." It is better for them to think: "I am on 10, and I am going to move back 2 steps. One step and I am on 9. Two steps and I am on 8."

Name _____

Use a Number Line to Subtract

Get Ready

Main Idea
I will use the number line to subtract.

You can use a number line to subtract.

Start at 9. Count back 3 to find the difference: 8, 7, 6.

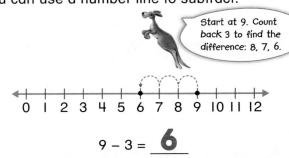

$$9 - 3 = \underline{6}$$

Check

Subtract. Write the difference.
Use the number line to help you.

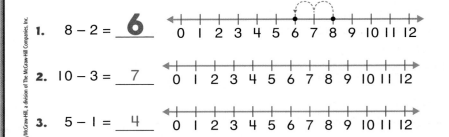

1. $8 - 2 = \underline{6}$ 0 1 2 3 4 5 6 7 8 9 10 11 12

2. $10 - 3 = \underline{7}$ 0 1 2 3 4 5 6 7 8 9 10 11 12

3. $5 - 1 = \underline{4}$ 0 1 2 3 4 5 6 7 8 9 10 11 12

4. $9 - 2 = \underline{7}$ 0 1 2 3 4 5 6 7 8 9 10 11 12

5. **Talk About It** How does the number line help you subtract?
   Sample answer: It shows the numbers in order.

Chapter 6   Lesson 3   one hundred eighty-nine   **189**

Reteach (p. 16)   BL

6-3 **Reteach**
Use a Number Line to Subtract

You can count back on a number line to subtract.
Find 9 − 3.

Start at 9. Count back 3. The difference is 6.

$9 - 3 = \underline{6}$

Use a number line to subtract. Start at the greater number. Count back.

1. $5 - 3 = \underline{2}$

2. $7 - 2 = \underline{5}$

3. $10 - 3 = \underline{7}$

4. $6 - 2 = \underline{4}$

5. $12 - 3 = \underline{9}$

Grade 1   16   Chapter 6

Skills Practice (p. 17)   OL

6-3 **Skills Practice**
Use a Number Line to Subtract

Use the number line to subtract.

1. $7 - 3 = \underline{4}$

2. $6 - 1 = \underline{5}$

3. $12 - 2 = \underline{10}$

4. $5 - 3 = \underline{2}$

Solve. Use the number line to help.

5. 8 cars start in the race.
   2 cars cannot finish.
   How many cars finish the race?

   $\underline{8} - \underline{2} = \underline{6}$ cars

6. Jess and her mom go to the post office.
   They buy 10 stamps. Jess puts a stamp on three letters. How many stamps are left?

   $\underline{10} - \underline{3} = \underline{7}$ stamps

Grade 1   17   Chapter 6

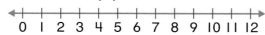

Practice

Subtract. Write the difference.
Use the number line to help you.

0 1 2 3 4 5 6 7 8 9 10 11 12

6.
$$
\begin{array}{r} 5 \\ -\ 3 \\ \hline 2 \end{array}
$$

7.
$$
\begin{array}{r} 8 \\ -\ 3 \\ \hline 5 \end{array}
$$

8.
$$
\begin{array}{r} 7 \\ -\ 3 \\ \hline 4 \end{array}
$$

9.
$$
\begin{array}{r} 10 \\ -\ 2 \\ \hline 8 \end{array}
$$

10.
$$
\begin{array}{r} 6 \\ -\ 2 \\ \hline 4 \end{array}
$$

11.
$$
\begin{array}{r} 9 \\ -\ 3 \\ \hline 6 \end{array}
$$

12.
$$
\begin{array}{r} 4 \\ -\ 3 \\ \hline 1 \end{array}
$$

13.
$$
\begin{array}{r} 11 \\ -\ 3 \\ \hline 8 \end{array}
$$

14. $7 - 2 = \underline{5}$ 15. $8 - 1 = \underline{7}$ 16. $9 - 2 = \underline{7}$

17. $3 - 1 = \underline{2}$ 18. $10 - 1 = \underline{9}$ 19. $11 - 2 = \underline{9}$

Data File

There are many horses in Kentucky. Kentucky's state horse is the Thoroughbred.

20. There are 12 horses in a field. 3 of them are brown. How many horses are not brown?

$\underline{12} - \underline{3} = \underline{9}$

190   one hundred ninety

 Math at Home Activity: Have your child show 12 – 6 using the number line.

Enrich (p. 20)   **AL**

6-3 Name _____
Enrich
Subtraction Solver

Look at the difference. Use the number line to show a subtraction sentence for the difference.

1.
7 8 9 10 11 12
☐ – ☐ = 8

2.
3 4 5 6 7 8
☐ – ☐ = 5

Answers will vary.

3.
6 7 8 9 10 11
☐ – ☐ = 7

Answers will vary.

4.
1 2 3 4 5 6
☐ – ☐ = 2

Answers will vary.

5.
6 7 8 9 10 11
☐ – ☐ = 6

Answers will vary.

Grade 1   20   Chapter 6

Homework Practice (p. 18)   **OL**

6-3 Name _____
Homework Practice
Use a Number Line to Subtract

Use the number line to subtract.

1. $10 - 1 = \underline{9}$ 0 1 2 3 4 5 6 7 8 9 10 11 12

2. $6 - 3 = \underline{3}$ 0 1 2 3 4 5 6 7 8 9 10 11 12

3. $12 - 3 = \underline{9}$ 0 1 2 3 4 5 6 7 8 9 10 11 12

4. $5 - 2 = \underline{3}$ 0 1 2 3 4 5 6 7 8 9 10 11 12

Solve. Use the number line to help.

5. Denise colors 8 pictures from her coloring book. She gives 3 pictures away. How many does she have left?

0 1 2 3 4 5 6 7 8 9 10 11 12

$\underline{8} - \underline{3} = \underline{5}$ pictures

6. Jan's mom has 6 juice boxes. Jan drinks 2 of them. How many are left?

0 1 2 3 4 5 6 7 8 9 10

$\underline{6} - \underline{2} = \underline{4}$ juice boxes

Grade 1   18   Chapter 6

BL **Alternate Teaching Strategy**

If ▶ students struggle with using a number line to subtract . . .

Then ▶ use one of the following reteach options.

1 **CRM** **Daily Reteach Worksheet** (p. 16)

2 **Play a Subtraction Game** Partners share number cards 1–20 and a single number cube. One partner takes a card from the deck and records the number. Then the other partner rolls the number cube. Together, partners construct a subtraction sentence using the two numbers and then find the difference on a number line.

③ Practice

Differentiate practice using these leveled assignments for Exercises 6–20.

Level	Assignment
BL Below/ Approaching Level	Guide students in using a number line to complete the exercises.
OL On Level	Complete the exercises independently.
AL Above/Beyond Level	Complete the exercises independently. Then, for each exercise, write another problem with the same difference.

④ Assess

Formative Assessment

Have students demonstrate subtracting 5 from 12 on a number line. Have them explain how they found the answer.

WRITING IN ▶**MATH** Ask students to explain how using a number line helps them to subtract.

Quick Check **Are students continuing to struggle with using a number line to subtract?**

If Yes → Small Group Options (p. 189B)
Strategic Intervention Guide (p. 90)

If No → Independent Work Options (p. 189B)
CRM Skills Practice Worksheet (p. 17)
CRM Enrich Worksheet (p. 20)

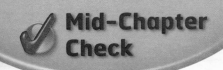

Mid-Chapter Check

Lessons 6-1 to 6-3

 Formative Assessment

Use the Mid-Chapter Check to assess student's progress in the first half of the chapter.

ExamView®
Assessment Suite Customize and create multiple versions of your Mid-Chapter Check and the test answer keys.

FOLDABLES® **Dinah Zike's Foldables**

Use these lesson suggestions to incorporate the Foldable during the chapter.

Lesson 6-1 On the second page of the subtraction journal, draw as "counting back." Subtract from a number by counting back 1, 2, or 3.

Lesson 6-2 On the third page of the subtraction journal, have students write three number sentences that show counting back 1, 2, or 3.

Lesson 6-3 On the fourth page of the subtraction journal, draw a number line starting with 0 and ending with 12.

Name _____

Count back to subtract.

1. $9 - 1 =$ __8__
2. $7 - 3 =$ __4__
3. $11 - 3 =$ __8__
4. $10 - 1 =$ __9__
5. $5 - 2 =$ __3__
6. $8 - 3 =$ __5__

7.
$$\begin{array}{r} 9 \\ - 3 \\ \hline 6 \end{array}$$

8.
$$\begin{array}{r} 4 \\ - 1 \\ \hline 3 \end{array}$$

9.
$$\begin{array}{r} 9 \\ - 2 \\ \hline 7 \end{array}$$

10.
$$\begin{array}{r} 12 \\ - 3 \\ \hline 9 \end{array}$$

Subtract. Write the difference. Use the number line to help you.

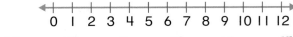
0 1 2 3 4 5 6 7 8 9 10 11 12

11.
$$\begin{array}{r} 10 \\ - 3 \\ \hline 7 \end{array}$$

12.
$$\begin{array}{r} 8 \\ - 2 \\ \hline 6 \end{array}$$

13.
$$\begin{array}{r} 12 \\ - 3 \\ \hline 9 \end{array}$$

14.
$$\begin{array}{r} 9 \\ - 3 \\ \hline 6 \end{array}$$

Write a number sentence to solve.

15. There were 10 boats at the dock. 2 boats left. How many boats are still at the dock?

__10__ ⊖ __2__ ⊜ __8__

16. There were 6 strawberries on the table. Tito ate 3 of them. How many are left?

__6__ ⊖ __3__ ⊜ __3__

Chapter 6   one hundred ninety-one **191**

Copyright © Macmillan/McGraw-Hill, a division of The McGraw-Hill Companies, Inc.

Data-Driven Decision-Making

Based on the results of the Mid-Chapter Check, use the following resources to review concepts that continue to give students problems.

Exercises	State/Local Standards	What's the Math?	Error Analysis	Resources for Review
1–10 Lesson 6-1		Show the meaning of subtraction. Use the counting back strategy.	Subtracts incorrectly. Adds numbers.	Strategic Intervention Guide (p. 90) **CRM** Chapter 6 Resource Masters (Reteach Worksheets)
11–14 Lesson 6-3		Use a number line to solve subtraction.	Goes wrong way on number line. Double counts when going left on number line.	**Math Online** Concepts in Motion Math Adventures
15–16 Lesson 6-2		Write and solve number sentences from problem situations.	Adds numbers. Does not write correct number sentence. Subtracts incorrectly.	

12 students were asked to choose their favorite shape.

Favorite Shape		
Shape	Votes	Total
♥	卌 I	6
●	II	2
■	IIII	4

Fill in the totals.
Then use the graph to answer the questions.

17. Which shape is the favorite?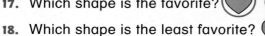

18. Which shape is the least favorite?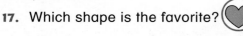

19. How many students in all chose the heart or square? __10__ students

---

Add or subtract.

20. 9 + 1 = __10__   **21.** 7 + 3 = __10__   **22.** 10 + 0 = __10__

23. 9 − 6 = __3__   **24.** 4 − 1 = __3__   **25.** 6 − 0 = __6__

Add. Use a doubles plus 1 fact to solve.
What doubles fact can help you?

26. Kelly saw 6 spiders. Ivy saw 7 spiders.
How many spiders did they see?

__6__ + __6__ = __12__

6 + 7 = __13__   __13__ spiders

Formative Assessment

Spiral Review

Reviews Chapters 1 to 6

Objective: Review and assess mastery of skills and concepts from previous chapters.

Resources for Review

Based on student results, refer to these lessons for remediation.

- **Exercises 17–19: Lesson 4-2** (p. 125)
- **Exercises 20–22: Lesson 2-8** (p. 69)
- **Exercises 23–25: Lesson 3-3, 3-4** (pp. 91, 95)
- **Exercise 26: Lesson 5-8** (p. 169)

Lesson Planner _____

Objective

Choose the best strategy to solve a problem.

Resources

Teacher Technology

- TeacherWorks

- **Real-World Problem Solving Library**
  Math and Science: *Rock Collections*
  Use these leveled books to reinforce and extend
  problem-solving skills and strategies.

  Leveled for:
  - **OL** On Level
  - **ELL** Sheltered English
  - **SP** Spanish

  For additional support, see
  the Real-World Problem
  Solving Teacher Guide

Daily Routine _____

Use these suggestions before beginning the lesson on p. 193.

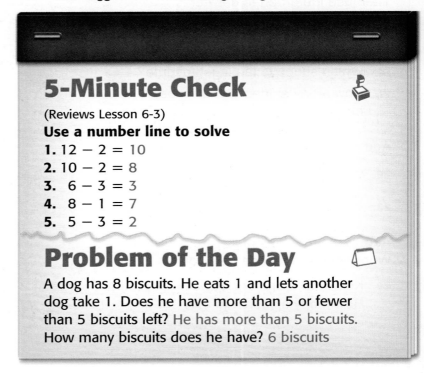

5-Minute Check

(Reviews Lesson 6-3)
Use a number line to solve
1. $12 - 2 = 10$
2. $10 - 2 = 8$
3. $6 - 3 = 3$
4. $8 - 1 = 7$
5. $5 - 3 = 2$

Problem of the Day

A dog has 8 biscuits. He eats 1 and lets another
dog take 1. Does he have more than 5 or fewer
than 5 biscuits left? He has more than 5 biscuits.
How many biscuits does he have? 6 biscuits

LINE UP Have students count off 1, 2, 1, 2, and so on.
Ask all the ones to line up. Count the number
lined up and then the number still seated. Point out that
the number is the same. Have the 2s line up and count
how many in all. **Is this an addition or a subtraction
problem?** addition **Is this a doubles or doubles plus one
problem? Explain.** Answers will vary depending on the
number of students.

Differentiated Instruction

Small Group Options

Option 1
Below/Approaching Level (BL)

LOGICAL, VISUAL/SPATIAL

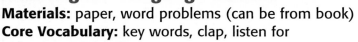

Materials: paper, pencil, bowl or basket containing 13 connecting cubes of one color and 7 of a second color

- Let students glance into the container and then guess how many of each color cube there are.
- Next, tell students there are twenty cubes in all. Invite them to revise their estimates.
- Snap together the cubes to make a separate bar for each color. Hold up the bars to allow students to compare the lengths without actually counting the cubes. Invite students to revise their estimates again.
- Have students count with you to find the actual number of cubes in each bar. Compare students' estimates with the actual count. Discuss how and why they changed their estimates during the activity.

Option 2
English Language Learners (ELL)

AUDITORY

Materials: paper, word problems (can be from book)
Core Vocabulary: key words, clap, listen for
Common Use Verb: hear

Hear Math This strategy sharpens students' listening skills and helps word recognition.

- Say, "**Key words** help us know what to do."
- Write *in all, more than one, less than one, how many more, how many are left.*
- Read various word problems. Direct students to clap when they hear one of the key words.
- Tally on the board every time they clap.
- Say: "Which **key words** did you hear?" Discuss what action they think they need to take with that problem as time permits.
- Continue reading another set of word problems, allowing small groups to decide how to record and sort them by action required.

Independent Work Options

Option 1
Early Finishers (OL) (AL)

KINESTHETIC, SPATIAL

Materials: paper plates, 12 pennies, missing-addend sentence strips for facts to 12 (ex. $7 + \square = 10$)

- Have partners study one of the missing-addend sentences and plan a way to use the paper plates and pennies to find the missing addend.
- To check their answer, ask partners to count the pennies to see if they match the addition sentence.

- Encourage partners to write a subtraction sentence that would provide the missing number.

Option 2
Student Technology

| Math Online | macmillanmh.com |

Option 3
Learning Station: Science (p. 181H)

Direct students to the Science Learning Station for more opportunities to explore and extend the lesson concept.

1 Introduce

Activity • Review

Write and read aloud the following problem:
The city needs 10 fire trucks. The city only owns 4 fire trucks. How many fire trucks does the city need to buy?

- **What do we know?** There are 4 fire trucks and the city needs 10.
- **What do we need to find?** How many more fire trucks it will take to make 10 in all.
- **What number sentence can we write to show what information is missing?** $4 + \_\_\_ = 10$
- **Do you think that the missing number will be more than or less than 2? Why?** Sample answer: More than 2; I know that $4 + 2$ is only 6 so it will take more than that to make 10.

2 Teach

Have students read the problem on p. 193. Guide them through the problem-solving steps.

Understand Using the questions, review what students know and what they need to find.

Plan Have them discuss their strategy.

Solve Guide students to use the *guess and check* method to solve the problem.

- **What should you do first, and how should you do it?** Guess the answer by writing the number sentence that matches this problem.
- **How should you check your answer?** Place the answer into the number sentence and decide if the number sentence is correct.

Check Have students look back at the problem to make sure that the answer fits the facts given.

⚠ COMMON ERROR!

If students rush to make wild guesses, explain that when they "guess and check," they should use what they know about numbers to make a reasonable guess.

193 Chapter 6 Develop Subtraction Strategies

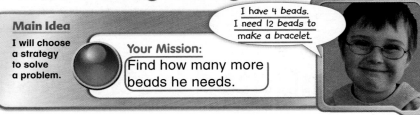

Name _____

Problem-Solving Investigation

Main Idea
I will choose a strategy to solve a problem.

Your Mission: Find how many more beads he needs.

I have 4 beads. I need 12 beads to make a bracelet.

Understand

What do I know?
Underline what you know.

What do I need to find?
Circle it.

Plan

How will I solve the problem?

Solve

One way is to guess and check.

$4 + 6 = 10$ No
$4 + 7 = 11$ No
$4 + 8 = 12$ Yes

_____8_____ more beads

Check

Look back.
Is my answer reasonable?

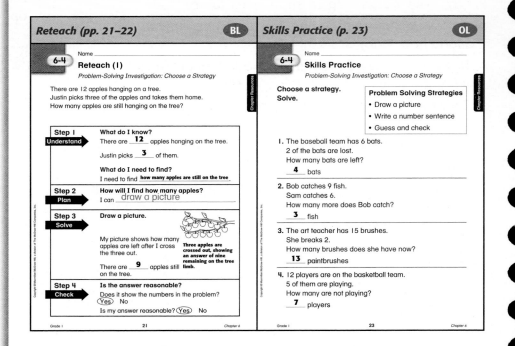

Mixed Problem Solving

Problem-Solving Strategies
- Guess and check
- Draw a picture
- Write a number sentence

Choose a strategy. Solve.

1. Rudy and Hector caught 14 fish. They threw 4 fish back in the water. How many fish were left?

____10____ fish

2. There were 15 pages in a book. Lisa read 6 pages of the book. How many pages did she still have to read?

____9____ pages

3. There are red and blue marbles in a basket. There are 11 marbles altogether. 5 marbles are red. How many marbles are blue?

____6____ are blue

4. Miss Bell passed out 9 pencils. 3 students still need pencils. How many pencils will Miss Bell pass out altogether?

____12____ pencils

194   one hundred ninety-four

Math at Home Activity: Take advantage of problem-solving opportunities during daily routines such as riding in the car, bedtime, doing laundry, putting away groceries, planning schedules, and so on.

Copyright © Macmillan/McGraw-Hill, a division of The McGraw-Hill Companies, Inc.

---

3 Practice

Mixed Problem Solving

Exercises 3–4 If students are having trouble understanding the problems, read them aloud. Slowly go through the problem-solving process until each student understands and is able to take over the completion of the problem.

4 Assess

✓ Formative Assessment

Have students solve the following problem: *Twelve people work at the factory. Five of the workers are women. How many are men?*

- **What steps will you use to solve this problem?**
  Decide what I know and what I need to find.

  Model the problem by writing a number sentence and/or drawing a picture.

  Guess the answer and then check it in the number sentence and/or picture.

Quick Check — **Are students continuing to struggle with the strategy?**

If Yes → Small Group Options (p. 191B)
  Strategic Intervention Guide (p. 90)

If No → Independent Work Options (p. 191B)
  CRM Skills Practice Worksheet (p. 23)
  CRM Enrich Worksheet (p. 25)

Chapter 6 Problem-Solving Investigation **194**

Lesson Planner

Objective
Use doubles facts to subtract.

Review Vocabulary
doubles

Resources
Materials: WorkMat 1: Ten-Frame

Manipulatives: two-colored counters

Literature Connection: *More Bugs? Less Bugs?* by Don L. Curry

Alternate Lesson: Use *IMPACT Mathematics:* Unit A to provide practice with using doubles to subtract.

Teacher Technology
- TeacherWorks • ♪ Math Songs Track 15 Lesson Plan

Focus on Math Background

When students see patterns develop while subtracting doubles, a foundation for "half" and "even" numbers is established. The concept of subtracting a number from its double is a reflexive process for the mind, which helps students readily comprehend this sort of symmetry. This is the inverse of adding doubles.

Daily Routine

Use these suggestions before beginning the lesson on p. 195.

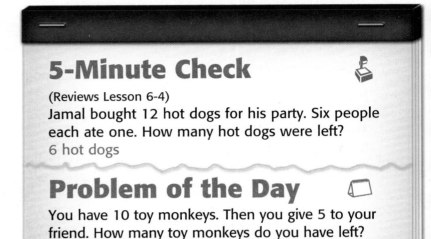

5-Minute Check
(Reviews Lesson 6-4)
Jamal bought 12 hot dogs for his party. Six people each ate one. How many hot dogs were left?
6 hot dogs

Problem of the Day
You have 10 toy monkeys. Then you give 5 to your friend. How many toy monkeys do you have left?
5 toy monkeys

LINE UP As students line up for recess, lunch, or dismissal, have each one answer questions similar to the following.

- **Look at today's date. Is it possible to subtract 3 (or 2, or 1)? If so, subtract and tell the answer.** Sample answer: Yes; $10 - 3 = 7$

▷ Review Math Vocabulary

Write **doubles** on the chalkboard and have students tell what they have learned about doubles.
- Have four students stand in front of the room.
- Ask a volunteer to separate the group to show that 4 is a double. Then ask 2 of the students to sit. **How many students did I "take away"? How many are left?** 2; 2
- Write the fact family for 4, 2, and 2. Encourage students to comment on patterns they see.
- Choose six new volunteers and repeat the demonstration for the 6, 3, 3 fact family.
- **Do you think doubles subtraction facts are easy to remember? Why?** Sample answer: Yes, because I know the difference will be the same number as the "take away" number.

Differentiated Instruction

Small Group Options

Option 1 — Gifted and Talented **AL**
SPATIAL, LOGICAL, SOCIAL

Materials: red number cube, paper, pencil

- Have students take turns rolling the red number cube and writing a doubles addition sentence using the number as an addend.
- On a second turn, players hold up the addition sentence they wrote and challenge another player to write the doubles subtraction fact that matches it.
- On a third turn, a player rolls the cube and tells whether the number is a double or not. If the number is a double, the player must state a subtraction fact that proves it.

Option 2 — English Language Learners **ELL**
LINGUISTIC, SOCIAL

Core Vocabulary: knee to knee, simultaneously, it's a fact.
Common Use Verb: pass

Talk Math This strategy helps students use doubles to subtract.

- Give a double domino to each student sitting knee to knee in a circle.
- Say: "Use doubles to subtract; it's a fact!"
- Using your domino say chant, clap, and read the answer. Prompt students to repeat.
- Repeat, passing doubles to the left around the circle. All students will speak simultaneously to shelter vocalization process.

Use this worksheet to provide additional support for English Language Learners.

English Language Learners (p. 75) **ELL**

23 Name _____

Addition and Subtraction Facts
Write the numbers from each spin.
Write the addition and subtraction facts.
Answers will vary.

Spin and record.	Addition facts	Subtraction facts
First spin	___ + ___ = ___	___ − ___ = ___
Second spin	___ + ___ = ___	___ − ___ = ___
First spin	___ + ___ = ___	___ − ___ = ___
Second spin	___ + ___ = ___	___ − ___ = ___
First spin	___ + ___ = ___	___ − ___ = ___
Second spin	___ + ___ = ___	___ − ___ = ___

Addition and Subtraction **75**

Independent Work Options

Option 1 — Early Finishers **OL** **AL**
SPATIAL, LOGICAL, SOCIAL

Materials: index cards, markers

- Have students make a card for each addition doubles fact and for each related subtraction fact.
- Tell students to mix the cards and lay them facedown in a grid. Then have students take turns turning over two cards to find a pair—one doubles addition fact and its matching subtraction fact.
- Play continues until all cards have been matched.

Option 2 — Student Technology

Math Online ▶ macmillanmh.com

♪ Math Songs, "Take It Away" Track 15 •
🎧 Math Adventures

Option 3 — Learning Station: Art (p. 181G)

Direct students to the Art Learning Station for more opportunities to explore and extend the lesson concept.

Option 4 — Problem-Solving Practice

Reinforce problem-solving skills and strategies with the Problem-Solving Practice worksheet.

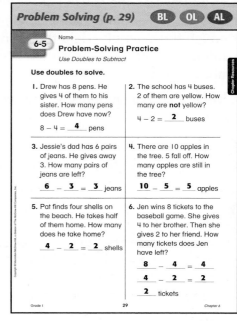

Problem Solving (p. 29) **BL** **OL** **AL**

Name _____
6-5 **Problem-Solving Practice**
Use Doubles to Subtract

Use doubles to solve.

1. Drew has 8 pens. He gives 4 of them to his sister. How many pens does Drew have now?
$8 - 4 =$ __**4**__ pens

2. The school has 4 buses. 2 of them are yellow. How many are **not** yellow?
$4 - 2 =$ __**2**__ buses

3. Jessie's dad has 6 pairs of jeans. He gives away 3. How many pairs of jeans are left?
__**6**__ − __**3**__ = __**3**__ jeans

4. There are 10 apples in the tree. 5 fall off. How many apples are still in the tree?
__**10**__ − __**5**__ = __**5**__ apples

5. Pat finds four shells on the beach. He takes half of them home. How many does he take home?
__**4**__ − __**2**__ = __**2**__ shells

6. Jen wins 8 tickets to the baseball game. She gives 4 to her brother. Then she gives 2 to her friend. How many tickets does Jen have left?
__**8**__ − __**4**__ = __**4**__
__**4**__ − __**2**__ = __**2**__
__**2**__ tickets

Grade 1   29   Chapter 6

1 Introduce

Activity Choice 1 • Hands-On

Have students cut a ten-frame in half to create two identical five-frames.

- Place the five-frames side by side and put five counters in each.
- **What doubles fact do these frames and counters show?** $5 + 5 = 10$
- Ask students to take away one of the groups of five counters and write the resulting subtraction sentence in both vertical and horizontal formats.

Activity Choice 2 • Literature

Introduce the lesson with *More Bugs? Less Bugs?* by Don L. Curry. For additional support, see p. TR50.

2 Teach

- Give each student 20 two-colored counters, and ask them to show 6 yellow and 6 red.
- **How many counters are in the group?** 12 counters **How many counters are yellow?** 6 counters **How many counters are red?** 6 counters **Six plus 6 is a doubles fact.**
- **You have 12. If you take away 6, how many will you have left?** 6
- **What number sentence will we write?** $12 - 6 = 6$ Write it on the board.
- Repeat with $8 - 4$, $6 - 3$, $4 - 2$.

Get Ready Use the section at the top of p. 195 to reinforce the lesson concept. Guide the students through the example. Help them understand that subtracting with doubles is the inverse of adding with doubles.

Check Observe students as you work through Exercises 1–5 as a class.

> **Exercise 5** Assess student comprehension before assigning practice exercises.

⚠ COMMON ERROR!

Students sometimes think the double subtraction sentence should look like the addition subtraction sentence. Help them remember that the greater number is first when subtracting.

Name _____

Use Doubles to Subtract

Get Ready

Main Idea

I will use doubles to add and subtract.

You know how to use doubles to add.

$4 + 4 = $ **8**

You can also use doubles to subtract.

$8 - 4 = $ **4**

✓ Check

Add the doubles. Then subtract.

1.

$2 + 2 = $ **4**

$4 - 2 = $ **2**

2.

$5 + 5 = $ 10

$10 - 5 = $ 5

3.

$1 + 1 = $ 2

$2 - 1 = $ 1

4.

$3 + 3 = $ 6

$6 - 3 = $ 3

5. **Talk About It** How can doubles facts help you subtract? Sample answer: They help you know the related facts.

Copyright © Macmillan/McGraw-Hill, a division of The McGraw-Hill Companies, Inc.

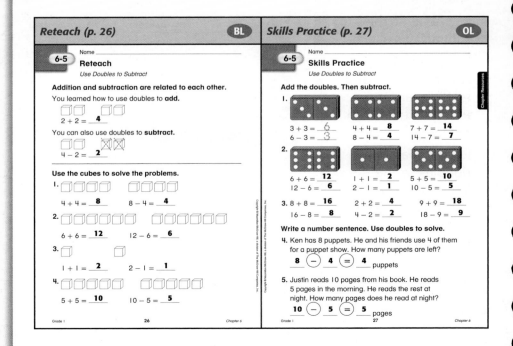

Reteach (p. 26) BL

6-5 Reteach
Use Doubles to Subtract

Addition and subtraction are related to each other.
You learned how to use doubles to **add**.

$2 + 2 = $ **4**

You can also use doubles to **subtract**.

$4 - 2 = $ **2**

Use the cubes to solve the problems.

1. $4 + 4 = $ **8** $8 - 4 = $ **4**

2. $6 + 6 = $ **12** $12 - 6 = $ **6**

3. $1 + 1 = $ **2** $2 - 1 = $ **1**

4. $5 + 5 = $ **10** $10 - 5 = $ **5**

Grade 1   26   Chapter 6

Skills Practice (p. 27) OL

6-5 Skills Practice
Use Doubles to Subtract

Add the doubles. Then subtract.

1. $3 + 3 = $ **6** $4 + 4 = $ **8** $7 + 7 = $ **14**
   $6 - 3 = $ **3** $8 - 4 = $ **4** $14 - 7 = $ **7**

2. $6 + 6 = $ **12** $1 + 1 = $ **2** $5 + 5 = $ **10**
   $12 - 6 = $ **6** $2 - 1 = $ **1** $10 - 5 = $ **5**

3. $8 + 8 = $ **16** $2 + 2 = $ **4** $9 + 9 = $ **18**
   $16 - 8 = $ **8** $4 - 2 = $ **2** $18 - 9 = $ **9**

Write a number sentence. Use doubles to solve.

4. Ken has 8 puppets. He and his friends use 4 of them for a puppet show. How many puppets are left?

   8 – **4** = **4** puppets

5. Justin reads 10 pages from his book. He reads 5 pages in the morning. He reads the rest at night. How many pages does he read at night?

   10 – **5** = **5** pages

Grade 1   27   Chapter 6

Add the doubles. Then subtract.

6.

$6 + 6 = \underline{12}$

$12 - 6 = \underline{6}$

7.

$2 + 2 = \underline{4}$

$4 - 2 = \underline{2}$

8.

$4 + 4 = \underline{8}$

$8 - 4 = \underline{4}$

9.

$1 + 1 = \underline{2}$

$2 - 1 = \underline{1}$

10.

$3 + 3 = \underline{6}$

$6 - 3 = \underline{3}$

11.

$5 + 5 = \underline{10}$

$10 - 5 = \underline{5}$

12. **WRITING IN** ►**MATH** Write a subtraction story using $6 - 3 = 3$.

Check students' work.

196   one hundred ninety-six

Math at Home Activity: Have your child subtract $12 - 6$ and tell what doubles fact helped solve the problem.

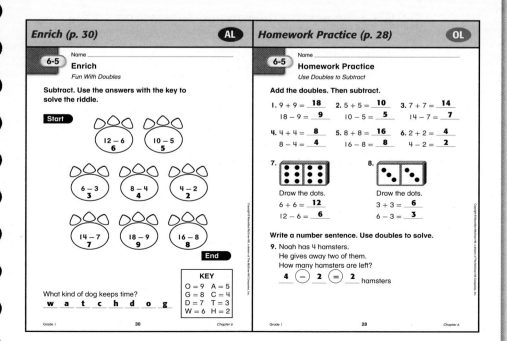

Enrich (p. 30)   **AL**

6-5   Name _____
Enrich
Fun With Doubles

Subtract. Use the answers with the key to solve the riddle.

Start

| $12 - 6$ | $10 - 5$ |
| **6** | **5** |

| $6 - 3$ | $8 - 4$ | $4 - 2$ |
| **3** | **4** | **2** |

| $14 - 7$ | $18 - 9$ | $16 - 8$ |
| **7** | **9** | **8** |

End

What kind of dog keeps time?
w a t c h d o g

KEY
O = 9   A = 5
G = 8   C = 4
D = 7   T = 3
W = 6   H = 2

Grade 1   30   Chapter 6

Homework Practice (p. 28)   **OL**

6-5   Name _____
Homework Practice
Use Doubles to Subtract

Add the doubles. Then subtract.

1. $9 + 9 = \underline{18}$ 2. $5 + 5 = \underline{10}$ 3. $7 + 7 = \underline{14}$
   $18 - 9 = \underline{9}$ $10 - 5 = \underline{5}$ $14 - 7 = \underline{7}$

4. $4 + 4 = \underline{8}$ 5. $8 + 8 = \underline{16}$ 6. $2 + 2 = \underline{4}$
   $8 - 4 = \underline{4}$ $16 - 8 = \underline{8}$ $4 - 2 = \underline{2}$

7.

Draw the dots.
$6 + 6 = \underline{12}$
$12 - 6 = \underline{6}$

8.

Draw the dots.
$3 + 3 = \underline{6}$
$6 - 3 = \underline{3}$

Write a number sentence. Use doubles to solve.

9. Noah has 4 hamsters.
   He gives away two of them.
   How many hamsters are left?

   $4 \;\boxed{-}\; 2 \;\boxed{=}\; 2$ hamsters

Grade 1   28   Chapter 6

BL **Alternate Teaching Strategy**

If ► students have difficulty using doubles facts to subtract . . .

Then ► use one of the following reteach options.

1 **CRM** **Daily Reteach Worksheet** (p. 26)

2 **Counter Contest** Display four yellow counters and four red counters as Set 1. Display five yellow counters and three red counters as Set 2. Have students write the subtraction sentences for each set. $8 - 4 = 4$; $8 - 5 = 3$ and $8 - 3 = 5$ **Which set can make more subtraction sentences?** Set 2 **Which set can make a doubles fact?** Set 1

③ Practice

Differentiate practice using these leveled assignments for Exercises 6–12. Exercise 12 asks students to create their own situation using the given number sentence. Make sure students understand how to create this.

Level	Assignment
BL Below/Approaching Level	Guide students through the exercises, using two-colored counters to set up and solve problems.
OL On Level	Complete the exercises independently, using counters as needed.
AL Above/Beyond Level	Complete the exercises independently without counters.

④ Assess

Formative Assessment

Have students model a subtraction sentence using doubles. Ask them to explain their model.

WRITING IN ►**MATH** Have students draw pictures of doubles found in nature and create a number sentence for each image.

Quick Check **Are students continuing to struggle using doubles facts to subtract?**

If Yes → **CRM** Reteach Worksheet (p. 26)

If No → Independent Work Options (p. 195B)

CRM Skills Practice Worksheet (p. 27)

CRM Enrich Worksheet (p. 30)

Lesson Planner

Objective

Relate addition and subtraction facts to solve problems.

Review Vocabulary

addition, subtraction

Resources

Materials: number cards, symbol cards $(+, -, =)$

Manipulatives: connecting cubes, number cubes

Literature Connection: *A Bag Full of Pups* by Dick Gackenbach

Alternate Lessons: Adapt "Peek Through the Wall" on pages 183 and 184 of *Math Their Way* for practice with addition and subtraction.
Use *IMPACT Mathematics:* Unit B to provide practice with related addition and subtraction facts.

Teacher Technology
- TeacherWorks

Focus on Math Background

Connecting Addition and Subtraction As students become more comfortable working the inverse relationship between addition and subtraction, the memorization of basic facts becomes easier. Multiple experiences with composing and decomposing numbers leads to the conceptual knowledge of the addition algorithm, the subtraction algorithm, and their inverse relationship to each other.

Daily Routine

Use these suggestions before beginning the lesson on p. 197.

5-Minute Check

(Reviews Lesson 6-5)

1. $6 + 6 = 12$ **2.** $5 + 5 = 10$
$12 - 6 = 6$ $10 - 10 = 0$

Problem of the Day

There are 7 blueberries left in the bowl. Dee looks at them and decides that he is not hungry. He eats none. How many blueberries are left in the bowl?
7 blueberries

 Have half the class line up. Ask students to create an addition and a subtraction story. Model using this example: *There are 8 students in line. If 8 more students join them, there will be 16 students in line. 8 + 8 = 16. There were 16 students sitting. Then 8 students got in line. So 8 students still are sitting. 16 − 8 = 8.*

Review Math Vocabulary

Write the words **addition** and **subtraction** on the chalkboard. Review the meanings of these words with students.
- **Which word means to join together sets to find the total or sum?** addition
- **Which word means to take away or find the difference?** subtraction

Differentiated Instruction

Small Group Options

Option 1 LINGUISTIC, AUDITORY

Gifted and Talented (AL)

- Explain that one group member in the circle will tell a story about subtraction, such as: *Once there were 5 frogs in the pond. Then 2 jumped out. Now there are 3 frogs in the pond.*
- Then all group members write the subtraction sentence for the story. $5 - 2 = 3$
- The next group member in the circle tells the related addition story: *Once there were 3 frogs in the pond. Then 2 more jumped in. Now there are 5 frogs in the pond.*
- Group members write the addition sentence for the story. $3 + 2 = 5$
- Students continue until everyone has had a turn to tell a story.

Option 2 VISUAL, AUDITORY

English Language Learners (ELL)

Materials: pictures of a bed, a blanket, a train, and a telephone.

Core Vocabulary: which picture, related facts, family
Common Use Verb: relate to

Hear Math This strategy helps students use their background knowledge to learn the vocabulary that describes related facts.

- Show a page with a picture of a bed, a blanket, a train, and a telephone
- Ask: "**Which picture *relates to*** (or is ***related to***) the bed?"
- Say: "Bed and blanket are ***related*** because people use a blanket on their bed."
- Have students say: "The blanket ***relates to*** the bed" (or "blanket and bed ***are related***.")
- Repeat for other items as time permits

Independent Work Options

Option 1 KINESTHETIC, LOGICAL

Early Finishers (OL) (AL)

Materials: beads in two colors, pipe cleaners, sentence strips (some blank, some with addition facts to 12)

- Have students read an addition sentence strip and model it by sliding beads onto a pipe cleaner.
- Partners work together to make bead models for both of the related subtraction sentences.
- Partners then write the subtraction sentences on blank sentence strips.

Option 2

Student Technology

Math Online ⟩ macmillanmh.com

Option 3

Learning Station: Health (p. 181H)

Direct students to the Health Learning Station for more opportunities to explore and extend the lesson concept.

Option 4

Problem-Solving Practice

Reinforce problem-solving skills and strategies with the Problem-Solving Practice worksheet.

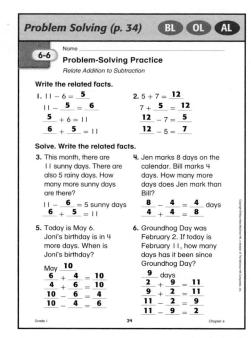

Problem Solving (p. 34) BL OL AL

6-6 Name _____
Problem-Solving Practice
Relate Addition to Subtraction

Write the related facts.

1. $11 - 6 = \underline{5}$
   $11 - \underline{5} = \underline{6}$
   $\underline{5} + 6 = 11$
   $\underline{6} + \underline{5} = 11$

2. $5 + 7 = \underline{12}$
   $7 + \underline{5} = \underline{12}$
   $\underline{12} - 7 = \underline{5}$
   $\underline{12} - 5 = \underline{7}$

Solve. Write the related facts.

3. This month, there are 11 sunny days. There are also 5 rainy days. How many more sunny days are there?
   $11 - \underline{6} = 5$ sunny days
   $\underline{6} + \underline{5} = 11$

4. Jen marks 8 days on the calendar. Bill marks 4 days. How many more days does Jen mark than Bill?
   $\underline{8} - \underline{4} = \underline{4}$ days
   $\underline{4} + \underline{4} = \underline{8}$

5. Today is May 6. Joni's birthday is in 4 more days. When is Joni's birthday?
   May $\underline{10}$
   $\underline{6} + \underline{4} = \underline{10}$
   $\underline{4} + \underline{6} = \underline{10}$
   $\underline{10} - \underline{6} = \underline{4}$
   $\underline{10} - \underline{4} = \underline{6}$

6. Groundhog Day was February 2. If today is February 11, how many days has it been since Groundhog Day?
   $\underline{9}$ days
   $\underline{2} + \underline{9} = \underline{11}$
   $\underline{9} + \underline{2} = \underline{11}$
   $\underline{11} - \underline{2} = \underline{9}$
   $\underline{11} - \underline{9} = \underline{2}$

Grade 1   34   Chapter 6

1 Introduce

Activity Choice 1 • Hands-On

- Give pairs of students ten connecting cubes. Show the students that every addition sentence has a subtraction sentence that goes with it. Use connecting cubes to demonstrate $4 + 2 = 6$ and $6 - 2 = 4$.

- One of the pair will use some or all of the cubes to make an addition problem. The other student will write it as a number sentence. The second student will then use the cubes to make the subtraction sentence that goes with the addition sentence. The other student will write the subtraction sentence.

Activity Choice 2 • Literature

Introduce the lesson with *A Bag Full of Pups* by Dick Gackenbach. For additional support, see p. TR50.

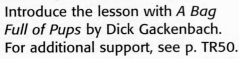

2 Teach

- Distribute number and symbol cards to groups. Ask students to use the cards to create an addition sentence with a sum no greater than 12.

- **How can you rearrange the cards to make a subtraction sentence?** Start with the sum and take away one of the smaller numbers to find out how many are left. **Do you need to use a different symbol card?** yes

Get Ready Use the section at the top of p. 197 to reinforce the lesson concept. As you work through the example with the students, reinforce that there is a subtraction sentence for each addition sentence.

Check Observe students as you work through Exercises 1–6 as a class.

 Exercise 6 Assess student comprehension before assigning practice exercises.

 COMMON ERROR!

Students may not realize that they can subtract either of the addends from a sum to make a related subtraction fact. Point out that in **Exercise 4**, 6 was subtracted from the sum, and subtracting 4 gives a second subtraction sentence: $10 - 4 = 6$.

Name _____

Relate Addition to Subtraction

Get Ready

Main Idea

I will use related addition and subtraction facts.

Related facts use the same numbers. These facts can help you add and subtract.

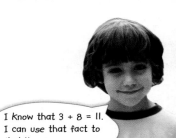

$$\begin{array}{r} 3 \\ + 8 \\ \hline 11 \end{array} \qquad \begin{array}{r} 11 \\ - 8 \\ \hline 3 \end{array}$$

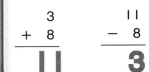 I know that $3 + 8 = 11$. I can use that fact to find $11 - 8$.

✓ Check

Use related facts to add and subtract.

1.		2.		3.	
$\begin{array}{r} 4 \\ + 7 \\ \hline 11 \end{array}$	$\begin{array}{r} 11 \\ - 4 \\ \hline 7 \end{array}$	$\begin{array}{r} 6 \\ + 5 \\ \hline 11 \end{array}$	$\begin{array}{r} 11 \\ - 6 \\ \hline 5 \end{array}$	$\begin{array}{r} 4 \\ + 8 \\ \hline 12 \end{array}$	$\begin{array}{r} 12 \\ - 4 \\ \hline 8 \end{array}$

Use the addition fact to write the related subtraction sentences.

4. $6 + 4 = \underline{10}$

$\underline{10} - \underline{6} = \underline{4}$

$\underline{10} - \underline{4} = \underline{6}$

5. $7 + 5 = \underline{12}$

$\underline{12} - \underline{7} = \underline{5}$

$\underline{12} - \underline{5} = \underline{7}$

6. Talk About It — Are $1 + 5 = 6$ and $6 - 1 = 5$ related facts? How do you know? Sample answer: Yes, because they use the same numbers.

Reteach (p. 31) — BL

6-6 Name _____

Reteach

Relate Addition to Subtraction

Related facts use the same numbers. These related addition facts use the numbers 3, 7, and 10.

$3 + 7 = 10 \quad 7 + 3 = 10$

These subtraction facts also use 3, 7, and 10. They are related to the addition facts.

$10 - 3 = 7 \quad 10 - 7 = 3$

Complete the related subtraction facts.

1. $6 + 3 = 9 \qquad 3 + 6 = \underline{9}$

$9 - 6 = \underline{3} \qquad 9 - 3 = \underline{6}$

2. $4 + 7 = 11 \qquad 7 + 4 = \underline{11}$

$11 - 4 = \underline{7} \qquad 11 - 7 = \underline{4}$

3. $5 + 3 = 8 \qquad 3 + 5 = \underline{8}$

$8 - \underline{5} = 3 \qquad 8 - 3 = \underline{5}$

4. $2 + 4 = 6 \qquad 4 + 2 = \underline{6}$

$6 - \underline{2} = \underline{4} \qquad 6 - \underline{4} = \underline{2}$

Grade 1   31   Chapter 6

Skills Practice (p. 32) — OL

6-6 Name _____

Skills Practice

Relate Addition to Subtraction

Use the related fact to write the related subtraction sentences.

1. $7 + 3 = \underline{10}$

$\underline{10} \ominus \underline{3} = \underline{7}$

$\underline{10} \ominus \underline{7} = \underline{3}$

2. $2 + 6 = \underline{8}$

$\underline{8} \ominus \underline{2} = \underline{6}$

$\underline{8} \ominus \underline{6} = \underline{2}$

3. $9 + 2 = \underline{11}$

$\underline{11} \ominus \underline{9} = \underline{2}$

$\underline{11} \ominus \underline{2} = \underline{9}$

4. $3 + 9 = \underline{12}$

$\underline{12} \ominus \underline{3} = \underline{9}$

$\underline{12} \ominus \underline{9} = \underline{3}$

5. $6 + 5 = \underline{11}$

$\underline{11} \ominus \underline{6} = \underline{5}$

$\underline{11} \ominus \underline{5} = \underline{6}$

6. $5 + 4 = \underline{9}$

$\underline{9} \ominus \underline{5} = \underline{4}$

$\underline{9} \ominus \underline{4} = \underline{5}$

Solve. Write the related addition fact.

7. This month, we picked 10 flowers. Last month, we picked 3. How many more flowers did we pick this month?

$10 - 7 = \underline{3}$ flowers

$\underline{7} + \underline{3} = 10$

8. Mrs. Jones' class has 8 goldfish. Mr. Kim's class has 4 goldfish. How many more goldfish does Mrs. Jones' class have?

$8 - 4 = \underline{4}$ goldfish

$\underline{4} + \underline{4} = 8$

Grade 1   32   Chapter 6

Practice

Use related facts to add and subtract.

7.
$$\begin{array}{r} 6 \\ + 5 \\ \hline 11 \end{array}$$
$$\begin{array}{r} 11 \\ - 5 \\ \hline 6 \end{array}$$

8.
$$\begin{array}{r} 4 \\ + 7 \\ \hline 11 \end{array}$$
$$\begin{array}{r} 11 \\ - 7 \\ \hline 4 \end{array}$$

9.
$$\begin{array}{r} 6 \\ + 4 \\ \hline 10 \end{array}$$
$$\begin{array}{r} 10 \\ - 4 \\ \hline 6 \end{array}$$

10.
$$\begin{array}{r} 8 \\ + 3 \\ \hline 11 \end{array}$$
$$\begin{array}{r} 11 \\ - 8 \\ \hline 3 \end{array}$$

Use the addition fact to write the related subtraction sentences.

11. $5 + 7 = \underline{12}$

$\underline{12} - \underline{7} = \underline{5}$

$\underline{12} - \underline{5} = \underline{7}$

12. $4 + 8 = \underline{12}$

$\underline{12} - \underline{4} = \underline{8}$

$\underline{12} - \underline{8} = \underline{4}$

Problem Solving

13. Number Sense Write two related facts for these numbers.
Possible answers:

11, 5, 6

$\underline{5} + \underline{6} = \underline{11}$

$\underline{11} - \underline{6} = \underline{5}$

 Math at Home Activity: Say an addition fact such as 3 + 9 = 12. Ask your child to name a related subtraction fact.

198   one hundred ninety-eight

Copyright © Macmillan/McGraw-Hill, a division of The McGraw-Hill Companies, Inc.

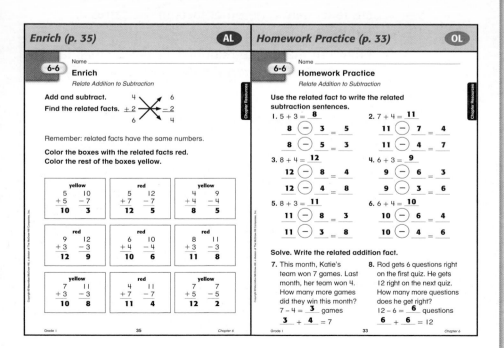

Lesson Planner _____

Objective
Write fact families to 12.

Vocabulary
fact family

Resources
Manipulatives: connecting cubes, number cubes
Literature Connection: *Math Fables* by Greg Tang
Alternate Lessons: Adapt "Beans" on page 174 of *Math Their Way* for practice writing addition fact families to 12. Use *IMPACT Mathematics:* Unit A to provide practice with fact families.

Teacher Technology
⊕ TeacherWorks • ♪ Math Songs Track 12 Lesson Plan

Focus on Math Background

As students become more comfortable composing and decomposing numbers in relation to addition and subtraction facts, their understanding of the inverse relationship between addition and subtraction grows. They become more comfortable with basic facts and mental retrieval. This facility makes them more efficient with computation in other areas of mathematics: measurement, data interpretation, and algebraic reasoning.

Daily Routine _____

Use these suggestions before beginning the lesson on p. 199.

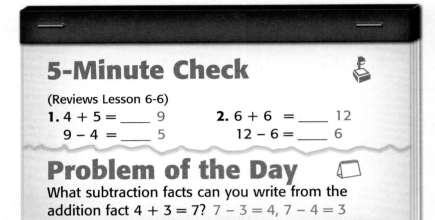

5-Minute Check
(Reviews Lesson 6-6)

1. $4 + 5 =$ ____ 9 **2.** $6 + 6 =$ ____ 12
$9 - 4 =$ ____ 5 $12 - 6 =$ ____ 6

Problem of the Day
What subtraction facts can you write from the addition fact $4 + 3 = 7$? $7 - 3 = 4, 7 - 4 = 3$

LINE UP When students line up for recess, lunch, or dismissal, have each one count the number of fingers on two hands and then create an addition sentence and a subtraction sentence using that number. Sample answer: $10 - 1 = 9; 9 + 1 = 10$

Building Math Vocabulary
Write the term **fact family** on the chalkboard and ask students to explain what they know about fact families.
- Write $5 + 2 = 7$ on the chalkboard and have students name the other facts in the same family. $2 + 5 = 7; 7 - 2 = 5; 7 - 5 = 2$
- Point out that related doubles facts are small fact families. **Can you name a doubles fact family?** Sample answer: $4 + 4 = 8$ and $8 - 4 = 4$

Visual Vocabulary Cards
Use Visual Vocabulary Card 18 to reinforce the vocabulary introduced in this lesson. (The Define/Example/Ask routine is printed on the back of each card.)

fact family

Differentiated Instruction

Small Group Options

Option 1
Gifted and Talented (AL)

Materials: 30 index cards

- Ask students to choose ten different fact families and write the numbers for each family on separate index cards. Have them put the cards in a pile.
- Then have each student in the group draw five cards.
- Explain that the goal of the game is to get all three numbers that make up a fact family.
- Students take turns asking one another for cards they need to complete their fact families. If no one has the card, the student chooses a card from the pile.

- Play continues until all the fact families are matched.

VISUAL/SPATIAL

Option 2
English Language Learners (ELL)

Materials: ten-frames, two-colored counters
Core Vocabulary: spots, occupied, empty
Common Use Verb: go together

See Math This strategy uses ten-frames to show fact families.

- Have students fill their ten-frames with counters, grouping colors together.
- Have them count how many are red, and yellow.
- Have students look for other students with corresponding numbers.
- Discuss if they all had the same colors with a given number. Use the discussion to discover fact families.

Use this worksheet to provide additional support for English Language Learners.

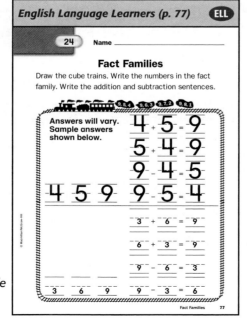

English Language Learners (p. 77) **ELL**

24 Name _____

Fact Families

Draw the cube trains. Write the numbers in the fact family. Write the addition and subtraction sentences.

Answers will vary. Sample answers shown below.

$4 + 5 = 9$
$5 + 4 = 9$
$9 - 4 = 5$

4 5 9   9 5 4

___ + ___ = ___   ___ + ___ = ___

___ + ___ = ___   ___ - ___ = ___

3   6   9   9 - 3 = 6

Fact Families 77

Independent Work Options

LOGICAL

Option 1
Early Finishers (OL) (AL)

Materials: index cards, markers

- Prepare fact-family flash cards ahead of time by writing one fact on each index card. In each fact, leave out one number and put a blank in its place. Write the missing number on the back of the card as well as the other number sentences in that fact family.
- Have partners use the cards like flash cards. After naming the missing number, students can name one, or all, of the other facts in the same family.

Option 2
Student Technology

Math Online macmillanmh.com

♪ Math Songs, "We Are Family" Track 12

Option 3
Learning Station: Art (p. 181G)

Direct students to the Art Learning Station for more opportunities to explore the lesson concept.

Option 4
Problem-Solving Practice

Reinforce problem-solving skills and strategies with the Problem-Solving Practice worksheet.

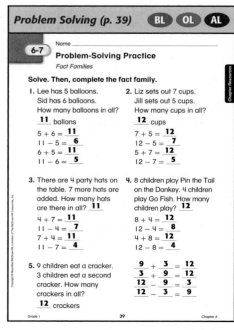

Problem Solving (p. 39) **BL OL AL**

6-7 Name _____
Problem-Solving Practice
Fact Families

Solve. Then, complete the fact family.

1. Lee has 5 balloons. Sid has 6 balloons. How many balloons in all?
___**11**___ ballons
$5 + 6 = 11$
$11 - 5 = 6$
$6 + 5 = 11$
$11 - 6 = 5$

2. Liz sets out 7 cups. Jill sets out 5 cups. How many cups in all?
___**12**___ cups
$7 + 5 = 12$
$12 - 5 = 7$
$5 + 7 = 12$
$12 - 7 = 5$

3. There are 4 party hats on the table. 7 more hats are added. How many hats are there in all? **11**
$4 + 7 = 11$
$11 - 4 = 7$
$7 + 4 = 11$
$11 - 7 = 4$

4. 8 children play Pin the Tail on the Donkey. 4 children play Go Fish. How many children play? **12**
$8 + 4 = 12$
$12 - 4 = 8$
$4 + 8 = 12$
$12 - 8 = 4$

5. 9 children eat a cracker. 3 children eat a second cracker. How many crackers in all?
___**12**___ crackers
$9 + 3 = 12$
$3 + 9 = 12$
$12 - 9 = 3$
$12 - 3 = 9$

Grade 1   39   Chapter 6

① Introduce

Activity Choice 1 • Hands-On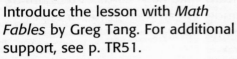

Ask students to write all the addition sentences with sums of 5 and the related subtraction sentences.

- List and discuss student responses. $0 + 5 = 5$, $5 + 0 = 5$, $5 - 0 = 5$, $5 - 5 = 0$, $4 + 1 = 5$, $1 + 4 = 5$, $5 - 1 = 4$, $5 - 4 = 1$, $2 + 3 = 5$, $3 + 2 = 5$, $5 - 2 = 3$, $5 - 3 = 2$
- **How many different facts are there?** 12
- **How are they the same? different?** they all include 5; they use different number combinations

Activity Choice 2 • Literature

Introduce the lesson with *Math Fables* by Greg Tang. For additional support, see p. TR51.

② Teach

- Give each student a number cube and two 6-cube trains of different colors. Have the student roll the cube and create a corresponding cube train. Then roll the cube again and create another cube train.

- Have the student combine the trains and tell the addition sentence. Then flip the train and tell the other addition number sentence.

- Have the student separate the train into its two parts and tell the two subtraction sentences.

- **What are the numbers in your fact family?** See students' work.

Get Ready Use the section at the top of student p. 199 to reinforce the lesson concept.

Check Observe students as you work through Exercises 1–3 as a class.

💬 **Exercise 3** Assess student comprehension before assigning practice exercises.

 COMMON ERROR!

Once students begin memorizing facts and fact families, they may think they must guess if they do not remember the answer. Remind them that they should still use manipulatives when they are not sure of an answer.

Name _____

Fact Families

Hands-On Activity

Get Ready

Main Idea
I will use fact families.

Vocabulary
fact family

3, 7, and 10 are the numbers in this fact family!

Related facts make a **fact family**.

$7 + \underline{3} = 10 \qquad 3 + \underline{7} = 10$

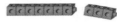

$10 - \underline{3} = 7 \qquad 10 - \underline{7} = 3$

Check

Use  to add and subtract.
Write the numbers in the fact family.

1. $8 + 1 = \underline{9} \qquad 1 + 8 = \underline{9}$

   $9 - 1 = \underline{8} \qquad 9 - 8 = \underline{1}$

   $\underline{1}, \underline{8}, \underline{9}$

2. $3 + 4 = \underline{7} \qquad 4 + 3 = \underline{7}$

   $7 - 3 = \underline{4} \qquad 7 - 4 = \underline{3}$

   $\underline{3}, \underline{4}, \underline{7}$

3. Talk About It — What fact family can you write with 2, 8, and 6? $2 + 6 = 8$, $6 + 2 = 8$, $8 - 2 = 6$, $8 - 6 = 2$

Chapter 6 Lesson 7   one hundred ninety-nine 199

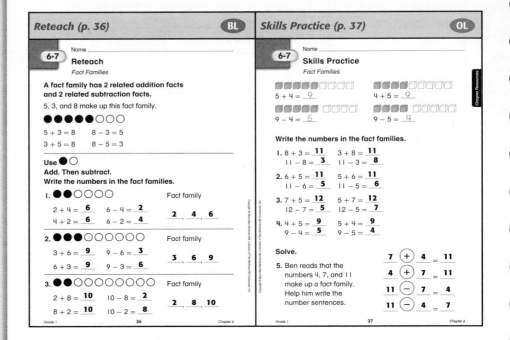

Use 🎲 to add and subtract.
Write the numbers in the fact family.

4. $4 + 7 = \underline{11}$ $7 + 4 = \underline{11}$

$11 - 7 = \underline{4}$ $11 - 4 = \underline{7}$

$\underline{4}, \underline{7}, \underline{11}$

5. $2 + 4 = \underline{6}$ $4 + 2 = \underline{6}$

$6 - 4 = \underline{2}$ $6 - 2 = \underline{4}$

$\underline{2}, \underline{4}, \underline{6}$

6. $1 + 9 = \underline{10}$ $10 \ominus 9 = \underline{1}$

$9 \oplus 1 = \underline{10}$ $10 \ominus 1 = \underline{9}$

7. $3 + 9 = \underline{12}$ $12 \ominus 3 = \underline{9}$

$9 \oplus 3 = \underline{12}$ $12 \ominus 9 = \underline{3}$

H.O.T. Problem

8. **Thinking Math**
When I am added to 7, the sum is 12.
What number am I?

$\underline{5}$

 Math at Home Activity: Have your child write a fact family for the numbers 1, 6, and 7.

BL Alternate Teaching Strategy

If students do not understand how fact families are related . . .

Then use one of the following reteach options.

1 CRM **Daily Reteach Worksheet** (p. 36)

2 **Connecting Cubes Subtraction** Display the sentences from one fact family. Help students model each one with connecting cubes. Have students use a different color cube for each addend in the family.

3 Practice

Differentiate practice using these leveled assignments for Exercises 4–8.

Level	Assignment
BL Below/ Approaching Level	Have students work in groups as you guide them through the exercises.
OL On Level	Complete the exercises independently.
AL Above/Beyond Level	Complete the exercises substituting facts with sums greater than 12.

4 Assess

Formative Assessment

Ask students to list the sentences in a fact family and use manipulatives to model each one. Have students explain how the equations are related.

WRITING IN ▶MATH Ask students to write the set of addition and subtraction number sentences for one of the fact families. Then have them write or illustrate a story based on one of those number sentences.

Quick Check: Are students continuing to struggle with generating fact families?

If Yes → CRM Reteach Worksheet (p. 36)

If No → Independent Work Options (p. 199B)

CRM Skills Practice Worksheet (p. 37)

CRM Enrich Worksheet (p. 40)

Enrich (p. 40) AL

6-7 Name _____
Enrich
Fact Family Stars

Look at each star.
Find 3 numbers that make a fact family.
Complete each fact family.   **See students' work.**

1. $\underline{5} + \underline{6} = 11$
$\underline{6} + \underline{5} = 11$
$11 - \underline{5} = \underline{6}$
$11 - \underline{6} = \underline{5}$

(star: 4, 4, 11, 5, 6, 3)

2. $\underline{9} + \underline{1} = 10$
$\underline{1} + \underline{9} = 10$
$10 - \underline{1} = \underline{9}$
$10 - \underline{9} = \underline{1}$

(star: 9, 2, 10, 6, 0, 1)

3. $\underline{4} + \underline{8} = 12$
$\underline{8} + \underline{4} = 12$
$12 - \underline{8} = \underline{4}$
$12 - \underline{4} = \underline{8}$

(star: 8, 5, 12, 1, 2, 4)

Grade 1   40   Chapter 6

Homework Practice (p. 38) OL

6-7 Name _____
Homework Practice
Fact Families

Write the numbers in the fact families.
1. $9 + 2 = \mathbf{11}$ $2 + 9 = \mathbf{11}$
$11 - 9 = \mathbf{2}$ $11 - 2 = \mathbf{9}$

2. $3 + 4 = \mathbf{7}$ $4 + 3 = \mathbf{7}$
$7 - 3 = \mathbf{4}$ $7 - 4 = \mathbf{3}$

Write the number sentences.
3. The numbers 2, 4, and 6 make up a fact family.
$2 \oplus 4 = 6$
$4 \oplus 2 = 6$
$6 \ominus 2 = 4$
$6 \ominus 4 = 2$

4. The numbers 5, 7, and 12 make up a fact family.
$5 \oplus 7 = 12$
$7 \oplus 5 = 12$
$12 \ominus 5 = 7$
$12 \ominus 7 = 5$

Grade 1   38   Chapter 6

Extra Practice

Reviews Lessons 6-1 to 6-7

Objective: Review and assess mastery of previous lessons' skills and concepts.

- Review with students how to subtract by counting back 1, 2, or 3.
- Have students help you build fact families to remind them how addition and subtraction are related.

Practice with Technology

Math Online Have students visit macmillanmh.com for additional practice with online activities, games, and quizzes.

Name _____

Add and subtract using fact families.

1. $3 + 5 = \underline{8}$ $5 + 3 = \underline{8}$

   $8 - 5 = \underline{3}$ $8 - 3 = \underline{5}$

2. $8 + 4 = \underline{12}$ $4 + 8 = \underline{12}$

   $12 - 4 = \underline{8}$ $12 - 8 = \underline{4}$

3. $1 + 6 = \underline{7}$ $6 + 1 = \underline{7}$

   $7 - 6 = \underline{1}$ $7 - 1 = \underline{6}$

4. $9 + 2 = \underline{11}$ $2 + 9 = \underline{11}$

   $11 - 2 = \underline{9}$ $11 - 9 = \underline{2}$

5. $6 + 4 = \underline{10}$ $4 + 6 = \underline{10}$

   $10 - 4 = \underline{6}$ $10 - 6 = \underline{4}$

Chapter 6   two hundred one   201

Game Time

Related or Not?
Fact Families

Play with a partner. Take turns.
- Put your game pieces under START.
- Roll the ⬛ and move your game piece.
- Decide whether the space you land on is part of a fact family. If it is, you can stay there. If it's not, move your game piece back to the space it was on before you rolled.
- The first person to FINISH wins!

You Will Need
⬛ ⚪ ⚫

START

| 1 + 4 | 3 + 5 | 4 + 6 | 2 + 8 | 3 + 2 |
| 5 − 1 | 8 − 3 | 11 − 6 | 10 − 8 | 6 − 3 |

7 + 5
12 − 6

10 + 1
12 − 1

| 6 + 5 | 8 + 3 | 9 + 2 | 5 + 1 | 3 + 7 | 1 + 7 |
| 12 − 6 | 11 − 3 | 11 − 9 | 6 − 2 | 9 − 3 | 8 − 1 |

4 + 4
9 − 4

9 + 3
12 − 3

| 2 + 2 | 6 + 2 | 8 + 2 | 1 + 8 | 3 + 4 |
| 4 − 2 | 8 − 3 | 10 − 2 | 10 − 1 | 7 − 4 |

FINISH

202 two hundred two

Related or Not?

Math Concept:
Fact Families

Manipulatives: two-colored counters, red number cube

Introduce the game on page 202 to students to play as a class, in small groups, or at a learning workstation to review concepts introduced in this chapter.

Instructions

- Put your game pieces on Start.
- Roll the number cube and move your game piece.
- Decide whether the space you land on shows problems in the same fact family. If it does, you can stay there. If it does not, move your game piece back to the space it was on before you rolled.
- The first person to Finish wins!

Extend the Game

When students finish the game, have them play a second time. In the second game, players who land on a fact family must name another problem in the same family.

Differentiated Practice

Use these leveling suggestions to differentiate the game for all learners.

Level	Assignment
BL Below/Approaching Level	Allow students to use a chart of fact families below 12 while playing the game. You could make the chart or use it as an assignment for a student who finishes early or is an advanced learner.
OL On Level	Have students play the game with the rules as written.
AL Above/Beyond Level	To finish each turn, players must correctly add all three numbers in the fact family shown on the space where they landed.

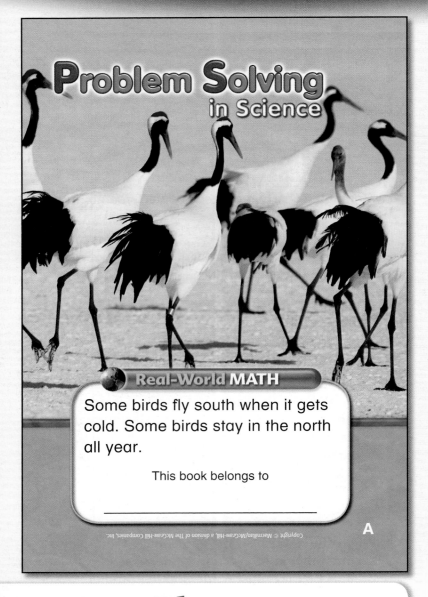

Problem Solving
in Science

Real-World MATH

Some birds fly south when it gets cold. Some birds stay in the north all year.

This book belongs to

_____

A

B

Alexa saw 12 birds eating seeds. 6 of them will fly south when it gets cold.

How many will stay for the winter?

0 1 2 3 4 5 6 7 8 9 10 11 12

____6____ birds

Lesson Planner

Objective

Use a number line to solve subtraction problems in science.

National Standard

Students should develop an understanding of organisms and environments.

Activate Prior Knowledge

Before students look at the pages, discuss ways that some animals deal with the change of seasons.

- **Some birds fly to warmer climates during the colder months. What do other animals do?** Sample answer: Bears sleep or hibernate. Some animals store food and grow thicker coats.

- **Why do animals change when it gets colder?** Sample answer: Animals change when it gets colder because they need to stay warm. Bears hibernate because less food is available during the cold weather.

Jose saw 11 birds. 3 of them will fly south when it gets cold.

How many will stay for the winter?

0 1 2 3 4 5 6 7 8 9 10 11 12

___8___ birds

C

In the winter, Raymond saw 6 birds eating from a bird feeder. None of them flew south.

How many stayed for the winter?

___6___ birds

D

Create the Book

Guide students to create their book.

- Have them fold the page in half.
- Ask them to write their name on page A.
- Explain that page A is the front cover and page D is the back cover. If necessary, have them practice flipping through the book in order.
- Guide them in reading the information and word problems on each of the pages.

Use the Student Pages

Have students work individually or in pairs to solve the word problems on pages B–D.

Page B Students may have problems setting up and solving this problem. Suggest that they break the word problem down into parts that answer the questions "What do I know?" and "What do I need to find out?" Their answers should help them set up the number sentence.

Page D This problem requires a clear understanding of zero. Suggest that students try drawing a picture of or act out the scenario.

WRITING IN ►MATH Have students write a subtraction problem related to birds flying south. Ask them to use counting back to solve the problem.

 **Dinah Zike's Foldables**

Use these lesson suggestions to incorporate the Foldables during the chapter. Students can then use their Foldable to review for the test.

Lesson 6-5 Show the subtraction of doubles with differences to 12 on the fifth page of the subtraction journal.

Lesson 6-6 Write one subtraction fact. Then write a related addition fact on the sixth page of the subtraction journal.

Lesson 6-7 On the last page of the subtraction journal, write four number sentences that make a fact family.

Vocabulary Review

Review chapter vocabulary using one of the following options.

- **Visual Vocabulary Card** (18)
- **eGlossary** at macmillanmh.com

Vocabulary Test

CRM **Chapter 6 Resource Masters** (p. 45)
Assess student comprehension of the chapter vocabulary with the Vocabulary Test.

Math Online ▷ **Chapter Test**
Alternative summative assessment options are available online at macmillanmh.com.

Name _____

Vocabulary

Circle the correct answer.

1. **count back**
   - **a.** $6 - 2 = 6, 5, 4$ (circled)
   - **b.** $6 - 2 = 6, 7, 8$

2. **fact family**
   - **a.** $7 + 3 = 10$ (circled)
     $3 + 7 = 10$
     $10 - 3 = 7$
     $10 - 7 = 3$
   - **b.** $6 + 4 = 10$
     $4 + 6 = 10$
     $5 + 5 = 10$
     $8 + 2 = 10$

Concepts

Count back to subtract.

3. $7 - 3 = \underline{4}$

4. $9 - 2 = \underline{7}$

Use a number line to subtract.

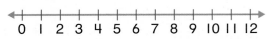

$$0 \quad 1 \quad 2 \quad 3 \quad 4 \quad 5 \quad 6 \quad 7 \quad 8 \quad 9 \quad 10 \quad 11 \quad 12$$

5. $5 - 2 = \underline{3}$ 6. $4 - 2 = \underline{2}$ 7. $8 - 4 = \underline{4}$

8. $6 - 2 = \underline{4}$ 9. $7 - 1 = \underline{6}$ 10. $10 - 1 = \underline{9}$

11. $10 - 5 = \underline{5}$ 12. $5 - 3 = \underline{2}$ 13. $12 - 6 = \underline{6}$

Chapter 6   two hundred five **205**

✓ Chapter 6 Project

My Story of Chapter 6

Alone, in pairs, or in small groups, have students discuss the results of their completed chapter project with the class. Assess their work using the Chapter Project rubric found in Chapter 6 Resource Masters on p. 50.

Find each difference.

14. $10 - 10 =$ ___0___   **15.** $12 - 7 =$ ___5___   **16.** $11 - 8 =$ ___3___

17. $10 - 4 =$ ___6___   **18.** $11 - 6 =$ ___5___   **19.** $9 - 8 =$ ___1___

20.	**21.**	**22.**	**23.**
10	12	11	10
− 5	− 6	− 4	− 7
5	6	7	3

24.	**25.**	**26.**	**27.**
8	5	12	8
− 3	− 2	− 4	− 6
5	3	8	2

Problem Solving

28. Write number sentences using these numbers.
Sample answers:

___8___ + ___4___ = ___12___

___12___ − ___8___ = ___4___

12, 8, 4

29. Cris has 6 jump ropes. What doubles fact shows the number of Cris's jump ropes?

___3___ + ___3___ = ___6___

Copyright © Macmillan/McGraw-Hill, a division of The McGraw-Hill Companies, Inc.

Summative Assessment

Summative Assessment

Use these alternate leveled chapter tests to differentiate assessment for the specific needs of your students.

Leveled Chapter 6 Tests			
Form	**Type**	**Level**	**CRM Pages**
1	Multiple Choice	BL	52–53
2A	Multiple Choice	OL	54–55
2B	Multiple Choice	OL	56–57
2C	Free Response	AL	58–59
2D	Free Response	AL	60–61

BL = below/approaching grade level
OL = on grade level
AL = above/beyond grade level

ExamView® Assessment Suite Customize and create multiple versions of your Chapter Test and their test answer keys.

Data-Driven Decision-Making

Based on the results of the Chapter Review/Test, use the following to review concepts that continue to present students with problems.

Exercises	State/Local Standards	What's the Math?	Error Analysis	Resources for Review
1 3–4 29		Show the meaning of subtraction by counting backwards. Understand doubles in subtraction.	Double counts a number when counting backwards. Does not recognize or use doubles as a tool.	Strategic Intervention Guide (p. 90) CRM Chapter 6 Resource Masters (Reteach Worksheets) **Math Online** Concepts in Motion Math Adventures
5–13		Use a number line to subtract.	Subtracts incorrectly.	
14–27		Show the meaning of subtraction.	Subtracts wrong numbers. Subtracts incorrectly.	
28		Know addition facts and corresponding subtraction facts and commit them to memory. Know fact families.	Does not know or recognize fact families.	

Test Practice

 Formative Assessment

- Use Student Edition pp. 207–208 as practice and cumulative review. The questions are written in the same style as many state tests.
- You can use these two pages to benchmark student progress, or as an alternative homework assignment.

Additional practice pages can be found in the Chapter 6 Resource Masters.

CRM **Chapter 6 Resource Masters**
Cumulative Test Practice

- Multiple Choice format (pp. 52–58, 62)
- Free Response format (pp. 59–61, 63)

ExamView **Assessment Suite** Create practice worksheets or tests that align to state standards.

Math Online For additional practice, visit macmillanmh.com.

Name _____

Listen as your teacher reads each problem.
Choose the correct answer.

1.
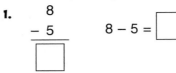

8 − 5 = ☐

  3 ⬤   4 ◯

  5 ◯   8 ◯

2.

9 − 3 = ☐

  5 ◯   6 ⬤

  7 ◯   12 ◯

3.

  11 − 1 ⬤   10 − 1 ◯

  12 − 2 ◯   11 − 10 ◯

4.
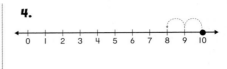

  9 − 1 ◯   8 − 2 ◯

  10 − 2 ⬤   10 − 3 ◯

5.
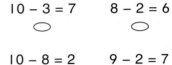
10 − 2 = 8

  10 − 3 = 7 ◯   8 − 2 = 6 ◯

  10 − 8 = 2 ⬤   9 − 2 = 7 ◯

6.
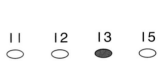
12 ☐ 14

  11 ◯ 12 ◯ 13 ⬤ 15 ◯

Chapter 6   two hundred seven **207**

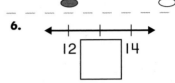

Test-Taking Tips

For the Teacher

- You may repeat orally administered directions if necessary.
- Read oral test questions at a moderate, steady pace.

For the Student

- Make sure to check that you have filled in an oval for each test question.
- Pay close attention when you hear the teacher's voice.

7.

$5 + 4 = 9$ ○ $2 + 3 = 5$ ○

$3 + 3 = 6$ ● $4 + 3 = 7$ ○

10.

$6 + 5 = 11$ ● $6 + 11 = 17$ ○

$5 + 11 = 16$ ○ $6 - 5 = 1$ ○

8.

$5 + \boxed{} = 10$

4 ○   5 ●

6 ○   10 ○

11. Kayla sees 4 stars. Len sees the same number of stars. How many stars do they see in all?

_8_ stars

9.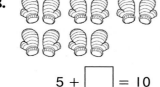

12. 9 hats are in the shop. Tess buys 2 hats. How many hats are left?

_7_ hats

STOP

Summative Assessment

Test Directions for Teachers

Read the following directions to students before they begin the test. Then read each question followed by a pause to allow students time to work on the problem and choose an answer. The first test item can be worked as a class example.

- **Write your name at the top of the page.**
- **I am going to read each question to you. Listen carefully to the entire question before you choose an answer.**

Multiple Choice

1. You can subtract across. You can also subtract down to find the difference. What is the difference?
2. What is the difference?
3. Look at the number line. Which problem does the number line show?
4. Look at the number line. Which problem does the number line show?
5. Look at the subtraction fact. What is the related subtraction fact for $10 - 2 = 8$?
6. What comes between 12 and 14?

- **Turn the page over.**

7. Look at the number facts. Which is a doubles fact?
8. Count the number of mittens. What number makes a doubles fact?
9. Look at the dominoes. Which domino shows $8 - 4 = 4$?
10. Which fact is a doubles plus one fact?

Short Response

11. Kayla sees 4 stars.
Len sees the same number of stars.
How many stars do they see in all?
12. Nine hats are in the shop.
Tess buys 2 hats.
How many hats are left?

Chapter Overview

Chapter-at-a-Glance

In Chapter 7, students order events and measure time to the hour and half hour on analog and digital clocks, and relate time to events.

Lesson	Math Objective	State/Local Standards
7-1 Ordering Events (pp. 213–214)	Put events in order.	
7-2 Time to the Hour (pp. 215–216)	Read and write time to the nearest hour.	
7-3 Time to the Half Hour (pp. 217–218)	Recognize time to the nearest half hour.	
7-4 Problem-Solving Strategy: Make a Table (pp. 219–220)	Use the *make a table* strategy to solve problems.	
7-5 Telling Time to the Hour and Half Hour (pp. 223–226)	Tell time to the hour and half hour on analog and digital clocks.	
7-6 Relate Time to Events (pp. 227–228)	Relate time and events.	
7-7 Problem-Solving Investigation: Choose a Strategy (pp. 231–232)	Choose the best strategy to solve a problem.	

Measure Time

BIG Idea To make sense of the passage of time, students need to learn to tell time to the hour and half hour and relate time to events. Students need experience ordering routines to determine which activities come before or after a particular event. Students need to compare duration of events with a common referent, such as sorting activities that last shorter or longer.

Algebra Readiness In Lesson 7-6, students put events in order using an abstract unit, duration of time.

Measurement Readiness In Lesson 7-5, students learn to tell time on both analog and digital clocks.

G1-FP5C *Measurement* **and** *Data Analysis:* Children strengthen their sense of number by solving problems involving measurements and data. Measuring by laying multiple copies of a unit end to end and then counting the units by using groups of tens and ones supports children's understanding of number lines and number relationships. Representing measurements and discrete data in picture and bar graphs involves counting and comparisons that provide another meaningful connection to number relationships.

Skills Trace
Vertical Alignment

Kindergarten

In kindergarten, students learned to:

- Understand concepts of time: morning, afternoon, evening, today, tomorrow, yesterday.
- Name the days of the week.
- Understand tools that measure time: clock, calendar.
- Identify the time to the nearest hour.

First Grade

During this chapter, students learn to:

- Tell time to the nearest hour and half hour.
- Relate time to events: before/after, shorter/longer.
- Tell time on both analog and digital clocks.

After this chapter, students learn to:

- Order and sort objects by measurement. (Chapter 9)

Second Grade

In second grade, students learn to:

- Tell time to the nearest quarter hour.
- Determine intervals of time in hours.
- Understand time relationships: how many minutes in an hour, days in a month, weeks in a year.

Backmapping and Vertical Alignment
McGraw-Hill's *Math Connects* program was conceived and developed with the final results in mind: student success in Algebra 1 and beyond. The authors, using the **NCTM Focal Points and Focal Connections** as their guide, developed this brand-new series by backmapping from Algebra 1 concepts, and vertically aligning the topics so that they build upon prior skills and concepts and serve as a foundation for future topics.

Math Vocabulary

The following math vocabulary words for Chapter 7 are listed in the glossary of the **Student Edition**. You can find interactive definitions in 13 languages in the **eGlossary** at macmillanmh.com.

after, before (p. 213)

b is before C
a b c d
b is after a

afternoon a time in the day between noon and sunset (p. 213)

analog a clock that has an hour hand and a minute hand (p. 223)

digital a clock that uses only numbers to show time (p. 223)

evening the time after school when it is dark (p. 213)

half hour one half of an hour is 30 minutes; sometimes called half past or half past the hour (p. 217)

half past half into the hour, like half hour. (p. 217)

hour a unit of time; 1 hour = 60 minutes (p. 215)

hour hand the shorter hand on a clock that tells the hour (p. 215)

minute hand the longer hand on a clock that tells the minutes (p. 215)

morning the period of time from sunrise to noon (p. 213)

o'clock at the beginning of the hour (p. 215)

Visual Vocabulary Cards Use Visual Vocabulary Cards 3, 14, 20, 21, 22, 27, and 31 to introduce and reinforce the vocabulary in this chapter. (The Define/Example/Ask routine is printed on the back of each card.)

hour

Chapter Planner

Suggested Pacing		
Instruction	**Review and Assessment**	**TOTAL**
7 days	2 days	**9 days**

Diagnostic Assessment
Are You Ready? (p. 210)

	Lesson 7-1 Pacing: 1 day	**Lesson 7-2** Pacing: 1 day	**Lesson 7-3** Pacing: 1 day
Lesson/ Objective	**Ordering Events** (pp. 213–214) **Objective:** Put events in order.	**Time to the Hour** (pp. 215–216) **Objective:** Read and write time to the nearest hour.	**Time to the Half Hour** (pp. 217–218) **Objective:** Recognize time to the nearest half hour.
State/Local Standards			
Math Vocabulary	**after**, **afternoon**, **before**, **evening**, **morning**	**hour**, **hour hand**, **minute hand**, **o'clock**	**half hour**, **half past**
Lesson Resources		**Materials** construction paper, markers **Manipulatives** student clocks, demonstration clocks **Other Resources** CRM Leveled Worksheets (pp. 11–15) Daily Reteach • 5-Minute Check Problem of the Day	**Manipulatives** demonstration clock, student clocks, number cubes **Other Resources** CRM Leveled Worksheets (pp. 16–20) Daily Reteach • 5-Minute Check Problem of the Day
	Other Resources CRM Leveled Worksheets (pp. 6–10) Daily Reteach • 5-Minute Check Problem of the Day		
Technology Math Online		Math Adventures	Math Adventures
Reaching All Learners	Gifted/Talented, p. 213B **AL** English Learners, p. 213B **ELL** Early Finishers, p. 213B **OL** **AL**	Below Level, p. 215B **BL** English Learners, p. 215B **ELL** Early Finishers, p. 215B **OL** **AL**	Gifted and Talented, p. 217B **AL** English Learners, p. 217B **ELL** Early Finishers, p. 217B **OL** **AL**
Alternate Lessons	*IMPACT Mathematics:* Unit F		

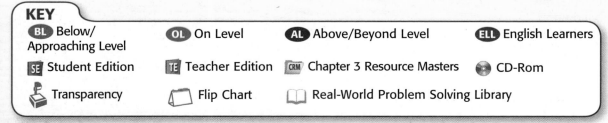

KEY

BL Below/ Approaching Level   **OL** On Level   **AL** Above/Beyond Level   **ELL** English Learners

SE Student Edition   **TE** Teacher Edition   **CRM** Chapter 3 Resource Masters   CD-Rom

Transparency   Flip Chart   Real-World Problem Solving Library

Lesson 7-4
Pacing: 1 day

Problem-Solving Strategy
Make a Table
(pp. 219–220)

Objective: Use the *make a table* strategy to solve problems.

Manipulatives
student clocks, connecting cubes

Other Resources
- CRM Leveled Worksheets (pp. 21–25)
- Daily Reteach • 5-Minute Check
- Problem of the Day
- *Getting Around Then and Now*

Gifted and Talented, p. 219B **AL**
English Learners, p. 219B **ELL**
Early Finishers, p. 219B **OL** **AL**

Formative Assessment:
Mid-Chapter Check (p. 221)
Spiral Review (p. 222)

Lesson 7-5
Pacing: 1 day

Telling Time to the Hour and Half Hour
(pp. 223–226)

Objective: Tell time to the hour and half hour on digital and analog clocks.

analog, digital

Materials
digital clock

Manipulatives
student clocks, demonstration clocks

Other Resources
- CRM Leveled Worksheets (pp. 26–30)
- Daily Reteach • 5-Minute Check
- Problem of the Day

Concepts in Motion

Below Level, p. 223B **BL**
English Learners, p. 223B **ELL**
Early Finishers, p. 223B **OL** **AL**

IMPACT Mathematics: Unit F

Lesson 7-6
Pacing: 1 day

Relate Time to Events
(pp. 227–228)

Objective: Relate time and events.

Manipulatives
demonstration clock, student clocks

Other Resources
- CRM Leveled Worksheets (pp. 31–35)
- Daily Reteach • 5-Minute Check
- Problem of the Day

Concepts in Motion

Below Level, p. 227B **BL**
English Learners, p. 227B **ELL**
Early Finishers, p. 227B **OL** **AL**

IMPACT Mathematics: Unit F

Extra Practice (p. 229)
Game Time: Switch It! (p. 230)

Lesson/Objective

State/Local Standards

Math Vocabulary

Lesson Resources

Technology

Math Online

Reaching All Learners

Alternate Lessons

CHAPTER 7

Chapter Planner

Lesson 7-7

Pacing: 1 day

Lesson/ Objective	**Problem-Solving Investigation** **Choose a Strategy** (pp. 231–232) **Objective:** Choose the best strategy to solve a problem.
State/Local Standards	
Math Vocabulary	
Lesson Resources	**Materials** paper, clock stamp **Manipulatives** student clocks **Other Resources** ⬛ Leveled Worksheets (pp. 36–40) ✍ Daily Reteach • 5-Minute Check 📖 Problem of the Day 📖 *Getting Around Then and Now*
Technology Math Online▶	
Reaching All Learners	Below Level, p. 231B **BL** English Learners, p. 231B **ELL** Early Finishers, p. 231B **OL** **AL**
Alternate Lessons	

Problem Solving in Music
(p. 233)

✓ Summative Assessment
Chapter Review/Test (p. 235)
Test Practice (p. 237)

Assessment Options

✓ Diagnostic Assessment
- **SE** *Option 1:* Are You Ready? (p. 210)
  Option 2: Online Quiz macmillanmh.com
- **CRM** *Option 3:* Diagnostic Test (p. 42)
- **CRM** *Option 4:* Chapter Pretest (p. 43)

✓ Formative Assessment
- **TE** Alternate Teaching Strategies (every lesson)
- **TE** Line Up (every lesson)
- **SE** Talk About It (every lesson)
- **SE** Writing in Math (every lesson)
- **SE** Check (every lesson)
- **SE** Mid-Chapter Check (p. 221)
- **CRM** Mid-Chapter Test (p. 44)

✓ Summative Assessment
- **SE** Chapter Review/Test (p. 235)
- **SE** Test Practice (p. 237)
- **CRM** Vocabulary Test (p. 45)
- **CRM** Leveled Chapter Tests (pp. 52–61)
- **CRM** Cumulative Test Practice (pp. 62–63)
- **CRM** Listening Assessment (pp. 48–49)
- **CRM** Oral Assessment (pp. 46–47)
- 🌐 Exam*View*® Assessment Suite
- A⁺ Advance Tracker

Mc Graw Hill **Professional Development**

Targeted professional development has been articulated throughout **McGraw-Hill's** *Math Connects* program. The **McGraw-Hill Professional Development Video Library** provides short videos that support the **NCTM Focal Points and Focal Connections.** For more information, visit macmillanmh.com.

Model Lessons	Instructional Strategies

What the Research Says . . .

Fredda J. Friederwitzer and Barbara Berman (1999) explain conceptual features of clocks that make telling time challenging for young children:

> The complex instrument that we use to measure time is multifaceted. To use it appropriately requires simultaneous processing of many variables. One must observe the position of hands, know the direction in which each hand is currently moving, remember the distinction between the hands, understand that each number on the clock has two different meanings, relate the position of the hands to the meaning of the numbers, and finally, tell the time.

Reference:
Friederwitzer, F. and B. Berman. "The Language of Time." *Teaching Children Mathematics* 6:4 (1999) : 254.

Teacher Notes

Reading

 pair | **VISUAL/ SPATIAL**

Hickory Dickory Dock

- Read the poem "Hickory Dickory Dock".
- Paste the poem on the left side of your paper.
- Illustrate the poem on the right side of your paper.
- Be sure to show a clock set to 1 o'clock in your picture.

Teacher Note: Provide a picture of a grandfather clock in case students aren't familiar with it.

Materials:
- copies of the poem "Hickory Dickory Dock"
- 11" × 14" construction paper
- glue or paste
- crayons, markers, and decorating materials

Art

 individual | **VISUAL/ SPATIAL**

Make Two Clocks

- Decorate two clocks. Paste one clock on each side of your paper.
- Decorate two hour hands and two minute hands.
- Paste on hands to show a time on one side of the paper and another time on the other side of the paper.
- Write what time it is. Then draw pictures of what you might do at that time.

Materials:
- clock patterns
- large, cut-out minute and hour hands
- glue or paste
- decorating materials
- 11" × 14" construction paper

Health

 individual | **LOGICAL, INTERPERSONAL**

Morning, Afternoon, Evening

- Think of at least one healthy food you eat in the morning and draw it in the part labeled *morning.*
- Think of at least one healthy food you eat in the afternoon and draw it in the part labeled *afternoon.*
- Think of at least one healthy food you eat in the evening and draw it in the part labeled *evening.*

Teacher Note: Help students understand what types of foods are healthy (e.g., fruit, whole grains, vegetables).

Materials:
- 11" × 14" construction paper divided into three labeled sections: *morning, afternoon, evening*
- markers or crayons

Science

  pair | SOCIAL

Birds and Bats

- Read *Stellaluna*.
- Choose at least three things that Stellaluna did when she thought she was a bird.
- Draw them in the part labeled *before.*
- Choose at least three things that Stellaluna did after she found out she was a bat.
- Draw them in the part labeled *after.*

Materials:
- 11" × 14" paper folded in half and labeled *before* and *after*
- *Stellaluna* by Janell Cannon
- crayons or markers

Language Arts

 individual | LOGICAL

Time Journal

- Write *Time* on the front of your journal.
- Label the pages of your journal with the following times: 9 o'clock, half past 9, 10:00, 10:30, 11 o'clock, half past 11.
- Write what happens during your school day at each of those times.
- Draw a picture to go with your words.

Teacher Note: Adjust the times to meet your students' needs.

10:00 I read.

10:30 We Play Outside

Materials:
- 2 sheets of paper folded and stapled into a 6-page booklet
- pencils, crayons, or markers

Calendar Time

Days of the Week: Before and After

- Before beginning the activity, have students practice representing dates in standard form by writing today's date.
- Write the name of the current month on the calendar poster.
- Fill in the numbers for just the current week from Sunday to Saturday.
- Point to Monday. **Is Monday before or after Sunday?** Monday is after Sunday.
- On a separate chart or the chalkboard write, *Monday is after Sunday.*
- Underline the word *after.* Continue asking *before* and *after* questions for the other days of the week. Be sure to mention each day at least once.

Introduce the Chapter

 Real World: What Time Is It?

Share with students that they are going to learn about telling time. Explain that learning to tell time will help them keep track of events in their lives.

- Have students sit in a circle on the floor.
- Display the demonstration clock. Set the clock to the current time, rounded to the hour.
- **What time is it now?** See students' answer should reflect the current time.
- **What time did you get up this morning?** Sample answer: 6 o'clock
- **Was it before or after the time it is now?** before

Have students turn to p. 209.

- **What time do you leave for school?** Sample answer: 7 o'clock
- **What time do you leave for home?** Sample answer: 3 o'clock

Key Vocabulary

Introduce key vocabulary in the chapter using the routine below.

Define: An **hour** is a unit of time.
Example: I played tennis for an hour.
Ask: How many hours are in a school day?

CHAPTER 7 Measure Time

Key Vocabulary
hour
half hour
analog clock
digital clock

Explore
What time do you go to school? _____
Check students' answers.

Chapter 7   two hundred nine **209**

 FOLDABLES Study Organizer **Dinah Zike's Foldables**

Guide students to create their Shutter Foldables for measuring time.

1. Begin as if you were going to make a hamburger but instead of creasing the paper, pinch it to show the midpoint.

2. Fold the outer edges of the paper to meet at the pinch, or midpoint, forming a shutter fold.

3. Use the Shutter Foldable for data occurring in twos.

When to Use It *Lessons 7-1, 7-2, 7-3, and 7-6. (Additional instructions for using the Foldable with these lessons are found on pp. 221 and 235.)*

Math Online
Take the Chapter Readiness
Quiz at macmillanmh.com.

Are You Ready for Chapter 7?

1. Circle the activity that takes *less* time.

eating breakfast   sleeping all night

2. Circle the activity that takes *more* time.

opening a door   reading a book

3. Write the number that comes *next*.

   6, 7, 8, ___9___

4. I come just *after* 10.
   I am just *before* 12.
   What number am I? ___11___

This page checks skills needed for Chapter 7.

Diagnostic Assessment

Check for students' prerequisite skills before beginning the chapter.

- **Option 1:** *Are You Ready for Chapter 7?*
  SE Student Edition, p. 210

- **Option 2:** *Online Assessment*
  Math Online > macmillanmh.com

- **Option 3:** *Diagnostic Tests*
  CRM Chapter 7 Resource Masters, p. 42

RTI (Response to Intervention)

Apply the Results Based on the results of the diagnostic assessment on student p. 210, use the chart below to address individual needs before beginning the chapter.

TIER 3 Intensive Intervention

If	students miss three or four of the exercises:
Then	use Chapters 4 and 6 of *Math Triumphs*, an intensive math intervention program from McGraw-Hill

TIER 2 Strategic Intervention
below/approaching grade level

If	students miss two in: **Exercises 1–4**
Then	choose a resource:

Strategic Intervention Guide (p. 116)

Math Online

TIER 1 On-Level

If	students miss one in: **Exercises 1–4**
Then	choose a resource:

TE Learning Stations (pp. 209G–209H)
TE Chapter Project (p. 211)
CRM Game: *Tic-Tac-Toe Time*
Math Adventures
My Math Zone Chapter 6
Math Online > Fact Dash

Above/Beyond Level

If	students miss zero: **Exercises 1–4**
Then	choose a resource:

TE Learning Stations (pp. 209G–209H)
TE Chapter Project (pp. 211)
Math Adventures
My Math Zone Chapters 6 and 7
Math Online > Games

Before you begin Chapter 7:

- Read the Math at Home letter on p. 211 with the class and have each student sign it.
- Send home copies of the Math at Home letter with each student.
- Use the Spanish letter on p. 212 for students with Spanish-speaking parents or guardians.

Starting the Chapter
Have students list what they do from the time they get up until the time they leave for school.

Read-Aloud Anthology
For an optional reading activity to introduce this chapter's math concepts, see the Read-Aloud Anthology on p. TR31.

MATH at HOME

Dear Family,
Today my class started Chapter 7, **Measure Time**. In this chapter, I will learn to tell time to the half hour and relate time to events. Here is an activity we can do and a list of books we can read together.

Love, _____

Activity
Have your child make a time book. Draw a clock that shows bedtime. Then draw clocks to show when you eat breakfast, go to school, and so on.

Key Vocabulary
minute hand
hour hand
analog clock
hour
digital clock

Math Online Click on the eGlossary link at macmillanmh.com to find out more about these words. There are 13 languages.

Books to Read
It's Justin Time, Amber Brown by Paula Danziger Putnam Juvenile, 2001.

Telling Time by Jules Older Charlesbridge Publishing, Inc., 2000.

It's about Time! by Stuart J. Murphy HarperCollins Publishing Company, 2005.

two hundred eleven 211

Chapter 7 Project

Time of Day Collages

- Provide students with four large sheets of 18 x 11 inch sheets of construction paper.
- At the top of three separate sheets of paper, have students write the headings: Morning, Afternoon, and Evening.
- Ask students to draw a clock on each sheet of paper to show a time during that part of the day.
- Have students find and cut out pictures of things they do during the morning, afternoon, and evening from old magazines. Students may also draw pictures that illustrate those things.
- Have each student make a cover for the book and share their collages in small groups or in front of the whole class.

Refer to Chapter 7 Resource Masters, p. 50 for a rubric to assess students' progress on this project.

MATEMÁTICAS en CASA

Estimada familia:

Hoy mi clase comenzó el Capítulo 7, **Mida tiempo**. En este capítulo, aprenderé a decir las medias horas y a relacionar la hora con eventos. A continuación, hay una actividad que podemos hacer y una lista de libros que podemos leer juntos.

Cariños, _____

Actividad

Pídanle a su hijo(a) que haga un libro del tiempo. Dibujen un reloj que muestre la hora de acostarse. Luego, dibujen relojes para mostrar cuándo toman desayuno, cuándo va su hijo(a) a la escuela y así sucesivamente.

Vocabulario clave

manecilla del minutero
manecilla del horario

reloj analógico

hora — 3:00

reloj digital

Math Online Visiten el enlace eGlossary en macmillanmh.com para averiguar más sobre estas palabras, las cuales se muestran en 13 idiomas.

Libros recomendados

Medir el tiempo: vuela un papelote!
de John Burstein
Gareth Stevens Publishing, 2006.

¿Cómo se mide el tiempo?
de Robert E Wells
Editorial Juventud, 2003.

212 two hundred twelve

Chapter 7 Literature List

Lesson	Book Title
7-1	**Telling Time with Big Mama Cat** Dan Harper
7-2	**What Time Is It? A Book of Math Riddles** Sheila Keenan
7-3	**It's About Time!** Stuart J. Murphy
7-4	**Time To …** Bruce McMillan
7-5	**Time To …** Bruce McMillan
7-6	**Get Up and Go!** Stuart J. Murphy
Any	**It's Justin Time, Amber Brown** Paula Danziger
Any	**Telling Time** Jules Older

TELLING TIME
written by Jules Older
illustrated by Megan Halsey

PAULA DANZIGER It's Justin Time, Amber Brown
illustrated by Tony Ross

ELL National ESL Standards Alignment for Chapter 7

Lesson, Page	ESL Standard	Modality	Level
7-1, p 213B	Goal 1, Standard 3, b	Auditory, Kinesthetic	Intermediate
7-2, p 215B	Goal 1, Standard 2, a	Auditory, Visual	Beginning
7-3, p 217B	Goal 1, Standard 1, c	Auditory	Intermediate
7-4, p 219B	Goal 2, Standard 2, f	Logical, Auditory	Intermediate
7-5, p 223B	Goal 2, Standard 3, c	Auditory, Kinesthetic	Intermediate
7-6, p 227B	Goal 2, Standard 1, f	Auditory, Kinesthetic	Intermediate
7-7, p 231B	Goal 2, Standard 1, f	Visual/Spatial	Intermediate

The National ESL Standards can be found in the Teacher Reference Handbook.

Lesson Planner

Objective
Put events in order.

Vocabulary
afternoon, evening, morning

Resources
Literature Connection: *Telling Time with Big Mama Cat* by Dan Harper

Alternate Lesson: Use *IMPACT Mathematics:* Unit F to provide practice ordering events.

Teacher Technology
 TeacherWorks

Focus on Math Background

In this lesson, students will categorize and sequence events that happen during three intervals of the day—morning, afternoon, and evening. By dividing the day into three parts, students can develop familiar reference points for ordering and sequencing a series of events from first to last. Coupled with this knowledge of how the day is partitioned into units, students need to learn how to use temporal vocabulary, such as *before* and *after*, to describe and sequence when certain activities take place in relation to other events. A thorough understanding of how time adheres to a repetitive sequence of three distinct intervals within a day lays the foundation for future work with measuring the duration of daily events using our standard numerical system of units represented by minutes and hours.

Daily Routine

Use these suggestions before beginning the lesson on p. 213.

5-Minute Check
(Reviews Lesson 6-7)
1. Write the fact family using the numbers 6, 7, and 13. $6 + 7 = 13$, $7 + 6 = 13$, $13 - 6 = 7$, $13 - 7 = 6$
2. Write the fact family using the numbers 8, 4, and 12. $8 + 4 = 12$, $4 + 8 = 12$, $12 - 8 = 4$, $12 - 4 = 8$

Problem of the Day
Susan and Mark collected 16 empty bottles. Susan collected 8 of the bottles. How many bottles did Mark collect? 8 bottles

 LINE UP When students line up for recess, lunch, or dismissal, ask four students in one section of the line to each give one of the facts from the fact family for 3, 4, and 7. Repeat with different students for the fact families 5, 3, and 8 and 6, 3, and 9.

Building Math Vocabulary
- Write the following words on the board: **afternoon, evening, and morning**.
- **In the morning, which comes after: waking up or brushing your teeth?** brushing my teeth
- **In the afternoon, which comes before: leaving school or getting home?** leaving school
- **In the evening, which comes after: eating dinner or cooking dinner?** eating dinner

Differentiated Instruction

Small Group Options

Option 1
Gifted and Talented (AL)

SOCIAL, VISUAL/SPATIAL

Materials: crayons

- Have each student label a sheet of paper: *morning, afternoon,* and *evening.*
- Ask the group to plan a fun day for themselves. Students should discuss and choose at least one activity that they would all like to do together for each.
- Have students use pictures and words to illustrate each activity. Use words like *early* and *late* to describe.

Option 2
English Language Learners (ELL)

AUDITORY, KINESTHETIC

Core Vocabulary: crunch, squish, spread, first, then
Common Use Verbs: prepare

Talk Math This strategy introduces a sequence of events on time by chanting.

- Recite and act out the chant for students.

  First you take the peanuts, and you crunch 'em, you crunch 'em (repeat)
  Chorus: For your peanut, peanut butter, and jelly. (repeat)
  Then you take the grapes, and you squish 'em, you squish 'em (repeat)
  Chorus
  Then you take the bread, and you spread it, you spread it (repeat)
  Chorus
  Then you take your sandwich, and you eat it, you eat it 'Cause it's good, peanut butter, and jelly (repeat)

- Have students join in and chant together from the beginning. Help students remember the order by pointing to the verses on the board.
- Talk about what you did first, and what you did *after* that. Emphasize the sequence or order of the actions.

Independent Work Options

Option 1
Early Finishers (OL) (AL)

VISUAL/SPATIAL

Materials: stapler, markers or crayons

- Help students make a daily journal by stapling three pages together along the left edge.
- Have students label the pages *morning, afternoon,* and *evening.*
- Ask students to draw or write about an activity their mother, father, or another adult they know does during each time of day.

Option 2
Student Technology

Math Online 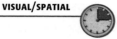 macmillanmh.com

Option 3
Learning Station: Health (p. 209G)

Direct students to the Health Learning Station for more opportunities to explore and extend the lesson concept.

Option 4
Problem-Solving Practice

Reinforce problem-solving skills and strategies with the Problem-Solving Practice worksheet.

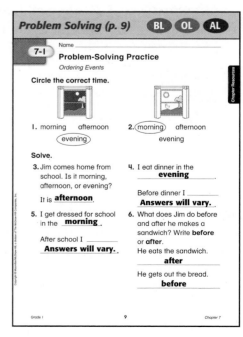

① Introduce

Activity Choice 1 • Hands-On

- Ask for volunteers to come to the front of the room and act out an activity associated with one of the times of day: **morning**, **afternoon**, or **evening**. For example, a student may act out brushing teeth or falling asleep.
- Have the class guess the activity and the time of the day. After they guess the activity, write it on the chalkboard.
- After students have guessed several activities, help them put the activities in order by asking before and after questions.

Activity Choice 2 • Literature

Introduce the lesson with *Telling Time with Big Mama Cat* by Dan Harper. For additional support see p. TR51.

② Teach

Explain that morning is the beginning of the day. It is when the sun comes up and the sky gets light. Noon is the middle of our day. We call the time before noon morning. We call the time after noon afternoon.

- **Does afternoon come before or after evening in one day?** before
- **Does evening come before or after morning in one day?** after

Get Ready Use the section at the top of p. 213 to reinforce the lesson concept. Guide the students as they associate time with events in their day.

Check Observe students as you work through Exercises 1–4 as a class.

 Exercise 4 Assess student comprehension before assigning practice exercises.

⚠ COMMON ERROR!

Many students have difficulty with the concept of naming time. Discuss the plans using time references. "The first thing this morning, we will read together. Later this morning we will do math."

Name _____

Ordering Events

Get Ready

Main Idea
I will put events in order.

Vocabulary
morning
afternoon
evening

Review Vocabulary
before
after

Morning, afternoon, and **evening** are times of the day.

morning	afternoon	evening

Carlo eats breakfast in the morning before school. Carlo brushes his teeth in the evening after dinner.

✓ Check

Draw what you do.

1. morning	2. afternoon	3. evening
Check students' drawing.	Check students' drawing.	Check students' drawing.

4. **Talk About It** What do you do in the morning *before* you leave for school? Sample answer: wake up, eat breakfast, brush teeth, get dressed

Chapter 7 Lesson 1   two hundred thirteen   213

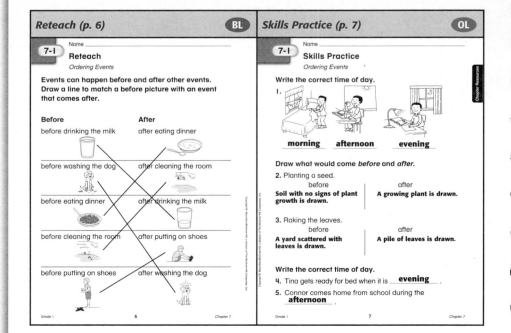

Reteach (p. 6) BL

7-1 Name _____ Reteach
Ordering Events

Events can happen before and after other events. Draw a line to match a before picture with an event that comes after.

Before	After
before drinking the milk	after eating dinner
before washing the dog	after cleaning the room
before eating dinner	after drinking the milk
before cleaning the room	after putting on shoes
before putting on shoes	after washing the dog

Grade 1   6   Chapter 7

Skills Practice (p. 7) OL

7-1 Name _____ Skills Practice
Ordering Events

Write the correct time of day.
1.

   morning   **afternoon**   **evening**

Draw what would come *before* and *after*.

2. Planting a seed.
before	after
Soil with no signs of plant growth is drawn.	A growing plant is drawn.

3. Raking the leaves.
before	after
A yard scattered with leaves is drawn.	A pile of leaves is drawn.

Write the correct time of day.
4. Tina gets ready for bed when it is **evening**

5. Connor comes home from school during the **afternoon**.

Grade 1   7   Chapter 7

Draw what you do.

5.

before lunch
Check students' drawing.

6.

after lunch
Check students' drawing.

7.

before school
Check students' drawing.

8.

after school
Check students' drawing.

Problem Solving

9. Reasoning Put these pictures in order.
Write 1, 2, and 3.

3	1	2

214   two hundred fourteen

Math at Home Activity: Ask your child to tell you about one event that happened at school. Then have your child tell you what happened before and after that event.

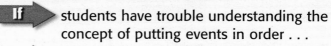

BL Alternate Teaching Strategy

If students have trouble understanding the concept of putting events in order . . .

Then use one of the following reteach options.

1 CRM **Daily Reteach Worksheet** (p. 6)

2 Draw a Timeline Help students draw a long arrow pointing to the right. Divide the arrow into three sections: morning, afternoon, evening. Label the left end of the arrow *before* and the right end *after*.

3 Practice

Differentiate practice using these leveled assignments for Exercises 5–9.

Level	Assignment
BL Below/ Approaching Level	Circle the words *before* and *after* in the exercises.
OL On Level	Complete the exercises independently.
AL Above/Beyond Level	Write a sentence about each picture they draw or photo on the page.

4 Assess

Formative Assessment

- **Describe the order of things you do before going to sleep at night.** Sample answer: Put on pajamas, read a story, brush teeth, get in bed, turn off light.

WRITING IN ►MATH Have students list three activities they do before school and three activities they do after school.

Quick Check **Are students continuing to struggle with ordering events?**

If Yes → Strategic Intervention Guide (p. 116)

If No → Independent Work Options (p. 213B)

CRM Skills Practice Worksheet (p. 7)

CRM Enrich Worksheet (p. 10)

Time to the Hour

Lesson Planner

Objective

Read and write time to the nearest hour.

Vocabulary

hour, **hour hand**, **minute hand**, **o'clock**

Resources

Materials: construction paper, markers

Manipulatives: student clocks, demonstration clock

Literature Connection: *What Time Is It? A Book of Math Riddles* by Sheila Keenan

Teacher Technology
⊙ TeacherWorks

Focus on Math Background

In this lesson, students will learn to tell time to the hour on an analog clock. Although first graders lack the proportional reasoning to make sense of how the hour hand moves one-twelfth the distance of the minute hand's progression, they can process simple facts about the clock, such as how the short hand always points to the hour, and how the long hand always indicates the minute. In addition to these basic rules, students need to remember that the hands on the clock always move in a clockwise motion—starting at 12, moving toward the right, and then revolving back around. Eventually, students will understand that when the minute hand has made one complete revolution around the clock, it has counted 60 minutes, which means that exactly one hour has passed.

Daily Routine

Use these suggestions before beginning the lesson on p. 215.

5-Minute Check

(Reviews Lesson 7-1)

1. Juan gets up and eats breakfast. Is it morning, afternoon, or evening? morning
2. Mary says, "Good night," to her family. Is it morning, afternoon, or evening? evening
3. Does Joe eat his sandwich before or after he makes it? after

Problem of the Day

Nico eats lunch at 12:00. He plays baseball at 4:00 in the afternoon. He goes to school at 8:00 in the morning. In what order to the events happen?
School, lunch, then baseball.

LINE UP When students line up for recess, lunch, or dismissal, ask: **Who got in line before you? Who got in line after you?**

Building Math Vocabulary

Draw a large analog clock on the chalkboard. Leave out the hour hand and the minute hand.

- Draw the **hour hand** at 3:00 in red chalk. Label the hour hand. Draw the **minute hand** at 12:00 in blue chalk. Label the minute hand.

- **The hour hand points to the hour and the minute hand points to the minutes.**

- Tell students that if the minute hand points to 12, they can say the hour and **"o'clock"** to tell the time.

- **If the time is six o'clock, where will the hour hand point?** to 6

Visual Vocabulary Cards

Use Visual Vocabulary Cards 21, 22, 27, and 31 to reinforce the vocabulary introduced in this lesson. (The Define/Example/Ask routine is printed on the back of each card.)

hour

Differentiated Instruction

Small Group Options

Option 1
Below Level (BL)

VISUAL/SPATIAL

Materials: clock

Give each group a clock.

- Have students take turns setting the hands on the clock to show a time to the hour. Remind students that the blue minute hand should stay pointing at the 12.

- Have students in the group write the times down using "o'clock."

- After each student has set the clock, have the group divide the times into two categories: before six o'clock and after six o'clock.

Option 2
English Language Learners (ELL)

AUDITORY/VISUAL

Materials: 12 paper plates numbered 1–12 in center
Core Vocabulary: between, across from, top of
Common Use Verbs: to stand

Do Math This strategy allows students to internalize the placement of an analog clock.

- Explain that students are going to make a human clock.

- Give a numbered plate to twelve students.

- Direct students to stand around the circle like a clock.

- Have one student stand in the center as the minute and hour hand.

- Allow students to switch places or remove numbers as a challenge for other students.

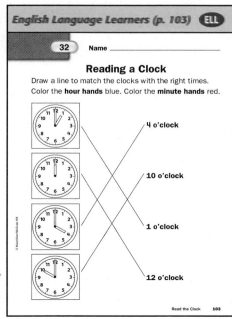

Use this worksheet to provide additional support for English Language Learners.

Independent Work Options

Option 1
Early Finishers (OL) (AL)

VISUAL/SPATIAL

Materials: clocks, blue number cubes

Give each student a clock and a blue number cube.

- Each student should start with both hands at 12.

- Have students take turns rolling the number cube and moving the minute hand that many big numbers around their clock.

- After the minute hand has made one revolution around the clock, students move the hour hand forward one number.

Option 2
Student Technology

Math Online ▷ macmillanmh.com

Math Adventures

Option 3
Learning Stations: Reading (p. 209G)

Direct students to the Reading Learning Station for more opportunities to explore and extend the lesson concept.

Option 4
Problem-Solving Practice

Reinforce problem-solving skills and strategies with the Problem-Solving Practice worksheet.

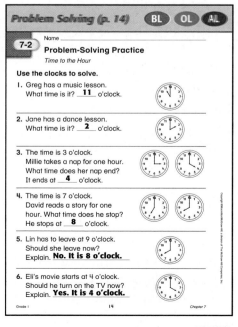

1 Introduce

Activity Choice 1 • Hands-On

- Discuss a few reasons people use clocks. Distribute the individual clocks.
- Explain that the little red hand marks the **hours**. Have students move the **hour hand** to each of the hours and say the hour name.
- Explain that the long blue hand marks the minutes. Have students set the **minute hand** on 12 and the hour hand on 1.
- Explain that when the hour hand is on 1 and the minute hand is on 12, we say one **o'clock**. **What time is it?** one o'clock

Activity Choice 2 • Literature

Introduce the lesson with *What Time Is It? A Book of Math Riddles* by Sheila Keenan. For additional support see p. TR51.

2 Teach

Pass out the student clocks.

- Have students show one o'clock.
- Show students that the hour hand is shorter than the minute hand.
- **Is four o'clock before or after seven o'clock?** before
- **If the time is nine o'clock, where does the minute hand point?** to 12
- **At what time are both hands pointing to the same number?** 12 o'clock

Get Ready Use the section at the top of p. 215 to reinforce the lesson concept. Guide students through the concepts of hour and o'clock.

Check Observe students as you work through Exercises 1–5 as a class.

 Exercise 5 Assess student comprehension before assigning practice exercises.

⚠ COMMON ERROR!

Some students may reverse the hands. Point out that *hour* is a shorter word than *minute*, so the shorter hand shows hours.

Name _____

Time to the Hour

Get Ready

Main Idea

I will read and write time to the hour.

Vocabulary
hour hand
hour
minute hand
o'clock

The hour hand is on 3. It is 3 o'clock

The clock has the numbers 1 to 12.
The **hour hand** is shorter.
It points to the **hour**.
The **minute hand** is longer.
It points to the minutes.

— minute hand

— hour hand

✓ Check

Use 🕐. Write the time.

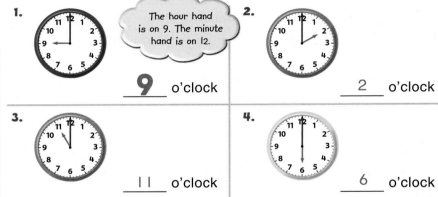

1.

The hour hand is on 9. The minute hand is on 12.

9 o'clock

2.

2 o'clock

3.

11 o'clock

4.

6 o'clock

5. **Talk About It** Where are the **hour hand** and the **minute hand** when it is 4 o'clock? on 4 and 12

Chapter 7   Lesson 2   two hundred fifteen   **215**

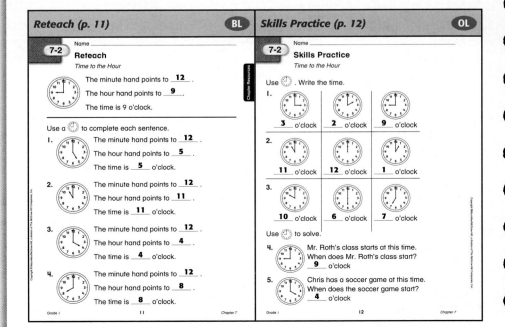

Reteach (p. 11) **BL**

7-2 Name ___ **Reteach**
Time to the Hour

The minute hand points to **12**.
The hour hand points to **9**.
The time is 9 o'clock.

Use a 🕐 to complete each sentence.

1. The minute hand points to **12**.
The hour hand points to **5**.
The time is **5** o'clock.

2. The minute hand points to **12**.
The hour hand points to **11**.
The time is **11** o'clock.

3. The minute hand points to **12**.
The hour hand points to **4**.
The time is **4** o'clock.

4. The minute hand points to **12**.
The hour hand points to **8**.
The time is **8** o'clock.

Grade 1   11   Chapter 7

Skills Practice (p. 12) **OL**

7-2 Name ___ **Skills Practice**
Time to the Hour

Use 🕐. Write the time.
1.
3 o'clock   **2** o'clock   **9** o'clock

2.
11 o'clock   **12** o'clock   **1** o'clock

3.
10 o'clock   **6** o'clock   **7** o'clock

Use 🕐 to solve.

4. Mr. Roth's class starts at this time. When does Mr. Roth's class start?
9 o'clock

5. Chris has a soccer game at this time. When does the soccer game start?
4 o'clock

Grade 1   12   Chapter 7

 **Practice**

Use 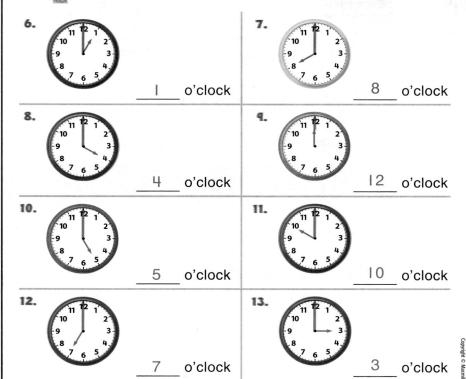. Write the time.

6. _____1_____ o'clock

7. _____8_____ o'clock

8. _____4_____ o'clock

9. _____12_____ o'clock

10. _____5_____ o'clock

11. _____10_____ o'clock

12. _____7_____ o'clock

13. _____3_____ o'clock

Problem Solving

Visual Thinking Draw the hands on the clock. Write the time. Use  to help.

14. Colin gets home at 3 o'clock.
Evan gets home 1 hour later.
What time does Evan get home? _____4_____ o'clock

216 two hundred sixteen

Math at Home Activity: Ask your child to say the times to the hour in order, beginning with 1 o'clock (1 o'clock, 2 o'clock, 3 o'clock, and so on).

Copyright © Macmillan/McGraw-Hill, a division of The McGraw-Hill Companies, Inc.

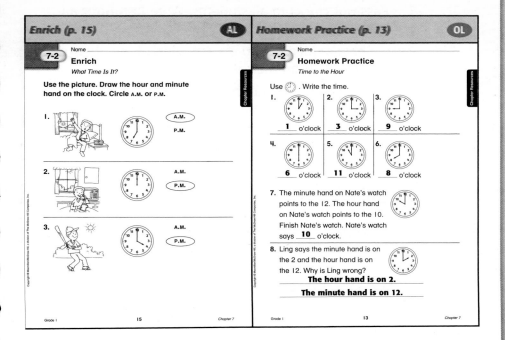

Alternate Teaching Strategy

If students have trouble understanding the concept of telling time to the hour . . .

Then use one of the following reteach options.

1 **Daily Reteach Worksheet** (p. 11)

2 **Clock Concentration** Make flash cards that show time in the "o'clock" format and another set of cards that show clocks telling time to the hour. Place all cards facedown. Have students find and match the times.

③ Practice

Differentiate practice using these leveled assignments for Exercises 6–14.

Level	Assignment
BL Below/ Approaching Level	Guide students through the exercises. Tell students to write in the answer blank the number the red hand points to.
OL On Level	Complete the exercises independently.
AL Above/Beyond Level	Have students put the answers in order from earliest (1 o'clock) to latest (12 o'clock).

④ Assess

Formative Assessment

• **Where is the minute hand when it is 2:00, 9:00, or 4:00?** The minute hand points to the 12.

WRITING IN ►MATH Have students draw a clock for the hour they have dinner and the hour they go to bed tonight.

Quick Check | **Are students continuing to struggle with telling time to the hour?**

If Yes → Small Group Options (p. 215B)

If No → Independent Work Options (p. 215B)
   Skills Practice Worksheet (p. 12)
   Enrich Worksheet (p. 15)

Lesson Planner

Objective
Recognize time to the nearest half hour.

Vocabulary
half hour, **half past**

Resources
Manipulatives: demonstration clock, student clocks, number cubes

Literature Connection: *It's About Time!* by Stuart J. Murphy

Teacher Technology
- TeacherWorks

Focus on Math Background

In this lesson, students will learn to tell time to the half hour on an analog clock. They will learn that half past means the same as telling time to the half hour. Since first graders are not required to tell time to the minute, they do not have to say, "two thirty" to describe the time when the clock shows half past two. To tell time to the half hour, students need to have a conceptual understanding of halves. Some activities in this lesson devote attention to helping students find the halfway point around the circumference of a clock.

Daily Routine

Use these suggestions before beginning the lesson on p. 217.

5-Minute Check

(Reviews Lesson 7-2)

Show each time on your clock.
1. 10 o'clock   See students' work.
2. 5:00   See students' work.
3. 12 o'clock   See students' work.

Problem of the Day

Marisa has 8 crayons. She loses 2. Daniel has 8 crayons. He gives away 4. Do both students have the same number of crayons left? Explain. No; 8 − 2 = 6, so Marisa has 6 crayons left. 8 − 4 = 4, so Daniel has 4 crayons left.

LINE UP When students line up for recess, lunch, or dismissal, have them tell you the time to the hour you show on the large demonstration analog clock.

Building Math Vocabulary

Pass out clocks to all students. Write **half hour** and **half past** on the board.

- Show students 7:30 on your clock. Have them show 7:30 on their clocks.
- Tell students when the minute hand is on the 6 a half hour has passed since the hour.
- Explain that when the clock shows the half hour, it is called half past. Model saying: "It is half past seven."

Visual Vocabulary Cards

Use Visual Vocabulary Card 20 to reinforce the vocabulary introduced in this lesson. (The Define/Example/Ask routine is printed on the back of each card.)

half hour

Differentiated Instruction

Small Group Options

Option 1 **Gifted/Talented** **AL** — VISUAL/SPATIAL, KINESTHETIC

Materials: index cards, red and blue crayons

- Have students work together to draw twelve clock faces on separate index cards. Each clock face should show a time at half past each hour starting with 1:30 and ending with 12:30. Make sure that students draw each hour hand pointing between the hour indicated and the following hour.

- Have students work together to write the "half past" times for each clock face on twelve separate index cards.

- Spread out all the cards facedown on a table.

- Students take turns flipping over two cards at a time. If a student matches a clock face and its corresponding time in words, he or she keeps both cards.

- Play continues until all matches have been made.

Option 2 **English Language Learners** **ELL** — AUDITORY

Materials: one kazoo per student
Core Vocabulary: shorter (chirp), longer (roar), a sound
Common Use Verbs: sounds like

Hear Math This strategy clarifies homonym sounds and allows students to internalize and label shorter and longer units of time.

- Introduce a kazoo, a toy instrument that makes a buzzing sound.

- Show students the mouthpiece and model making a sound.

- Demonstrate how to hum into the mouthpiece to make shorter and longer sounds.

- Model how to play *bird* songs (use visual) with shorter tones and longer *lion* (use visual) *roaring* sounds. Encourage students to play.

- Elicit other animal zoo sounds from students asking if this animal makes *shorter* or *longer* sounds, then playing them with the *ka-zoo*.

Independent Work Options

Option 1 **Early Finishers** **OL** **AL** — AUDITORY, SOCIAL

Materials: clocks
Pair students and provide each with a clock.

- Have one student set his or her clock to a time on the hour and say the time aloud. This student hides the clock face from his or her partner.

- Have the other student say the time that is a half hour later and set clock to the "half past" time.

- Have partners compare clocks and discuss the positions of the hands.

Option 2 **Student Technology**

Math Online ▶ macmillanmh.com

Math Adventures

Option 3 **Learning Station: Art** (p. 209G)

Direct students to the Art Learning Station for more opportunities to explore and extend the lesson concept.

Option 4 **Problem-Solving Practice**

Reinforce problem-solving skills and strategies with the Problem-Solving Practice worksheet.

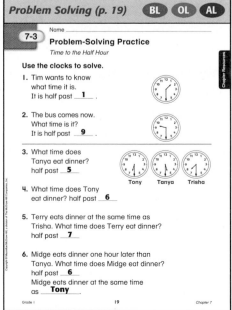

Problem Solving (p. 19) **BL** **OL** **AL**

Name _____
7-3 **Problem-Solving Practice**
Time to the Half Hour

Use the clocks to solve.

1. Tim wants to know what time it is. It is half past **1**.

2. The bus comes now. What time is it? It is half past **9**.

3. What time does Tanya eat dinner? half past **5**
   Tony   Tanya   Trisha

4. What time does Tony eat dinner? half past **6**

5. Terry eats dinner at the same time as Trisha. What time does Terry eat dinner? half past **7**

6. Midge eats dinner one hour later than Tanya. What time does Midge eat dinner? half past **6**
   Midge eats dinner at the same time as **Tony**.

Grade 1   19   Chapter 7

1 Introduce

Activity Choice 1 • Hands-On

- Give pairs of students two number cubes and a clock. One student rolls one or both cubes. The other, sets the clock to the time indicated by the cubes.

- After five rolls, the students switch jobs.

- As an option, the student rolling the cubes may say "**half past**" before rolling. The other student would then set the clock at half past the time indicated by the cubes.

Activity Choice 2 • Literature

Introduce the lesson with *It's About Time!* by Stuart J. Murphy. For additional support see p. TR51.

2 Teach

Display an analog clock that shows 10:00.

- **What time does this clock show?** ten o'clock

- **How do you know?** The hour hand is at 10. The minute hand is at 12.

- Move the minute hand around to 6. **What time does the clock show when the minute hand is at 6?** half past 10

- **Did the hour hand move as I moved the minute hand?** yes **Where is the hour hand now?** between 10 and 11

- Explain that as the minute hand moves, the hour hand moves towards the next hour.

Get Ready Use the section at the top of p. 217 to reinforce the lesson concept. Reinforce the concepts of hour and half past or **half hour**.

Check Observe students as you work through Exercises 1–5 as a class.

 Exercise 5 Assess student comprehension before assigning practice exercises.

! COMMON ERROR!

When drawing half-past times, some students will draw the hour hand pointing directly to the number of the hour. Use geared clocks to show students that the hour hand moves halfway to the next number as the minute hand moves halfway around the circle.

Name _____

Time to the Half Hour

Get Ready

Main Idea
I will recognize time to the half hour.

Vocabulary
half hour
half past

The clock shows time to the **half hour**.
The minute hand points to 6.
The hour hand is between 4 and 5.
It is 4:30 or **half past** 4.

✓ Check

Use . Write the time.

1. half past __9__

2. half past __1__

3. half past __6__

4. half past __3__

5. **Talk About It** It is half past 8. Explain what *half past* means. The hour hand is halfway between 8 and 9 or 8:30.

Chapter 7 Lesson 3 two hundred seventeen 217

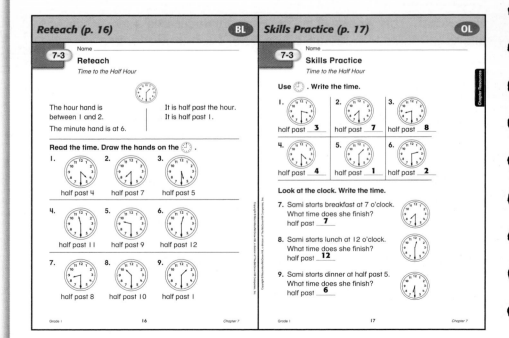

Reteach (p. 16) **BL**

7-3 Name _____
Reteach
Time to the Half Hour

The hour hand is between 1 and 2. The minute hand is at 6. | It is half past the hour. It is half past 1.

Read the time. Draw the hands on the ⏰.

1. half past 4
2. half past 7
3. half past 5
4. half past 11
5. half past 9
6. half past 12
7. half past 8
8. half past 10
9. half past 1

Grade 1   16   Chapter 7

Skills Practice (p. 17) **OL**

7-3 Name _____
Skills Practice
Time to the Half Hour

Use ⏰. Write the time.

1. half past __3__
2. half past __7__
3. half past __8__
4. half past __4__
5. half past __1__
6. half past __2__

Look at the clock. Write the time.

7. Sami starts breakfast at 7 o'clock. What time does she finish? half past __7__

8. Sami starts lunch at 12 o'clock. What time does she finish? half past __12__

9. Sami starts dinner at half past 5. What time does she finish? half past __6__

Grade 1   17   Chapter 7

Use . Write the time.

6.

half past ___10___

7.

half past ___2___

8.

half past ___5___

9.

half past ___11___

10.

half past ___4___

11.

half past ___7___

12. WRITING IN ►MATH What is one difference between the **minute hand** and **hour hand**?

Sample answer: The hour hand is shorter and tells the

hour. The minute hand is longer and tells the minute.

218 two hundred eighteen

Math at Home Activity: Give your child a time to the hour. Have him/her tell you where the clock hands would be for half-past that hour.

BL Alternate Teaching Strategy

If ► students have trouble reading time to the half hour . . .

Then ► use one of the following reteach options.

1 CRM Daily Reteach Worksheet (p. 16)

2 Be a Clock Have students model the time by using one arm as the hour hand and the other arm as a minute hand.

3 Practice

Differentiate practice using these leveled assignments for Exercises 6–12.

Level	Assignment
BL Below/ Approaching Level	Guide students through the exercises. Help them use their clocks correctly.
OL On Level	Complete the exercises independently.
AL Above/Beyond Level	Complete the exercises without the student clocks.

4 Assess

✓ **Formative Assessment**

Show your manipulative clock with the minute hand pointing to 6 and the hour hand pointing directly to 9.

• **What is wrong with this clock?** Sample answer: The hour hand should be pointing halfway between 9 and 10.

WRITING IN ►MATH Have students write about activities that can be finished in a half hour.

Quick Check **Are students continuing to struggle telling time to the half hour?**

If Yes → CRM Reteach Worksheet (p. 16)

If No → Independent Work Options (p. 217B)
　　　　　CRM Skills Practice Worksheet (p. 17)
　　　　　CRM Enrich Worksheet (p. 20)

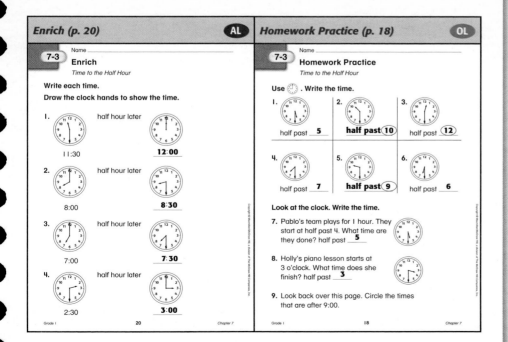

Problem-Solving Strategy
Make a Table

Lesson Planner

Objective

Use the *make a table* strategy to solve problems.

Resources

Manipulatives: student clocks

Literature Connection: *Time to . . .* by Bruce McMillan

Teacher Technology

 TeacherWorks

Real-World Problem Solving Library
Math and Social Studies: *Getting Around Then and Now*
Use these leveled books to reinforce and extend problem-solving skills and strategies.

📖 Leveled for:

- **OL** On Level
- **ELL** Sheltered English
- **SP** Spanish

For additional support, see the Real-World Problem Solving Teacher Guide.

Daily Routine

Use these suggestions before beginning the lesson on p. 219.

5-Minute Check

(Reviews Lesson 7-3)
What time is it when the hour hand is between 6 and 7 and the minute hand is on 6? 6:30

Problem of the Day

Six children are eating lunch. Four more children sit down at their table. How many children are at the lunch table? 10 children

LINE UP Have students hold up fingers to show which they do first in the morning: (1) get dressed, (2) eat breakfast, or (3) wash their face. Ask students holding up two fingers to stand and line up. Repeat with other questions about afternoon and evening activities until all students are in line.

Differentiated Instruction

Small Group Options

Option 1
Gifted and Talented (AL)

LOGICAL

Materials: paper, pencils

- Have each student survey classmates to find out their usual bedtime.
- After students collect the data, have them make a column-by-row table to show the bedtimes.
- Explain that the names of students surveyed should be listed down the left side of the table and bedtimes should be listed across the top of the table. Students should put X's in the table boxes to show each classmate's bedtime.

Option 2
English Language Learners (ELL)

LOGICAL, AUDITORY

Materials: two-column table labeled *short* and *long*, index cards, tape, paste or glue stick
Core Vocabulary: same, different, paste
Common Use Verbs: match

Hear Math This strategy uses background knowledge to demonstrate making a table.

- Define "same" and "different" by demonstrating examples with short and long animal sounds from lesson 7-3 (you make them, not with a kazoo).
- Ask students to draw a picture of their favorite animal or bird on an index card.
- Draw one yourself (have the other ready) and demonstrate to students the sound it makes. Identify the sound as short or long.
- Demonstrate how to stick your index card onto the table under the appropriate sound length.
- Help students match and paste their pictures under the right heading.
- Review each sound on the table.

Independent Work Options

Option 1
Early Finishers (OL) (AL)

SPATIAL

Materials: table with rows labeled *red, orange, yellow, purple*; connecting cubes

- Have each student take a handful of red, orange, yellow, and purple connecting cubes.
- Ask students to count the number of each color of connecting cubes they have.
- Challenge students to complete the table by drawing cubes to show how many of each color they have.

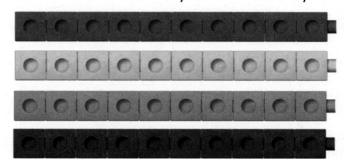

Option 2
Student Technology

Math Online macmillanmh.com

Option 3
Learning Station: Language Arts (p. 209H)

Direct students to the Language Arts Learning Station for more opportunities to explore and extend the lesson concept.

7-4

1 Introduce

Activity Choice 1 • Review

Draw a clock with the hour hand past 9.

- **What do we know?** It is past 9:00.
- **What time will it be when the minute hand is on 6?** Half past nine, or 9:30
- **How do we know?** The hour hand is past 9 and the minute hand is half past the hour.
- Help students use their clocks to model.

Activity Choice 2 • Literature

Introduce the lesson with Bruce McMillan's, *Time to . . . .* For additional support, see p. TR51.

2 Teach

Understand Using the questions, review what students know and what they need to find.

Plan Have them discuss their strategy.

Solve Before students use the table to answer the questions, ask:

- **What headings are on the table?** Bus Number and Time Bus is Leaving
- **Where do you look to find information about the headings?** Look across the rows or down the columns.

Check Ask students where they found the times the buses were leaving. Are their answers reasonable?

- **Which column tells the times the buses leave?** the second column

! COMMON ERROR!

Students may not stay in the same column or row as they try to track information. Show them how to use two index cards or other straightedge guides to pinpoint the information related to a certain row heading and column heading.

Name _____

Problem-Solving Strategy
Make a Table

Main Idea
I will make a table to solve a problem.

The buses leave in order every half hour. Bus 1 leaves at 9:30.
What time do buses 2, 3, 4, and 5 leave?

Bus Number	Time Bus is Leaving
1	9:30
2	10:00
3	10:30
4	11:00
5	11:30

Understand

What do I know?
Underline what you know.
What do I need to find?
Circle the question.

Plan

How will I solve the problem?

Solve

Make a table.

See table above.

Check

Look back.
Is my answer reasonable?

Check students' explanations.

Reteach (pp. 21–22) **BL**

Name _____

7-4 Reteach (1)
Problem-Solving Strategy: Make a Table

Art Center Fall Class Schedule		
Class	Time Class Begins	Time Class Ends
Photography	9:30	11:30
Drawing	10:30	12:00
Jewelry Making	11:00	12:30

What time does drawing class begin?

Step 1 Understand	What do I know? When the classes begin. When the classes end. What do I need to find out? The time **drawing** class begins.
Step 2 Plan	How will I find when the drawing class begins? I will make a **table**. The **table** shows the information I need.
Step 3 Solve	Use the table. Look at the table. What time does drawing class begin? **10:30**
Step 4 Check	Look back. Does my answer tell what time drawing class begins? **yes**

Grade 1   21   Chapter 7

Skills Practice (p. 23) **OL**

Name _____

7-4 Skills Practice
Problem-Solving Strategy: Make a Table

Use the table to answer the questions.
Circle or write your answer.

Ms. Kahl's Class Schedule		
Subject	Time Subject Begins	Time Subject Ends
Reading	9:00	10:00
Writing	10:00	11:00
Art/Music	11:00	12:00
Lunch	12:00	12:30
Recess	12:30	1:00
Math	1:00	2:00
Science	2:00	2:30
Social Sciences	2:30	3:30

1. Sean has to visit the dentist. He will leave at the same time that science begins. What time will Sean leave school?
   9:00   10:00   (2:00)   2:30

2. Lucy's favorite subject begins at 10:00. What is Lucy's favorite subject?
   Math   (Writing)   Art/Music   Social Studies

3. What is the first subject taught after recess?
   Math

4. **Reading** ends at 10:00.

Grade 1   23   Chapter 7

Try It

Remember
Understand
Plan
Solve
Check

Make a table and solve.

1. In the morning Ms. Kim's students change activities every hour. Reading starts at 8:30. Fill in the chart to show what time each activity starts.

Morning Schedule	
Activity	**Time**
Reading	8:30
Music	9:30
Learning Stations	10:30

2. Students work in learning stations for 1 hour. Then they go to recess. What time do students go to recess? __11:30__

Your Turn

Make a table to solve.

Afternoon Schedule	
Activity	**Time**
Math	1:00
Art	1:30
Writing	2:00
Science	2:30

3. In the afternoon the students in Ms. Kim's class change activities every half hour. Math starts at 1:00. Fill in the chart to show what time each activity starts.

4. What activity happens after writing? __science__

5. What activity do the students do just before art? __math__

220 two hundred twenty

Copyright © Macmillan/McGraw-Hill, a division of The McGraw-Hill Companies, Inc.

Try It Observe students as you work through Exercises 1–2 as a class.

BL Alternate Teaching Strategy

If students have trouble using a table in Exercises 1–2 . . .

Then use one of these reteach options . . .

1 CRM **Daily Reteach Worksheet** (pp. 21–22)

2 **Tables in the Real-World** Give each student a list of current children's movies and the times they are playing at the theater. Ask students to show the movie times in a table. Have students ask each other questions regarding their tables. For example: *What movie can you see at 6:00?*

3 Practice

Your Turn

Exercises 3–5 Be sure students can read and understand the problems. Model again how to read and understand the table in order to obtain the necessary information.

4 Assess

Formative Assessment

Have students use the table on page 220 to find and write the answers to the following questions:

- **What time is Writing?** 2:00
- **Is Art before or after Math?** after
- **Where did you look to find your answers?** the second column

---

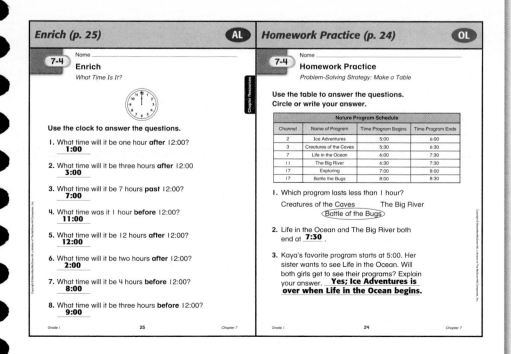

Quick Check — **Are students continuing to struggle with reading a table?**

If Yes → CRM Reteach Worksheet (pp. 21–22)

If No → Independent Work Options (p. 219B)

CRM Skills Practice Worksheet (p. 23)

CRM Enrich Worksheet (p. 25)

Lessons 7-1 to 7-4

✓ **Formative Assessment**

Use the Mid-Chapter Check to assess student's progress in the first half of the chapter.

ExamView® Assessment Suite Customize and create multiple versions of your Mid-Chapter Check and the test answer keys.

FOLDABLES® Dinah Zike's Foldables

Use these lesson suggestions to incorporate the Foldable during the chapter.

Lesson 7-1 Divide the back of the shutter Foldable into three sections and label them morning, afternoon, and evening. Record events that occur during these times.

Lesson 7-2 Use a sheet of poster board to make a large shutter Foldable. Make and place a minute and hour hand on the clock using a brad. Move the hands to make the clock show the hours. On the left inside tab of the shutter Foldable write the hours using "o'clock."

Lesson 7-3 Use the hour and minute hands to form half hours. Write the half hours on the inside right tab using the terms "half past." Close the door of the shutter Foldable. Open the right door to show a half hour and open the left door to show the second half hour. Note that two half hours make an hour.

Name _____

1. Draw what you do.

before recess
Check students' answers.

Write the time.

2.	**3.**	**4.**
___3___ o'clock	___10___ o'clock	___9___ o'clock
5.	**6.**	**7.**
half past ___7___	half past ___3___	half past ___4___

8. Solve the riddle.
Draw the hands on the clock.
My minute hand is on 6. My hour hand is halfway between 1 and 2.

What time am I? __1:30__

Chapter 7   two hundred twenty-one **221**

Data-Driven Decision-Making

Based on the results of the Mid-Chapter Check, use the following resources to review concepts that continue to give students problems.

Exercises	State/Local Standards	What's the Math?	Error Analysis	Resources for Review
1 Lesson 7-1		Order events.	Does not number each set of houses.	**Strategic Intervention Guide** (p. 116) **CRM** Chapter 7 Resource Masters (Reteach Worksheets) **Math Online** Concepts in Motion 🌐 Math Adventures
2–4 Lessons 7-2		Tell time to the nearest hour.	Does not know how to write time. Confuses hands of clock. Does not write time.	
5–8 Lessons 7-3		Tell time to the nearest half hour.	Confuses hands of clock. Does not know how to write time. Does not write time. Does not understand "halfway."	

Spiral Review   Chapters 1–7

Count. Write the number. Write the name of the number.

9.

_____

___2___   ___two___

10.

_____

___9___   ___nine___

11.

_____

___3___   ___three___

Subtract.

12. 6 − 3 = ___3___   **13.** 8 − 2 = ___6___

14. 2 − 1 = ___1___   **15.** 4 − 2 = ___2___

Add.

16. 1 + 4 = ___5___   **17.** 2 + 7 = ___9___

18. 9 + 3 = ___12___   **19.** 3 + 6 = ___9___

20. Ava has 11 grapes.
She eats 3 grapes.
How many grapes are left? ___8___ grapes.
Write the number sentence.

___11___ ⊖ ___3___ ⊜ ___8___

Formative Assessment

Spiral Review

Reviews Chapters 1 to 7

Objective: Review and assess mastery of skills and concepts from previous chapters.

Resources for Review

Based on student results, refer to these lessons for remediation.

- **Exercises 9–11: Lesson 1-4** (p. 23)
- **Exercises 12–15: Lesson 6-1** (p. 185)
- **Exercises 16–19: Lesson 2-8** (p. 69)
- **Exercise 20: Lesson 3-3** (p. 91)

Telling Time to the Hour and Half Hour

Lesson Planner

Objective

Tell time to the hour and half hour on digital and analog clocks.

Vocabulary

analog, digital

Resources

Materials: digital clock

Manipulatives: student clocks, demonstration clock

Literature Connection: *Time to . . .* by Bruce McMillan

Alternate Lesson: Use *IMPACT Mathematics:* Unit F to provide practice telling time to the hour and half hour.

Teacher Technology

⊙ TeacherWorks • Concepts in Motion

Focus on Math Background

To accurately tell time to the half hour on an analog clock, a first grader has to understand how both hands have moved half the distance from where they were at the top of the hour. The student can easily become confused when the position of the hands on the half hour does not correspond to the way the time is said. For example, when the student hears "half past 9," the hour hand is between 9 and 10, instead of directly at 9; the minute hand is at 6. Unlike the analog clock, the digital clock displays time more explicitly. In Lesson 5, students will learn to read a digital clock and tell time to the hour and half hour on both an analog and a digital clock.

Daily Routine

Use these suggestions before beginning the lesson on p. 223.

5-Minute Check

(Reviews Lesson 7-4)
Make a table that shows what time you eat breakfast, lunch, and dinner. Use your clock to show the times. See students' work.

Problem of the Day

Kim is going on a trip. She packs 3 pieces of cheese, and 4 crackers. How many pieces of food is Kim taking with her? 7 pieces of food

LINE UP When students line up for recess, lunch, or dismissal, write several digital times to the hour or half hour on the chalkboard. Go through the line, having students each read times in order.

Building Math Vocabulary

- Draw an **analog** clock showing 4:30 on the chalkboard.
- **What time does this clock show?** half past 4
- **How do you tell time on this clock?** with the hour hand and the minute hand
- Draw a **digital** clock showing 4:30 on the chalkboard. Draw and label arrows pointing to the hours and the minutes.
- Ask students to help you list ways the two clocks are alike and different.

Visual Vocabulary Cards

Use Visual Vocabulary Cards 3 and 14 to reinforce the vocabulary introduced in this lesson. (The Define/Example/Ask routine is printed on the back of each card.)

Differentiated Instruction

Small Group Options

LINGUISTIC, SOCIAL

Option 1
Below/Approaching Level BL

Materials: student clocks, white boards

Divide students into groups of three. Help students draw an outline of a digital clock with four blanks and a colon on the white board.

- Have one student say a time using *o'clock* or *half past.*
- One of the other students writes the time in digital format on the white board. The third student sets the time on the analog clock.
- Students compare clocks and check answers.
- Have students erase the time on the white board, switch roles, and repeat.

AUDITORY, KINESTHETIC

Option 2
English Language Learners ELL

Materials: clock, ruler
Core Vocabulary: minute/hour hand, in, out
Common Use Verb: put

Talk Math This strategy uses background knowledge of students' body parts to connect with clock vocabulary.

- Explain that in math, *hand* is a pointer on a clock. It is also a body part.
- Have students stand in a circle.
- Give students a ruler to hold as their minute hand.
- Model a revised version of the Hokey Pokey song: ("You put your minute hand in . . . ")
- Substitute with *hour hand* in the next verse.
- Repeat as time permits.

Use this worksheet to provide additional support for English Language Learners.

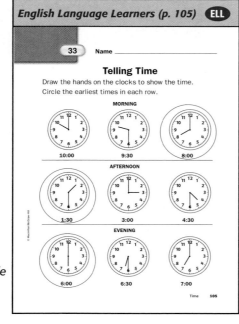

Independent Work Options

VISUAL/SPATIAL, LOGICAL

Option 1
Early Finishers OL AL

Materials: Six pairs of index cards with matching digital and analog times

- Have students place the cards facedown.
- Students take turns turning over two cards.
- If the times on the digital and analog clocks match, the student keeps them.

Option 2
Student Technology

Math Online macmillanmh.com

Option 3
Learning Station: Science (p. 209H)

Direct students to the Science Learning Station for more opportunities to explore and extend the lesson concept.

Option 4
Problem-Solving Practice

Reinforce problem-solving skills and strategies with the Problem-Solving Practice worksheet.

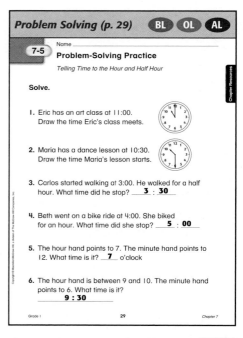

① Introduce

Activity Choice 1 • Hands-On

- Show students an analog clock and a number line with the numbers 1–12.
- **What is the same about the number line and the clock?** Sample answers: They both have the numbers 1–12; The numbers are in order from least to greatest.
- As a class, count from 1 to 12. Ask one volunteer to point to the numbers on the clock, starting at 1. Have another volunteer point to the numbers on the number line.
- Then give each student a copy of the number line. Have students cut slits between each number.
- Then have students bring together each end of the number line, so it is in the shape of a circle. Encourage the students to position the number line, so it looks like a clock with the 12 on the top and the 6 on the bottom.

Activity Choice 2 • Literature

Introduce the lesson with *Time To . . .* by Bruce McMillan. For additional support, see p. TR52.

⚠ COMMON ERROR!

Students may think that :06 minutes is half-past on a digital clock because that is what the minute hand points to on an analog clock. Explain that the numbers on an analog clock are hours only and that there are 60 minutes in one hour, so 30 minutes is half an hour.

Name _____

Telling Time to the Hour and Half Hour

These are two kinds of clocks.

This is an analog clock.

This is a digital clock.

Main Idea
I will tell time to the hour and the half hour.

Vocabulary
analog
digital

1 hour is 60 minutes long.

1 half hour is 30 minutes long.

start here

start here

the hour | 5:00 | the minutes

the hour | 5:30 | the minutes

It is five o'clock or 5:00.

It is five thirty or 5:30. We could also say it is half past 5 or 30 minutes after 5.

Chapter 7 Lesson 5   two hundred twenty-three **223**

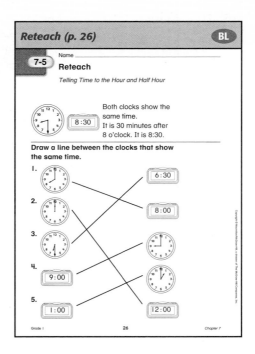

Reteach (p. 26) — BL

7-5 Reteach

Telling Time to the Hour and Half Hour

Both clocks show the same time. It is 30 minutes after 8 o'clock. It is 8:30.

Draw a line between the clocks that show the same time.

1.   6:30
2.   8:00
3.
4. 9:00
5. 1:00   12:00

Grade 1   26   Chapter 7

 Check

7. Sample answer: The analog clock shows the time using hands, the digital uses numbers.

Draw the missing clock hands to show each time.
Use  to help. Then write the time.

1. half past 9

9:30

2. 3 o'clock

3:00

3. 8:00

8:00

4. 5:30

5:30

5. 30 minutes after 11

11:30

6. 1:00

1:00

Copyright © Macmillan/McGraw-Hill, a division of The McGraw-Hill Companies, Inc.

7. **Talk About It** How are an analog clock and a digital clock different?

GO on

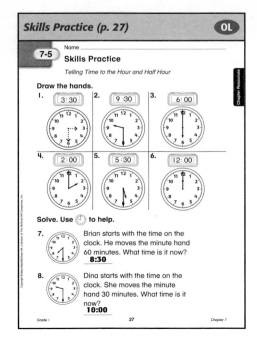

Skills Practice (p. 27) — OL

7-5 **Skills Practice**
Name _____

Telling Time to the Hour and Half Hour

Draw the hands.
1. 3:30
2. 9:30
3. 6:00
4. 2:00
5. 5:30
6. 12:00

Solve. Use 🕐 to help.
7. Brian starts with the time on the clock. He moves the minute hand 60 minutes. What time is it now? **8:30**
8. Dina starts with the time on the clock. She moves the minute hand 30 minutes. What time is it now? **10:00**

Grade 1   27   Chapter 7

---

2 Teach

Display an **analog** clock and a **digital** clock side by side, set to 11:00.

- **What time does the analog clock show?** 11 o'clock
- Point to the hour on the digital clock. **How many hours?** 11 hours
- Point to the minutes. **How many minutes?** 0 minutes
- Tell students that eleven hours and zero minutes is eleven o'clock, so these clocks show the same time.
- **How many minutes are in an hour?** 60 minutes
- **How many minutes are in half an hour?** 30 minutes
- **If the digital clock was at half past 11, how many hours and minutes would it show?** 11 hours and 30 minutes

Get Ready Use the section at the top of p. 223 to reinforce the lesson concept. Reinforce the concept that analog and digital clocks show time in different ways, but both ways mean the same.

Check Observe students as you work through Exercises 1–7 as a class.

Exercise 7 Assess student comprehension before assigning practice exercises.

BL Alternate Teaching Strategy

If students have trouble telling time to the hour and half hour on digital and analog clocks . . .

Then use one of the following reteach options.

1 **CRM** **Daily Reteach Worksheet** (p. 26)

2 **Break It Down** Have students read hours and minutes from an analog clock separately as a number of hours *and* a number of minutes. Then translate that to a digital time.

Lesson 7-5 Telling Time to the Hour and Half Hour **224**

③ Practice

Differentiate practice using these leveled assignments for Exercises 8–21.

Level	Assignment
BL Below/Approaching Level	Guide students through the exercises. Help them interpret *o'clock* as no minutes and *half* past as 30 minutes
OL On Level	Complete independently.
AL Above/Beyond Level	Complete exercises without student clocks.

Name _____

> **Practice**

Draw the missing clock hands to show each time.
Use 🕐 to help. Then write the time.

8. half past 3

3 : 30

9. 11:00

11:00

10. 2 o'clock

2 : 00

11. 30 minutes after 7

7 : 30

12. 5 o'clock

5 : 00

13. thirty minutes after 1

1 : 30

Write the time.

14. half past 6

6 : 30

15. 4 o'clock

4 : 00

16. half past 10

10 : 30

Chapter 7   Lesson 5

two hundred twenty-five   225

Copyright © Macmillan/McGraw-Hill, a division of The McGraw-Hill Companies, Inc.

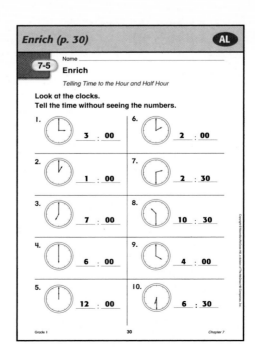

Enrich (p. 30) — **AL**

7-5 **Enrich**

Telling Time to the Hour and Half Hour

Look at the clocks.
Tell the time without seeing the numbers.

1. 3 : 00
2. 1 : 00
3. 7 : 00
4. 6 : 00
5. 12 : 00
6. 2 : 00
7. 2 : 30
8. 10 : 30
9. 4 : 00
10. 6 : 30

Grade 1   30   Chapter 7

Draw the missing hands to show each time.
Use  to help. Then write the time.

17. 4 o'clock

4:00

18. 6:30

6:30

19. 12 o'clock

12:00

H.O.T. Problems

Thinking Math

20. The hour hand is between 8 and 9.
The minute hand is on 6.

What time is it? __8__ : __30__
Draw the hands on the clock.

21. The hour hand is on 9.
The minute hand is on 12.

What time is it? __9__ : __00__
Draw the hands on the clock.

 Math at Home Activity: Practice telling time on analog and digital clocks with your child by drawing a time on one and then draw the same time on the other.

Copyright © Macmillan/McGraw-Hill, a division of The McGraw-Hill Companies, Inc.

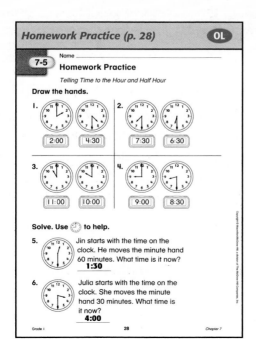

---

④ Assess

✏️ Formative Assessment

- **When the analog clock shows 6 o'clock, what does the digital clock look like?** 6:00
- **When the analog clock show half past six, what does the digital clock look like?** 6:30

WRITING IN ▶ MATH Have students show the time they go to bed and the time they get up in analog and digital formats.

Have students complete the appropriate sections of their Foldables using information from the lesson.

Quick Check | **Are students continuing to struggle with telling time on digital and analog clocks?**

If Yes → Small Group Options (p. 223B)
If No → Independent Work Options (p. 223B)
    CRM Skills Practice Worksheet (p. 27)
    CRM Enrich Worksheet (p. 30)

Lesson Planner _____

Objective
Relate time and events.

Review Vocabulary
analog, half past

Resources
Manipulatives: demonstration clock, student clocks

Literature Connection: *Get Up and Go!* by Stuart J. Murphy

Alternate Lesson: Use *IMPACT Mathematics:* Unit F to provide practice relating time to events.

Teacher Technology
🌐 TeacherWorks • Concepts in Motion

Focus on Math Background

When comparing the lengths of two objects, students can determine which one is longer by visualizing the distance between the end points on both objects. Unlike length, however, time is not as easily identifiable because students cannot see its duration. Before first graders can appreciate the importance of measuring the passage of time with a standard system of units such as minutes and hours, they must have experiences comparing two events using a nonstandard unit, such as a minute sand timer. In this lesson, students will compare the duration of activities and determine which events take a longer or a shorter amount of time.

Daily Routine _____

Use these suggestions before beginning the lesson on p. 227.

5-Minute Check 🔊
(Reviews Lesson 7-5)
What time is it?

1. half past 7

2. 9:00 9 o'clock

Problem of the Day 📖
Jeff and Stephanie have 8 strawberries to share. Stephanie eats 4 strawberries. Jeff eats 2 fewer strawberries than Stephanie. How many strawberries does Jeff eat? How many strawberries are left? Jeff eats 2 strawberries; 2 strawberries are left.

LINE UP Have students leave their desks in four groups to line up. Ask students to order the groups by length of time it took to get into line, using the words *shortest, shorter, longer*, and *longest*.

Review Math Vocabulary
Draw a large analog clock on the board. Leave out the hour hand and the minute hand.

- **What kind of clock is this?** an analog clock
- **If the time is half past 8, where does the minute hand point?** to 6 **Where does the hour hand point?** between 8 and 9
- Draw the hands on the clock.

Visual Vocabulary Cards
Use Visual Vocabulary Card 3 to reinforce the vocabulary reviewed in this lesson. (The Define/Example/Ask routine is printed on the back of each card.)

analog

Differentiated Instruction

Small Group Options

Option 1

Below Level **BL**

VISUAL/SPATIAL, SOCIAL

Materials: crayons, markers

- Ask students to draw pictures of the following: brushing their teeth, eating, doing their homework, playing outside, and opening a door.
- Have students estimate how long it takes in minutes to do each of the activities. Remind students that one hour is 60 minutes.
- Next, have students compare their time estimates with other students. Have them decide if they estimated an appropriate amount of time for each activity and then order the activities from shortest to longest.

20 minutes
Michelle

5 minutes
Emelio

Option 2

English Language Learners **ELL**

AUDITORY, KINESTHETIC

Core Vocabulary: music/sing, lunch/eat, class/learn
Common Use Verb: replace

Talk Math This strategy helps students vocalize and remember their daily schedule by replacing lyrics with it.

- Ask, "What do we do first at school? Then what?"
- Model student responses using the "Peanut Butter and Jelly" chant (see lesson 7.1).
- For example:

  First we hear a story. Then I read it. I read it.
  Then we go to Music, and I sing it, I sing it.
  Then we go to lunch and I eat it, I eat it.

- Students do the chant, adding actions if appropriate.

Independent Work Options

Option 1

Early Finishers **OL** **AL**

KINESTHETIC

Materials: sand timer (about 1 minute timer), connecting cubes

- Instruct one partner to watch a sand timer while the other partner connects as many cubes as he or she can into one train before the timer runs out.
- Have students switch roles and repeat with a different set of cubes.
- When both partners finish, have them count and compare the results of their experiment.

Option 2

Student Technology

Math Online ▷ macmillanmh.com

Option 3

Learning Station: Language Arts (p. 209H)

Direct students to the Language Arts Learning Station for more opportunities to explore and extend the lesson concept.

Option 4

Problem-Solving Practice

Reinforce problem-solving skills and strategies with the Problem-Solving Practice worksheet.

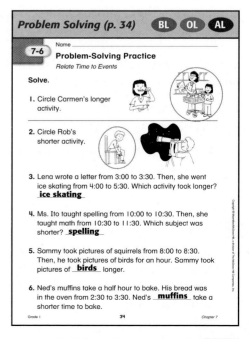

Problem Solving (p. 34) **BL** **OL** **AL**

Name

7-6

Problem-Solving Practice
Relate Time to Events

Solve.

1. Circle Carmen's longer activity.

2. Circle Rob's shorter activity.

3. Lena wrote a letter from 3:00 to 3:30. Then, she went ice skating from 4:00 to 5:30. Which activity took longer? **ice skating**

4. Ms. Ito taught spelling from 10:00 to 10:30. Then, she taught math from 10:30 to 11:30. Which subject was shorter? **spelling**

5. Sammy took pictures of squirrels from 8:00 to 8:30. Then, he took pictures of birds for an hour. Sammy took pictures of **birds** longer.

6. Ned's muffins take a half hour to bake. His bread was in the oven from 2:30 to 3:30. Ned's **muffins** take a shorter time to bake.

Grade 1   34   Chapter 7

7-6

1 Introduce

Activity Choice 1 • Hands-On

- Set two chairs in front of the group and ask two volunteers to sit in them. Explain that you will give each person instructions, and when you say "go," they will do what you said. The audience will decide which person took longer.

- Tell one student he or she will stand up quickly and then sit down quickly. Tell the other student he or she will stand up, turn around, jump three times, and sit down.

- Discuss the activities using time references such as *longer, shorter, more time, less time*.

Activity Choice 2 • Literature

Introduce the lesson with *Get Up and Go!* by Stuart J. Murphy. For additional support see p. TR52.

2 Teach

- Have available four student analog clocks.

- Display two clocks. Set the clock on the left at the time school starts and the one on the right at the time school ends. Label the display "Our School Day."

- Display two more clocks, showing the time school starts and the time students go to lunch. Label the display "Our School Morning."

- Explain what the clocks show.

- **Which takes longer?** our school day

- Invite a volunteer to show the passage of time on the clocks.

Get Ready Use the section at the top of p. 227 to reinforce the lesson concept.

Check Observe students as you work through Exercises 1–2 as a class.

 Exercise 2 Assess student comprehension before assigning practice exercises.

 COMMON ERROR!

Students may focus only on the minute hand. Remind them that if the hour hand points between two numbers, the lesser number names the hour.

Name _____

Relate Time to Events

Get Ready

Main Idea
I will relate time to events.

Events take different amounts of time.

5:30 to 6:30   6:30 to 7:00

Which takes longer? **dinner**

Check   2. Sample answer: tying a shoe—less; driving to vacation—more

Circle the activity that takes longer.

1.

4:00 to 4:30   4:30 to 5:30

2. **Talk About It** Name an activity that would take more than an hour. Name an activity that would take less than an hour.

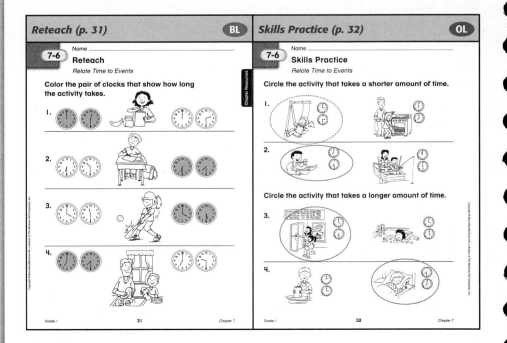

Reteach (p. 31) **BL**

7-6 Reteach
Relate Time to Events

Color the pair of clocks that show how long the activity takes.

Skills Practice (p. 32) **OL**

7-6 Skills Practice
Relate Time to Events

Circle the activity that takes a shorter amount of time.

Circle the activity that takes a longer amount of time.

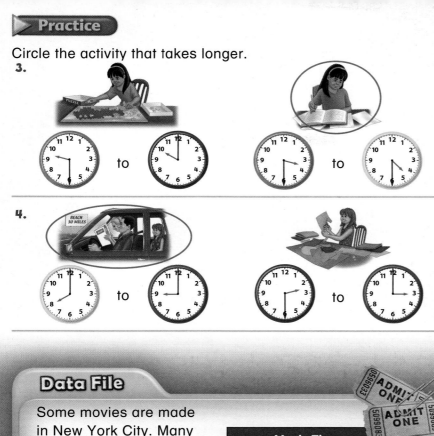

> **Practice**

Circle the activity that takes longer.

3.

to   to

4.

to   to

Data File

Some movies are made in New York City. Many people work together to make movies.

5. Ray and Tori want to see Wolf Cub. Circle the clock that shows what time this movie starts.

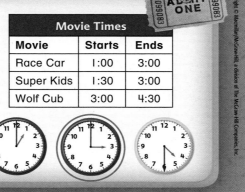

Movie Times		
Movie	**Starts**	**Ends**
Race Car	1:00	3:00
Super Kids	1:30	3:00
Wolf Cub	3:00	4:30

228 two hundred twenty-eight

Math at Home Activity: Give your child two things to do. Talk about what is likely to take more time and less time.

Enrich (p. 35)   **AL**

7-6 Name _____

Enrich

How Long?

Use one of the words below to complete each sentence.

| minutes | hours | days | weeks | months | years |

1. I sleep for about 8 **hours** each night.

2. It takes me about 20 **minutes** to eat lunch.

3. I am 6 **years** old.

4.
| Sunday | Monday | Tuesday | Wednesday |
| Thursday | Friday | Saturday | |

There are 7 **days** in one week.

5. We go to school for about 9 **months** each year.

Grade 1   35   Chapter 7

Homework Practice (p. 33)   **OL**

7-6 Name _____

Homework Practice

Relate Time to Events

Circle the activity that takes a shorter amount of time.

1.

2.

Solve.

3. Owen rode his bike from 10:00 to 10:30. Then, he cleaned his room from 10:30 to 11:30. Which activity was longer?
cleaning

4. Keiko played piano from 4:00 to 5:00. Then, she read from 5:00 to 5:30. Which activity was shorter? **reading**

Grade 1   33   Chapter 7

BL Alternate Teaching Strategy

If students have trouble relating time and events . . .

Then use one of the following reteach options.

1 **CRM** **Daily Reteach Worksheet** (p. 31)

2 **Convert to Digital** Have students write the digital time beneath each analog clock. This will help some students calculate the different lengths of time.

③ Practice

Differentiate practice using these leveled suggestions for Exercises 3–5.

Level	Assignment
BL Below/ Approaching Level	Have students use clocks and move in 30-minute increments from the start time to the end time.
OL On Level	Complete the exercises independently.
AL Above/Beyond Level	Have students write the duration of each event in hours and minutes.

④ Assess

✓ Formative Assessment

- **What can you use to measure how long something takes?** Sample answers: a clock, a timer, a stopwatch

- **What words do you use to tell how long something takes?** Sample answers: minutes, hours, seconds

WRITING IN ►MATH Ask students to write about something that takes a very long time and explain why it takes so long.

Quick Check **Are students continuing to struggle with relating time and events?**

If Yes → Small Group Options (p. 227B)

If No → Independent Work Options (p. 227B)
CRM Skills Practice Worksheet (p. 32)
CRM Enrich Worksheet (p. 35)

Extra Practice

Reviews Lessons 7-1 to 7-6

Objective: Review and assess mastery of previous lessons' skills and concepts.

- Review with students that *comes first* means that one action happened at a time before the other action.

- Students may wish to make a timeline. Draw a horizontal line with an arrow pointing to the right on the chalkboard. Write *earlier, before,* and *first* towards the left end and *later, after,* and *second* toward the right end.

Practice with Technology

Math Online Have students visit macmillanmh.com for additional practice with online activities, games, and quizzes.

Name _____

Circle which comes first.

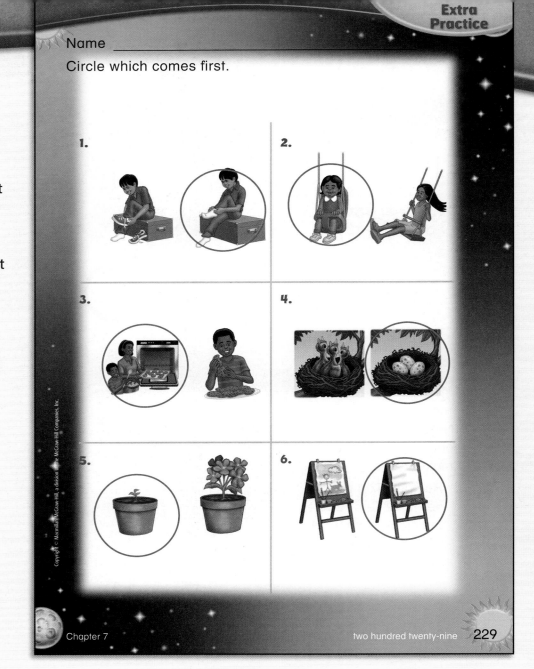

1.
2.
3.
4.
5.
6.

Chapter 7
two hundred twenty-nine 229

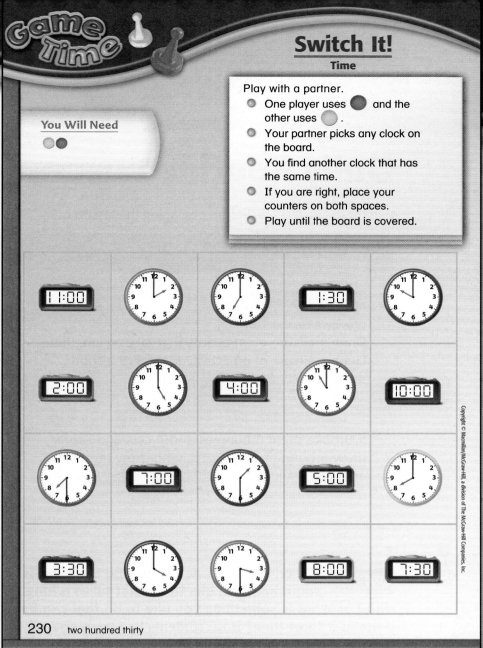

Switch It!

Time

Play with a partner.
- One player uses ⬤ and the other uses ◯ .
- Your partner picks any clock on the board.
- You find another clock that has the same time.
- If you are right, place your counters on both spaces.
- Play until the board is covered.

You Will Need
◯⬤

11:00 1:30 2:00 4:00 10:00 7:00 5:00 3:30 8:00 7:30

Copyright © Macmillan/McGraw-Hill, a division of The McGraw-Hill Companies, Inc.

230 two hundred thirty

Switch It!

Math Concept:
Tell Time on Digital and Analog Clocks

Manipulatives: two-colored counters

Introduce the game on page 230 to your students to play as a class, in small groups, or at a learning workstation to review concepts introduced in this chapter.

Instructions

- Assign each student a color.
- Students play in pairs.
- The first player picks any clock on the game board.
- The second player finds a clock with the same time.
- If the second player is correct, he or she places counters on both clocks.
- Students take turns and play until the board is covered. The winner is the player who has more counters on the board.

Extend the Game

Have students create their own game board using matching analog and digital clocks.

Differentiated Practice

Use the leveling suggestions to differentiate the game for all learners.

Level	Assignment
BL Below/Approaching Level	Allow students to match only the clocks with times to the hour or half hour. Cover the other clocks before play starts.
OL On Level	Have students play the game with the rules as written.
AL Above/Beyond Level	Give students a time limit to complete the game. If time runs out before the board is covered, neither player wins!

Lesson Planner

Objective

Choose the best strategy to solve a problem.

Resources

Materials: paper, clock stamp

Manipulatives: student clocks

Teacher Technology

💿 TeacherWorks

Real-World Problem Solving Library
Math and Social Studies: *Getting Around Then and Now*
Use these leveled books to reinforce and extend problem-solving skills and strategies.

📖 Leveled for:

- **OL** On Level
- **ELL** Sheltered English
- **SP** Spanish

For additional support, see the Real-World Problem Solving Teacher Guide.

Daily Routine

Use these suggestions before beginning the lesson on p. 231.

5-Minute Check

(Reviews Lesson 7-6)
Draw a picture of an activity that takes a long time. Draw a picture of an activity that takes a short time. See students' work.

Problem of the Day

If Brooke drew 6 bunnies and 4 cats and Laura drew 5 bunnies and 7 cats, who drew the most animals? Laura; Brooke drew 6 + 4 = 10; Laura drew 5 + 7 = 12.

LINE UP Call on students one by one and ask **What is something you like to do that takes a long time?** or **What is something you like to do that can be done in a short time?** Have students line up as soon as they have had a turn to respond.

Differentiated Instruction

Small Group Options

Option 1 — Below Level (BL) LOGICAL

Materials: paper, pencils, large index cards each labeled with a different activity such as *wake up, go to bed,* or *eat lunch* (for each student)

- Give each student a set of labeled cards. Ask students to draw a picture to match the label on each card.
- Have students decide what time they usually do the activity on each card. Ask them to show that time by drawing an analog clock and a digital clock on each card.
- Invite students to compare their pictures and times to those of other students.

Option 2 — English Language Learners (ELL) VISUAL/SPATIAL

Materials: number cards to 12, model clock
Core Vocabulary: begin/end time, over time, lunch
Common Use Verb: pass time

Do Math This strategy allows students to internalize telling time and relating time to events.

- Have 12 students form a circle, using cards to show a clock.
- Using a model clock, demonstrate and write "12:00" (or whenever lunch starts).
- Have two new students act out noon in the center of the human clock.
- Write "2:30" (the end time of lunch or recess as appropriate).
- Model moving hands with the clock.
- Have students repeat, acting out the passage over time.
- Repeat with new students and time as time permits.
- Discuss the strategies each student uses to demonstrate the passage of time.

Independent Work Options

Option 1 — Early Finishers (OL) (AL) SPATIAL

Materials: index cards each with a different time (to the hour), paper, markers, clocks

- Have students choose a card and write that time at the top of a sheet of paper. Ask students to draw a clock and a picture of themselves doing an activity they might do at that time.
- Next, have students choose a second card and write that time on their paper. Ask them to draw a clock and a different activity for that time.
- Ask students to use their clocks to decide how many hours there are between the two times they chose.
- Invite them to write captions about their times and activities.

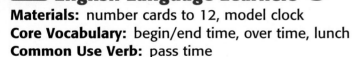

Option 2 — Student Technology

Math Online macmillanmh.com

Option 3 — Learning Station: Science (p. 209H)

Direct students to the Science Learning Station for more opportunities to explore and extend the lesson concept.

1 Introduce

Activity • Review

- Divide students into small groups. Give each group an index card with two activities such as the following: *tie your shoes, 10 jumping jacks, stand up, sing the ABC's,* and *count to 20.*

- Explain to the students that the *act it out* strategy is one strategy they can use to solve a problem.

- Assign two students in each group to act out the activities on their group's index cards. The other student(s) will decided which activity takes more time.

- Mix up and rotate the index cards from group to group until each student has an opportunity to act out an activity.

2 Teach

Understand Using the questions, review what students know and what they need to find.

Plan Have them discuss their strategy.

Solve Before students choose a strategy ask:

- **What do you know?** The party starts at 1:30. Shemar needs to leave a half hour before the party starts.

- **What do you need to know?** what time Shemar needs to leave

- **What strategies could you use to solve the problem?** Sample answers: act it out, work backward, draw a picture

Check Ask students if they counted back 30 minutes.

- **What time does Shemar need to leave?** 1:00

! **COMMON ERROR!**

Some students may always count clockwise, even when a problem requires them to count back on their clocks. Provide plenty of practice finding times that are earlier or later than a given time, modeling for students the correct direction to move their clock hands.

Name _____

Problem-Solving Investigation

Shemar is going to a party that starts at 1:30. He needs to leave home a half hour before the party starts. What time should Shemar leave?

Main Idea

I will choose a strategy to solve a problem.

Your Mission: Find what time Shemar needs to leave.

Understand

What do I know?
Underline what you know.

What do I need to find?
Circle it.

Plan

How will I solve the problem?

Solve

One way is to act it out.

See students' answers.

Check

Look back.
Is my answer reasonable?

Check students' explanations.

Chapter 7   Lesson 7   two hundred thirty-one   231

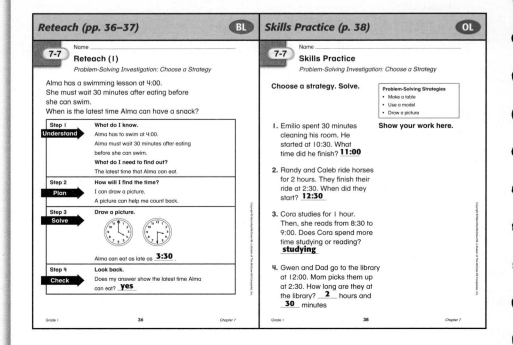

Reteach (pp. 36–37)   BL

7-7   Name _____
Reteach (1)
Problem-Solving Investigation: Choose a Strategy

Alma has a swimming lesson at 4:00.
She must wait 30 minutes after eating before she can swim.
When is the latest time Alma can have a snack?

| Step 1 Understand | What do I know.
Alma has to swim at 4:00.
Alma must wait 30 minutes after eating before she can swim.
What do I need to find out?
The latest time that Alma can eat. |

| Step 2 Plan | How will I find the time?
I can draw a picture.
A picture can help me count back. |

| Step 3 Solve | Draw a picture.

Alma can eat as late as **3:30**. |

| Step 4 Check | Look back.
Does my answer show the latest time Alma can eat? **yes** |

Grade 1   36   Chapter 7

Skills Practice (p. 38)   OL

7-7   Name _____
Skills Practice
Problem-Solving Investigation: Choose a Strategy

Choose a strategy. Solve.

Problem-Solving Strategies
- Make a table
- Use a model
- Draw a picture

1. Emilio spent 30 minutes cleaning his room. He started at 10:30. What time did he finish? **11:00**

Show your work here.

2. Randy and Caleb ride horses for 2 hours. They finish their ride at 2:30. When did they start? **12:30**

3. Cora studies for 1 hour. Then, she reads from 8:30 to 9:00. Does Cora spend more time studying or reading? **studying**

4. Gwen and Dad go to the library at 12:00. Mom picks them up at 2:30. How long are they at the library? **2** hours and **30** minutes

Grade 1   38   Chapter 7

Mixed Problem Solving

Problem-Solving Strategies
- Act it out
- Draw a picture
- Make a table

Solve.

1. Diego started hiking at 3:00. He hiked for 30 minutes. What time did he stop?

___3:30___

2. Erin eats breakfast at 7:00. She leaves for school at 7:30. How long does Erin have to eat breakfast?

___30___ minutes

3. Lindsay's piano lesson is 30 minutes. Sofia's lesson is 1 hour. Who has the longer piano lesson?

___Sofia___

4. At Angie's school, lunch is at 1:00. Recess is at 12:00. Does Angie go to lunch or recess first?

___recess___

232 two hundred thirty-two

Copyright © Macmillan/McGraw-Hill, a division of The McGraw-Hill Companies, Inc.

BL **Alternate Teaching Strategy**

If students have trouble using the draw a picture strategy to solve time problems . . .

Then use one of these reteach options.

1. **CRM** **Daily Reteach Worksheet** (pp. 36–37)

2. **Draw a Picture** Have students use their clocks to count back 30 minutes. Allow them to use a clock stamp on their paper and then draw only the clock hands to show the time they see on their clocks.

③ Practice

Mixed Problem Solving

Exercises 1–4 Review problem-solving strategies.

Help students choose which strategy will work best for each problem. Allow them to use their clocks.

④ Assess

Formative Assessment

Tell students the following story:
Mark is hungry. He checks his watch and sees that it is 4:00. He eats dinner at 6:00. How long must Mark wait until dinner time?

- **How will you solve the problem?** Sample answers: act it out; draw a picture

- **What picture could you draw to solve the problem?** Sample answer: an analog clock showing 4:00

- Have students draw a picture to solve the problem.

Quick Check **Are students continuing to struggle with using pictures to solve time problems?**

If Yes → Small Group Options (p. 231B)

If No → Independent Work Options (p. 231B)

　　　CRM Skills Practice Worksheet (p. 38)

　　　CRM Enrich Worksheet (p. 40)

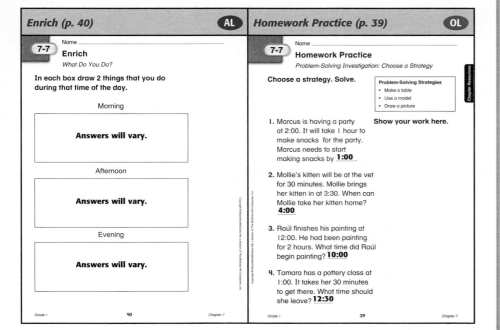

Enrich (p. 40) **AL**

7-7 **Enrich**
What Do You Do?

In each box draw 2 things that you do during that time of the day.

Morning
Answers will vary.

Afternoon
Answers will vary.

Evening
Answers will vary.

Grade 1　　40　　Chapter 7

Homework Practice (p. 39) **OL**

7-7 **Homework Practice**
Problem-Solving Investigation: Choose a Strategy

Choose a strategy. Solve.

Problem-Solving Strategies
- Make a table
- Use a model
- Draw a picture

1. Marcus is having a party at 2:00. It will take 1 hour to make snacks for the party. Marcus needs to start making snacks by **1:00**.

Show your work here.

2. Mollie's kitten will be at the vet for 30 minutes. Mollie brings her kitten in at 3:30. When can Mollie take her kitten home? **4:00**

3. Raúl finishes his painting at 12:00. He had been painting for 2 hours. What time did Raúl begin painting? **10:00**

4. Tamara has a pottery class at 1:00. It takes her 30 minutes to get there. What time should she leave? **12:30**

Grade 1　　39　　Chapter 7

Lesson 7-7 Problem-Solving Investigation **232**

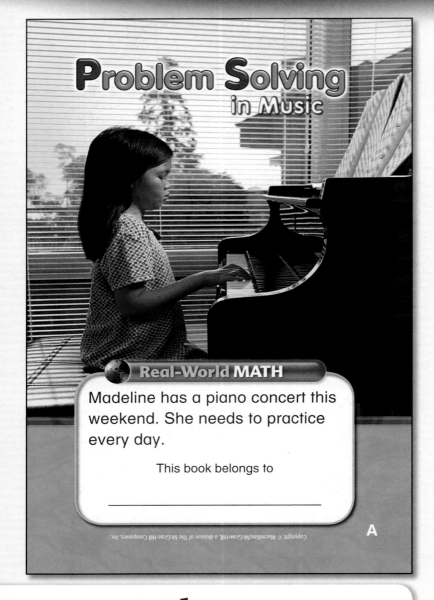

Problem Solving in Music

Real-World MATH

Madeline has a piano concert this weekend. She needs to practice every day.

This book belongs to

A

She is going to play a song called "Minute Waltz."

B

Lesson Planner

Objective

Use manipulative clocks to solve addition problems in music.

National Standard

Students identify uses of music in their daily experiences and describe characteristics that make certain music suitable for each use.

Activate Prior Knowledge

- **Does anyone have a piano at home? Who plays the piano in your house?** See students' explanations.
- **Why is practice important?** Sample answer: Practice will help you get better at doing something.
- **What are some things you practice?** Sample answers: sports; math; reading
- **What is your favorite musical instrument? Why?** Sample answer: guitar; I like to pluck the strings.
- Explain that a musician is any person who performs music. **Where have you seen a musician?** Sample answer: my mom plays piano at home; our music teacher plays guitar.

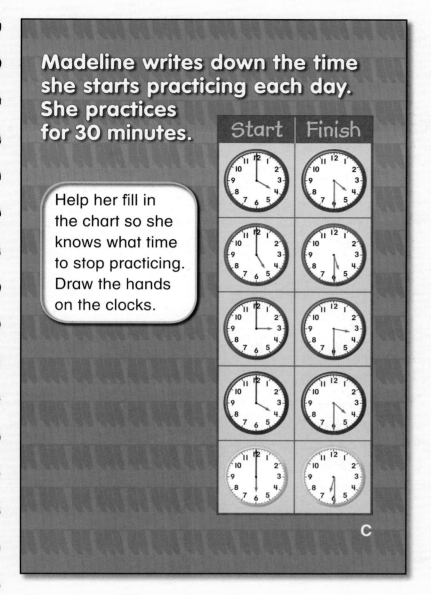

Madeline writes down the time she starts practicing each day. She practices for 30 minutes.

Help her fill in the chart so she knows what time to stop practicing. Draw the hands on the clocks.

Start	Finish

C

Practicing has helped Madeline play the piano.

Madeline practiced everyday for 30 minutes. How many hours total did she practice in 6 days?

___3___ hours

FOLD DOWN

D

Create the Book

Guide students to create their book.

- Have them fold the page in half.
- Ask them to write their name on page A.
- Explain that page A is the front cover and page D is the back cover. If necessary, have them practice flipping through the book in order.
- Guide them in reading the information and word problems on each of the pages.

Use the Student Pages

Have students work individually or in pairs to complete the problems on pages C–D.

Page C Refer students to page C to find for how long Madeline practices.

Page D Adding several half hours into a total is a new skill. For practice, let students move forward half hours starting from 12:00 on a clock. Students should arrive at 2:30, which is two and a half hours.

WRITING IN ▸MATH Have students choose an activity and write how often and for how long they practice in a week.

Extend the Activity

Tell students that the class will practice music for five minutes each day next week. During that time, sing, hum, clap to rhythms, and so on. Be sure to draw students' attention to a clock at the beginning and end of each practice; point out that the minute hand moved one number in five minutes.

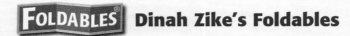 **Dinah Zike's Foldables**

Use this lesson suggestion to incorporate the Foldable during the chapter. Students can then use their Foldable to review for the test.

Lesson 7-6 Discuss which of the events recorded on the back of the Foldable as occurring before or after another event. Discuss whether one of the events takes more or less time than another event. Also use the terms "shorter" and "longer" in discussions.

Vocabulary Review

Review chapter vocabulary using one of the following options.

- **Visual Vocabulary Cards (3, 14, 20, 21, 22, 27, and 31)**
- **eGlossary at** macmillanmh.com

Vocabulary Test

CRM **Chapter 7 Resource Masters** (p. 45)
Assess Student comprehension of the chapter vocabulary with the Vocabulary Test.

Math Online **Chapter Test**
Alternative summative assessment options are available online at macmillanmh.com.

Name _____

Vocabulary

Write the missing word. Use the word box to help.

| longer | analog |
| shorter | digital |

1. The **minute hand** is the ____longer____ hand.

2. The **hour hand** is the ____shorter____ hand.

3. ____analog____ clock

4. ____digital____ clock

Concepts

Write the time on each digital clock.

5. 5:30
   5:30

6. 30 minutes after 11
   11:30

7. 1:00
   1:00

8. half past 4
   4:30

Chapter 7   two hundred thirty-five **235**

Chapter 7 Project

Time of Day Collages

Have students discuss the results of their completed chapter project as a class. Assess their work using the Chapter Project rubric found in Chapter 7 Resource Masters on p. 50.

Write the time.

9. 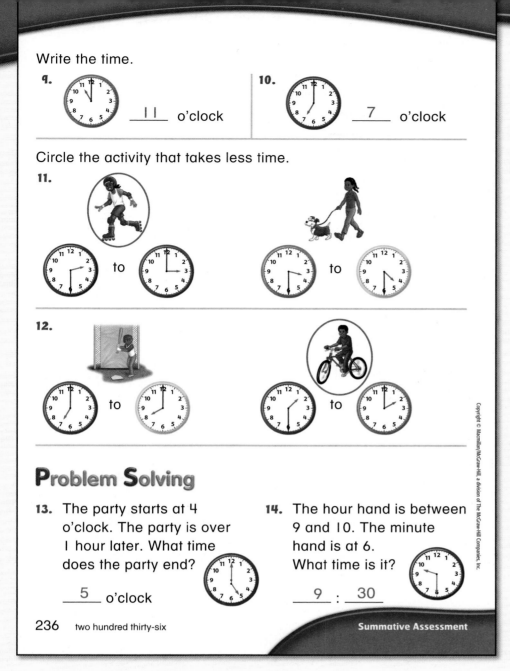 __11__ o'clock

10. __7__ o'clock

Circle the activity that takes less time.

11. to   to

12. to   to

Problem Solving

13. The party starts at 4 o'clock. The party is over 1 hour later. What time does the party end?

__5__ o'clock

14. The hour hand is between 9 and 10. The minute hand is at 6. What time is it?

__9__ : __30__

Summative Assessment

Copyright © Macmillan/McGraw-Hill, a division of The McGraw-Hill Companies, Inc.

Summative Assessment

Use these alternate leveled chapter tests to differentiate assessment for the specific needs of your students.

Leveled Chapter 7 Tests			
Form	**Type**	**Level**	**CRM Pages**
1	Multiple Choice	**BL**	52–53
2A	Multiple Choice	**OL**	54–55
2B	Multiple Choice	**OL**	56–57
2C	Multiple Choice	**AL**	58–59
2D	Free Response	**AL**	60–61

BL = below/approaching grade level
OL = on grade level
AL = above/beyond grade level

ExamView® Assessment Suite   Customize and create multiple versions of your Chapter Test and their test answer keys.

Data-Driven Decision-Making

Based on the results of the Chapter Review/Test, use the following to review concepts that continue to present students with problems.

Exercises	State/Local Standards	What's the Math?	Error Analysis	Resources for Review
1–4		Know and use vocabulary for digital and analog clocks.	Does not know words "analog," "digital." Reverses hands of clock.	Strategic Intervention Guide (p. 116) CRM Chapter 7 Resource Masters (Reteach Worksheets)
5–10		Tell time to the nearest hour or half hour.	Confuses hands of clock. Does not draw two hands. Cannot write time.	**Math Online** Concepts in Motion Math Adventures
11–12		Use an analog clock to tell time. Relate time to events.	Confuses word "less." Circles both answers.	

Test Practice

Formative Assessment

- Use Student Edition pp. 237–238 as practice and cumulative review. The questions are written in the same style as found on many state tests.

- You can also use these two pages to benchmark student progress, or as an alternative homework assignment.

Additional practice pages can be found in the Chapter 7 Resource Masters.

CRM Chapter 7 Resource Masters
Cumulative Test Practice

- Multiple Choice format (pp. 52–58, 62)

- Free Response format (pp. 59–61, 63)

Exam_View_
Assessment Suite Create practice worksheets or tests that align to state standards.

Math Online For additional practice, visit macmillanmh.com.

Name _____

Listen as your teacher reads each problem.
Choose the correct answer.

1.

2.

3.

4.

5.

6.

For the Teacher

- Before starting a test, tell students about how much time the test or each section will take.

- Encourage students to look their test over carefully before they turn it in.

For the Student

- Remind students to ask for help if they do not understand the instructions.

- Encourage students to listen carefully when you give instructions.

7.

Tim's Marbles	
Color	Number
Red	4
Green	6
Blue	3

7   9   10   13

10. $7 + 4 = 11$

$4 + 7 = 11$ $7 - 4 = 3$

$11 - 4 = 7$ $7 - 3 = 4$

8.

$4 - 0 = 4$ $4 - 2 = 2$

$4 + 2 = 6$ $4 + 0 = 4$

11. It is 8 o'clock. School starts at half past 8. How many minutes until school starts?

_____30_____ minutes

9.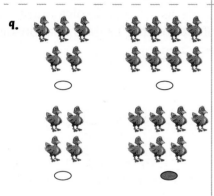

12. There were 3 butterflies sitting on the flower. Then 3 butterflies flew away. How many butterflies are left?

_____0_____ butterflies

STOP

238   two hundred thirty-eight

Summative Assessment

Test Directions for Teachers

Read the following directions to students before they begin the test. Then read each question followed by a pause to allow students time to work on the problem and choose an answer. The first test item can be worked as a class example.

- **Write your name at the top of the page.**
- **I am going to read each question to you. Listen carefully to the entire question before you choose an answer.**

Multiple Choice

1. Myra told her father she would be home by 5:00. Which clock shows when Myra will be home?
2. Aaron started soccer practice at 10:00. Which clock shows 10:00?
3. Which clock shows 8 o'clock?
4. Look at the pictures. Mark the picture that shows what you do **after** dinner?
5. Look at the clocks. Mark the clock that shows what time it be will one-half hour **after** 2:00.
6. Which clock shows half past 4?

- **Turn the page over.**

7. Look at the table. It shows the number of red, green, and blue marbles Tim has. How many red and blue marbles does Tim have in all?
8. Look at the flower pots. Which number sentence shows how many are left?
9. Look at the birds. Which group of birds shows 7 birds?
10. Look at the number sentence. Which is a related subtraction fact for $7 + 4 = 11$?

Short Response

11. It is 8 o'clock. School starts at half past 8. How many minutes until school starts.
12. There were 3 butterflies sitting on the flower. Then 3 butterflies flew away. How many butterflies are left?

CHAPTER 8

Chapter Overview

Chapter-at-a-Glance

In Chapter 8, the emphasis is on making, counting, and reading numbers from 11 to 20, counting and estimating with 10s, counting and skip counting by 2s, 5s, and 10s on a hundred chart, and using strategies to solve problems.

Lesson		Math Objective	State/Local Standards
8-1	**Counting to 20** (pp. 243–244)	Make, count, and write numbers to 20. Tell how many tens and ones there are in numbers to 20.	
8-2	**Counting by Tens** (pp. 245–246)	Make, count, and write tens to 100.	
8-3	**Problem-Solving Strategy: Look for a Pattern** (pp. 247–248)	Use the *look for a pattern* strategy to solve problems.	
8-4	**Hundred Chart** (pp. 249–252)	Count and order numbers from 1 to 100 on a hundred chart.	
8-5	**Estimating with Groups of Ten** (pp. 255–256)	Use a group of 10 as a guide to estimate quantities up to 100.	
8-6	**Problem-Solving Investigation: Choose a Strategy** (pp. 257–258)	Choose the best strategy to solve a problem.	
8-7	**Skip Counting by 2s, 5s, and 10s** (pp. 259–260)	Use patterns to skip count by twos, fives, and tens.	
8-8	**Skip Counting on a Hundred Chart** (pp. 261–262)	Use a hundred chart to identify and continue skip-counting patterns.	
8-9	**Even and Odd** (pp. 263–264)	Find patterns in numbers such as even and odd numbers.	

Recognize Number Patterns

BIG Idea Hundred charts are effective in showing patterns in our number system. Using a hundred chart, students develop a strong foundation for understanding the relationships between numbers, skip-counting patterns, and number sense. A hundred chart also provides opportunities to see the results of increasing and decreasing patterns as students count on and back by one and by ten.

Algebra Readiness In Lessons 8-1 and 8-2, students prepare for algebra through the use of tens and ones to represent two-digit numbers, which will lay the foundation for understanding the idea of an equation as two balanced equalities. In Lesson 8-6, students write and solve number sentences from problem situations that express relationships involving addition and subtraction.

Focal Points and Connections

G1-FP2 *Number and Operations:* **Developing an understanding of whole number relationships, including grouping in tens and ones**

Children compare and order whole numbers (at least to 100) to develop an understanding of and solve problems involving the relative sizes of these numbers. They think of whole numbers between 10 and 100 in terms of groups of tens and ones (especially recognizing the numbers 11 to 19 as 1 group of ten and particular numbers of ones). They understand the sequential order of the counting numbers and their relative magnitudes and represent numbers on a number line.

Skills Trace
Vertical Alignment

Kindergarten
In kindergarten, students learned to:
- Read, write, order, and compare numbers 0 to 30.

First Grade
During this chapter, students learn to:
- Tell how many tens and ones there are in numbers to 20. Make, count, and write tens.
- Count and order numbers from 1 to 100 on a hundred chart.
- Find patterns in numbers such as even and odd numbers.
- Use a hundred chart to identify and continue skip-counting patterns.

After this chapter, students learn to:
- Use place value with tens and ones. (Chapter 13)
- Count, read, write, compare, and order numbers to 100. (Chapter 13)
- Use estimation strategies in computation and problem-solving that involve numbers that use the ones and tens places. (Chapter 13)

Second Grade
In second grade, students learn to:
- Understand the relationship between numbers, quantities, and place value in whole numbers up to 100.
- Count, read, and write numbers to 100 (1,000) and identify the place value for each digit.

Backmapping and Vertical Alignment McGraw-Hill's *Math Connects* program was conceived and developed with the final results in mind: student success in Algebra 1 and beyond. The authors, using the **NCTM Focal Points and Focal Connections** as their guide, developed this brand-new series by backmapping from Algebra 1 concepts, and vertically aligning the topics so that they build upon prior skills and concepts and serve as a foundation for future topics.

▷ Math Vocabulary
The following math vocabulary words for Chapter 8 are listed in the glossary of the *Student Edition*. You can find interactive definitions in 13 languages in the *eGlossary* at macmillanmh.com.

hundred chart a chart that shows numbers 1–100 (p. 249)

1	2	3	4	5	6	7	8	9	10
11	12	13	14	15	16	17	18	19	20
21	22	23	24	25	26	27	28	29	30
31	32	33	34	35	36	37	38	39	40
41	42	43	44	45	46	47	48	49	50
51	52	53	54	55	56	57	58	59	60
61	62	63	64	65	66	67	68	69	70
71	72	73	74	75	76	77	78	79	80
81	82	83	84	85	86	87	88	89	90
91	92	93	94	95	96	97	98	99	100

ones Example: (p. 243) This number has 3 ones.

skip count to count objects in equal groups of two or more (p. 259)

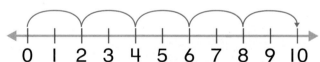

estimate to find a number close to an exact amount (p. 255)

even 0, 2, 4, 6, 8 (p. 263)

odd 1, 3, 5, 7, 9 (p. 263)

Visual Vocabulary Cards Use Visual Vocabulary Cards 17 and 32 to reinforce the vocabulary in this chapter. (The Define/Example/Ask routine is printed on the back of each card.)

ones

Chapter Planner

Suggested Pacing		
Instruction	Review and Assessment	TOTAL
9 days	2 days	**11 days**

Diagnostic Assessment
Are You Ready? (p. 240)

	Lesson 8-1 — Pacing: 1 day	Lesson 8-2 — Pacing: 1 day	Lesson 8-3 — Pacing: 1 day
Lesson/ Objective	**Counting to 20** (pp. 243–244) **Objective:** Make, count, and write numbers to 20. Tell how many tens and ones there are in numbers to 20.	**Counting by Tens** (pp. 245–246) **Objective:** Make, count, and write tens to 100.	**Problem-Solving Strategy** **Look for a Pattern** (pp. 247–248) **Objective:** Use the *look for a pattern* strategy to solve problems.
State/Local Standards			
Math Vocabulary	ones		
Lesson Resources	**Materials** pencils, overhead marker, overhead projector, WorkMat1: Ten-Frame **Manipulatives** two-colored counters, connecting cubes **Other Resources** CRM Leveled Worksheets (pp. 6–10) Daily Reteach • 5-Minute Check Problem of the Day	**Materials** pencils, overhead markers, 10 × 10 grid on a transparency, overhead projector **Manipulatives** base-ten blocks, connecting cubes **Other Resources** CRM Leveled Worksheets (pp. 11–15) Daily Reteach • 5-Minute Check Problem of the Day	**Other Resources** CRM Leveled Worksheets (pp. 16–20) Daily Reteach • 5-Minute Check Problem of the Day Look Again
Technology Math Online	♪ Math Song Track 10 Math Adventures	♪ Math Song Track 8 Math Tool Chest, Place Value Concepts in Motion	
Reaching All Learners	Gifted and Talented, p. 243B **AL** English Learners, p. 243B **ELL** Early Finishers, p. 243B **OL** **AL**	Gifted and Talented, p. 245B **AL** English Learners, p. 245B **ELL** Early Finishers, p. 245B **OL** **AL**	Gifted and Talented, p. 247B **AL** English Learners, p. 247B **ELL** Early Finishers, p. 247B **OL** **AL**
Alternate Lessons		*Math Their Way*, p. 314 *IMPACT Mathematics:* Unit H	

KEY

BL Below/Approaching Level **OL** On Level **AL** Above/Beyond Level **ELL** English Learners

SE Student Edition **TE** Teacher Edition **CRM** Chapter 3 Resource Masters CD-Rom

Transparency Flip Chart Real-World Problem Solving Library

Lesson 8-4	**Lesson 8-5**	**Lesson 8-6**	

Pacing: 1 day (Lesson 8-4)
Pacing: 1 day (Lesson 8-5)
Pacing: 1 day (Lesson 8-6)

Lesson 8-4

Hundred Chart
(pp. 249–252)

Objective: Count and order numbers from 1 to 100 on a hundred chart.

Lesson 8-5

Estimating with Groups of Ten
(pp. 255–256)

Objective: Use a group of 10 as a guide to estimate quantities up to 100.

Lesson 8-6

Problem-Solving Investigation
Choose a Strategy
(pp. 257–258)

Objective: Choose the best strategy to solve a problem.

Lesson/Objective

State/Local Standards

Math Vocabulary

hundred chart

estimate

Lesson Resources

Materials
class-size number line, overhead projector, hundred chart

Materials
yarn, pennies

Manipulatives
connecting cubes, two-colored counters

Materials
pencils

Manipulatives
two-colored counters, connecting cubes

Other Resources
- CRM Leveled Worksheets (pp. 21–25)
- Daily Reteach • 5-Minute Check
- Problem of the Day

Other Resources
- CRM Leveled Worksheets (pp. 26–30)
- Daily Reteach • 5-Minute Check
- Problem of the Day

Other Resources
- CRM Leveled Worksheets (pp. 31–35)
- Daily Reteach • 5-Minute Check
- Problem of the Day

Technology

♪ Math Song Track 8

♪ Math Song Track 8
Concepts in Motion

Math Online

Reaching All Learners

Below Level, p. 249B **BL**
English Learners, p. 249B **ELL**
Early Finishers, p. 249B **OL** **AL**

Gifted and Talented, p. 255B **AL**
English Learners, p. 255B **ELL**
Early Finishers, p. 255B **OL** **AL**

Below Level, p. 257B **BL**
English Learners, p. 257B **ELL**
Early Finishers, p. 257B **OL** **AL**

Alternate Lessons

IMPACT Mathematics: Unit H

Formative Assessment
- Mid-Chapter Check (p. 253)
- Spiral Review (p. 254)

Chapter Planner

	Lesson 8-7 Pacing: 1 day	**Lesson 8-8** Pacing: 1 day	**Lesson 8-9** Pacing: 1 day
Lesson/ Objective	**Skip Counting by 2s, 5s, and 10s** (pp. 259–260) **Objective:** Skip count by 2s, 5s, and 10s to 100.	**Skip Counting on a Hundred Chart** (pp. 261–262) **Objective:** Use a hundred chart to identify and continue skip-counting patterns.	**Even and Odd** (pp. 263–264) **Objective:** Find patterns in numbers such as even and odd numbers.
State/Local Standards			
Math	skip count		even, odd
Lesson Resources	**Materials** pencils **Manipulatives** connecting cubes, two-colored counters **Other Resources** CRM Leveled Worksheets (pp. 36–40) Daily Reteach • 5-Minute Check Problem of the Day	**Materials** stickers, overhead projector, hundred chart transparency **Other Resources** CRM Leveled Worksheets (pp. 41–45) Daily Reteach • 5-Minute Check Problem of the Day	**Materials** hundred chart, pencils, crayons **Manipulatives** two-colored counters **Other Resources** CRM Leveled Worksheets (pp. 46–58) Daily Reteach • 5-Minute Check Problem of the Day
Technology Math Online	♪ Math Song Track 9 Math Adventures	♪ Math Song Track 9	Math Adventures
Reaching All Learners	Gifted and Talented, p. 259B AL English Learners, p. 259B ELL Early Finishers, p. 259B OL AL	Below Level, p. 261B BL English Learners, p. 261B ELL Early Finishers, p. 261B OL AL	Below Level, p. 263B BL English Learners, p. 263B ELL Early Finishers, p. 263B OL AL
Alternate Lessons		*IMPACT Mathematics:* Unit D	*IMPACT Mathematics:* Unit D

Extra Practice (p. 265)
Game Time (p. 266)
Problem Solving in Social Studies (p. 267)

Summative Assessment
• Chapter Review/Test (p. 269)
• Test Practice (p. 271)

Assessment Options

✓ Diagnostic Assessment

- **SE** *Option 1:* Are You Ready? (p. 240)
  Option 2: Online Quiz (macmillanmh.com)
- **CRM** *Option 3:* Diagnostic Test (p. 52)
- **CRM** *Option 4:* Chapter Pretest (p. 53)

✓ Formative Assessment

- **TE** Alternate Teaching Strategies (every lesson)
- **SE** Talk About It (every lesson)
- **SE** Writing in Math (every lesson)
- **SE** Check (every lesson)
- **TE** Line Up (every lesson)
- **SE** Mid-Chapter Check (p. 253)
- **CRM** Mid-Chapter Test (p. 54)

✓ Summative Assessment

- **SE** Chapter Review/Test (pp. 269–270)
- **SE** Test Practice (pp. 271–272)
- **CRM** Vocabulary Test (p. 55)
- **CRM** Leveled Chapter Tests (pp. 62–71)
- **CRM** Cumulative Test Practice (pp. 72–73)
- **CRM** Listening Assessment (pp. 58–59)
- **CRM** Oral Assessment (pp. 56–57)
- ⊙ Exam*View*® Assessment Suite
- ⋏ Advance Tracker

Mc Graw Hill Professional Development

Targeted professional development has been articulated throughout the **McGraw-Hill's *Math Connects* program**. The **McGraw-Hill Professional Development Video Library** provides short videos that support the **NCTM Focal Points and Focal Connections.** For more information, visit macmillanmh.com.

| Model Lessons | Instructional Strategies |

Assessment Tips

Counting, ordering, and comparing numbers to 100 are important prerequisite skills that are necessary for learning addition and subtraction concepts.

- Use a clipboard that has a list of the students' names and the concepts you want to assess.
- As students count, order, and compare numbers, write down your observations on the clipboard.
- These observations should help you plan next steps with the students.
- Make sure you record the date of the observation so you can begin to see progress over time.

Teacher Notes

Social Studies

 group | LOGICAL, KINESTHETIC

Stars and Stripes

- Count the number of red and white stripes on the American flag.
- Use groups of ten to find the number of stars on the flag.
- Count the number of stars on the flag.
- How many groups of ten stars are there on the flag?

Materials:
- an American flag

 Art

individual | LOGICAL, VISUAL/SPATIAL

Counting to 20

- Make a counting book called *Counting to 20*. Write the title on the cover of your book. Use crayons or markers to decorate the cover.
- Write one number at the top of each page. Make your pages show 0 through 20 in order.
- Draw or stamp stars, circles, squares, or other shapes to show each number in your book. Use groups of tens and ones.

Materials:
- a blank book
- markers
- stamps

 Language Arts

individual | LOGICAL, KINESTHETIC

Counting by Tens

- Look at the number on each card. Read the number name.
- Mix up the cards. Put them on the table with the words showing.
- Put the cards in order. Count by tens.

Teacher Note: For this learning station, make a number card for each multiple of 10 from 10 to 100. On the back of each card, write out the number name.

Materials:
- cards with numbers and number names

Science

group | VISUAL/SPATIAL, KINESTHETIC

How Many Petals?

- Find photos of flowers.
- Count the petals by two. Write down how many petals each flower has.
- Which flower has the most petals?
- Draw your own flower with any number of petals.

Teacher Note: Some flowers will be harder to count than others. Point students towards pictures with clearly "countable" petals.

Materials:
- science magazines
- paper
- crayons

Health

group | KINESTHETIC

Hop, Skip, Jump!

- See how high you can skip count while jumping rope.
- Count by twos each time you jump.
- Repeat the activity, but skip count by fives and tens.

Materials:
- jump ropes

Calendar Time

Skip-Counting Calendar

- Before beginning the activity, have students practice representing dates in numberic form (1-5-2009, for example) by writing today's date.
- Write the name of the current month on the calendar. Fill in the numbers for the days of the month.
- Point to the square for each date named as you lead students in counting by twos. Have a volunteer color a green stripe across the top of each square.
- Next, have students count dates by fives. Have a volunteer color a yellow stripe across the top of each square.
- Count dates by tens and have a volunteer color a red stripe across the top of each square.
- Ask students to describe patterns they see and tell ways that a calendar is similar to a hundred chart.

Introduce the Chapter

🌐 Real World: How Many?

Share with students that they are going to learn how to count a lot of objects in ways that are much faster than counting objects one by one.

- Divide the class into groups of five and have each group form a circle. Have students take off their shoes and place them in the middle of the circle.
- **How many shoes are in the middle?** 10 shoes
- **How did you solve the problem?** Sample answers: counted them all; counted by twos
- Explain that it is faster and easier to count objects in groups.

Have students turn to p. 239.

- Ask students to count the marbles and write the number.
- Then have students write how many groups of ten they can make from the number.

Key Vocabulary

Introduce key vocabulary in the chapter using the routine below.

Define: I **estimate** when I find a number close to the real amount.
Example: I can estimate how many fish are in the aquarium without counting them.
Ask: Estimate how many students are your class.

CHAPTER 8

Recognize Number Patterns

Key Vocabulary
hundred chart
skip count
even
odd

Explore

How many groups of ten are in 30?

_____3_____

Chapter 8   two hundred thirty-nine **239**

FOLDABLES Study Organizer — Dinah Zike's Foldables

Guide students to create their Matchbook Foldables for recognizing number patterns to 100.

① Fold an 8½ x 10 sheet of paper like a hamburger, but fold it so that one side is one inch longer than the other side.

② Fold the one-inch tab over the short side forming an envelope-like fold.

③ Cut the front flap in half toward the mountain top to create two flaps.

When to Use It *Lessons 8-1, 8-4, and 8-7. (Additional instructions for using the Foldable with these lessons are found on pp. 253 and 269.)*

1	2	3	4	5	6	7	8	9	10
11	12	13	14	15	16	17	18	19	20
21	22	23	24	25	26	27	28	29	30
31	32	33	34	35	36	37	38	39	40
41	42	43	44	45	46	47	48	49	50
51	52	53	54	55	56	57	58	59	60
61	62	63	64	65	66	67	68	69	70
71	72	73	74	75	76	77	78	79	80
81	82	83	84	85	86	87	88	89	90
91	92	93	94	95	96	97	98	99	100

Name _____

✓ Are You Ready for Chapter 8?

1. Write the missing numbers.

1	2	3	4	5
6	7	8	9	10
11	12	13	14	15

Write the number.

2.  ___6___ hats

3. ♥♥♥♥♥♥♥♥♥♥ ___10___ hearts

4.  ___9___ sandwiches

5. Seth has 12 flowers. He gives away 4 flowers.
How many flowers are left? ___8___ flowers

240   two hundred forty   This page checks skills needed for Chapter 8.

Copyright © Macmillan/McGraw-Hill, a division of The McGraw-Hill Companies, Inc.

Diagnostic Assessment

Check for students' prerequisite skills before beginning the chapter.

- **Option 1:** *Are You Ready for Chapter 8?*

  SE Student Edition, p. 240

- **Option 2:** *Online Assessment*

  Math Online macmillanmh.com

- **Option 3:** *Diagnostic Tests*

  CRM Chapter 8 Resource Masters, p. 52

RTI (Response to Intervention)

Apply the Results Based on the results of the diagnostic assessment on student p. 84, use the chart below to address individual needs before beginning the chapter.

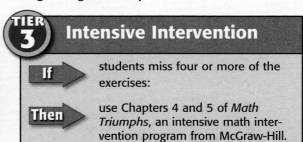

TIER 3 **Intensive Intervention**

If → students miss four or more of the exercises:

Then → use Chapters 4 and 5 of *Math Triumphs*, an intensive math intervention program from McGraw-Hill.

TIER 2 **Strategic Intervention**
below/approaching grade level

If → students miss two or three in:
Exercises 1–5

Then → choose a resource:

Strategic Intervention Guide (p. 26)

CRM Chapter 5 Resource Masters
(Reteach Worksheets)

Math Online Concepts in Motion

TIER 1 **On-Level**

If → students miss one in:
Exercises 1–5

Then → choose a resource:

TE Learning Stations (pp. 239G–239H)

TE Chapter Project (p. 241)

CRM Game: *Skip Cards*

● Math Adventures

My Math Zone Chapter 7

Math Online Fact Dash

Above/Beyond Level

If → students miss none in:
Exercises 1–5

Then → choose a resource:

TE Learning Stations (pp. 239G–239H)

TE Chapter Project (p. 241)

▯ Real-World Problem Solving: *Look Again*

My Math Zone Chapters 7, 8

Math Online Game

Before you begin Chapter 8:

- Read the Math at Home letter found on p. 241 with the class and have each student sign it.
- Send home copies of the Math at Home letter with each student.
- Use the Spanish letter on p. 242 for students with Spanish-Speaking parents or guardians.

Starting the Chapter

Ask students to write about a time when they used numbers to 100. Give an example, such as working on a 100-piece puzzle or counting pennies in a piggy bank.

Read-Aloud Anthology

For an optional reading activity to introduce this chapter's math concepts, see the Read-Aloud Anthology on page TR32.

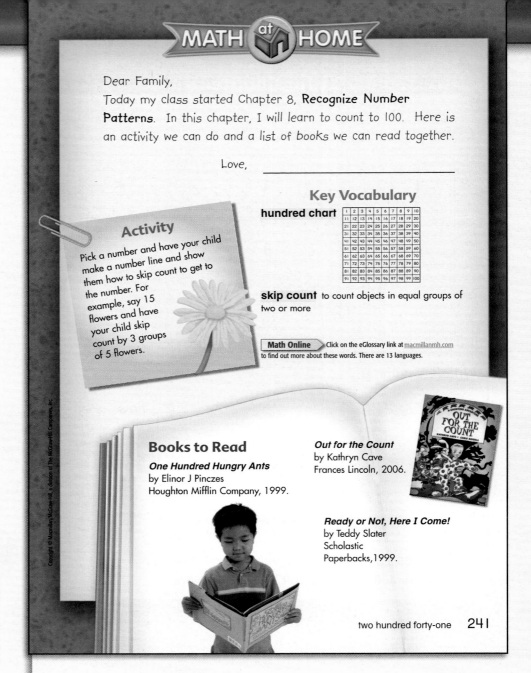

Chapter 8 Project

Patterns on a Hundred Chart

- Provide copies of the hundred chart for individual students to use to color in counting patterns.
- At the top of each hundred chart, students should write the number they are skip counting by (e.g., 2s, 5s, 10s) and use a crayon to color in the number squares as they skip count through the chart beginning at 0.
- At the bottom of each hundred chart, students can write the number patterns they notice.
- Ask students to arrange the hundred charts in order from the least skip counting number to the greatest skip counting number, and compile the charts to make a book.

CRM *Refer to Chapter 8 Resource Masters, p. 60 for a rubric to assess students'progress on this project.*

Estimada Familia,

Hoy mi clase comenzó el Capítulo 8, **Reconoce patrones numéricos**. En este capítulo, aprenderé a contar hasta 100. A continuación, hay una actividad que podemos hacer y una lista de libros que podemos leer juntos.

Cariños, _____

Actividad

Seleccionen un número y pídanle a su hijo(a) que dibuje una imagen que muestre cómo contar salteado hasta llegar al número.
Por ejemplo, digan 15 flores y pídanle a su hijo(a) que dibuje 3 grupos de 5 flores.

Vocabulario clave

tabla de centenas

1	2	3	4	5	6	7	8	9	10
11	12	13	14	15	16	17	18	19	20
21	22	23	24	25	26	27	28	29	30
31	32	33	34	35	36	37	38	39	40
41	42	43	44	45	46	47	48	49	50
51	52	53	54	55	56	57	58	59	60
61	62	63	64	65	66	67	68	69	70
71	72	73	74	75	76	77	78	79	80
81	82	83	84	85	86	87	88	89	90
91	92	93	94	95	96	97	98	99	100

conteo salteado- contar de 2 en 2, de 5 en 5 ó de 10 en 10 para llegar más rápido a un número mayor

Math Online Visiten el enlace eGlossary en macmillanmh.com para averiguar más sobre estas palabras, las cuales se muestran en 13 idiomas.

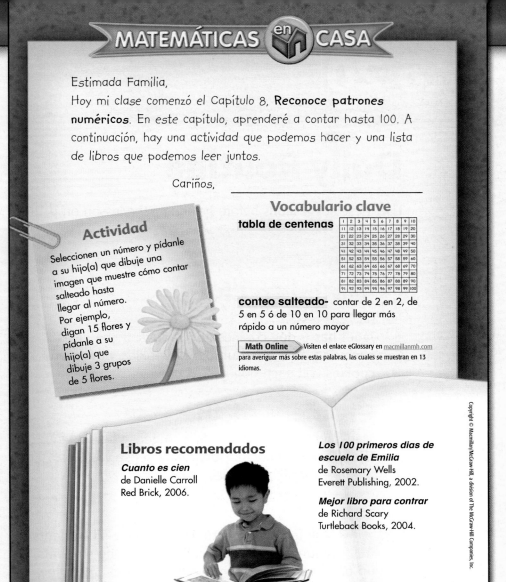

Libros recomendados

Cuanto es cien
de Danielle Carroll
Red Brick, 2006.

Los 100 primeros días de escuela de Emilia
de Rosemary Wells
Everett Publishing, 2002.

Mejor libro para contrar
de Richard Scary
Turtleback Books, 2004.

242 two hundred forty-two

Chapter 8 Literature List

Lesson	Book Title
8-1	**Let's Count it Out, Jesse Bear** Nancy White Carlstrom
8-2	**From One to One Hundred** Teri Sloat
8-3	**One Hundred Hungry Ants** Elinor J. Pinczes
8-4	**Out for the Count: A Counting Adventure** Kathryn Cave
8-5	**100 Days of Fun at School** Janet Craig
8-7	**One Hundred Hungry Ants** Elinor J. Pinczes
8-8	**One Hundred Hungry Ants** Elinor J. Pinczes
8-9	**Jump Kangaroo, Jump** Stuart J. Murphy
Any	**100 Days of School** Trudy Harris
Any	**Ready or Not, Here I Come!** Teddy Slater

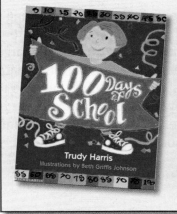

ELL National ESL Standards Alignment for Chapter 8

Lesson, Page	ELL Standard	Modality	Level
8-1, p 243B	Goal 1, Standard 3, K	Linguistic	Beginning
8-2, p 245B	Goal 3, Standard 2, B	Auditory, Linguistic	Intermediate
8-3, p 247B	Goal 2, Standard 1, D	Logical, Spatial	Intermediate
8-4, p 249B	Goal 2, Standard 2, D	Auditory, Spatial	Beginning
8-5, p 255B	Goal 2, Standard 2, J	Visual/Spatial	Intermediate
8-6, p 257B	Goal 3, Standard 3, D	Linguistic, Interpersonal	Advanced
8-7, p 259B	Goal 2, Standard 1, F	Auditory, Kinesthetic	Intermediate
8-8, p 261B	Goal 2, Standard 2, I	Visual/Spatial	Intermediate
8-9, p 263B	Goal 2, Standard 1, F	Logical, Social	Intermediate

The National ESL Standards can be found in the Teacher Reference Handbook.

Lesson Planner

Objectives

Make, count, and write numbers to 20. Tell how many tens and ones there are in numbers to 20.

Vocabulary

ones

Resources

Materials: pencils, overhead marker, overhead projector, WorkMat 1: Ten-Frame

Manipulatives: two-colored counters, connecting cubes

Literature Connection: *Let's Count It Out, Jesse Bear* by Nancy White Carlstrom

Teacher Technology
🔘 TeacherWorks • Math Songs Track 10 Lesson Plan

Focus on Math Background

In this lesson the students will practice counting by ones to 20. Mastery of this skill is critical before students can begin unitizing and quantifying larger amounts using more efficient skip counting strategies. By first grade, most first graders should be able to accomplish counting by ones with relative ease and accuracy and have an efficient strategy for organizing and keeping track of quantities greater than 20.

Daily Routine

Use these suggestions before beginning the lesson on p. 243.

5-Minute Check

(Reviews Lesson 7-7)
Janet has 9 dog cookies and 3 dogs. If she gives each dog the same number of cookies, how many cookies will each dog get? 3 cookies

Problem of the Day

Matt saw 9 geese on the lake. 4 geese flew away. Then 5 geese flew in. How many geese were on the lake then? 10 geese

LINE UP Ask ten students to line up. Have all students count up from 10 as the rest of the students line up one at a time. When twenty students are in line, ask: **How many groups of ten are there?**

Building Math Vocabulary

Materials: base-ten blocks, overhead projector
- Show the number 23. Explain that the 3 is in the **ones** place, so this number has 3 ones.
- Write the number 11 on a transparency. Explain that the number 11 represents one group of tens and 1 one. Show this number with 1 rod and 1 unit.
- Review eleven, twelve, thirteen, fourteen, fifteen, sixteen, seventeen, eighteen, nineteen, and twenty in the same way. Write each number on the overhead and model building it with base-ten blocks. Have students use base-ten blocks at their desk to build each number along with you.

Visual Vocabulary Cards

Use Visual Vocabulary Card 32 to reinforce the vocabulary introduced in this lesson. (The Define/Example/Ask routine is printed on the back of each card.)

Differentiated Instruction

Small Group Options

VISUAL/SPATIAL, KINESTHETIC, LOGICAL

Option 1 Gifted and Talented AL

Materials: pencils, paper, connecting cubes

- Prepare ten "trains" with varying numbers of connecting cubes up to twenty in each. Explain that students should make each train twenty cubes long.

- Have students count and record the total number of cubes in each train.

- For each train, have students decide whether they need to add cubes to make it exactly twenty cubes long.

- Each time students make a train the correct length, help them write an addition sentence that shows what they did.

- Ask students to put each train back in its original form so it will be ready for the next group of students to use.

Option 2 English Language Learners ELL

LINGUISTIC

Materials: poster of garden chant
Core Vocabulary: garden, rhyming, showing
Common Use Verb: growing

Talk Math This strategy uses rhyming and background knowledge to help students count to 20.

- Draw or show a picture of a garden on the board. Ask children what they know about a garden.

> One, two, three, The garden is growing.
> Four, five, six, Now it needs hoeing.
> Seven, eight, nine, Down go the weeds.
> Ten, eleven, twelve, Water it needs.
> Thirteen, fourteen, Here comes a shower.
> Fifteen, sixteen, A carrot and a flower.
> Seventeen, eighteen, The sun is showing.
> Nineteen, twenty! The garden is growing!

- As you chant the poem, act it out.

- Repeat, encourage students to speak and act out the poem chorally.

Independent Work Options

VISUAL/SPATIAL, KINESTHETIC, SOCIAL

Option 1 Early Finishers OL AL

Materials: thin markers, chart paper

- Have students work together to make a chart that uses tally marks to illustrate the numbers 11–20.

- Ask students to write each number and then make the correct number of tallies next to it.

- In each set of tallies, have students circle the tens (2 groups of 5) in red and circle the ones in green.

11	卌 卌 I
12	卌 卌 II
13	卌 卌 III
14	卌 卌 IIII
15	卌 卌 卌
16	卌 卌 卌 I
17	卌 卌 卌 II
18	卌 卌 卌 III
19	卌 卌 卌 IIII
20	卌 卌 卌 卌

Option 2 Student Technology

Math Online macmillanmh.com

♪ Math Songs, "The Number Line" Track 10 • 🎮 Math Adventures

Option 3 Learning Station: Art (p. 239G)

Direct students to the Art Learning Station for more opportunities to explore and extend the lesson concept.

Option 4 Problem-Solving Practice

Reinforce problem-solving skills and strategies with the Problem-Solving Practice worksheet.

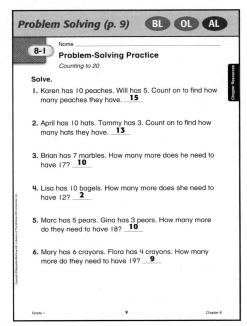

Problem Solving (p. 9) BL OL AL

Name _____
8-1 **Problem-Solving Practice**
Counting to 20

Solve.

1. Karen has 10 peaches. Will has 5. Count on to find how many peaches they have. **15**

2. April has 10 hats. Tammy has 3. Count on to find how many hats they have. **13**

3. Brian has 7 marbles. How many more does he need to have 17? **10**

4. Lisa has 10 bagels. How many more does she need to have 12? **2**

5. Marc has 5 pears. Gina has 3 pears. How many more do they need to have 18? **10**

6. Mary has 6 crayons. Flora has 4 crayons. How many more do they need to have 19? **9**

Grade 1   9   Chapter 8

1 Introduce

Activity Choice 1 • Hands-On

Give each student a handful of counters and have students separate the counters into groups of ten.

- **How many groups of ten do you have?**
  Sample answers: 0, 1, or 2 groups of ten
- **How many ones are left over?** See students' work.

Activity Choice 2 • Literature

Introduce the lesson with *Let's Count It Out, Jesse Bear* by Nancy White Carlstrom. For additional support, see p. TR52.

2 Teach

- On the overhead, display vertically a ten-frame with ten counters on the left and five counters on the right.

- As you write 1 above the group of ten and 5 above the group of 5, explain that there is 1 group of ten and 5 ones. The counters represent 15.

- Repeat with 1 group of ten and 8 ones.

- **How many groups of ten are there?** 1 group

- **How many ones are there?** 8 ones

- **What number do the tens and ones represent?** 18

- Have students use place value to compare.
  Which number is greater, 15 or 18? 18

Get Ready Use the top of p. 243 to reinforce the lesson concept. Guide students through the process of making 11 through 19 as tens and ones.

Check Observe students as you work through Exercises 1–5 as a class.

 **Exercise 5** Assess student comprehension before assigning practice exercises.

⚠ COMMON ERROR!

Students may forget to use 0 as a place holder and write 2 rather then 20 for example. When recording tens and ones, ask students to draw two blanks and to point to the blank where they will record the number in each category.

Name _____

Counting to 20

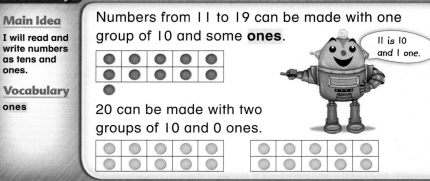

Get Ready

Main Idea
I will read and write numbers as tens and ones.

Vocabulary
ones

Numbers from 11 to 19 can be made with one group of 10 and some **ones**.

11 is 10 and 1 one.

20 can be made with two groups of 10 and 0 ones.

✓ Check

Use ⬤ ◯ and WorkMat 1. Read the number.
Then write as 10 and some ones.

1. twelve
   12 is __10__ and __2__ ones.

2. thirteen
   13 is __10__ and __3__ ones.

3. fourteen
   14 is __10__ and __4__ ones.

4. fifteen
   15 is __10__ and __5__ ones.

5. **Talk About It** How is 2 different from 20? Sample answer: 2 is two ones, 20 is two tens

Chapter 8   Lesson 1   two hundred forty-three   243

Copyright © Macmillan/McGraw-Hill, a division of The McGraw-Hill Companies, Inc.

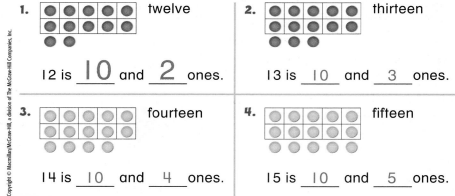

Reteach (p. 6) — BL

8-1 Reteach
Counting to 20

Numbers from 11 to 19 can be made with one group of 10 and some ones.

16 can be made with one group of 10 and 6 ones.

Write each number as 10 and some ones left over.

1. 13 is __10__ and __3__ ones.
2. 14 is __10__ and __4__ ones.
3. 15 is __10__ and __5__ ones.
4. 17 is __10__ and __7__ ones.
5. 18 is __10__ and __8__ ones.
6. 19 is __10__ and __9__ ones.

Grade 1   6   Chapter 8

Skills Practice (p. 7) — OL

8-1 Skills Practice
Counting to 20

Write each number as 10 and some ones left over.

1. 11 is __10__ and __1__ ones.
   eleven
2. 14 is __10__ and __4__ ones.
   fourteen
3. 16 is __10__ and __6__ ones.
   sixteen

Answer the questions.

4. If you have 10 apples, how many more do you need to have 15? __5__
5. If you have 2 carrots, how many more do you need to have 12? __10__
6. If you have 10 bananas, how many more do you need to have 19? __9__

Grade 1   7   Chapter 8

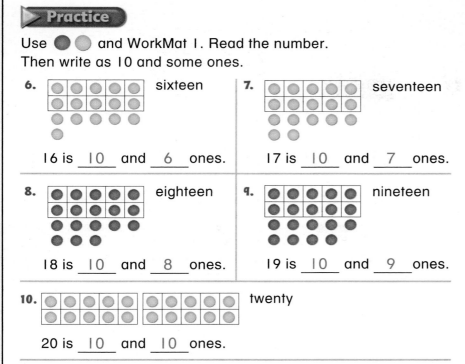

Use ⬤⬤ and WorkMat 1. Read the number.
Then write as 10 and some ones.

6. sixteen

16 is __10__ and __6__ ones.

7. seventeen

17 is __10__ and __7__ ones.

8. eighteen

18 is __10__ and __8__ ones.

9. nineteen

19 is __10__ and __9__ ones.

10. twenty

20 is __10__ and __10__ ones.

Write each number as 10 and some ones.

11. fifteen   15 is __10__ and __5__ ones.

12. eleven   11 is __10__ and __1__ one.

13. nineteen   19 is __10__ and __9__ ones.

H.O.T. Problem

14. Thinking Math You have 6 pencils in your pencil box. How many more do you need to get 16? __10__ pencils

244   two hundred forty-four

Math at Home Activity: Have your child count different objects of which there are 11–20. Ask your child to tell how many tens and ones.

BL Alternate Teaching Strategy

If students do not understand the place-value concepts of tens and ones in two-digit numbers . . .

Then use one of these reteach options.

1 CRM **Daily Reteach Worksheet** (p. 6)

2 Quantity Value Versus Column Value Build understanding of column value (25 is 2 tens and 5 units), by first describing the quantity value (25 is 20 plus 5).

③ Practice

Differentiate practice using these leveled assignments for Exercises 6–14.

Level	Assignment
BL Below/Approaching Level	Guide students through the exercises.
OL On Level	Complete independently, using workmat and counters as needed.
AL Above/Beyond Level	Complete the exercises without the workmat and counters.

④ Assess

Formative Assessment

Provide a double ten-frame workmat and counters.

- **How can you model 14 with counters?** Students should fill the first frame and put four counters in the second.
- **Write 14. What do the 1 and 4 in 14 represent?** 1 ten and 4 ones

WRITING IN ▶**MATH** Display two 10-cube towers. **About how many cubes in all?** 20 cubes Have students write about how to decide how many cubes without counting each one.

Quick Check **Are students continuing to struggle with tens and ones in numbers to 20?**

If Yes → Strategic Intervention Guide (p. 34)

If No → Independent Work Options (p. 243B)
   CRM Skills Practice Worksheet (p. 7)
   CRM Enrich Worksheet (p. 10)

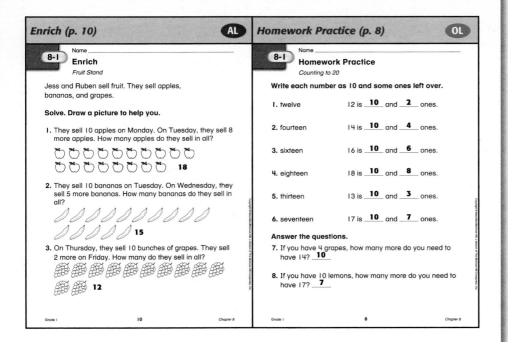

Enrich (p. 10) **AL**

8-1 Name ___
Enrich
Fruit Stand

Jess and Ruben sell fruit. They sell apples, bananas, and grapes.

Solve. Draw a picture to help you.

1. They sell 10 apples on Monday. On Tuesday, they sell 8 more apples. How many apples do they sell in all?
18

2. They sell 10 bananas on Tuesday. On Wednesday, they sell 5 more bananas. How many bananas do they sell in all?
15

3. On Thursday, they sell 10 bunches of grapes. They sell 2 more on Friday. How many do they sell in all?
12

Grade 1   10   Chapter 8

Homework Practice (p. 8) **OL**

8-1 Name ___
Homework Practice
Counting to 20

Write each number as 10 and some ones left over.

1. twelve   12 is __10__ and __2__ ones.

2. fourteen   14 is __10__ and __4__ ones.

3. sixteen   16 is __10__ and __6__ ones.

4. eighteen   18 is __10__ and __8__ ones.

5. thirteen   13 is __10__ and __3__ ones.

6. seventeen   17 is __10__ and __7__ ones.

Answer the questions.

7. If you have 4 grapes, how many more do you need to have 14? __10__

8. If you have 10 lemons, how many more do you need to have 17? __7__

Grade 1   8   Chapter 8

Lesson Planner _____

Objectives
Make, count, and write tens to 100.

Review Vocabulary
ten

Resources
Materials: pencils, overhead markers, 10 × 10 grid on a transparency, overhead projector

Manipulatives: base-ten blocks, connecting cubes

Literature Connection: *From One to One Hundred* by Teri Sloat

Alternate Lessons Use "Base-Ten Unifix Patterns" on page 314 in *Math Their Way* to provide practice making, counting, and writing by tens.

Use *IMPACT Mathematics*: Unit H to provide practice with counting by tens.

Teacher Technology
🌐 TeacherWorks • Concepts in Motion • 🎵 Math Tool Chest • Math Songs Track 10 Lesson Plan

Focus on Math Background

This lesson focuses counting by tens to quantify amounts up to 100. To be able to accurately skip count by tens, the student has to know the counting sequence and names of each decade—e.g. twenty, thirty, forty—all the way to 100. Also, as the student counts out 100 items, he/she must remember to group the objects into units of ten while reciting the corresponding skip counting sequence.

Daily Routine _____

Use these suggestions before beginning the lesson on p. 245.

5-Minute Check
(Reviews Lesson 8-1)
1. I have 1 ten and 9 ones. What number am I? 19
2. I have 1 ten and 3 ones. What number am I? 13
3. How many tens and ones are in seventeen? 1 ten and 7 ones
4. How many tens and ones are in twenty? 2 tens and 0 ones

Problem of the Day
Ted and his brother baked 12 muffins. They each ate 2 muffins. They gave their mother and sister each 1 muffin. How many muffins were left?
6 muffins

LINE UP Have students line up. Then have them count off by tens. When students get to 100, have them start over counting backwards to 10.

▷ Review Math Vocabulary
Materials: connecting cubes
- Write on the board the word **ten** and the numeral 10. Remind students that a ten is a group of ten objects.
- Have each student count out ten cubes and connect them to make a ten-train. Ask students to check for accuracy by comparing the length of their ten-train with classmates' trains.
- Have students sit in a circle. Ask ten students to place their ten-trains in the center of the circle. Count by tens as you point to each ten-train. Review the words ten, twenty, thirty, forty, fifty, sixty, seventy, eighty, ninety, and one hundred.
- Explain that 10 tens equal one hundred. Then have students count by tens to 100 with you.

Differentiated Instruction

Small Group Options

VISUAL/SPATIAL, LOGICAL

Gifted and Talented (AL)

Materials: index cards, markers

- Have students make a set of cards for the numbers 20 through 40.
- To model the activity, display several cards in order with one missing, as shown below. **Which card is missing?**
- Then have students do the same in groups. Group members take turns displaying a sequence of numbers with one missing. The other group members skip count to recognize the missing card.

AUDITORY/LINGUISTIC

English Language Learners (ELL)

Materials: 13–19 and 30, 40, 50, 60, 70, 80, 90 cards
Core Vocabulary: sound, end of the word, tap
Common Use Verb: listen

Hear Math This strategy helps students hear the differences in ending sounds.

- Model saying "13" and "30" while holding up the number cards.
- Explain that "13" has an *n* sound at the end of the word (thir-teen) and "30" has a *d* sound at the end (thir-*d*) when naturally spoken.
- Put the teen and ten card on a chalkboard ledge.
- Ask students to tap on numbers that end with the *d* sound while you say random numbers like "40" emphasizing the ending.

Use this worksheet to provide additional support for English Language Learners.

English Language Learners (p. 17) **ELL**

4 Name _____

Tens and Ones

Spin the tens spinner. Write that number.
Spin the ones spinner. Write that number.
Write the number of tens and ones in the chart.

	TENS	ONES	
Spin 1:	7	5	75
Spin 2:			
Spin 3:			
Spin 4:			
Spin 5:			

Check student responses.

Tens and Ones **17**

Independent Work Options

VISUAL/SPATIAL

Early Finishers (OL) (AL)

Materials: grid paper, crayons

- Distribute grid paper and crayons. **How many squares do we need to color to show a group of ten?** 10 squares Have students color ten squares in one row and write 10 next to that row.
- **How many squares would show two groups of ten?** 20 squares On another sheet of grid paper, have students fill in two rows of ten squares and write 20 next to them.

Student Technology

Math Online ▷ macmillanmh.com

♪ Math Songs, "Grouping by Tens" Track 8 • Math Tool Chest • Math Adventures

Learning Station: Language Arts (p. 239G)

Direct students to the Language Arts Learning Station for more opportunities to explore and extend the lesson concept.

Problem-Solving Practice

Reinforce problem-solving skills and strategies with the Problem-Solving Practice worksheet.

Problem Solving (p. 14) **BL** **OL** **AL**

Name _____

8-2 **Problem-Solving Practice**
Counting by Tens

Count by tens. Solve.

1. Matt has 4 sets of 10 trading cards. How many cards does he have?
   40
   forty

2. Ashley has 6 sets of ten markers. How many markers does she have?
   60
   sixty

3. Todd has 10 marbles. Chris has 10 marbles. Susan has 10 marbles. How many marbles are there in all?
   30
   thirty

4. Ann and Beth each have 10 peas. How many peas do they have?
   20
   twenty

5. Sara has 10 pencils. Jake, Joshua, Larry, and Michelle each have 10 pencils. How many total pencils are there?
   50
   fifty

6. Don, Jerry, Ben, Tom, Terry, Sally, and Sam each have 10 flowers. How many flowers do they have?
   70
   seventy

Grade 1 14 Chapter 8

 **8-2**

1 Introduce

Activity Choice 1 • Hands-On

- On the overhead, display ten base-ten units and one base-ten rod. Show a unit block and explain that it is one.
- Stack ten unit blocks, counting each one to show ten ones.
- Place a rod beside the ten unit blocks. Explain that ten unit blocks are the same as one ten. So when you have ten units, you exchange them and use one ten rod instead.
- Have them count out two stacks of ten unit blocks. Then exchange them for two rods.

Activity Choice 2 • Literature

Introduce the lesson with *From One to One Hundred* by Teri Sloat. For additional support, see p. TR52.

2 Teach

- Gather 30 connecting cubes. Display ten of them. Explain that when you have ten units, you can link them together and make one rod that stands for ten.
- Count until you get to 10. **How many cubes?** 10 cubes **What can I do when I get 10 cubes?** Link them together to make a rod.
- Show that now you have one rod made of ten ones.
- Continue the activity to show the number 30.

Get Ready Use the section at the top of p. 245 to reinforce the lesson concept.

Check Observe students as you work through Exercises 1–3 as a class.

💬 **Exercise 3** Assess student comprehension before assigning practice exercises.

⚠️ **COMMON ERROR!**

Students may lose count more easily when counting by tens because the numbers are less familiar than ones. Show students that counting by tens is a lot like counting by ones. Ten begins with a 1, 20 begins with a 2, etc.

245 **Chapter 8** Recognize Number Patterns

Name _____

Counting by Tens

Get Ready

Main Idea
I will count groups of ten.

You can count objects by ones. Or you can put objects into groups of ten then count by tens.

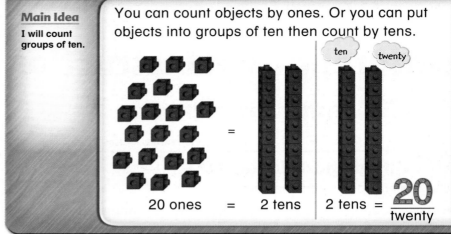

20 ones = 2 tens | 2 tens = **20** twenty

✔️ **Check**

Use 🎲. Count by tens. Read and write the number.

1. **6** tens / **60** sixty

2. **3** tens / **30** thirty

3. 💬 **Talk About It** How many groups of ten are in 50? Explain how you know. Sample answer: 5; I counted by tens to fifty. 10, 20, 30, 40, 50

Chapter 8   Lesson 2   two hundred forty-five **245**

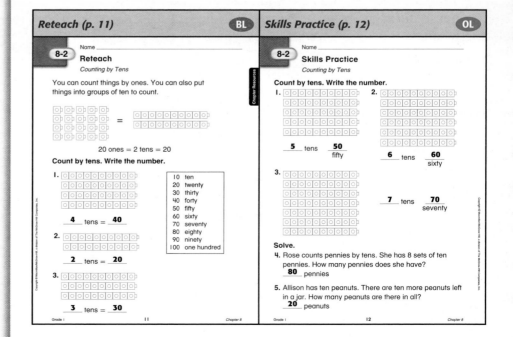

Reteach (p. 11) **BL**

8-2 Reteach
Counting by Tens

You can count things by ones. You can also put things into groups of ten to count.

20 ones = 2 tens = 20

Count by tens. Write the number.

1. **4** tens = **40**

2. **2** tens = **20**

3. **3** tens = **30**

10	ten
20	twenty
30	thirty
40	forty
50	fifty
60	sixty
70	seventy
80	eighty
90	ninety
100	one hundred

Skills Practice (p. 12) **OL**

8-2 Skills Practice
Counting by Tens

Count by tens. Write the number.

1. **5** tens **50** fifty

2. **6** tens **60** sixty

7 tens **70** seventy

Solve.

4. Rose counts pennies by tens. She has 8 sets of ten pennies. How many pennies does she have? **80** pennies

5. Allison has ten peanuts. There are ten more peanuts left in a jar. How many peanuts are there in all? **20** peanuts

Use . Count by tens. Read and write the number.

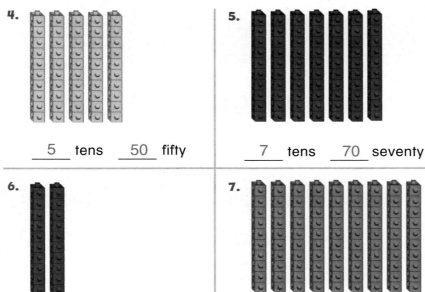

4.
_____5_____ tens _____50_____ fifty

5.
_____7_____ tens _____70_____ seventy

6.
_____2_____ tens _____20_____ twenty

7.
_____9_____ tens _____90_____ ninety

Write the number.

8. 6 tens = _____60_____
sixty

9. 3 tens = _____30_____
thirty

10. 8 tens = _____80_____
eighty

Problem Solving

11. Logical Reasoning Luisa is counting to 100 by tens. She starts with 10. She writes 8 numbers on her paper. What is the last number Luisa writes? _____80_____

246 two hundred forty-six

Math at Home Activity: Have your child find the number of fingers in your family. Ask how your child could count by tens to find the answer.

BL Alternate Teaching Strategy

If ▶ students have trouble counting by tens . . .

Then ▶ use one of these reteach options.

1 **CRM** **Daily Reteach Worksheet** (p. 11)

2 **Use Pennies to Count by Tens** Give students 40, 50, 60 70, 80, or 90 pennies. Have students stack the pennies into groups of ten. Ask students to write the number of stacks. Then have students point to each stack as they count by tens. Ask students to write the total number of pennies.

3 **TechLink** Have students use Math Tool Chest to help complete the problem-solving exercises.

③ Practice

Differentiate practice using these leveled assignments for Exercises 4–11.

Level	Assignment
BL Below/ Approaching Level	Guide students through the exercises. Have them use ten-trains for assistance.
OL On Level	Complete the exercises with a partner.
AL Above/Beyond Level	Complete the exercises independently.

④ Assess

✐ Formative Assessment

Have students use base-ten blocks, grid paper, or ten-trains to count by tens to 100.

WRITING IN ▶**MATH** Have students write about a situation where they would count by tens. For example, counting the students in the classroom.

Quick Check **Are students continuing to struggle with counting by tens to 100?**

If Yes → Strategic Intervention Guide (p. 44)

If No → Independent Work Options (p. 245B)
CRM Skills Practice Worksheet (p. 12)
CRM Enrich Worksheet (p. 15)

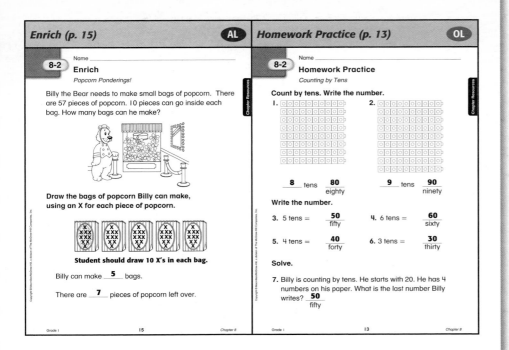

Enrich (p. 15) **AL**

8-2 Name _____
Enrich
Popcorn Ponderings!

Billy the Bear needs to make small bags of popcorn. There are 57 pieces of popcorn. 10 pieces can go inside each bag. How many bags can he make?

Draw the bags of popcorn Billy can make, using an X for each piece of popcorn.

Student should draw 10 X's in each bag.

Billy can make ____5____ bags.

There are ____7____ pieces of popcorn left over.

Grade 1   15   Chapter 8

Homework Practice (p. 13) **OL**

8-2 Name _____
Homework Practice
Counting by Tens

Count by tens. Write the number.

1.
____8____ tens ____80____
eighty

2.
____9____ tens ____90____
ninety

Write the number.

3. 5 tens = ____50____
fifty

4. 6 tens = ____60____
sixty

5. 4 tens = ____40____
forty

6. 3 tens = ____30____
thirty

Solve.

7. Billy is counting by tens. He starts with 20. He has 4 numbers on his paper. What is the last number Billy writes? ____50____
fifty

Grade 1   13   Chapter 8

Lesson Planner

Objective

Use the *look for a pattern* strategy to solve problems.

Resources

Literature Connection: *One Hundred Hungry Ants* by Elinor J. Pinczes

Teacher Technology

- TeacherWorks

📖 **Real-World Problem Solving Library**
Math and Science: *Look Again*

Use these leveled books to reinforce and extend problem-solving skills and strategies.

Leveled for:

- **OL** On Level
- **ELL** Sheltered English
- **SP** Spanish

For additional support, see the Real-World Problem Solving Teacher Guide.

Daily Routine

Use these suggestions before beginning the lesson on p. 247.

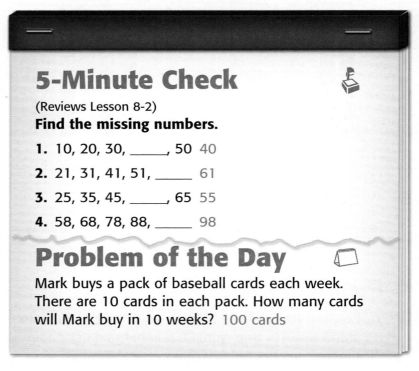

5-Minute Check

(Reviews Lesson 8-2)

Find the missing numbers.

1. 10, 20, 30, _____, 50   40

2. 21, 31, 41, 51, _____   61

3. 25, 35, 45, _____, 65   55

4. 58, 68, 78, 88, _____   98

Problem of the Day

Mark buys a pack of baseball cards each week. There are 10 cards in each pack. How many cards will Mark buy in 10 weeks?   100 cards

LINE UP Give students a number between 1 and 20. Have students start with that number and count by tens as they line up.

Differentiated Instruction

Small Group Options

Option 1 **Gifted and Talented** (AL)

LOGICAL

Materials: paper, pencils

Students will develop a plan to figure out how many doors are in their house.

- Have students list all of the rooms in their house.
- Then have them mentally picture each room, one by one, and list the number of doors in each. Remind students to count all doors, including closet doors.
- Finally, have students add to find the total number of doors in their house.
- Invite group members to compare their results to see whether there is a pattern. Remind students to compare the number of rooms, too. Ask them why the number of rooms might be important in using logical reasoning. Sample answer: Houses with more rooms would probably have more doors.

> Bedroom – 2
>
> Kitchen – 2
>
> Family Room – 1
>
> Bathroom – 1

Option 2 **English Language Learners** (ELL)

LOGICAL, SPATIAL

Materials: 1 inch, 1 foot, and 1 yard lengths of string

Core Vocabulary: that would be good, what would be better, which make sense?

Common Use Verb: could

See Math This strategy helps students understand what makes sense by recognizing patterns.

- Display string that is 1 inch, 1 foot, and 1 yard long.
- Ask students if they can measure the chalkboard using the inch string. Say: "Yes we *could*, **that would be good**—but **what would be better**?"
- Repeat for the foot long string, and the yard string, using the rhyming phrase each time.
- Discuss which length of string makes sense. Extend the strategy to other objects as time permits.

Independent Work Options

Option 1 **Early Finishers** (OL) (AL)

KINESTHETIC, VISUAL/SPATIAL, LOGICAL

Materials: chart paper; thin, colored markers

- Tell students that they will make a poster to complete a pattern.
- Display and discuss examples such as *I ate 30 sandwiches*, and *I ate 3 sandwiches*. Then invite students to write two sentences of their own in two different columns of a chart—one that uses a single digit and one that uses the corresponding ten.
- Ask students to draw a picture on their poster to illustrate each sentence.
- Finally, have students circle the reasonable sentence.

Option 2 **Student Technology**

 Math Online macmillanmh.com

Option 3 **Learning Station: Science** (p. 239H)

Direct students to the Science Learning Station for more opportunities to explore and extend the lesson concept.

1 Introduce

Activity Choice 1 • Review

Write and read aloud the following:

Jonathan scored 10 points in the game. Sheila scored 4 fewer points than Jonathan. How many points did Sheila score?

- **Which problem-solving strategy would be best for solving this problem?** Sample answer: write a number sentence
- **What number sentence would help you solve the problem?** 10 − 4 = 6
- **How many points did Sheila score?** 6 points

Activity Choice 2 • Literature

Introduce the lesson with *One Hundred Hungry Ants* by Elinor J. Pinczes. For additional support, see p. TR52.

2 Teach

Have students read the problem on page 247. Guide them through the problem-solving steps.

Understand Using the questions, review what students know and what they need to find.

Plan Have them discuss their strategy.

Solve Guide students to *look for a pattern* to solve the problem.

- **What is the pattern unit for the pattern on Kareem's backpack?** up arrow, down arrow, down arrow
- **What will come next in this pattern?** up arrow

Check Have students look back at the problem to make sure that the answer fits the facts given.

Name _____

Problem-Solving Strategy
Look for a Pattern

Main Idea
I will look for a pattern to solve a problem.

Kareem saw this pattern on his backpack. What will come next?

↑ ↓ ↓ ↑ ↓ ↓

Understand
What do I know? Underline what you know.
What do I need to find? Circle the question.

Plan
How will I solve the problem?

Solve
Look for a pattern.
Sample answer: The pattern unit is up arrow, down arrow, down arrow. The up arrow will come next.

Check
Look back.
Is my answer reasonable? Check students' explanations.

Chapter 8   Lesson 3   two hundred forty-seven   **247**

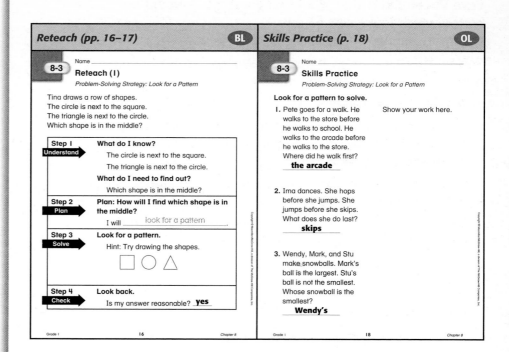

Try It

Look for a pattern to solve.

1. Martina saw this pattern.
   Circle what comes next.

2. Mia saw this pattern.
   Circle what comes next.

Your Turn

Look for a pattern to solve.

3. Thomas saw this pattern.
   Circle what comes next.

4. Sari saw this pattern.
   Circle what comes next.

248 two hundred forty-eight

Math at Home Activity: Look for patterns around your home. Ask your child what you would need to extend the patterns you find.

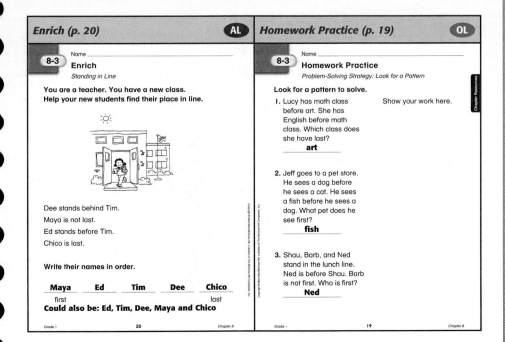

Enrich (p. 20) **AL**

8-3 Name _____
Enrich
Standing in Line

You are a teacher. You have a new class.
Help your new students find their place in line.

Dee stands behind Tim.

Maya is not last.

Ed stands before Tim.

Chico is last.

Write their names in order.

Maya	Ed	Tim	Dee	Chico
first				last

Could also be: Ed, Tim, Dee, Maya and Chico

Grade 1   20   Chapter 8

Homework Practice (p. 19) **OL**

8-3 Name _____
Homework Practice
Problem-Solving Strategy: Look for a Pattern

Look for a pattern to solve.

1. Lucy has math class   Show your work here.
   before art. She has
   English before math
   class. Which class does
   she have last?
   art

2. Jeff goes to a pet store.
   He sees a dog before
   he sees a cat. He sees
   a fish before he sees
   a dog. What pet does he
   see first?
   fish

3. Shau, Barb, and Ned
   stand in the lunch line.
   Ned is before Shau. Barb
   is not first. Who is first?
   Ned

Grade 1   19   Chapter 8

Try It Observe students as you work through Exercises 1–2 as a class.

BL Alternate Teaching Strategy

If ➤ students have difficulty finding a pattern . . .

Then ➤ use one of these reteach options.

1 **CRM Daily Reteach Worksheet** (pp. 16–17)

2 **Find the Clues** As students work through the problems, have them underline the pattern unit. Then ask them to say the pattern aloud before circling their answer. Have students say the pattern aloud with their answer to check their work.

③ Practice

Your Turn

Exercises 3–4 Be sure students can read and understand the problems. Remind them to think about what they know and circle the answer that makes the most sense.

④ Assess

Formative Assessment

On the board, draw a sock with the following pattern along the top: star, star, sun, star, star, sun.

- **What is the pattern unit?** star, star, sun

- Have students continue the pattern unit until there are four suns in all. star, star, sun, star, star, sun, star, star, sun, star, star, sun

Quick Check **Are students continuing to struggle looking for a pattern to solve?**

If Yes ➤ **CRM** Reteach Worksheet (p. 16–17)

If No ➤ Independent Work Options (p. 247B)

CRM Skills Practice Worksheet (p. 18)

CRM Enrich Worksheet (p. 20)

Lesson 8-3 Problem-Solving Strategy **248**

Lesson Planner

Objective

Count and order numbers from 1 to 100 on a hundred chart.

Vocabulary

hundred chart

Resources

Materials: class-size number line, overhead projector, hundred chart

Literature Connection: *Out for the Count: A Counting Adventure* by Kathryn Cave

Teacher Technology
- TeacherWorks • Math Songs Track 8 Lesson Plan

Focus on Math Background

Students use a hundred chart in this lesson in order to visualize the resulting patterns that unfold as the numbers are organized and displayed in a 10 by 10 grid. When students look at a hundred chart, they will notice, among many other patterns, how the digits in the ones place repeat in a 1–9 sequence and how the digits in the tens place remain the same going horizontally from left to right.

Daily Routine

Use these suggestions before beginning the lesson on p. 249.

5-Minute Check

(Reviews Lesson 8-3)

Look at the number patterns. Find the missing numbers.

1. 40, 50, ___ , 70, 80 60
2. 12, 22, 32, 42, ___ 52
3. 9, 19, 29, ___, 49 39

Problem of the Day

Carmen caught 10 frogs. Then she let 8 of the frogs hop away. How many frogs did she have left? 2 frogs

LINE UP Have students count by tens as they line up. The first student should say *ten*, the second student *twenty*, and so on. After 10 students have lined up, have the next student begin again at *ten*.

▷ Building Math Vocabulary

Materials: connecting cubes, hundred chart

- Write the word **hundred chart** on the board. Beside it, display a class-size hundred chart or a hundred chart on an overhead projector. Explain that it is called a hundred chart. Have children call out what they notice about the hundred chart. Sample answers: The numbers are in order; the numbers at the end of each row have a zero/are tens; there are patterns reading across and reading down.

- Explain that a hundred chart is a table that has ten rows, ten columns, and the numbers 1–100 in order. A hundred chart is read from left to right with return sweeps the same direction that you read a book.

Differentiated Instruction

Small Group Options

Option 1
Below Level **BL**

Materials: hundred chart

- Point to and say a number on the hundred chart, for example, **17.** Then have a student read that whole number and count on the next five numbers in order from memory: 18, 19, 20, 21, 22.

1	2	3	4	5	6	7	8	9	10
11	12	13	14	15	16	17	18	19	20
21	22	23	24	25	26	27	28	29	30
31	32	33	34	35	36	37	38	39	40
41	42	43	44	45	46	47	48	49	50
51	52	53	54	55	56	57	58	59	60
61	62	63	64	65	66	67	68	69	70
71	72	73	74	75	76	77	78	79	80
81	82	83	84	85	86	87	88	89	90
91	92	93	94	95	96	97	98	99	100

- Have the rest of the group check the numbers by following along on the hundred chart. Repeat with greater and greater numbers to help students build fluency reading a hundred chart and counting on.

Option 2
English Language Learners **ELL**

Materials: 100's chart, counters
Core Vocabulary: across, up and down, diagonally
Common Use Verb: cover

Do Math This strategy introduces the 100's chart and how to verbalize movement around a grid.

- Model *across*, *diagonal*, and *up and down* on a bingo chart.
- Put numbers 1–100 in a container.
- Give each student a 100's chart and counters.
- Pull and read the number. Prompt students to cover it with a counter. Use the vocabulary to help them find the number as necessary.
- Repeat as time permits.

Independent Work Options

Option 1
Early Finishers **OL** **AL**

Materials: hundred chart, crayons

- Have partners take turns secretly coloring in a number on a hundred chart.
- Have one student describe a number by telling the number that comes before, after, above, and below it. Then the partner guesses.
- Have to other student use place value.

1	2	3	4	5	6	7	8	9	10
11	12	13	14	15	16	17	18	19	20
21	22	23	24	25	26	27	28	29	30
31	32	33	34	35	36	37	38	39	40
41	42	43	44	45	46	47	48	49	50
51	52	53	54	55	56	57	58	59	60
61	62	63	64	65	66	67	68	69	70
71	72	73	74	75	76	77	78	79	80
81	82	83	84	85	86	87	88	89	90
91	92	93	94	95	96	97	98	99	100

Option 2
Student Technology

Math Online macmillanmh.com

♪ Math Songs, "Grouping By Tens" Track 8

Option 3
Learning Station: Health (p. 239H)

Direct students to the Health Learning Station for more opportunities to explore and extend the lesson concept.

Option 4
Problem-Solving Practice

Reinforce problem-solving skills and strategies with the Problem-Solving Practice worksheet.

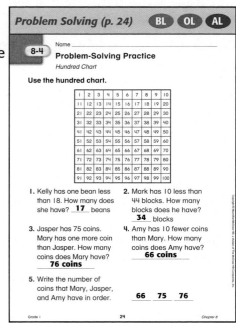

1 Introduce

Activity Choice 1 • Hands-On

- Display a **hundred chart**. Explain that one of the fun things we can do with a hundred chart is start any place and count forward or backward.
- Start at 1. Touch each number and count to 15.
- Distribute hundred chart to the students. Ask a volunteer to name or point to a number. Have students tell the number that comes before and after the number chosen by the volunteer.
- Count on several numbers with the group.

Activity Choice 2 • Literature

Introduce the lesson with *Out for the Count: A Counting Adventure* by Kathryn Cave. For additional support, see p. TR53.

2 Teach

- Display a hundred chart on the overhead. Touch a number and have students say the number aloud. Then count with the students to 100. Repeat the activity.
- Next, on the overhead, write a set of five or six numbers in order with a number missing. Have students use the hundred chart to tell what number is missing from the set.
- Then on the overhead, write four or five random numbers. Have students use the hundred chart to help them put the numbers in order.

Get Ready Use the section at the top of p. 249 to reinforce the lesson concept.

Check Observe students as you work through Exercises 1–12 as a class.

> **Exercise 12** Assess student comprehension before assigning practice exercises.

! COMMON ERROR!

Students may not understand that numbers that are not consecutive can be placed in order. Use a number line to reinforce the idea that putting in order means telling which comes before and which comes after, even if other numbers come between.

Name _____

Hundred Chart

Get Ready

Main Idea

I will read and count numbers in order on a hundred chart.

Vocabulary

hundred chart

You can use a **hundred chart** to read and count numbers in order.

1	2	3	4	5	6	7	8	9	10
11	12	13	14	15	16	17	18	19	20
21	22	23	24	25	26	27	28	29	30
31	32	33	34	35	36	37	38	39	40
41	42	43	44	45	46	47	48	49	50
51	52	53	54	55	56	57	58	59	60
61	62	63	64	65	66	67	68	69	70
71	72	73	74	75	76	77	78	79	80
81	82	83	84	85	86	87	88	89	90
91	92	93	94	95	96	97	98	99	100

If I start at 21, what number will I say next? 22

Check

1. Count from 1 to 25. Color the numbers as you read them.

2. Count from 26 to 50. Color the numbers as you read them.

3. Count from 51 to 100. Color the numbers as you read them.

1	2	3	4	5	6	7	8	9	10
11	12	13	14	15	16	17	18	19	20
21	22	23	24	25	26	27	28	29	30
31	32	33	34	35	36	37	38	39	40
41	42	43	44	45	46	47	48	49	50
51	52	53	54	55	56	57	58	59	60
61	62	63	64	65	66	67	68	69	70
71	72	73	74	75	76	77	78	79	80
81	82	83	84	85	86	87	88	89	90
91	92	93	94	95	96	97	98	99	100

Reteach (p. 21)   **BL**

8-4   Name _____

Reteach
Hundred Chart

Find number patterns on a hundred chart.

Look at 23 on the chart.

10 less than 23
Go ↑ to 13.

I less
Go ← to 22.

13

22 | 23 | 24

I more
Go → to 24.

33

10 more
Go ↓ to 33.

Write each number. Use the hundred chart.

1. (48) I more Go → 49   10 more Go ↓ 58
   I less Go ← 47   10 less Go ↑ 38

2. (73) I more Go → 74   10 more Go ↓ 83
   I less Go ← 72   10 less Go ↑ 63

3. (67) I more Go → 68   10 more Go ↓ 77
   I less Go ← 66   10 less Go ↑ 57

Grade 1   21   Chapter 8

Use the hundred chart.
Write the numbers in order.

1	2	3	4	5	6	7	8	9	10
11	12	13	14	15	16	17	18	19	20
21	22	23	24	25	26	27	28	29	30
31	32	33	34	35	36	37	38	39	40
41	42	43	44	45	46	47	48	49	50
51	52	53	54	55	56	57	58	59	60
61	62	63	64	65	66	67	68	69	70
71	72	73	74	75	76	77	78	79	80
81	82	83	84	85	86	87	88	89	90
91	92	93	94	95	96	97	98	99	100

4. 13 31 23   __13__ __23__ __31__

5. 35 27 20   __20__   __27__   __35__

Remember
The numbers are in order on the hundred chart.

6. 24 21 30   __21__   __24__   __30__

7. 85 68 59 74   __59__   __68__   __74__   __85__

8. 52 36 48 65   __36__   __48__   __52__   __65__

9. 98 100 99 97   __97__   __98__   __99__   __100__

10. 59 84 63 49   __49__   __59__   __63__   __84__

11. 30 72 18 39   __18__   __30__   __39__   __72__

12. **Talk About It** How many numbers on the hundred chart are less than 20? 19

250   two hundred fifty

GO on

BL **Alternate Teaching Strategy**

If students have trouble putting in order numbers between 1 and 100 . . .

Then use one of these reteach options.

1. **CRM** **Daily Reteach Worksheet** (p. 21)

2. **Count to 100** Have student pairs practice counting from 1–100, using objects such as pennies, corn kernels, macaroni noodles, or other similar items.

Skills Practice (p. 22)   **OL**

8-4   Name _____

Skills Practice
Hundred Chart

Use the hundred chart. Find each number below on the chart. Find 1 less. Find 1 more.

1	2	3	4	5	6	7	8	9	10
11	12	13	14	15	16	17	18	19	20
21	22	23	24	25	26	27	28	29	30
31	32	33	34	35	36	37	38	39	40
41	42	43	44	45	46	47	48	49	50
51	52	53	54	55	56	57	58	59	60
61	62	63	64	65	66	67	68	69	70
71	72	73	74	75	76	77	78	79	80
81	82	83	84	85	86	87	88	89	90
91	92	93	94	95	96	97	98	99	100

1. 25   1 less is __24__.   1 more is __26__.

2. 46   1 less is __45__.   1 more is __47__.

3. 90   1 less is __89__.   1 more is __91__.

Write the numbers in order.

4. There are 10 kids in Mary's class. There are 8 kids in Mark's class. There are 6 kids in David's class. Write the numbers in order.   __6__   __8__   __10__

Grade 1   22   Chapter 8

③ Practice

Differentiate practice using these leveled assignments for Exercises 13–23.

Level	Assignment
BL Below/Approaching Level	Guide students through the exercises.
OL On Level	Complete the exercises with a partner.
AL Above/Beyond Level	Complete the exercises independently.

Name _____

▶ Practice

13. Read and write the missing numbers.

1	2	3	4	5	6	7	8	9	10
11	12	13	14	15	16	17	18	19	20
21	22	23	24	25	26	27	28	29	30
31	32	33	34	35	36	37	38	39	40
41	42	43	44	45	46	47	48	49	50
51	52	53	54	55	56	57	58	59	60
61	62	63	64	65	66	67	68	69	70
71	72	73	74	75	76	77	78	79	80
81	82	83	84	85	86	87	88	89	90
91	92	93	94	95	96	97	98	99	100

Chapter 8 Lesson 4   two hundred fifty-one 251

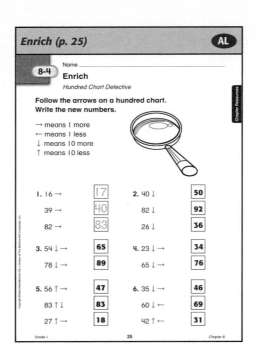

Enrich (p. 25)   **AL**

Use the hundred chart.
Write the numbers in order.

1	2	3	4	5	6	7	8	9	10
11	12	13	14	15	16	17	18	19	20
21	22	23	24	25	26	27	28	29	30
31	32	33	34	35	36	37	38	39	40
41	42	43	44	45	46	47	48	49	50
51	52	53	54	55	56	57	58	59	60
61	62	63	64	65	66	67	68	69	70
71	72	73	74	75	76	77	78	79	80
81	82	83	84	85	86	87	88	89	90
91	92	93	94	95	96	97	98	99	100

14. 44   14   41

   14   41   44

15. 89   81   18

   18   81   89

16. 38   29   47

   29   38   47

17. 22   14   87   78

   14   22   78   87

18. 74   8   49

   8   49   74

19. 18   96   37   3

   3   18   37   96

20. 55   16   38   4

   4   16   38   55

21. 17   85   46   71

   17   46   71   85

22. 63   14   93   8

   8   14   63   93

WRITING IN ►MATH

23. Count from 91 to 100. Count backward from 100 to 91. How are counting forward and counting backward alike? How are they different?   Sample answers:

Alike: You say the same numbers when you count forward and when you count backward. Different: When you count

forward, each number is one more than the one before it. When you count backward, each number is one less than the one before it.

Math at Home Activity: Have your child choose a number on the hundred chart and show you how to count backward to 1 and forward to 100 from that number.

252   two hundred fifty-two

 Assess

Formative Assessment

Have students use a hundred chart to count to 100 by tens.

- **How can you use a hundred chart to put three numbers in order from least to greatest?** Find them on the chart and see which one comes first, second, and last.

- **Put these numbers in order from least to greatest: 52, 14, 33.** 14, 33, 52

WRITING IN ►**MATH** Display a hundred chart. **Write about how you can use a hundred chart to count by tens.** Sample answer: Read the numbers in the tens column in order.

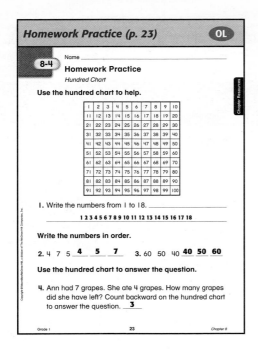

Homework Practice (p. 23) **OL**

8-4   Name _____

Homework Practice
Hundred Chart

Use the hundred chart to help.

1	2	3	4	5	6	7	8	9	10
11	12	13	14	15	16	17	18	19	20
21	22	23	24	25	26	27	28	29	30
31	32	33	34	35	36	37	38	39	40
41	42	43	44	45	46	47	48	49	50
51	52	53	54	55	56	57	58	59	60
61	62	63	64	65	66	67	68	69	70
71	72	73	74	75	76	77	78	79	80
81	82	83	84	85	86	87	88	89	90
91	92	93	94	95	96	97	98	99	100

1. Write the numbers from 1 to 18. _____
   1 2 3 4 5 6 7 8 9 10 11 12 13 14 15 16 17 18

Write the numbers in order.

2. 4 7 5 **4   5   7**   3. 60 50 40 **40 50 60**

Use the hundred chart to answer the question.

4. Ann had 7 grapes. She ate 4 grapes. How many grapes did she have left? Count backward on the hundred chart to answer the question. ___**3**___

Grade 1   23   Chapter 8

Quick Check   Are students continuing to struggle with using a hundred chart?

If Yes → Small Group Options (p. 251B)
Strategic Intervention Guide (p. 98)

If No → Independent Work Options (p. 251B)
CRM Skills Practice Worksheet (p. 22)
CRM Enrich Worksheet (p. 25)

 **Mid-Chapter Check**

Lessons 8-1 to 8-4

 Formative Assessment

Use the Mid-Chapter Check to assess students' progress in the first half of the chapter.

ExamView®
Assessment Suite
Customize and create multiple versions of your Mid-Chapter Check and the test answer keys.

FOLDABLES® Dinah Zike's Foldables

Use these lesson suggestions to incorporate the Foldable during the chapter.

Lesson 8-1 Make ten Matchbook Foldables and use them for numbers 11–20. Add these cards to those made in Chapter 1 to form the numbers 1–20. Make new Foldables if Foldables from Chapter 1 are no longer available.

Lesson 8-4 Divide students into groups and have them make Matchbook Foldables for numbers 21–99. Use the Foldables to make a hundred chart. Discuss how students could represent 100 on the hundred chart.

Name _____

Read the number. Then write as 10 and some ones.

1. eighteen   18 is __10__ and __8__ ones.

2. thirteen   13 is __10__ and __3__ ones.

3. sixteen   16 is __10__ and __6__ ones.

Count by tens.
Read and write the number.

4. 5 tens = ___50___   5. 2 tens = ___20___
         fifty   twenty

Use the hundred chart.
Write the numbers in order.

1	2	3	4	5	6	7	8	9	10
11	12	13	14	15	16	17	18	19	20
21	22	23	24	25	26	27	28	29	30
31	32	33	34	35	36	37	38	39	40
41	42	43	44	45	46	47	48	49	50
51	52	53	54	55	56	57	58	59	60
61	62	63	64	65	66	67	68	69	70
71	72	73	74	75	76	77	78	79	80
81	82	83	84	85	86	87	88	89	90
91	92	93	94	95	96	97	98	99	100

6. 54 86 12   __12__ __54__ __86__

7. 41 94 7   __7__ __41__ __94__

8. 84 19 26   __19__ __26__ __84__

Solve.

9. Julie read 7 pages of a book.
   She has 5 pages left to read.
   How many pages are in the book?
   __7__ (+) __5__ (=) __12__ pages

Chapter 8   two hundred fifty-three **253**

Data-Driven Decision Making

Based on the results of the Mid-Chapter Check, use the following resources to review concepts that continue to give students problems.

Exercises	State/Local Standards	What's the Math?	Error Analysis	Resources for Review
1–3 Lesson 8-1		Create sets of tens and ones.	Does not count tens and ones correctly.	Strategic Intervention Guide (p. 98) **CRM** Chapter 8 Resource Masters (Reteach Worksheets)
4–5 Lesson 8-2		Find the whole number from a set of tens.	Does not add tens correctly.	**Math Online** Concepts in Motion Math Adventures
6–8 Lesson 8-4		Use a hundred chart to order numbers.	Incorrectly orders numbers. Puts numbers in reverse order.	

Write the time.

10.

___ 3 ___ : ___ 30 ___

11.

___ 8 ___ : ___ 00 ___

12.

___ 11 ___ : ___ 30 ___

13.

___ 6 ___ : ___ 00 ___

Add. Then subtract.

14. $4 + 4 =$ ___ 8 ___

$8 - 4 =$ ___ 4 ___

15. $6 + 5 =$ ___ 11 ___

$11 - 5 =$ ___ 6 ___

16. Jake is planning a pool party. If the weather pattern continues, will Friday be a good day for swimming? Explain your answer.

Monday	Tuesday	Wednesday	Thursday	Friday
⚡	☀	⚡	☀	

No, because the pattern shows that there will be lightning on Friday. It is not safe to swim when there is lightning.

Formative Assessment

Spiral Review

Review Chapters 1 to 8

Objective: Review and assess mastery of skills and concepts from previous chapters.

Resources for Review

Based on student results, refer to these lessons for remediation.

- **Exercises 10–13: Lesson 7-5** (p. 223)
- **Exercises 14–15: Lesson 6-5** (p. 195)
- **Exercise 16: Lesson 1-1** (p. 17)

Estimating with Groups of Ten

Lesson Planner

Objective

Use a group of tens as a guide to estimate quantities up to 100.

Vocabulary

estimate

Resources

Materials: yarn, pennies

Manipulatives: connecting cubes, two-colored counters

Literature Connection: *100 Days of Fun at School* by Janet Craig

Alternate Lessons Adapt "Perimeters" on page 315 of *Math Their Way* for practice in estimating quantities up to 100. Use *IMPACT Mathematics:* Unit H to provide practice with estimating quantities up to 100.

Teacher Technology
TeacherWorks • Concepts in Motion

Focus on Math Background

In this lesson, students will estimate with groups of tens. All multiples of ten (numbers that can be broken down into equal groups of ten—i.e. 20, 30, 40, etc.) are important landmarks, or friendly numbers, because they are easy to count. For example, it is much easier to think of 19 as close to 20, or two sets of ten, instead of one ten and nine singles.

Daily Routine

Use these suggestions before beginning the lesson on p. 255.

5-Minute Check

(Reviews Lesson 8-4)
Use a hundred chart to solve the riddles:
1. The numbers above and below me are 34 and 54. What number am I? 44
2. The numbers before and after me are 17 and 19. What number am I? 18

Problem of the Day

Juan has a jar of pennies. He needs to find how many pennies he has. What are some was to find the number of pennies? Sample answer: Count them by tens.

 LINE UP Ask students to estimate how many steps they must take from their seat to the classroom door. Then count the actual number of steps. **Was your estimate higher or lower than the actual number of steps you took?**

Building Math Vocabulary

Materials: two identical jars—one filled with jellybeans and one filled with marbles

- Write the word **estimate** on the board. Explain that to find an answer close to an exact amount, they can estimate.

- Display the jars. Tell students how many marbles are in the jar. Then have each student guess the number of jellybeans in the jar.

- Have students count the jellybeans. Discuss which estimates were closest.

Visual Vocabulary Cards

Use Visual Vocabulary Card 17 to reinforce the vocabulary introduced in this lesson. (The Define/Example/Ask routine is printed on the back of each card.)

estimate

Differentiated Instruction

Small Group Options

Option 1 — Gifted and Talented (AL)

Materials: index cards, markers

- Have students work together to count the number of desks in one group or row in the classroom.
- Then challenge them to use that number of desks to estimate about how many desks there are altogether in the classroom.
- Finally, have students take an actual count of desks in the classroom.

Option 2 — English Language Learners (ELL)

Materials: paper bag, objects, 9 small paper plates
Core Vocabulary: bag, paper clips, about
Common Use Verb: guess

Do Math This strategy uses counters as a tool to teach estimation.

- Put a number of paper clips (or other like objects) in a paper bag and shake.
- Say: "guess about how many are in the bag."
- Explain that students can make 10 guesses in all.
- Count the objects by putting each group of ten on a paper plate.
- Change the objects and number and repeat as time permits.

Use this worksheet to provide additional support for English Language Learners.

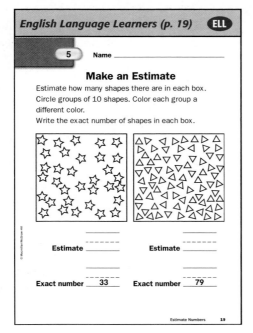

English Language Learners (p. 19) **ELL**

5   Name _____

Make an Estimate

Estimate how many shapes there are in each box.
Circle groups of 10 shapes. Color each group a different color.
Write the exact number of shapes in each box.

Estimate _____   Estimate _____

Exact number __33__   Exact number __79__

Estimate Numbers   19

Independent Work Options

Option 1 — Early Finishers (OL) (AL)

Materials: four baby food jars with objects

- Have students estimate the number of objects in each jar and write their estimates on a sheet of paper.
- Ask students to count out ten objects from each jar and then revise their estimates. Have them record their revised estimate.
- Finally, have students count the objects in each jar and record the actual number.

Jar	Est. 1	Est. 2	Actual
1			
2			
3			
4			

Option 2 — Student Technology

Math Online > macmillanmh.com

Online Games

Option 3 — Learning Station: Social Studies (p. 239G)

Direct students to the Social Studies Learning Station for more opportunities to explore and extend the lesson concept.

Option 4 — Problem-Solving Practice

Reinforce problem-solving skills and strategies with the Problem-Solving Practice worksheet.

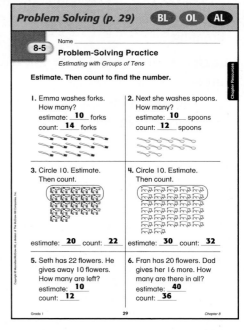

Problem Solving (p. 29) **BL OL AL**

Name _____

8-5   **Problem-Solving Practice**
Estimating with Groups of Tens

Estimate. Then count to find the number.

1. Emma washes forks. How many?
estimate: __10__ forks
count: __14__ forks

2. Next she washes spoons. How many?
estimate: __10__ spoons
count: __12__ spoons

3. Circle 10. Estimate. Then count.
estimate: __20__ count: __22__

4. Circle 10. Estimate. Then count.
estimate: __30__ count: __32__

5. Seth has 22 flowers. He gives away 10 flowers. How many are left?
estimate: __10__
count: __12__

6. Fran has 20 flowers. Dad gives her 16 more. How many are there in all?
estimate: __40__
count: __36__

Grade 1   29   Chapter 8

① Introduce

Activity Choice 1 • Hands-On

Give students ten yellow, ten purple, ten red, ten green, and ten orange cubes. Have students count and connect all of their yellow cubes.

- **How many connecting cubes are yellow?** 10
- **How many colors are left?** 4 colors
- **Estimate how many connecting cubes you have in all.** See students' work.
- Have students connect the cubes of each color separately and make a new estimate.
- **Were your estimates the same or different?** See students' explanations.

Activity Choice 2 • Literature

Introduce the lesson with *100 Days of Fun at School* by Janet Craig. For additional support, see p. TR53.

② Teach

- Put together ten yellow connecting cubes, eight red, nine green, and two purple. Display the yellow chain on the overhead.
- Place the chain of eight red cubes below the yellow cubes. **Are there almost as many reds as there are yellows?** yes
- Explain that this is a way to estimate.
- Replace the red with the green, and repeat.

Get Ready Use the section at the top of p. 255 to reinforce the lesson concept. Guide students through estimating.

Check Observe students as you work through Exercises 1–4 as a class.

💬 **Exercise 4** Assess student comprehension before assigning practice exercises.

⚠ COMMON ERROR!

Some students may have difficulty generating reasonable estimates rather than wild guesses. Think "out loud" to model estimation strategies, such as counting groups of ten or comparing part to whole.

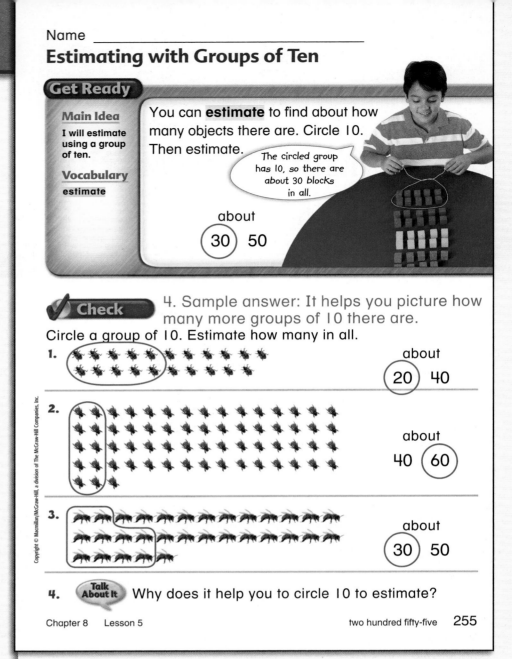

Name _____

Estimating with Groups of Ten

Get Ready

Main Idea
I will estimate using a group of ten.

Vocabulary
estimate

You can **estimate** to find about how many objects there are. Circle 10. Then estimate.

The circled group has 10, so there are about 30 blocks in all.

about
(30) 50

Check — 4. Sample answer: It helps you picture how many more groups of 10 there are.

Circle a group of 10. Estimate how many in all.

1. about (20) 40

2. about 40 (60)

3. about (30) 50

4. **Talk About It** Why does it help you to circle 10 to estimate?

Chapter 8   Lesson 5   two hundred fifty-five   255

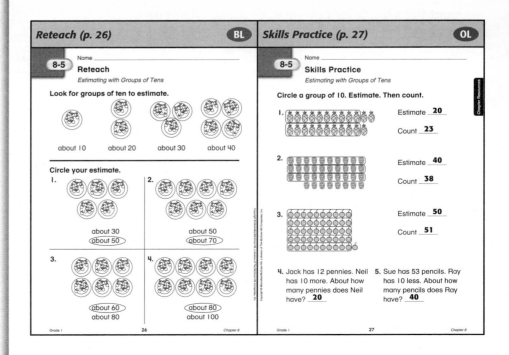

Reteach (p. 26) — BL

8-5 **Reteach**
Estimating with Groups of Tens

Look for groups of ten to estimate.

about 10   about 20   about 30   about 40

Circle your estimate.

1. about 30 / (about 50)

2. about 50 / (about 70)

3. (about 60) / about 80

4. (about 80) / about 100

Grade 1   26   Chapter 8

Skills Practice (p. 27) — OL

8-5 **Skills Practice**
Estimating with Groups of Tens

Circle a group of 10. Estimate. Then count.

1. Estimate **20**   Count **23**

2. Estimate **40**   Count **38**

3. Estimate **50**   Count **51**

4. Jack has 12 pennies. Neil has 10 more. About how many pennies does Neil have? **20**

5. Sue has 53 pencils. Ray has 10 less. About how many pencils does Ray have? **40**

Grade 1   27   Chapter 8

Circle a group of 10. Estimate how many in all.

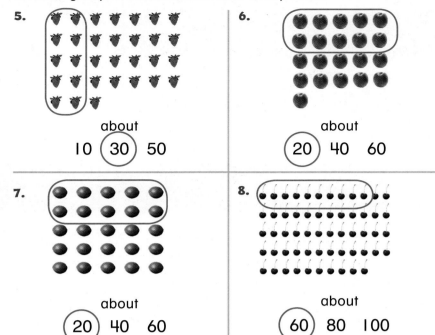

5.

about

10 (30) 50

6.

about

(20) 40 60

7.

about

(20) 40 60

8.

about

(60) 80 100

Problem Solving

9. Logical Reasoning Rey started with 10 bags of cups for his lemonade stand. Each bag had 10 cups. At the end of the day, Rey had 5 cups left. Is 10 or 100 a better estimate for how many cups of lemonade he sold? Explain.

Sample answer: 100 because 10 packs of 10 cups each is 100.

Math at Home Activity: Give your child a handful of small objects. Have your child estimate how many. Then count.

256 two hundred fifty-six

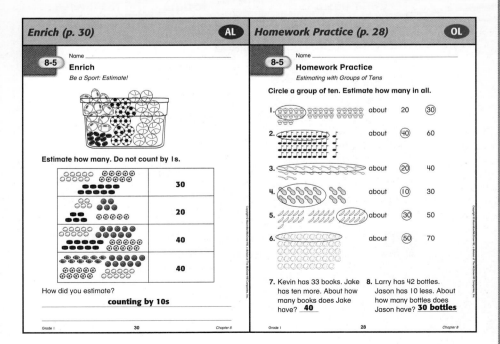

Enrich (p. 30) AL

8-5 Name _____

Enrich
Be a Sport: Estimate!

Estimate how many. Do not count by 1s.

	30
	20
	40
	40

How did you estimate?

counting by 10s

Grade 1   30   Chapter 8

Homework Practice (p. 28) OL

8-5 Name _____

Homework Practice
Estimating with Groups of Tens

Circle a group of ten. Estimate how many in all.

1. about 20 (30)
2. about (40) 60
3. about (20) 40
4. about (10) 30
5. about (30) 50
6. about (50) 70

7. Kevin has 33 books. Jake has ten more. About how many books does Jake have? **40**

8. Larry has 42 bottles. Jason has 10 less. About how many bottles does Jason have? **30 bottles**

Grade 1   28   Chapter 8

BL Alternate Teaching Strategy

If students have trouble estimating . . .

Then use one of the following reteach options.

1 CRM Daily Reteach Worksheet (p. 26)

2 Use Manipulatives Have students spread out two handfuls of counters. Help them use yarn to circle ten of the counters. Have students compare their group of ten to the counters outside the yarn.

- **Are there more or fewer than ten outside the yarn? Do you think there are 2 groups of ten outside the yarn?** See students' work.

- **Use your ideas to estimate how many counters you have.** See students' work.

③ Practice

Differentiate practice using these leveled assignments for Exercises 5–9.

Level	Assignment
BL Below/Approaching Level	Guide students through the exercises. Have them use manipulatives for support
OL On Level	Complete the exercises with a partner.
AL Above/Beyond Level	Complete the exercises independently.

④ Assess

Formative Assessment

Arrange 68 counters on the overhead in six rows of 10 and one row of 8.

Which estimate is closer—70 or 90? Why do you think so? 70; There are almost 7 groups of 10.

WRITING IN ►MATH Give students an opportunity to estimate objects found in nature. Take a walk outside. Have students record estimations of objects such as flowers in the garden.

Quick Check **Are students continuing to struggle with estimating?**

If Yes → Strategic Intervention Guide (p. 48)

If No → Independent Work Options (p. 255B)

CRM Skills Practice Worksheet (p. 27)

CRM Enrich Worksheet (p. 30)

Problem-Solving Investigation
Choose a Strategy

Lesson Planner _____

Objective

Choose the best strategy to solve problems.

Resources

Materials: pencils

Manipulatives: two-colored counters, connecting cubes

Teacher Technology

🌐 TeacherWorks

📖 **Real-World Problem Solving Library**
Math and Science: *Look Again*
Use these leveled books to reinforce and extend
problem-solving skills and strategies.

Leveled for:

OL On Level

ELL Sheltered English

SP Spanish

For additional support,
see the Real-World
Problem Solving
Teacher Guide.

Daily Routine _____

Use these suggestions before beginning the lesson on p. 257.

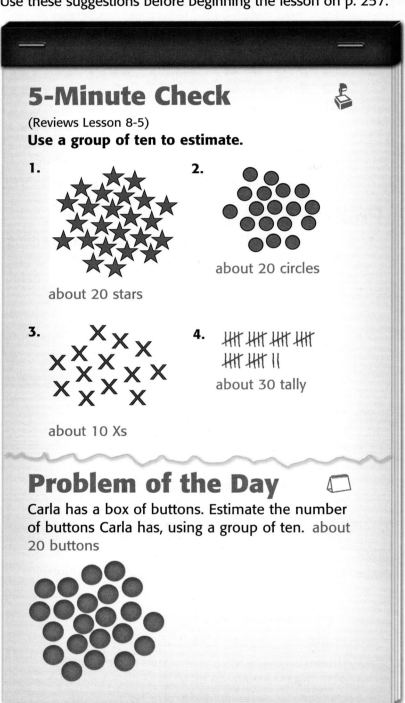

5-Minute Check

(Reviews Lesson 8-5)
Use a group of ten to estimate.

1.

about 20 stars

2.

about 20 circles

3.

about 10 Xs

4.

about 30 tally

Problem of the Day

Carla has a box of buttons. Estimate the number
of buttons Carla has, using a group of ten. about
20 buttons

 Have students count by tens to 100 and back to
10 as they line up.

Differentiated Instruction

Small Group Options

Option 1

LOGICAL, VISUAL/SPATIAL, KINESTHETIC

Below/Approaching Level

Materials: 12″ × 18″ sheets of construction paper, 100 connecting cubes

Have students use connecting cubes for counting in groups.

- Place a large sheet of construction paper in front of each student. Divide the cubes into random sets, putting a pile of cubes on each student's sheet.

- Have students work together to find the total number of connecting cubes. After students count their own cubes, coach them as needed to find a way to add all the groups together.

- When students have arrived at a total number of cubes, invite them to discuss ways they grouped and counted the cubes.

- **How does grouping make it easier to count large numbers?** Sample answer: Groups with equal numbers of items can be added together so that each individual item does not have to be counted separately.

Option 2

LINGUISTIC, INTERPERSONAL

English Language Learners

Materials: number cards 0 to 100
Core Vocabulary: model, show, do it
Common Use Verb: say

Talk Math This strategy gives the students practice vocalizing numbers and available language.

- With students in a circle, give the stack of number cards to a student.

- Have the student look at the number of the top card and choose a strategy to say, act out or model the number.

- When the student has demonstrated the number, the group estimates the demonstrated number by showing a number card and the student keeps the number card.

- Allow students to discuss why or how they reached their estimate. Repeat the process as time permits.

Independent Work Options

Option 1

LOGICAL

Early Finishers

Materials: two-colored counters

- Have students use two-colored counters as models to solve this problem:
  Anthony has 6 packs of gum. Each pack has 10 pieces. He gave 1 pack of gum to his friend. How many packs of gum does Anthony have left? How many pieces of gum? 5 packs; 50 pieces of gum

Option 2

Student Technology

Math Online ▷ macmillanmh.com

Option 3

Learning Station: Social Studies (p. 239G)

Direct students to the Social Studies Learning Station for more opportunities to explore and extend the lesson concept.

1 Introduce

Activity Choice 1 • Review

Write and read aloud the following:

Ken has 18 toy soldiers. Brett has 6 soldiers. How many soldiers do the boys have together?

- **Which problem-solving strategies would be good ways to solve this problem?** Sample answers: write a number sentence; draw a picture
- **What number sentence would you write?** $18 + 6 = 24$
- **What picture could you draw to model the problem? How would you use the picture to solve the problem?** Sample answer: Draw 18 symbols to represent soldiers and then draw 6 more. Count, or group and count, to find the total number of symbols, 24.

2 Teach

Have students read the problem on page 257. Guide them through the problem-solving steps.

Understand Using the questions, review what students know and what they need to find.

Plan Have them discuss their strategy.

Solve Guide students to *use logical reasoning* to solve the problem.

- Have students answer questions to reason the answer.
- **How many groups of ten does Maria have?** 2 groups
- **How many books does Maria have?** 20 books

Check Have students look back at the problem and use connecting cubes to make sure that the answer fits the facts given.

- **Do you have two groups of ten cubes?** yes
- **Do you have twenty cubes?** yes

COMMON ERROR!

Students may lose count as they reason to solve a problem. Have them use manipulatives to make sure they have counted the correct number of symbols.

Name _____

Problem-Solving Investigation

Main Idea
I will choose a strategy to solve a problem.

I have a lot of books. To count them, I put them in groups of 10. I have 2 groups of ten. How many books do I have?

Your Mission: Find the number of books that Libby has.

Understand

What do I know? Underline what you know.
What do I need to find? Circle it.

Plan

How will I solve the problem?

Solve

One way is to use logical reasoning.

Use connecting cubes and make 2 groups of ten. Count the cubes.

Check

____20____ books

Look back.
Is my answer reasonable?

Check students' explanations.

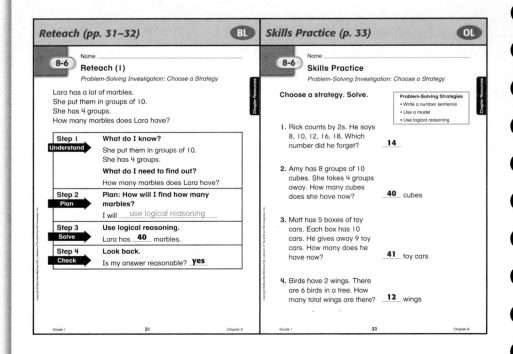

Reteach (pp. 31–32) **BL**

8-6   Name _____
Reteach (1)
Problem-Solving Investigation: Choose a Strategy

Lara has a lot of marbles.
She put them in groups of 10.
She has 4 groups.
How many marbles does Lara have?

Step 1 Understand	What do I know? She put them in groups of 10. She has 4 groups. What do I need to find out? How many marbles does Lara have?
Step 2 Plan	Plan: How will I find how many marbles? I will ___use logical reasoning___
Step 3 Solve	Use logical reasoning. Lara has __40__ marbles.
Step 4 Check	Look back. Is my answer reasonable? __yes__

Grade 1   31   Chapter 8

Skills Practice (p. 33) **OL**

8-6   Name _____
Skills Practice
Problem-Solving Investigation: Choose a Strategy

Choose a strategy. Solve.

Problem-Solving Strategies
- Write a number sentence
- Use a model
- Use logical reasoning

1. Rick counts by 2s. He says 8, 10, 12, 16, 18. Which number did he forget? __14__

2. Amy has 8 groups of 10 cubes. She takes 4 groups away. How many cubes does she have now? __40__ cubes

3. Matt has 5 boxes of toy cars. Each box has 10 cars. He gives away 9 toy cars. How many does he have now? __41__ toy cars

4. Birds have 2 wings. There are 6 birds in a tree. How many total wings are there? __12__ wings

Grade 1   33   Chapter 8

Mixed Problem Solving

Problem-Solving Strategies
- Use logical reasoning
- Act it out
- Write a number sentence

Choose a strategy. Solve.

1. Dogs have 2 ears.
There are 9 dogs at the park.
How many dog ears
are there altogether?

_____18_____

---

2. Brandon has 12 toy boats.
That is 3 more than Dale has.
How many toy boats does Dale have?

_____9_____ boats

---

3. Jaylynn has 2 boxes of frozen juice bars.
Each box has 10 in it. If she eats
2 frozen juice bars, how many will
she have left?

_____18_____ frozen juice bars

---

4. Joanne has 5 groups of 10 cubes.
She takes 10 away.
How many cubes does she have left?

_____40_____ cubes

258 two hundred fifty-eight

 Math at Home Activity: Take advantage of problem-solving opportunities during daily routines such as riding in the car, bedtime, doing laundry, putting away groceries, planning schedules, and so on.

BL **Alternate Teaching Strategy**

If students have difficulty reasoning the problem out . . .

Then use one of these reteach options.

1 **CRM** **Daily Reteach Worksheet** (pp. 31–32)

2 **Make a Model** Have students use counters to model problems. Then suggest that they draw a picture by writing an X in place of each counter.

3 Practice

Mixed Problem Solving

Exercises 1–4 Be sure students can read and understand the problems. Remind students to think about the problem-solving strategies they have learned. Have them decide which strategy would best help them solve each problem.

4 Assess

Formative Assessment

Tell the following math story: *Leo has 14 toy cars. He has a carrying case that holds 25 cars. How many more cars will Leo need to fill the carrying case?*

- **Which problem-solving strategies could you use to solve the problem?** Act it out; draw a picture; write a number sentence.

- To check for understanding, have students choose one strategy and solve the problem. Strategies will vary, but should lead to the answer of 11 more cars.

Quick Check **Are students continuing to struggle with choosing a strategy?**

If Yes → Small Group Options (p. 257B)

If No → Independent Work Options (p. 257B)
  CRM Skills Practice Worksheet (p. 33)
  CRM Enrich Worksheet (p. 35)

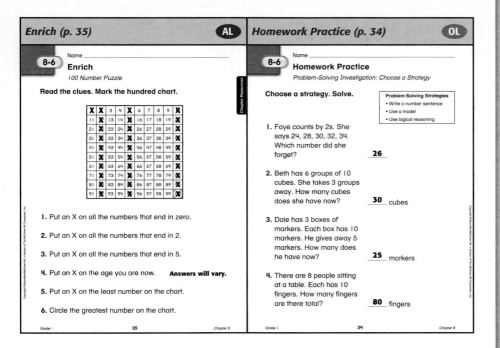

Enrich (p. 35) **AL**

8-6 Name _____
Enrich
100 Number Puzzle

Read the clues. Mark the hundred chart.

1. Put an X on all the numbers that end in zero.
2. Put an X on all the numbers that end in 2.
3. Put an X on all the numbers that end in 5.
4. Put an X on the age you are now. **Answers will vary.**
5. Put an X on the least number on the chart.
6. Circle the greatest number on the chart.

Grade 1   35   Chapter 8

Homework Practice (p. 34) **OL**

8-6 Name _____
Homework Practice
Problem-Solving Investigation: Choose a Strategy

Choose a strategy. Solve.

Problem-Solving Strategies
- Write a number sentence
- Use a model
- Use logical reasoning

1. Faye counts by 2s. She says 24, 28, 30, 32, 34. Which number did she forget? **26**

2. Beth has 6 groups of 10 cubes. She takes 3 groups away. How many cubes does she have now? **30** cubes

3. Dale has 3 boxes of markers. Each box has 10 markers. He gives away 5 markers. How many does he have now? **25** markers

4. There are 8 people sitting at a table. Each has 10 fingers. How many fingers are there total? **80** fingers

Grade 1   34   Chapter 8

Lesson Planner

Objective

Use patterns to skip count by twos, fives, and tens.

Vocabulary

skip count

Resources

Materials: pencils

Manipulatives: connecting cubes, two-colored counters

Literature Connection: *One Hundred Hungry Ants* by Elinor J. Pinczes

Teacher Technology

TeacherWorks • Math Songs Track 9 Lesson Plan

Focus on Math Background

This lesson focuses on skip counting by 10s, 5s, and 2s. Flexibility with skip counting allows students to choose a quantification strategy that best and most efficiently quantifies a particular number. For example, when counting 48, the child could start skip counting by 10s until reaching 40 and then switch to a counting by 2s strategy to quantify the remaining eight objects.

Daily Routine

Use these suggestions before beginning the lesson on p. 259.

5-Minute Check

(Reviews Lesson 8-6)

Kuy has 10 toy trucks. That is 4 more than Taya. How many toy trucks does Taya have? 6

Problem of the Day

Tim's father bought a package of 12 candles for Tim's birthday cake. It was Tim's 7th birthday. His father used 1 candle for each year of Tim's age. How many candles were left? 5 candles

LINE UP Have students hold up five fingers and count off by fives, starting over at the beginning of the line each time another student lines up. When they reach 50, the next student in line starts again with 5.

Building Math Vocabulary

Materials: class number line, student number lines, hundred chart

- Write the term **skip count** on the board. Explain that skip counting is counting in equal groups of two or more.
- Let's count by ones. Model "finger-hopping" from one number to the next while counting to 10 on a number line.
- **Did we skip any numbers?** no
- **When you skip count by twos, your finger moves two times but you only say the second number.** Model skip counting by twos on a number line. Repeat with students.
- Model skip counting by fives and tens using a hundred chart. Explain that to skip count by any number you must skip that amount each time.

Differentiated Instruction

Small Group Options

VISUAL/SPATIAL, KINESTHETIC

Gifted and Talented (AL)

Materials: walk-on number line made with butcher paper (or large index cards), masking tape

- Have a student start at 0 and alternate between hopping on one foot and jumping on the numbers. The student should use both feet to jump on every other number. Ask classmates to count aloud the numbers the student jumps on. **How are you counting?** by twos

- Repeat the activity by having students hop and jump to count by fives. Guide students to notice that they hop four times, then jump the fifth time.

- Repeat the activity by having students hop and jump to count by tens.

| 20 |
| 19 |
| 18 |
| 17 |
| 16 |
| 15 |
| 14 |
| 13 |
| 12 |
| 11 |
| 10 |
| 9 |
| 8 |
| 7 |
| 6 |
| 5 |
| 4 |
| 3 |
| 2 |
| 1 |

Option 2

AUDITORY, KINESTHETIC

English Language Learners (ELL)

Materials: paper plate numbers, frog puppet
Core Vocabulary: frog, lily pad, skipping
Common Use Verb: skip over

Do Math This strategy demonstrates the common and mathematical meanings of "skip" by activating background knowledge.

- Demonstrate skipping by holding arms out and touching alternate knees. Say: "This movement is called skipping. Skipping is faster."

- Use a frog puppet to model skip counting on a number line. Say: "The frog is skipping over the numbers. This kind of skipping helps us count faster."

- Lay out the "lilly pads" and allow students to practice skip counting with the frog puppet or as pretend frogs.

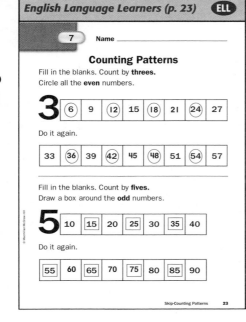

Use this worksheet to provide additional support for English Language Learners.

Independent Work Options

Option 1

VISUAL/SPATIAL, KINESTHETIC

Early Finishers (OL) (AL)

- Have students line up. Explain that they are making a human number line. Have them count by ones and remember their number.

- Then have students skip count by twos. Then by fives.

Option 2

Student Technology

Math Online ▶ macmillanmh.com

♪ Math Songs, "Skip Counting (2, 4, 6, 8)" Track 9 •
🌐 Math Adventures

Option 3

Learning Station: Science (p. 239H)

Direct students to the Science Learning Station for more opportunities to explore and extend the lesson concept.

Option 4

Problem-Solving Practice

Reinforce problem-solving skills and strategies with the Problem-Solving Practice worksheet.

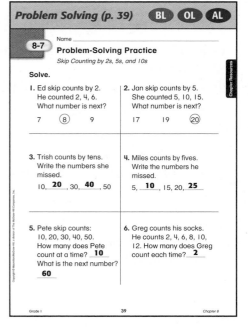

① Introduce

Activity Choice 1 • Hands-On

Have several students sit in a row at the front of the room and hold their hands or feet out in front of them.

- **How many hands (or feet) does each person have?** 2
- **What is a fast way to figure out how many hands (or feet) in all?** Count by twos
- Count by twos with the students.
- **How many fingers (or toes) does each person have?** 10
- **What is a fast way to figure out how many fingers (or toes) in all?** Count by fives or tens
- Count by fives or tens with the students.

Activity Choice 2 • Literature

Introduce the lesson with *One Hundred Hungry Ants* by Elinor J. Pinczes. For additional support, see p. TR53.

② Teach

- Give each pair of students twenty counters. Have students arrange their counters in groups of two. Tell them to touch each group of two as they count them by twos. **How many counters?** 20 counters

- Have students put the counters in groups of five. Lead students in counting by fives. **How many counters?** 20 counters

- Repeat the activity with groups of ten.

Get Ready Use the section at the top of student p. 259 to reinforce the lesson concept. Help students **skip count** by using the number line.

Check Observe students as you work through Exercises 1–4 as a class.

Exercise 4 Assess student comprehension before assigning practice exercises.

⚠ COMMON ERROR!

If students do not understand the concept, try making a "number chart" with groups of two counters in columns and write the twos on the right side of the chart. Count with the students, emphasizing the twos.

Name _____

Skip Count by 2s, 5s, and 10s

Main Idea
I will use patterns to skip count by twos, fives, and tens.

Vocabulary
skip count

You can **skip count** on a number line.

I can count by twos. 2, 4, 6, 8, 10, 12, 14, 16, 18, 20

✓ **Check**

4. Counting by 2s the numbers end with 0, 2, 4, 6, or 8. By 5s and 10s the numbers end with 0 or 5.

Use a number line. Skip count.

0 1 2 3 4 5 6 7 8 9 10 11 12 13 14 15 16 17 18 19 20 21 22 23 24 25 26 27 28 29 30

1. 2, 4, **6**, _8_ , _10_ , _12_ , _14_ ☁ Count by 2s.

2. 5, 10, _15_ , _20_ , _25_ , _30_ ☁ Count by 5s.

3. 10, 20, _30_ , _40_ , _50_ , _60_ ☁ Count by 10s.

4. **Talk About It** What patterns do you see when you count by 2s? By 5s and 10s?

Chapter 8   Lesson 7   two hundred fifty-nine **259**

Reteach (p. 36) `BL`

8-7 **Reteach**
Skip Counting by 2s, 5s, and 10s

Skip counting by 2s.
2, 4, 6, 8, 10, 12, 14, 16, 18, 20

Skip counting by 5s.
5, 10, 15, 20, 25, 30, 35, 40, 45, 50

Skip counting by 10s.
10, 20, 30, 40, 50, 60, 70, 80, 90, 100

I. Skip count by 2s. Count 2 🚲 at a time.

2, 4, **6**, 8, **10**, 12, **14**, 16, **18**, **20**

2. Skip count by 5s. Count 5 🍇 at a time.

5, **10**, 15, 20, **25**, **30**, 35, **40**

3. Skip count by 10s. Count 10 ▬ at a time.

10, 20, **30**, **40**, 50

Grade 1   36   Chapter 8

Skills Practice (p. 37) `OL`

8-7 **Skills Practice**
Skip Counting by 2s, 5s, and 10s

1. Count the leaves.

2, 4, **6**, **8**, **10** leaves

2.

5, **10**, **15**, **20**, **25**, **30** leaves

3.

10, **20**, **30**, **40**, **50**, **60**, **70** leaves

Solve.

4. Lucy has 4 apples.
Molly has 2 more apples than Lucy.
Sara has two more apples than Molly.
How many apples does Molly have? **6**
How many apples does Sara have? **8**

Grade 1   37   Chapter 8

Skip count by 2s, 5s, or 10s.

5.

___2___, ___4___, ___6___, ___8___ seeds

6.

___5___, ___10___, ___15___, ___20___, ___25___, ___30___ seeds

7.

___10___, ___20___, ___30___, ___40___, ___50___ seeds

8.

___5___, ___10___, ___15___, ___20___, ___25___, ___30___, ___35___ seeds

H.O.T. Problem

9. **Make It Right**
Chris skip counts by tens like this.

Tell why Chris is wrong. Make it right.

10, 20, 30, 40
45, 50, 55, 60

Sample answer: Chris counted by 5s and 10s. He should

have counted 10, 20, 30, 40, 50, 60

260   two hundred sixty

Math at Home Activity: Have your child find objects to skip count, such as pairs of shoes or sets of stairs and skip count to find how many.

Enrich (p. 40) **AL**

8-7   Name _____
Enrich
Count by 2s to the Circus

Ellie the elephant needs to get back to the circus.
Color the peanut path that counts by 2s.

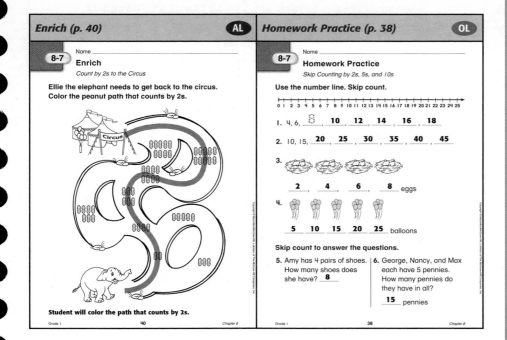

Student will color the path that counts by 2s.

Grade 1   40   Chapter 8

Homework Practice (p. 38) **OL**

8-7   Name _____
Homework Practice
Skip Counting by 2s, 5s, and 10s

Use the number line. Skip count.

0 1 2 3 4 5 6 7 8 9 10 11 12 13 14 15 16 17 18 19 20 21 22 23 24 25

1. 4, 6, _8_, __10__, __12__, __14__, __16__, __18__

2. 10, 15, __20__, __25__, __30__, __35__, __40__, __45__

3.

___2___, ___4___, ___6___, ___8___ eggs

4.

___5___, ___10___, ___15___, ___20___, ___25___ balloons

Skip count to answer the questions.

5. Amy has 4 pairs of shoes. How many shoes does she have? __8__

6. George, Nancy, and Max each have 5 pennies. How many pennies do they have in all?

__15__ pennies

Grade 1   38   Chapter 8

BL **Alternate Teaching Strategy**

If ▶ students have trouble skip counting . . .

Then ▶ use one of these reteach options.

1 **CRM** **Daily Reteach Worksheet** (p. 36)

2 **Skip Counting with Counters** Help students put counters on a number line or hundred chart to show which numbers to skip and which numbers to say when counting by fives. Have them count "1, 2, 3, 4" as they place yellow counters on the chart and "5" as they place a red one.

❸ Practice

Differentiate practice using these leveled assignments for Exercises 5–9.

Level	Assignment
BL Below/Approaching Level	Give students a number line. Guide students through the exercises. Have them use their finger to keep their place on the number line.
OL On Level	Complete the exercises independently.
AL Above/Beyond Level	Complete the exercises without using a number line.

❹ Assess

✓ Formative Assessment

- **How is skip counting different from counting by ones?** In skip counting, you do not say all the numbers. You skip over the same amount each time.

WRITING IN ▶MATH Have students draw pictures and label things that come in twos, fives, or tens. Sample answers: twos: shoes, feet, arms; fives: fingers, points on a star; tens: toes, fingers

Quick Check Are students continuing to struggle with skip counting by twos, fives, and tens?

If Yes → Strategic Intervention Guide (p. 42)

If No → Independent Work Options (p. 259B)

CRM Skills Practice Worksheet (p. 37)

CRM Enrich Worksheet (p. 40)

Skip Counting on a Hundred Chart

Lesson Planner

Objective
Use a hundred chart to identify and continue skip-counting patterns.

Review Vocabulary
skip count

Resources
Materials: stickers, overhead projector, hundred chart transparency

Literature Connection: *One Hundred Hungry Ants* by Elinor J. Pinczes

Alternate Lesson: Use *IMPACT Mathematics:* Unit D to provide practice with skip counting.

Teacher Technology
- TeacherWorks • Math Songs Track 9 Lesson Plan

Focus on Math Background

This lesson connects students' prior knowledge of repeating patterns and labels, such as AB or ABC, to the patterns that unfold on a hundred chart when skip counting by different numbers. For instance, students will readily notice how skip counting by 2s results in an alternating AB pattern. Visualizing skip counting patterns in this way lays the foundation for future work understanding the concept of multiples and eventually leads to instantaneous recall of multiplication facts.

Daily Routine

Use these suggestions before beginning the lesson on p. 261.

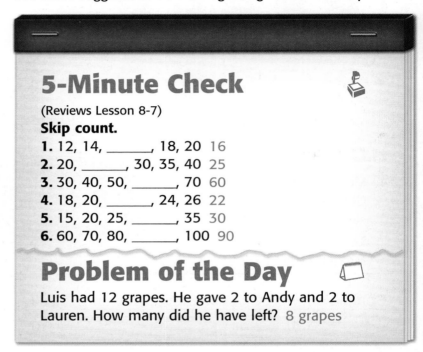

5-Minute Check
(Reviews Lesson 8-7)
Skip count.
1. 12, 14, _____, 18, 20 16
2. 20, _____, 30, 35, 40 25
3. 30, 40, 50, _____, 70 60
4. 18, 20, _____, 24, 26 22
5. 15, 20, 25, _____, 35 30
6. 60, 70, 80, _____, 100 90

Problem of the Day
Luis had 12 grapes. He gave 2 to Andy and 2 to Lauren. How many did he have left? 8 grapes

LINE UP Have volunteers give a paper clip to every second student in line as students count aloud. Guide them to start softly with 1 and emphasize every second student who receives a paper clip: 1, **2**, 3, **4**, 5, **6**, 7, **8**, 9, **10**.

Review Math Vocabulary
Materials: paper, crayons
- Write the term **skip count** on the board and have volunteers tell what they know about skip counting.

- Have students stand in a line and hold up their hands. **How many fingers on each hand?** 5 fingers **How many fingers on all of the hands in the line?** Sample answer: 90 fingers.

- **We can count by fives to find out how many fingers in all.** As you skip count together, have each student wiggle the fingers on the hand being counted.

- Then have students trace one hand several times on paper and skip count to find how many fingers in all. Direct students to label their drawings with the term *skip count*.

Differentiated Instruction

Small Group Options

Option 1 VISUAL/SPATIAL, KINETHESTIC, SOCIAL

Below Level BL

Materials: hundred chart for each group

- Give each group a hundred chart.
- Have the first student choose a number between 0 and 10.
- The second student then colors that number in on the hundred chart, counts ten more than the number, and colors in the square.
- Then another student counts ten more and colors in the square.
- Have students continue counting and coloring until they reach the last row of the chart.
- Students can switch roles, pick a new starting number, and repeat the activity.
- **What pattern do you see?** Each number has the same last digit.

Option 2 VISUAL/SPATIAL

English Language Learners ELL

Materials: hundred chart for each player, tokens
Core Vocabulary: finger on, every other, space
Common Use Verb: place

Hear Math This strategy connects auditory and visual representations of numbers and allows them to practice skip counting.

- Show students a hundred chart. Say: "You can jump over numbers on a number chart too."
- Direct students to put a token on number 1, and their finger on number 2, repeating the action until the chart is covered. Use the vocabulary, emphasizing that on every other space, a token is placed.
- Have students put their fingers on the numbers as you read them, skip counting by 2.
- Repeat for skip counting by 5 and 10 as time permits.

Independent Work Options

Option 1 VISUAL/SPATIAL, KINETHESTIC, LOGICAL

Early Finishers OL AL

Materials: hundred chart for each student, crayons

- Have students use a hundred chart to count by twos. Direct them to make a green stripe on the square of each number they say.
- Next, have students count by fives, making a red stripe on every fifth square.
- Finally, have students count by tens and make a blue stripe on every tenth square.

Option 2

Student Technology

Math Online macmillanmh.com

♪ Math Songs, "Skip Counting (2, 4, 6, 8)" Track 9

Option 3

Learning Station: Science (p. 239H)

Direct students to the Science Learning Station for more opportunities to explore and extend the lesson concept.

Option 4

Problem-Solving Practice

Reinforce problem-solving skills and strategies with the Problem-Solving Practice worksheet.

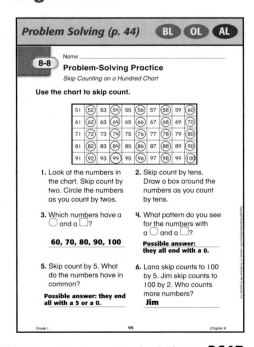

8-8

1 Introduce

Activity Choice 1 • Hands-On

- Have students skip count by tens, patting their knees with each count.
- Then have students count by fives and clap on each number.
- After practicing several times, have half the class count slowly by fives and clap while the other half counts by tens and pats knees. Remind those counting by tens to count and pat only on tens and to sit silent on numbers that end in 5.
- **What pattern did you notice?** We clapped and tapped on every other number.

Activity Choice 2 • Literature

Introduce the lesson with *One Hundred Hungry Ants* by Elinor J. Pinczes. For additional support, see p. TR53.

2 Teach

- Display a hundred chart on the overhead. Remind students that they have counted backward and forward by one. Tell them that they are now going to count by twos.
- Explain that when you count by 2s, you say a number, skip a number, and say the next number.
- Demonstrate on the hundred charts, starting with 2. Have students count with you as you touch the twos. Repeat with fives and tens.

Get Ready Use the section at the top of p. 261 to reinforce the lesson concept.

Check Observe students as you work through Exercises 1–4 as a class.

> **Exercise 4** Assess student comprehension before assigning practice exercises.

COMMON ERROR!

Some students may be confused about why, when counting by fives and tens, some of the numbers are the same. Point out that $5 + 5 = 10$ and show them how each two groups of 5 on a hundreds chart ends at a ten.

Name _____

Skip Counting on a Hundred Chart

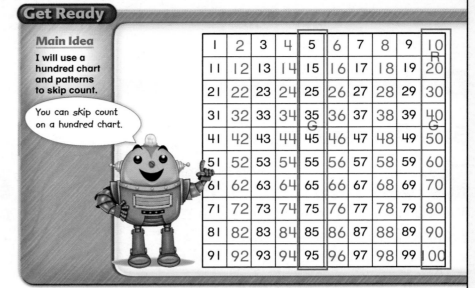

Get Ready

Main Idea
I will use a hundred chart and patterns to skip count.

You can skip count on a hundred chart.

✓ Check

Use the hundred chart and patterns to skip count.

1. Count by 2s. **Write** the missing numbers.

_____

2. Count by 5s. **Color** the numbers .

_____

3. Count by 10s. **Color** the numbers .

_____

4. Talk About It — Why are the numbers in the tens column both colors? They show counting by 2s and counting by 5s numbers.

Chapter 8   Lesson 8   two hundred sixty-one   261

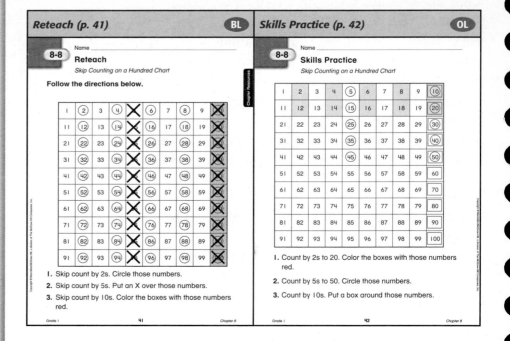

Reteach (p. 41) — BL

8-8 Reteach
Skip Counting on a Hundred Chart

Follow the directions below.

1. Skip count by 2s. Circle those numbers.
2. Skip count by 5s. Put an X over those numbers.
3. Skip count by 10s. Color the boxes with those numbers red.

Grade 1   41   Chapter 8

Skills Practice (p. 42) — OL

8-8 Skills Practice
Skip Counting on a Hundred Chart

1. Count by 2s to 20. Color the boxes with those numbers red.
2. Count by 5s to 50. Circle those numbers.
3. Count by 10s. Put a box around those numbers.

Grade 1   42   Chapter 8

Practice

5. Count by 5s. Circle the numbers.
6. Count by 10s. Mark an X on the numbers.
7. Count by 2s. Color the numbers crayon.

The 2s, 4s, 6s, 8s and 10s column should be colored blue.

1	2	3	4	5	6	7	8	9	10
11	12	13	14	15	16	17	18	19	20
21	22	23	24	25	26	27	28	29	30
31	32	33	34	35	36	37	38	39	40
41	42	43	44	45	46	47	48	49	50
51	52	53	54	55	56	57	58	59	60
61	62	63	64	65	66	67	68	69	70
71	72	73	74	75	76	77	78	79	80
81	82	83	84	85	86	87	88	89	90
91	92	93	94	95	96	97	98	99	100

Data File

People drive cars and trucks on highways. State Highway 51 in Oklahoma is a popular highway for cars, trucks, and buses.

Answer the questions.

8. There are 5 cars on the highway. Each car has two people inside. How many people are in all the cars? 10 people
9. There are 3 buses on the highway. There are 10 people on each bus. How many people are on all the buses? 30 people

Math at Home Activity: Have your child practice skip counting objects around the house.

Enrich (p. 45) AL

8-8 Name ______

Enrich

100s of Ways to Count!

1	2	3	X	5	6	7	X	9	10
11	X	13	14	15	X	17	18	19	X
21	22	23	X	25	26	27	X	29	30
31	X	33	34	35	X	37	38	39	X
41	42	43	X	45	46	47	X	49	50
51	X	53	54	55	X	57	58	59	X
61	62	63	X	65	66	67	X	69	70
71	X	73	74	75	X	77	78	79	X
81	82	83	X	85	86	87	X	89	90
91	X	93	94	95	X	97	98	99	X

1. Start with 2. Skip count by 2s to 100. Color those numbers.
2. Start with 3. Skip count by 3s to 100. Circle the numbers.
3. Start with 4. Skip count by 4s to 100. Put an X over the boxes.
4. How many boxes are colored and circled? **16**
5. How many boxes are circled and have Xs? **8**
6. How many boxes are colored and have Xs? **8**

Grade 1 45 Chapter 8

Homework Practice (p. 43) OL

8-8 Name ______

Homework Practice

Skip Counting on a Hundred Chart

Use the hundred chart to skip count.

1	2	3	4	5	6	7	8	9	X
11	12	13	14	15	16	17	18	19	X
21	22	23	24	25	26	27	28	29	X
31	32	33	34	35	36	37	38	39	X
41	42	43	44	45	46	47	48	49	X
51	52	53	54	55	56	57	58	59	X
61	62	63	64	65	66	67	68	69	X
71	72	73	74	75	76	77	78	79	X
81	82	83	84	85	86	87	88	89	X
91	92	93	94	95	96	97	98	99	X

1. Skip count by 2s to 40. Circle them.
2. Skip count by 5s to 100. Circle them.
3. Skip count by 10s. Put an X through them.
4. Did you circle any numbers two times? Which ones?

yes, 10, 20, 30 and 40

Grade 1 43 Chapter 8

Chapter Resources

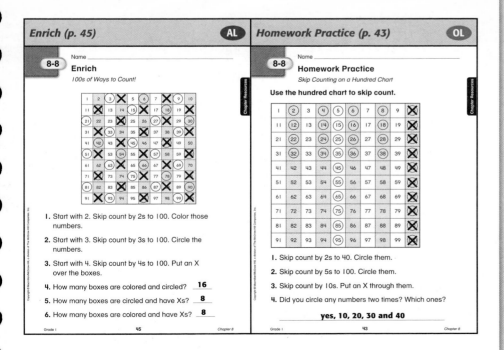

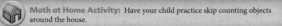

BL Alternate Teaching Strategy

If students start skip counting from the wrong number on a hundred chart . . .

Then use one of these reteach options.

1 CRM **Daily Reteach Worksheet** (p. 41)

2 **Use Cues** Give students a special sticker to mark where to begin counting on the hundred chart.

3 Practice

Differentiate practice using these leveled assignments for Exercises 5–9.

Level	Assignment
BL Below/ Approaching Level	Pair student with a classmate performing above level.
OL On Level	Complete exercises independently.
AL Above/Beyond Level	Pair student with a classmate performing below level.

4 Assess

Formative Assessment

- **How can you know which number comes next when you skip count?** Sample answer: Use a hundred chart and skip over the same number of squares each time.

WRITING IN MATH Have students draw several pairs of mittens or shoes and write the answer to the following question: **What number would you use to count mittens or shoes? Why?** Twos; they come in pairs, or groups of two.

Quick Check **Are students having trouble skip counting on a hundred chart?**

If Yes → Small Group Options (p. 261B)
Strategic Intervention Guide (p. 44)

If No → Independent Work Options (p. 261B)
CRM Skills Practice Worksheet (p. 42)
CRM Enrich Worksheet (p. 45)

Lesson Planner

Objective
Find patterns in numbers such as even and odd numbers.

Vocabulary
even, odd

Resources
Materials: hundred chart, pencils, crayons
Manipulatives: two-colored counters
Literature Connection: *Jump Kangaroo, Jump* by Stuart J. Murphy
Alternate Lesson: Use *IMPACT Mathematics:* Unit D to provide practice with even and odd numbers.

Teacher Technology
 TeacherWorks • Concepts in Motion

Daily Routine

Use these suggestions before beginning the lesson on p. 263.

5-Minute Check
(Reviews Lesson 8-8)
Use a hundred chart to skip count.
1. Skip count by 2s from 1 to 19. 1, 3, 5, 7, 9, 11, 13, 15, 17, 19
2. Skip count by 2s from 2 to 20. 2, 4, 6, 8, 10, 12, 14, 16, 18, 20
3. Skip count by 5s from 5 to 25. 5, 10, 15, 20, 25
4. Skip count by 10s from 13 to 63. 13, 23, 33, 43, 53, 63

Problem of the Day
Ben had 20 toy cars. He gave away 12 of them. How many toy cars does Ben have left? 8 toy cars

LINE UP Have 13 students line up. Lead students in counting by 2s to decide whether 13 is even or odd. Have the rest of the students line up. Have them count the students by 2s to find whether that number is even or odd.

Building Math Vocabulary

• Write on the board **even–0, 2, 4, 6, 8** and **odd–1, 3, 5, 7, 9**
• Explain that an **even** number ends with 0, 2, 4, 6, or 8, and an **odd** number ends with 1, 3, 5, 7, or 9.
• Explain that If you can start with 2 and count to a number by 2s the number is even. Place 12 counters on the overhead.
• **Is this number of counters even or odd? Why?** Together with students, count by 2s. even; Sample answers: We counted by 2s and there were no counters left over; the number 12 ends with 2.
• Place 17 counters on the overhead.
• **Is the number of counters even or odd? Why?** odd; Sample answers: If you count by 2s there is one counter left over; the number 17 ends with 7.

Differentiated Instruction

Small Group Options

LOGICAL, KINESTHETIC

Option 1 — Below Level (BL)

Materials: hundred chart, blue crayon, green crayon

- Distribute a hundred chart to each student.
- Have the students color all even numbers green and all odd numbers blue.
- Have students notice the patterns they see and compare their charts to see if they have the same squares colored the same colors.

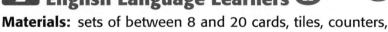

1	2	3	4	5	6	7	8	9	10
11	12	13	14	15	16	17	18	19	20
21	22	23	24	25	26	27	28	29	30
31	32	33	34	35	36	37	38	39	40
41	42	43	44	45	46	47	48	49	50
51	52	53	54	55	56	57	58	59	60
61	62	63	64	65	66	67	68	69	70
71	72	73	74	75	76	77	78	79	80
81	82	83	84	85	86	87	88	89	90
91	92	93	94	95	96	97	98	99	100

LOGICAL, SOCIAL

Option 2 — English Language Learners (EL)

Materials: sets of between 8 and 20 cards, tiles, counters, beans, etc.

Core Vocabulary: even, left over, odd

Common Use Verb: share

See Math This strategy helps students make a connection between odd and left over.

- Say: "We will **share** materials today. We want to make sure we have the same number for each person."
- Demonstrate as you say: "One for you, one for me, one for you…" with a partner.
- Say: "If we have the same number after sharing all, our materials were **even**. If your partner has one more, our materials were **odd**; we did not start with the same number."
- Give each pair a set of materials. Allow students to figure out if their number is even or odd.

Independent Work Options

VISUAL/SPATIAL, KINESTHETIC, SOCIAL

Option 1 — Early Finishers (OL) (AL)

Materials: hundred chart, connecting cubes

- Have partners take turns making a connecting cube train and determining whether the number of cubes is even or odd by breaking the trains into pairs of cubes. Remind students that if they can make all the cubes into pairs, the number is even. If they make pairs and there is one left over, the number is odd.
- Each time they break apart a train and discover whether a number is even or odd, have students record their findings on a hundreds chart. Have them color even-numbered squares in red and odd-numbered squares in blue.

Option 2 — Student Technology

Math Online — macmillanmh.com

Math Adventures

Option 3 — Learning Station: Art (p. 239G)

Direct students to the Art Learning Station for more opportunities to explore the lesson concept.

Option 4 — Problem-Solving Practice

Reinforce problem-solving skills and strategies with the Problem-Solving Practice worksheet.

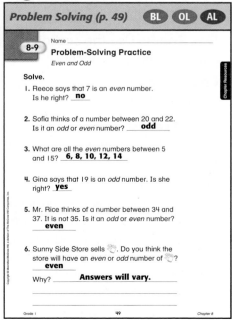

Problem Solving (p. 49) (BL) (OL) (AL)

8-9 Name _____

Problem-Solving Practice
Even and Odd

Solve.

1. Reece says that 7 is an *even* number. Is he right? **no**

2. Sofia thinks of a number between 20 and 22. Is it an *odd* or *even* number? **odd**

3. What are all the *even* numbers between 5 and 15? **6, 8, 10, 12, 14**

4. Gina says that 19 is an *odd* number. Is she right? **yes**

5. Mr. Rice thinks of a number between 34 and 37. It is not 35. Is it an *odd* or *even* number? **even**

6. Sunny Side Store sells 🖐. Do you think the store will have an *even* or *odd* number of 🖐? **even** Why? **Answers will vary.**

Grade 1   49   Chapter 8

1 Introduce

Activity Choice 1 • Hands-On

- Give each student a handful of counters. Have students count the counters by 2s.
- **Could you count all the counters by 2s or did you have a counter left over?** Answers will vary.
- Draw two columns on the board; label one **even** and one **odd**.
- List in the appropriate column the number of counters each student has.
- **Can you find a pattern in the even column?** Even numbers end with 0, 2, 4, 6, or 8.
- **Can you find a pattern in the odd column?** Odd numbers end with 1, 3, 5, 7, or 9.

Activity Choice 2 • Literature

Introduce the lesson with *Jump Kangaroo, Jump* by Stuart J. Murphy. For additional support, see p. TR53.

2 Teach

- Ask students to circle numbers on the hundred chart that end with 0, 2, 4, 6, or 8 with a red crayon.
- Then have them circle the numbers on the hundred chart that end with 1, 3, 5, 7, or 9 with a green crayon.
- **Which numbers are even? Why?** The numbers circled in red are even; even numbers end in 0, 2, 4, 6, or 8.
- **Which digits do odd numbers end with?** 1, 3, 5, 7, or 9

Get Ready Use the section at the top of p. 263 to teach the lesson concept.

Check Observe students as you work through Exercises 1–6 as a class.

Exercise 6 Assess student comprehension before assigning practice exercises.

⚠ COMMON ERROR!

Students may make an error while counting pairs, which will cause them to incorrectly identify a number as even or odd. Have students use manipulatives and push each pair away from the others so they can clearly see whether or not they have paired all the counters.

Name _____

Even and Odd

 Hands-On Activity

Get Ready

Main Idea
I will find even and odd numbers in number patterns.

Vocabulary
even
odd

You can find pattern in even and odd numbers.

6	7
If you can make pairs, the number is **even**.	If you make pairs and one cube is left over, the number is **odd**.

✓ Check

Use 🎲 to show the number. Circle *even* or *odd*.

1. **4** (even) / odd

2. **5** even / (odd)

3. **8** (even) / odd

4. **9** even / (odd)

Color even numbers 🖍 and odd numbers 🖍.
Use 🎲 to help.

5.

1	2	3	4	5	6	7	8	9	10
11	12	13	14	15	16	17	18	19	20

Even numbers should be shaded red.
Odd numbers should be shaded blue.

6. **Talk About It** What patterns do you see in the chart above?
Students should notice that every other number is even/odd.

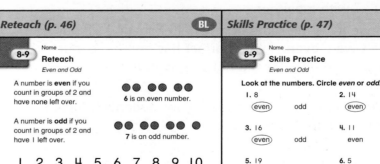

Practice

Use  to show the number. Circle *even* or *odd*.

7. **11**   even
         (odd)

8. **12**   (even)
          odd

Color even numbers ━━ and odd numbers ━━.
Use 🎲 to help.

9.

1	2	3	4	5	6	7	8	9	10
11	12	13	14	15	16	17	18	19	20
21	22	23	24	25	26	27	28	29	30

Even numbers should be shaded in orange. Odd numbers should be shaded in green.

10. Are the green numbers even or odd?

odd

11. Are the orange numbers even or odd?

even

Problem Solving

12. Visual Thinking Color odd numbers ━━ and even numbers ━━. Count by 5's on the chart. What pattern do you see? Would you color the number 65 blue or yellow? How do you know?

1	2	3	4	5	6	7	8	9	10
11	12	13	14	15	16	17	18	19	20
21	22	23	24	25	26	27	28	29	30
31	32	33	34	35	36	37	38	39	40

Students should notice that numbers ending in 5 are odd
and colored in blue; numbers ending in 0 are even and
colored yellow. 65 would be odd.

Math at Home Activity: Work with your child to create a number line from 1 to 20. Have him or her circle the even numbers and draw a line under the odd numbers. Ask him or her to tell you about the pattern that even and odd numbers make.

264   two hundred sixty-four

BL Alternate Teaching Strategy

If students have difficulty finding patterns in even and odd numbers . . .

Then use one of these reteach options.

1 CRM **Daily Reteach Worksheet** (p. 46)

2 Use Skip Counting on a Hundred Chart Give students a hundred chart and have them count by 2s beginning with 0 to find even numbers, and beginning with 1 to find odd numbers.

③ Practice

Differentiate practice using these leveled assignments for Exercises 7–12.

Level	Assignment
BL Below/Approaching Level	Guide students through the exercises. Use connecting cubes for support.
OL On Level	Complete the exercises with connecting cubes for support.
AL Above/Beyond Level	Complete the exercises independently.

④ Assess

Formative Assessment

- **Is 18 an even or odd number? Explain.** Sample answer: Even; you can count by 2s to 18; 18 ends with an 8.

WRITING IN ▶MATH Have students write about how they will remember to find patterns in even and odd numbers. Sample answers: You can count by 2s to find even numbers; odd numbers end with 1, 3, 5, 7, or 9.

Quick Check   **Are students continuing to struggle with finding patterns in even and odd numbers?**

If Yes → Small Group Options (p. 263B)

If No → Independent Work Options (p. 263B)

CRM Skills Practice Worksheet (p. 47)

CRM Enrich Worksheet (p. 50)

Review Lessons 8-1 to 8-9

Objective: Review and assess mastery of previous lessons' skills and concepts.

- Review with students how to skip count by twos, fives, and tens.
- Explain that they will have to decide what number is being used for skip counting and then skip count by that number to find the missing numbers.
- Students may want to use a hundred chart for help.

Practice with Technology

Math Online > Have students visit macmillanmh.com for additional practice with online activities, games, and quizzes.

Name _____

Skip count.

1. 8, 10, 12, 14, __16__, __18__, __20__, __22__, __24__, __26__

2. 25, 30, 35, 40, __45__, __50__, __55__, __60__, __65__

3. 40, 50, 60, __70__, __80__, __90__, __100__

4. 50, 55, 60, 65, 70, __75__, __80__, __85__, __90__, __95__, __100__

5. 22, 24, 26, 28 __30__, __32__, __34__, __36__, __38__, __40__

Count by 2s to connect the dots.

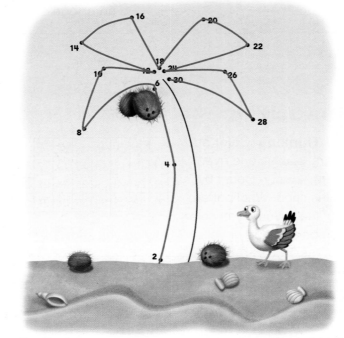

Chapter 8   Extra Practice   two hundred sixty-five   265

Slide Through the Digits
Comparing Numbers

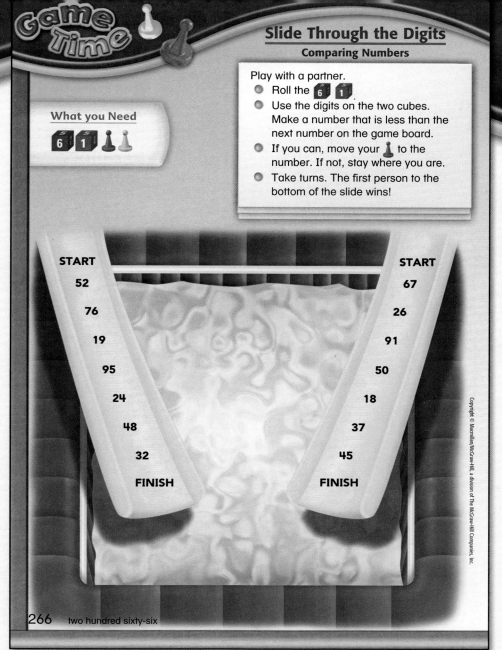

Play with a partner.
- Roll the [6] [1].
- Use the digits on the two cubes. Make a number that is less than the next number on the game board.
- If you can, move your ♟ to the number. If not, stay where you are.
- Take turns. The first person to the bottom of the slide wins!

What you Need
[6] [1] ♟ ♟

START
52
76
19
95
24
48
32
FINISH

START
67
26
91
50
18
37
45
FINISH

266 two hundred sixty-six

Copyright © Macmillan/McGraw-Hill, a division of The McGraw-Hill Companies, Inc.

Slide Through the Digits

Math Concept:
Numbers to 100
Manipulatives: red and blue number cubes, two-colored counters

Instructions
- Have each student choose a red or yellow colored counter to use as a game piece.
- Have each student roll the blue number cube. The person who rolls the greater number plays first.
- Players take turns rolling both number cubes. After rolling, the player tries to use the digits on the two cubes to make a number that is less than the next number on the board. (Do not use zero in the tens.)
- If the digits on the cubes can make a lesser number, the player moves his or her game piece to the next number. If not, the player does not move.
- The first one to the bottom of the slide wins!

Extend the Game
Have students tell whether the number they made is greater than or less than the next number on the board.

Differentiated Practice
Use these leveling suggestions to differentiate the game for all learners.

Level	Assignment
BL Below/Approaching Level	Have students roll the number cubes. If they can make any number on their slide, they may move their game piece to that number. The first person to get the last number on their slide wins!
OL On Level	Have students play the game with the rules as written.
AL Above/Beyond Level	Have students determine how much greater than or less than the next number on the board their roll of the dice is.

Problem Solving in Social Studies

Real-World MATH

Many schools celebrate their 100th day. Some schools have parties. Some schools make crafts.

This book belongs to

_____

A

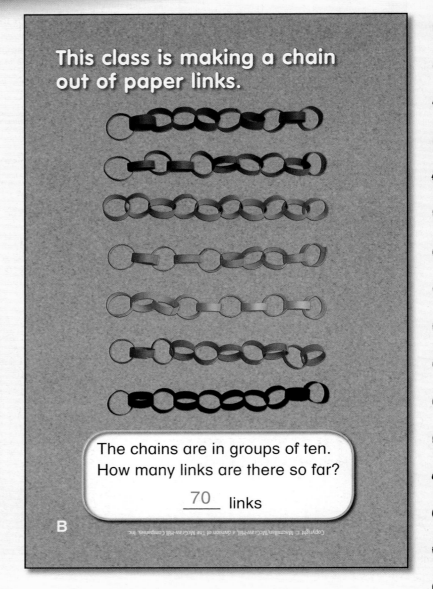

This class is making a chain out of paper links.

The chains are in groups of ten. How many links are there so far?

___70___ links

B

Lesson Planner

Objective

Use a hundred chart to count by tens in art.

National Standard

Student understands family life now and in the past, and family life in various places long ago.

Activate Prior Knowledge

Before you turn students' attention to the pages, discuss celebrations.

- Explain that a celebration is a special event in honor of a special person or day.
- **Can you name a person or day that your family celebrates?** See students' explanations.
- **Do you think people everywhere celebrate these events?** See students' explanations.
- Share a story with students of an event you celebrated as a child.
- Have students ask adults in their families to describe the traditions they have kept over the years.

This class made a school bus on big paper.

The bus has five big windows. The children wanted to draw ten faces in each window. How many people would be on the bus?

__50__ people

How many buses would they need for 100 people? Make a table to find the answer.

__2__ buses

C

This school has a guest. She is 100 years old!

What questions would you ask a person who is 100 years old?

FOLD DOWN

D

Create the Book

Guide students to create their book.

- Have them fold the page in half.

- Ask them to write their name on page A.

- Explain that page A is the front cover and page D is the back cover. If necessary, have them practice flipping through the book in order.

- Guide them in reading the information and word problems on each of the pages.

Use the Student Pages

Have students work individually or in pairs to solve the word problems on pages B–D.

Page B Students may have problems counting by groups of ten. Suggest that students use a hundred chart to help if needed.

Page C Students may have problems counting the number of people on the bus. Suggest that they try counting by tens.

Extend the Activity

Have students work in small groups to count different objects to 100. Then ask students to divide the objects into groups of ten.

FOLDABLES **Dinah Zike's Foldables**

Use this lesson suggestion to incorporate the Foldables during the chapter. Students can then use their Foldable to review for the test.

Lesson 8-7 Use the hundred chart to count by 2s, 5s, and 10s. Use the hundred chart for skip counting.

Vocabulary Review

Review chapter vocabulary using one of the following options.

- **Visual Vocabulary Cards** (17 and 32)
- **eGlossary** at macmillanmh.com

Vocabulary Test

CRM **Chapter 8 Resource Masters** (p. 55)
Assess student comprehension of the chapter vocabulary with the Vocabulary Test.

Math Online **Chapter Test**
Alternative summative assessment options are available online at macmillanmh.com.

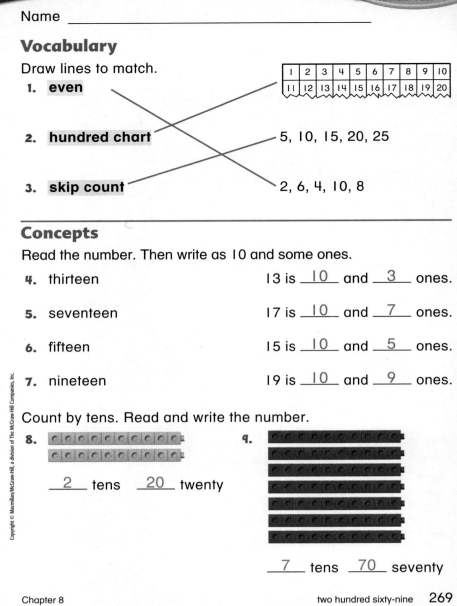

Name _____

Vocabulary

Draw lines to match.

1	2	3	4	5	6	7	8	9	10
11	12	13	14	15	16	17	18	19	20

1. **even**

2. **hundred chart** 5, 10, 15, 20, 25

3. **skip count** 2, 6, 4, 10, 8

Concepts

Read the number. Then write as 10 and some ones.

4. thirteen 13 is __10__ and __3__ ones.

5. seventeen 17 is __10__ and __7__ ones.

6. fifteen 15 is __10__ and __5__ ones.

7. nineteen 19 is __10__ and __9__ ones.

Count by tens. Read and write the number.

8.

__2__ tens __20__ twenty

9.

__7__ tens __70__ seventy

Chapter 8 two hundred sixty-nine **269**

✓ Chapter 8 Project

Patterns on a Hundred Chart

Alone, in pairs, or in small groups, have students discuss the results of their completed chapter project with the class. Assess their work using the Chapter Project rubric found in Chapter 8 Resource Masters, p. 60.

Use the number line. Skip count.

0 1 2 3 4 5 6 7 8 9 10 11 12 13 14 15 16 17 18 19 20 21 22 23 24 25 26 27 28 29 30

10. 2, 4, _6_, _8_, _10_   **11.** 10, 15, _20_, 25, _30_

12. 5, 10, _15_, _20_, _25_   **13.** _10_, 20, 30

14. 10, _20_, 30   **15.** 12, _14_, _16_, 18, 20

Circle *even* or *odd*.

16. 5    even
(odd)

---

17. 12    (even)
odd

Problem Solving

18. Abbey has 3 groups of 10 pencils. She takes 10 away. How many pencils does she have left?
_20_

Copyright © Macmillan/McGraw-Hill, a division of The McGraw-Hill Companies, Inc.

Summative Assessment

Use these alternate leveled chapter tests to differentiate assessment for the specific needs of your students.

Leveled Chapter 8 Tests			
Form	**Type**	**Level**	**CRM Pages**
1	Multiple Choice	BL	62–63
2A	Multiple Choice	OL	64–65
2B	Multiple Choice	OL	66–67
2C	Free Response	AL	68–69
2D	Free Response	AL	70–71

BL = below/approaching grade level
OL = on grade level
AL = above/beyond grade level

ExamView® Assessment Suite Customize and create multiple versions of your Chapter Test and their test answer keys.

Data-Driven Decision Making

Based on the results of the Chapter Review/Test, use the following to review concepts that continue to present students with problems.

Exercises	State/Local Standards	What's the Math?	Error Analysis	Resources for Review
1–3		Understand vocabulary "hundred chart", "tens", and "skip counting.	Does not understand words "even," "skip counting," "hundred chart." Does not draw three lines.	Strategic Intervention Guide (p. 98) CRM Chapter 8 Resource Masters (Reteach Worksheets)
4–9		Count, read, and write by 10's.	Adds numbers incorrectly. Does not use tens place value.	**Math Online** Concepts in Motion
10–15		Use a number line to skip count by 2s, 5s, and 10s to 100.	Does not write on all spaces given. Adds and counts incorrectly and writes wrong numbers.	Math Adventures
16–17		Identify even and odd numbers.	Does not understand the words "even" and "odd".	

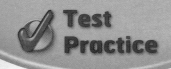

Test Practice

 Formative Assessment

- Use Student Edition pp. 271–272 as practice and cumulative review. The questions are written in the same style as many state tests.
- You can use these two pages to benchmark student progress, or as an alternative homework assignment.

Additional practice pages can be found in the Chapter 8 Resource Masters.

CRM Chapter 8 Resource Masters

Cumulative Test Practice

- Multiple Choice format (pp. 65–68, 72)
- Free Response format (pp. 69–71, 73)

Exam*View* **Assessment Suite** Create practice worksheets or tests that align to your state standards.

Math Online For additional practice visit macmillanmh.com.

Name _____

Listen as your teacher reads each problem. Choose the correct answer.

1.

5	4
○	○
6	8
⬤	○

4.

5	4
○	○
6	8
⬤	○

2. 26, 81, 4

26, 81, 4	81, 26, 4
○	○
4, 26, 81	4, 81, 26
⬤	○

5.   8 ☐ 5 = 3

−	=	>	+
⬤	○	○	○

3.

(clock showing 2:00)

4:00	2:00	12:00	8:00
○	⬤	○	○

6.   2 ☐ 5 = 7

>	+
○	⬤
−	=
○	○

Copyright © Macmillan/McGraw-Hill, a division of The McGraw-Hill Companies, Inc.

Chapter 8   two hundred seventy-one **271**

Test-Taking Tips

For the Teacher

- Before starting a test, tell students about how much time the test or each section will take.
- Remind students to check their answers.

For the Student

- Tell students to clearly fill the bubble so everyone can read their answers.
- Tell students that if they cannot answer a question, cross out the answer choices they know are wrong, then choose an answer from the choices that remain.

7. 5, 10, 15, 20, _____

21	25	15	5
○	⬤	○	○

10.   5 − 3

3 − 1	8 − 5
⬤	○

4 − 3	5 − 2
○	○

8.

○	○

⬤	○

11. There are 9 cars. 5 are blue. The rest are green. How many cars are green?

____4____ cars

9.

10	16
○	○

17	19
⬤	○

12. Nate wrote 9 tens and 3 ones. What number did he write?

____93____

STOP

Summative Assessment

Test Directions for Teachers

Read the following directions to students before they begin. Then read each questions followed by a pause to allow student time to work and choose an answer. The first test item can be worked as a class example.

- **Write your name at the top of the page.**
- **I am going to read each question to you. Listen carefully to the entire question before you choose an answer.**

Multiple Choice

1. How many tens in 60?
2. Look at the group of numbers. Which group shows the numbers in order from least to greatest?
3. Look at the clock. What time does it show?
4. How many ones in 96?
5. Which sign is missing?
6. Which sign is missing?

- **Turn the page over.**

7. Look at the number pattern. Which number comes next?
8. Which clock shows 4 o'clock?
9. Which number is 1 ten and 7 ones?
10. Look at 5 minus 3. Which fact makes the same difference?

Short Response

11. There are 9 cars. 5 are blue. The rest are green. How many cars are green?
12. Nate wrote 9 tens and 3 ones. What number did he write?

Student Handbook

Built-In Workbook

Facts Practice **FP1**

WorkMats 1–8

Reference

English-Spanish Picture Glossary **G1**

Photo Credits

Hundred Chart, Number
Words, and Measurement . . . **Inside Back Cover**

How to Use the Student Handbook

Use the Student Handbook

You, or your teacher, may decide that working through some additional problems would be helpful. The **Facts Practice** section is useful:

- when you need more practice with addition facts and subtraction facts

- when you need to show different ways to make numbers, show the order of numbers, count on to add, count back to subtract, or write numbers as hundreds, tens, and ones

- when you need to know the meaning of a math word

- when you need to find number patterns, to order numbers, or to skip count

- when you need help writing the number names

Preparing for Standardized Tests

It's time to review how to take a standardized test. You have been building your math skills in class. Soon you will have a chance to put them to work.

Tips for Success!

Before a Test

- Go to bed early the night before.
- Eat a good breakfast the next morning.

During a Test

- Listen carefully as your teacher reads each question.
- Work carefully.

Whatever you do...

- Do not rush.
- Do not give up.

RELAX. Just do your best.

Preparing for Standardized Tests

Multiple-Choice

You will fill in bubbles to answer questions.

Make sure to:
- Fill in the bubble completely.
- Make your marks dark.
- If you make a mistake, erase it all.

Correct		
2	5	7	9
○	○	⬤	○

Not Correct		
2	5	7	9
○	○	⦿	○

Short-Response

You will solve problems and write your answers on the line.

Make sure to:
- Work slowly and carefully.
- Use your neatest handwriting.
- Check your work.
- Make sure that you answered the question.

Name _____

Multiple-Choice Practice

Directions

Listen as your teacher reads each problem. Choose the correct answer.

1. There are twenty-two cows on a farm. There are nine pigs. About how many animals are there in all?

   ○ about 10   ○ about 20

   ○ about 25   ⬤ about 30

2. Jeremy has thirty-one crayons. Ana has fifty-two crayons. About how many more crayons does Ana have than Jeremy?

   ○ about 10   ⬤ about 20

   ○ about 25   ○ about 30

3. Which sign makes the number sentence true?

   $$9 - 5 \boxed{} 4$$

   ○ +   ⬤ =   ○ >   ○ <

4. Three bees are on a flower. Four more bees join them. Which number sentence shows how many bees there are in all?

   ○ $4 + 3 = 7$ ○ $4 - 3 = 1$

   ⬤ $3 + 3 = 6$ ○ $7 - 4 = 3$

5. What time is shown on the clock?

   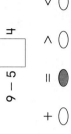

   ○ 3 o'clock   ○ 6 o'clock

   ⬤ 9 o'clock   ○ 10 o'clock

6. Which activity takes the most time?

   ○ brushing your teeth

   ⬤ watching a movie

   ○ walking a dog

   ○ taking a bath

Short-Response Practice

Name _____

Directions
Listen as your teacher reads each problem. Write the correct answer.

1. Jenny has 4 pencils. She buys 3 more at the store. How many pencils does she have in all?

7 pencils

2. Kiah put eleven beads on a bracelet. Then she added twenty-one more beads. About how many beads did she use?

about **30** beads

3. Megan's family has 3 dogs and 2 cats. How many pets do they have in all?

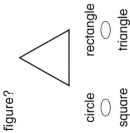

5 pets

4. Amy skipped rope sixty-two times at recess. Michael skipped rope eighteen times. About how many more times did Amy skip rope than Michael?

about **40** times

5. Andy had ten colored pencils. He gave four of them to Marta. Write a number sentence to show how many colored pencils Andy has left.

10 − 4 = 6

6. Vicky's school begins at the time shown on the clock. What time is shown on the clock?

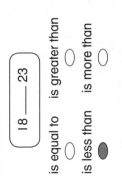

8:00 or 8 o'clock

Short-Response Practice   TP5

Multiple-Choice Practice

Directions
Listen as your teacher reads each problem. Choose the correct answer.

7. What shape makes up the faces of the figure below?

○ circle   ○ line
● square   ○ triangle

8. What is the name of this figure?

○ circle   ○ rectangle
○ square   ● triangle

9. What rule could you use to find the next number in the pattern?

1, 3, 5, 7, 9, 11, 13, 15

○ add 1   ○ subtract 1
● add 2   ○ subtract 2

10. Kareem made a number pattern showing the amount of money in nickels. What is the next amount of money in the pattern?

5¢, 10¢, 15¢, 20¢, 25¢, 30¢

○ 30¢   ● 35¢   ○ 40¢   ○ 45¢

11. Look at the number below. How do you read this number?

32

○ thirty-two   ○ three two
○ twenty-three   ● twenty-two

12. Look at the numbers below. What can you replace the blank with to make a true statement?

18 ____ 23

○ is equal to   ○ is greater than
● is less than   ○ is more than

Glossary/Glosario

English	Español
add (adding, addition) To join together sets to find the total or sum. (page 53)	**sumar (suma, adición)** Unir conjuntos para hallar el total o la suma.
 $2 + 5 = 7$	$2 + 5 = 7$
addend Any numbers or quantities being added together. (page 155)	**sumando** Números o cantidades que se suman.
$2 + 3$	$2 + 3$
2 is an addend and 3 is an addend.	2 es un sumando y 3 es un sumando.
addition sentence An expression using numbers and the + and = signs. (page 55)	**expresión de suma** Expresión que usa números y los signos + y =.
$4 + 5 = 9$	$4 + 5 = 9$
after To follow in place or time. (page 39)	**después** Que sigue en lugar o en tiempo.
 5 6 7 8	5 6 7 8
6 is just after 5	6 viene inmediatemente *después* del 5

Short-Response Practice

Directions
Listen as your teacher reads each problem. Write the correct answer.

7. What is the value of this coin?

10 ¢

8. What shape is this party hat?

cone

9. What is this shape?

cube

10. Miles had nine tennis balls. He gave two of them to Matthew. Write a number sentence to show how many tennis balls Miles has left.

$9 - 2 = 7$

11. Name the shape that comes next in this pattern.

circle

12. What rule could you use to find the next number in the pattern?

4, 5, 6, 7, 8, 9, 10, 11, 12

add 1

13. Look at the pattern of numbers below. Which number comes next?

10, 20, 30, 40

50

14. What rule could you use to find the next number in the pattern?

3, 6, 9, 12, 15

add 3

Glossary/Glosario

English	Español

A

afternoon A time in the day between noon and sunset. (page 213)

tarde Momento del día entre el mediodía y el atardecer.

afternoon

tarde

analog A clock that has an hour hand and a minute hand. (page 223)

analógico Reloj que tiene manecilla horaria y minutero.

minute hand — hour hand

minutero — manecilla horaria

B

bar graph A graph that uses bars to show data. (page 133)

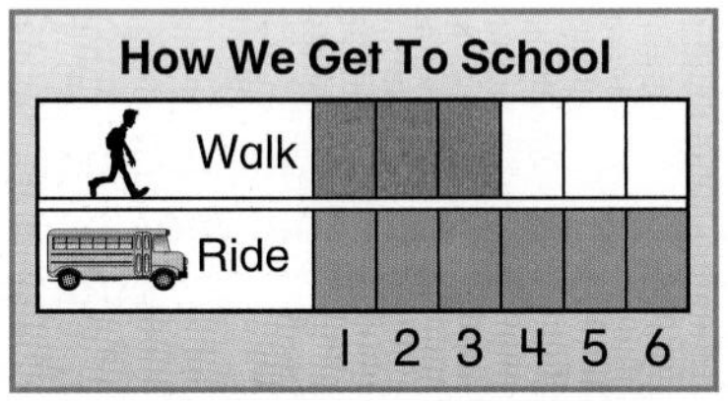

gráfica de barras Gráfica que usa barras para mostrar datos.

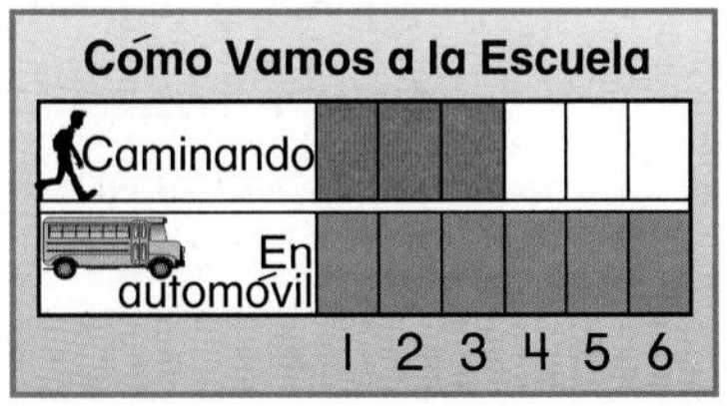

How We Get To School
Walk
Ride
1 2 3 4 5 6

Cómo Vamos a la Escuela
Caminando
En automóvil
1 2 3 4 5 6

Glossary/Glosario

English	Español

B

before (page 39)

antes

5 6 7 8

6 is just *before* 7

6 viene inmediatamente *antes* del 7

between (page 39)

entre

The kitten is *between* the two dogs.

El gatito está *entre* dos perros.

C

cent ¢ (page 351)

centavo ¢

1¢   1 cent

1¢   1 centavo

Glossary/Glosario

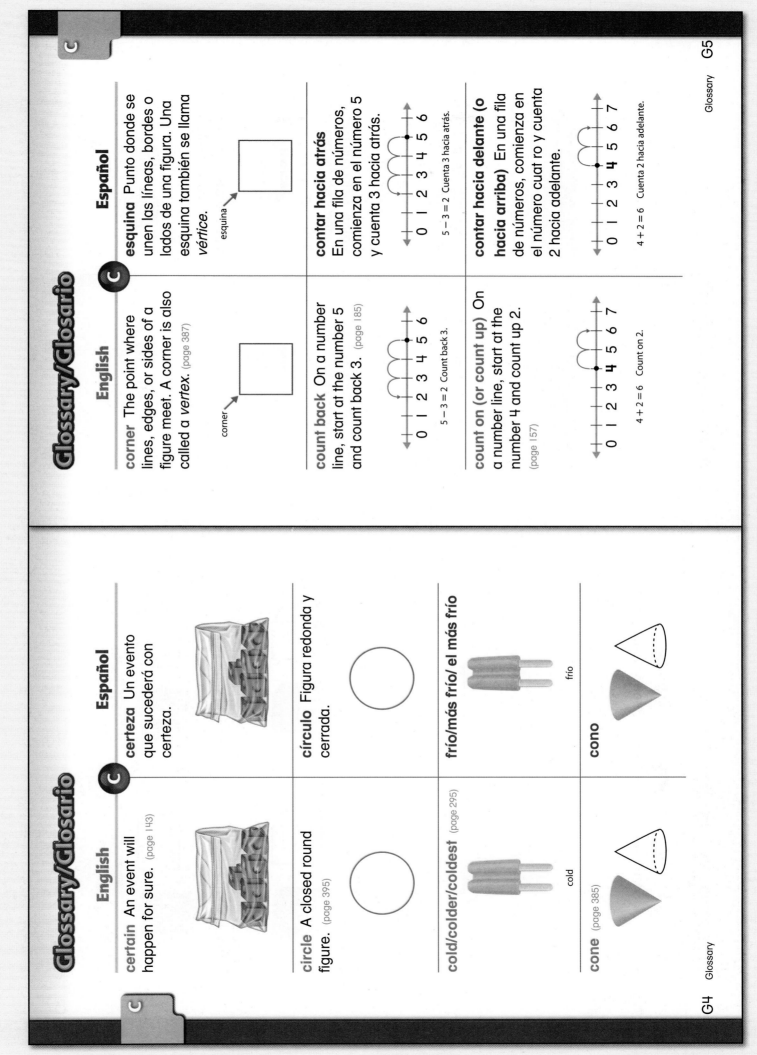

C

English	Español
certain An event will happen for sure. (page 143)	**certeza** Un evento que sucederá con certeza.
circle A closed round figure. (page 395)	**círculo** Figura redonda y cerrada.
cold/colder/coldest (page 295) cold	**frío/más frío/ el más frío** frío
cone (page 385)	**cono**

C

English	Español
corner The point where lines, edges, or sides of a figure meet. A corner is also called a *vertex*. (page 387) corner	**esquina** Punto donde se unen las líneas, bordes o lados de una figura. Una esquina también se llama *vértice*. esquina
count back On a number line, start at the number 5 and count back 3. (page 185) 0 1 2 3 4 5 6 5 – 3 = 2 Count back 3.	**contar hacia atrás** En una fila de números, comienza en el número 5 y cuenta 3 hacia atrás. 0 1 2 3 4 5 6 5 – 3 = 2 Cuenta 3 hacia atrás.
count on (or count up) On a number line, start at the number 4 and count up 2. (page 157) 0 1 2 3 4 5 6 7 4 + 2 = 6 Count on 2.	**contar hacia delante (o hacia arriba)** En una fila de números, comienza en el número cuatro y cuenta 2 hacia adelante. 0 1 2 3 4 5 6 7 4 + 2 = 6 Cuenta 2 hacia adelante.

Glossary/Glosario

English		Español
C		**C**

covers less/least (page 301)

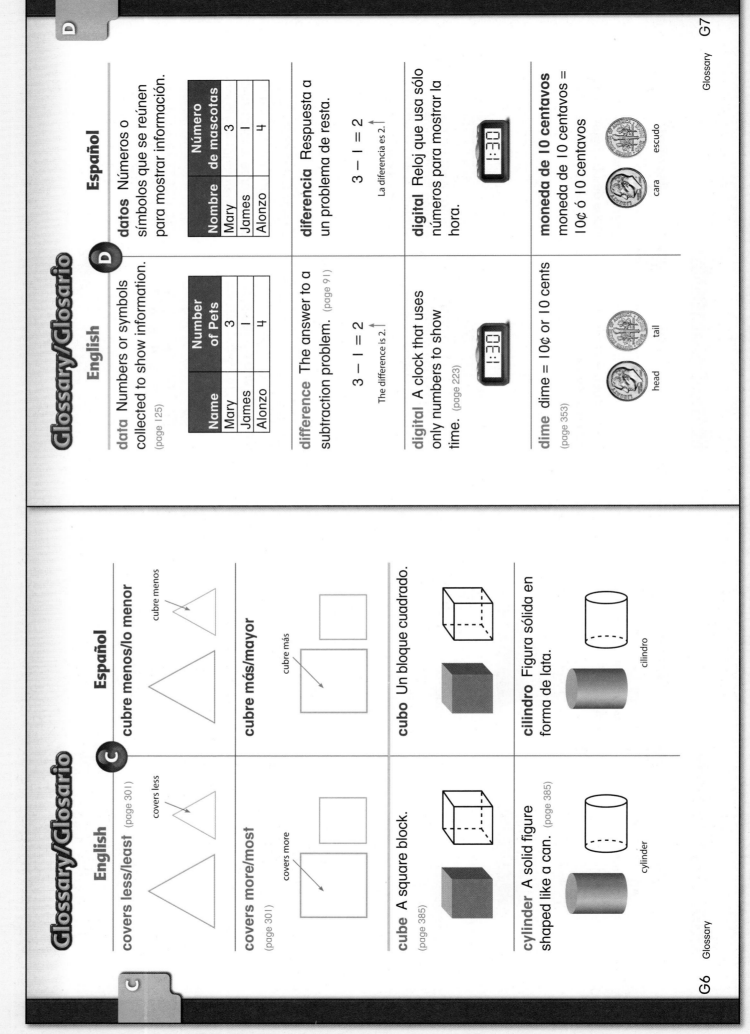

covers less

cubre menos/lo menor

cubre menos

covers more/most (page 301)

covers more

cubre más/mayor

cubre más

cube A square block. (page 385)

cubo Un bloque cuadrado.

cylinder A solid figure shaped like a can. (page 385)

cylinder

cilindro Figura sólida en forma de lata.

cilindro

English		Español
D		**D**

data Numbers or symbols collected to show information. (page 125)

Number of Pets	
Name	
Mary	3
James	1
Alonzo	4

datos Números o símbolos que se reúnen para mostrar información.

Número de mascotas	
Nombre	
Mary	3
James	1
Alonzo	4

difference The answer to a subtraction problem. (page 91)

$$3 - 1 = 2$$

The difference is 2.

diferencia Respuesta a un problema de resta.

$$3 - 1 = 2$$

La diferencia es 2.

digital A clock that uses only numbers to show time. (page 223)

1:30

digital Reloj que usa sólo números para mostrar la hora.

1:30

dime dime = 10¢ or 10 cents (page 353)

head   tail

moneda de 10 centavos moneda de 10 centavos = 10¢ ó 10 centavos

cara   escudo

Glossary/Glosario

E

English	Español
doubles (and doubles plus 1) Two addends that are the same number. (pages 169 and 171)	**dobles (y dobles más 1)** Dos sumandos que son el mismo número.

2 + 2 = 4

2 + 3 = 5

2 + 2 = 4

2 + 3 = 5

English	Español
equal parts Each part is the same size. (page 457)	**partes iguales** Cada parte es del mismo tamaño.
A muffin cut in equal parts.	Un panecillo cortado en partes iguales.

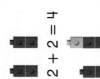

English	Español
equals (=) Having the same value as or is the same as. (page 55)	**igual (=)** Que tienen el mismo valor o son iguales a.

2 + 4 = 6
↑
equal sign

2 + 4 = 6
↑
signo de igual

English	Español
estimate To find a number close to an exact amount. (page 255)	**estimar** Hallar un número cercano a la cantidad exacta.

E F

English	Español
even Numbers that end with 0, 2, 4, 6, 8. (page 263)	**par** Números que terminan en 0, 2, 4, 6, 8.

English	Español
evening The time after school when it is dark. (page 213)	**anochecer** Hora después de la escuela cuando está oscuro.

evening

anochecer

English	Español
face The flat part of a 3-dimensional figure. (page 387)	**cara** Parte plana de una figura de 3 dimensiones.

face

cara

Glossary/Glosario

F

English	Español
fact family Addition and subtraction sentences that use the same numbers. Sometimes called *related facts*. (page 199)	**familia de datos** Expresiones de suma y resta que utilizan los mismos números. Algunas veces se llaman *datos relacionados*.

$$6 + 7 = 13 \qquad 13 - 7 = 6$$
$$7 + 6 = 13 \qquad 13 - 6 = 7$$

$$6 + 7 = 13 \qquad 13 - 7 = 6$$
$$7 + 6 = 13 \qquad 13 - 6 = 7$$

English	Español
fraction A number that represents part of a whole or part of a set. (page 461)	**fracción** Número que representa la parte de un todo o la parte de un conjunto.

$$\frac{1}{2}, \frac{1}{3}, \frac{1}{4}, \frac{3}{4}$$

$$\frac{1}{2}, \frac{1}{3}, \frac{1}{4}, \frac{3}{4}$$

G

English	Español
graph A way to present data collected. Also a type of chart. (page 125)	**gráfica** Forma de presentar datos recogidos. También tipo de tabla.

Our Favorite Sports

Soccer / Football / Baseball

Number of Participants 1 2 3 4 5 6 7 8 9

bar graph

Nuestros Deportes Favoritos

Balón / Fútbol / Beisbol

Número de Participantes 1 2 3 4 5 6 7 8 9

una gráfica de barras

Glossary/Glosario

H

English	Español
half hour (or half past) One half of an hour is 30 minutes. Sometimes called *half past* or *half past the hour*. (page 217)	**media hora (o y media)** Media hora son 30 minutos. Algunas veces se llama 'y media'.

English	Español
heavy (heavier, heaviest) Weighs more. (page 285) An elephant is heavier than a mouse.	**pesado (más pesado, el más pesado)** Pesa más. Un elefante es más pesado (pesa más) que un ratón.

heavier

más pesado

English	Español
holds less/least (page 291)	**contener menos**

The glass holds less than the pitcher.

El vaso contiene menos que la jarra.

Glossary/Glosario

English

hundred chart A chart that shows numbers 1–100. (page 249)

1	2	3	4	5	6	7	8	9	10
11	12	13	14	15	16	17	18	19	20
21	22	23	24	25	26	27	28	29	30
31	32	33	34	35	36	37	38	39	40
41	42	43	44	45	46	47	48	49	50
51	52	53	54	55	56	57	58	59	60
61	62	63	64	65	66	67	68	69	70
71	72	73	74	75	76	77	78	79	80
81	82	83	84	85	86	87	88	89	90
91	92	93	94	95	96	97	98	99	100

impossible An event that cannot happen. (page 143)

You cannot pick a blue cube.

is equal to = (page 35)

6 = 6

6 is equal to 6

Español

tabla de cien Tabla que muestra los números. 1–100.

1	2	3	4	5	6	7	8	9	10
11	12	13	14	15	16	17	18	19	20
21	22	23	24	25	26	27	28	29	30
31	32	33	34	35	36	37	38	39	40
41	42	43	44	45	46	47	48	49	50
51	52	53	54	55	56	57	58	59	60
61	62	63	64	65	66	67	68	69	70
71	72	73	74	75	76	77	78	79	80
81	82	83	84	85	86	87	88	89	90
91	92	93	94	95	96	97	98	99	100

imposible Un evento que no puede ocurrir.

No puedes elegir un cubo azul.

igual a =

6 = 6

6 es igual a 6

Glossary/Glosario

English

holds more/most (page 291)

The pitcher holds more than the glass.

hot/hotter/hottest (page 295)

hot

hour A unit of time 1 hour = 60 minutes (page 215)

hour hand The hand on a clock that tells the hour. It is the shorter hand. (page 215)

hour hand

Español

contener más

El vaso contiene más que la jarra.

caliente/más caliente/ el más caliente

caliente

hora Unidad de tiempo. 1 hora = 60 minutos

manecilla horaria Manecilla del reloj que dice la hora. Es la manecilla más corta.

manecilla horaria

Glossary/Glosario

Glossary/Glosario

English | Español

I

is greater than > (page 35)

7 > 2

7 is greater than 2

mayor que >

7 > 2

7 es mayor que 2

is less than < (page 35)

4 < 7

4 is less than 7

menor que <

4 < 7

4 es menor que 7

L

length (page 277)

length

longitud

longitud

Glossary/Glosario

English | Español

L

light (lighter, lightest) (page 285) Weighs less. The mouse is lighter than the elephant.

lighter

liviano (más liviano, el más liviano) Pesa menos. El ratón es más liviano (pesa menos) que el elefante.

más liviano

long (longer, longest) (page 277) A way to compare the lengths of two objects.

long

longer

longest

largo (más largo, el más largo) Forma de comparar la longitud de dos objetos.

largo

más largo

el más largo

M

measure To find the length, height, or weight using standard or nonstandard units. (page 279)

medir Hallar la longitud, estatura o peso mediante unidades estándar o no estándar.

Glossary/Glosario

Glossary/Glosario

G16

English	Español
M	
minus (−) The sign used to show subtraction. (page 91) $5 - 2 = 3$ ↑ minus sign	**resta (−)** Signo que se usa en la resta. $5 - 2 = 3$ ↑ signo de resta
minute hand The longer hand on a clock that tells the minutes. (page 215)  minute hand	**minutero** La manecilla más larga de un reloj que indica los minutos. 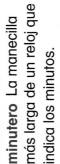 minutero
missing addend $9 + \underline{\quad} = 16$ The missing addend is 7. (page 211)	**sumando desconocido** $9 + \underline{\quad} = 16$ El sumando desconocido es 7.
morning The period of time from sunrise to noon. (page 213) 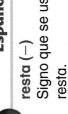 morning	**mañana** Período de tiempo que va del amanecer al mediodía. mañana

G17

English	Español
N	
nickel 5¢ or 5 cents (page 351)  head tail	**moneda de cinco centavos** 5¢ ó 5 centavos  cara escudo
number Tells how many. 1, 2, 3, 4, 5, 6, 7, 8, 9, 10, … (page 23)  There are 3 chicks.	**números** Decir cuántos. 1, 2, 3, 4, 5, 6, 7, 8, 9, 10, …  Hay 3 pollito.
number line A line with number labels. (page 39) 0 1 2 3 4 5 6 7 8 9 10	**línea de números** Línea con rótulos de números. 0 1 2 3 4 5 6 7 8 9 10
O	
o'clock At the beginning of the hour. (page 215) It is 3 o'clock.	**en punto** Al comienzo de la hora.  Son las 3 en punto.
odd Numbers that end with 1, 3, 5, 7, 9. (page 263)	**impar** Números que terminan en 1, 3, 5, 7, 9.

Glossary/Glosario

English	Español
one fourth A fraction that shows 1 piece out of 4 equal pieces. (page 463) $\frac{1}{4}$	**un cuarto** Fracción que muestra 1 de 4 partes iguales. $\frac{1}{4}$
one half A fraction that shows 1 piece out of 2 equal pieces. (page 461) $\frac{1}{2}$	**un medio** Fracción que muestra 1 de 2 partes iguales. $\frac{1}{2}$
one third A fraction that shows 1 piece out of the 3 equal pieces. (page 463) $\frac{1}{3}$	**un tercio** Fracción que muestra 1 de 3 partes iguales. $\frac{1}{3}$
ones This number has 3 ones. 2 3	**unidades** Este número tiene 3 unidades. 2 3

Glossary/Glosario

English	Español
order 1, 3, 6, 7, 9 (page 39) These numbers are in order from least to greatest.	**orden** 1, 3, 6, 7, 9 Estos números están en orden del menor al mayor.
pattern An order that a set of objects or numbers follows over and over. (page 17) A, A, B, A, A, B, A, A, B  pattern unit	**patrón** Orden que sigue continuamente un conjunto de objetos o números. A, A, B, A, A, B, A, A, B unidad de patrón
penny 1¢ or 1 cent (page 351) head tail	**moneda de un centavo** 1¢ ó 1 centavo cara escudo
picture graph A graph that has different pictures to show information collected. (page 125) Our Favorite Toys	**gráfica con imágenes** Gráfica que tiene diferentes imágenes para mostrar la información recogida. Nuestros Juguetes Favoritos

Glossary/Glosario

G20

English	Español
P	**P**
plane figure See 2-dimensional figure. (page 375)	**figura plana** Ver figuras de 2 dimensiones.
plus (+) A symbol to show addition. (page 55)	**suma (+)** Símbolo para mostrar la suma.
$4 + 5 = 9$ plus sign	$4 + 5 = 9$ signo de suma
position Tell where an object is. (page 401)  above	**posición** Dice dónde está un objeto. 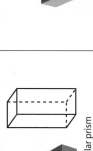 arriba
pyramid A solid figure with a polygon as a base and triangular shaped faces. (page 385) 	**pirámide** Figura sólida con un polígono como base y caras de forma triangular.
Q	**Q**
quarter 25¢ or 25 cents (page 365) head tail	**moneda de 25 centavos** 25¢ ó 25 centavos cara escudo

Glossary/Glosario

G21

English	Español
R	**R**
rectangle A shape with four sides and four corners. (page 395) 	**rectángulo** Figura con cuatro lados y cuatro esquinas. 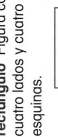
rectangular prism A 3-dimensional shape. (page 385) 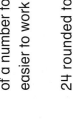 rectangular prism	**prisma rectangular** Figura de 3 dimensiones.  Prisma rectangular
regroup To take apart a number to write it in a new way. (page 423) 1 ten + 2 ones becomes 12 ones 	**reagrupar** Separar un número para escribirlo en una nueva forma. 1 decena + 2 unidades se convierten en 12 unidades.
round To change the *value* of a number to one that is easier to work with. (page 495) 24 rounded to the nearest 10 is 20.	**redondear** Cambiar el *valor* de un número a uno con el que es más fácil trabajar. 24 redondeado a la decena más cercana es 20.

Glossary/Glosario

English	Español
sort To group together like items. (page 123)	**ordenar** Agrupar elementos iguales.
sphere A solid figure that has the shape of a round ball. (page 367)	**esfera** Figura sólida con la forma de una pelota redonda.
square A rectangle that has four equal sides. (page 395)	**cuadrado** Rectángulo que tiene cuatro lados iguales.
subtract (subtracting, subtraction) To take away, take apart, separate, or find the difference between two sets. The opposite of addition. (page 89) 4−1=3	**restar (resta, sustracción)** Eliminar, quitar, separar o hallar la diferencia entre dos conjuntos. Lo opuesto de la suma. 4−1=3

Glossary/Glosario

English	Español
short (shorter, shortest) To compare length or height of two (or more) objects. (page 277) short / shorter / shortest	**corto (más corto, el más corto)** Comparar la longitud o la altura de dos (o más) objetos. corto / más corto / el más corto
side (page 395) side	**lado** lado
skip count To count objects in equal groups of two or more. (page 259) 2,4,6,8,10 0 1 2 3 4 5 6 7 8 9 10	**conteo en grupos** Contar objetos en grupos iguales de dos o más. 2,4,6,8,10 0 1 2 3 4 5 6 7 8 9 10
solid figure See 3-dimensional figure. (page 385)	**figura sólida** Ver figura de 3 dimensiones.

Glossary/Glosario

G24

English	Español
subtraction sentence An expression using numbers and the − and = signs. (page 91) $9 - 5 = 4$	**expresión de resta** Expresión que contiene números y los signos de − y =. $9 - 5 = 4$
sum The answer to an addition problem. (page 55) $2 + 4 = 6$ ↑ sum	**suma** Respuesta a un problema de suma. $2 + 4 = 6$ ↑ suma
survey To collect data by asking people the same question. (page 129) This survey shows favorite foods.	**encuesta** Recoger datos haciendo las mismas preguntas a las personas. Esta encuesta muestra las comidas favoritas.
tally chart A way to show data collected using tally marks. (page 129) 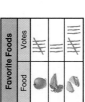	**tabla de conteo** Forma de mostrar los datos recogidos utilizando marcas de contar. 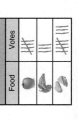

G25

English	Español
tens (page 419) This number has 2 tens. 	**decenas** Este número tiene 2 decenas. 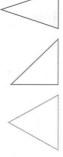
three-dimensional figure A solid figure. (page 385) 	**figura de 3 dimensiones** Figura solida.
triangle A shape with three sides. (page 395)	**triángulo** Figura con tres lados.
two-dimensional figure The outline of a figure such as a triangle, square, or rectangle. (page 395)	**figura de 2 dimensiones** Esquema de una figura como un triángulo, cuadrado o rectángulo.

Glossary/Glosario

English	Español

U

unit An object used to measure. (page 279)

unidad Objeto que se usa para medir.

V

venn diagram A drawing that uses circles to sort and show data. (page 123)

diagrama de Venn Dibujo que utiliza círculos para ordenar y mostrar datos.

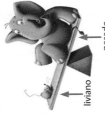

W

weight (page 285)

peso

light — heavy

liviano — pesado

Z

zero 0 The number zero equals none or nothing. (page 59)

cero 0 El número cero es igual a nada o ninguno.

Photo Credits

Name _____

Count On 1, 2, and 3 (Use with Chapter 5)

1. $1+7=8$ $3+3=6$ $8+1=9$ $7+1=8$ $5+1=6$ $9+1=10$

2. $2+3=5$ $1+6=7$ $2+5=7$ $6+3=9$ $3+5=8$ $1+5=6$

3. $2+2=4$ $2+7=9$ $3+1=4$ $4+2=6$ $2+4=6$ $7+3=10$

✂ -

Name _____

Count Back 1, 2, and 3 (Use with Chapter 6)

1. $9-3=6$ $4-1=3$ $7-2=5$ $3-3=0$ $5-3=2$ $7-3=4$

2. $10-2=8$ $3-1=2$ $9-2=7$ $2-1=1$ $6-2=4$ $3-2=1$

3. $4-2=2$ $10-3=7$ $5-1=4$ $8-2=6$ $5-2=3$ $4-3=1$

Facts Practice

Name _____

Doubles and Doubles Plus 1 (Use with Chapter 7)

1.
$$6+6=12 \quad 4+5=9 \quad 5+5=10 \quad 3+2=5 \quad 2+1=3 \quad 3+4=7$$

2.
$$6+5=11 \quad 3+2=5 \quad 2+2=4 \quad 4+3=7 \quad 5+4=9 \quad 4+4=8$$

3.
$$2+3=5 \quad 3+3=6 \quad 1+1=2 \quad 1+0=1 \quad 5+2=3 \quad 5+6=11$$

✂

Name _____

Use Doubles or Count Back (Use with Chapter 8)

1.
$$4-2=2 \quad 11-3=8 \quad 3-2=1 \quad 7-3=4 \quad 10-5=5$$

2.
$$8-3=5 \quad 7-2=5 \quad 8-4=4 \quad 12-3=9 \quad 6-2=4$$

3.
$$12-6=6 \quad 2-2=0 \quad 11-2=9 \quad 5-2=3 \quad 8-3=5$$

Name _____

Count On 1, 2, and 3 (Use with Chapter 5)

4.
$$1+9=10 \quad 3+6=9 \quad 6+2=8 \quad 1+4=5 \quad 3+7=10 \quad 4+3=7$$

5.
$$3+2=5 \quad 3+6=9 \quad 2+7=9 \quad 5+2=7 \quad 5+2=7 \quad 1+3=4$$

6.
$$5+3=8 \quad 3+4=7 \quad 4+1=5 \quad 6+1=7 \quad 2+8=10 \quad 2+6=8$$

Name _____

Count Back 1, 2, and 3 (Use with Chapter 6)

4.
$$6-3=3 \quad 10-2=8 \quad 3-2=1 \quad 5-3=2 \quad 2-1=1 \quad 7-3=4 \quad 8-2=6$$

5.
$$5-2=3 \quad 4-2=2 \quad 10-1=9 \quad 2-2=0 \quad 7-3=4$$

6.
$$9-3=6 \quad 10-3=7 \quad 4-1=5 \quad 6-1=5 \quad 8-2=6$$

Name _____

Doubles and Doubles Plus 1 (Use with Chapter 7)

4.

0	1	3	2	3	5
+0	+2	+2	+2	+4	+5
0	3	5	4	7	10

5.

4	5	2	6	3	4
+3	+4	+3	+5	+3	+4
7	9	5	11	6	8

6.

6	5	2	3	4	1
+6	+6	+1	+4	+5	+1
12	11	3	7	9	2

Name _____

Use Doubles or Count Back (Use with Chapter 8)

4.

12	11	6	5	4	3
−6	−3	−1	−3	−2	−2
6	8	5	2	2	1

5.

8	7	11	8	10	6
−3	−3	−2	−2	−5	−3
5	4	9	6	5	3

6.

12	8	9	2	9	6
−3	−4	−2	−2	−3	−3
9	4	7	0	6	3

Name _____

Make a Ten (Use with Chapter 9)

1.

4	6	5	8	4	8
+6	+7	+8	+6	+6	+5
10	13	13	14	10	13

2.

2	5	9	1	3	7
+8	+9	+7	+9	+7	+9
10	14	16	10	10	16

3.

7	6	6	7	9	4
+8	+4	+5	+3	+8	+9
15	10	10	10	17	13

Name _____

Subtract Zero and All (Use with Chapter 10)

1.

1	5	3	2	6	8
−0	−0	−3	−0	−0	−8
1	5	0	2	6	0

2.

2	7	8	6	7	5
−2	−7	−0	−6	−0	−5
0	0	8	0	7	0

3.

4	3	9	9	1	4
−4	−0	−9	−0	−1	−0
0	3	0	9	0	4

Name _____

Facts to 10 (Use with Chapter 10)

1.
$$4 + 6 = 10 \quad 4 + 5 = 9 \quad 3 + 2 = 5 \quad 2 + 6 = 8 \quad 2 + 5 = 7 \quad 1 + 3 = 4$$

2.
$$1 + 7 = 8 \quad 1 + 1 = 2 \quad 3 + 7 = 10 \quad 5 + 1 = 6 \quad 7 + 3 = 10 \quad 7 + 2 = 9$$

3.
$$4 + 3 = 7 \quad 0 + 5 = 5 \quad 8 + 2 = 10 \quad 5 + 3 = 8 \quad 9 + 1 = 10 \quad 5 + 4 = 9$$

✂

Name _____

Subtract from 10 or Less (Use with Chapter 11)

1.
$$10 - 2 = 8 \quad 9 - 4 = 5 \quad 10 - 7 = 3 \quad 10 - 8 = 2 \quad 9 - 6 = 3 \quad 10 - 7 = 3$$

2.
$$10 - 4 = 6 \quad 8 - 6 = 2 \quad 9 - 7 = 2 \quad 9 - 1 = 8 \quad 10 - 9 = 1 \quad 8 - 5 = 3$$

3.
$$9 - 8 = 1 \quad 10 - 5 = 5 \quad 8 - 7 = 1 \quad 10 - 3 = 7 \quad 10 - 4 = 6 \quad 10 - 6 = 4$$

Name _____

Make a Ten (Use with Chapter 9)

4.
$$6 + 8 = 14 \quad 9 + 4 = 13 \quad 2 + 9 = 11 \quad 5 + 7 = 12 \quad 8 + 9 = 17 \quad 9 + 1 = 10$$

5.
$$7 + 7 = 14 \quad 8 + 2 = 10 \quad 3 + 8 = 11 \quad 8 + 4 = 12 \quad 9 + 6 = 15 \quad 7 + 3 = 10$$

6.
$$9 + 5 = 14 \quad 6 + 9 = 15 \quad 4 + 7 = 11 \quad 7 + 5 = 12 \quad 8 + 8 = 16 \quad 3 + 9 = 12$$

Name _____

Subtract Zero and All (Use with Chapter 10)

4.
$$6 - 0 = 6 \quad 2 - 0 = 2 \quad 8 - 0 = 8 \quad 6 - 6 = 0 \quad 7 - 7 = 0 \quad 9 - 0 = 9$$

5.
$$8 - 8 = 0 \quad 1 - 1 = 0 \quad 9 - 9 = 0 \quad 4 - 4 = 0 \quad 2 - 2 = 0$$

6.
$$3 - 3 = 0 \quad 5 - 0 = 5 \quad 7 - 0 = 7 \quad 1 - 0 = 1 \quad 3 - 0 = 3 \quad 5 - 5 = 0$$

Name _____

Facts to 12 (Use with Chapter 11)

1.
$$3 + 5 = 8 \qquad 4 + 8 = 12 \qquad 8 + 4 = 12 \qquad 0 + 8 = 8 \qquad 5 + 2 = 7 \qquad 3 + 4 = 7$$

2.
$$6 + 5 = 11 \qquad 2 + 5 = 7 \qquad 4 + 2 = 6 \qquad 9 + 1 = 10 \qquad 5 + 6 = 11 \qquad 7 + 4 = 11$$

3.
$$5 + 4 = 9 \qquad 4 + 4 = 8 \qquad 7 + 1 = 8 \qquad 0 + 6 = 6 \qquad 4 + 7 = 11 \qquad 8 + 1 = 9$$

✂

Name _____

Subtract from 12 or Less (Use with Chapter 12)

1.
$$12 - 9 = 3 \qquad 12 - 7 = 5 \qquad 12 - 4 = 8 \qquad 12 - 7 = 5 \qquad 11 - 5 = 6 \qquad 12 - 6 = 6$$

2.
$$12 - 3 = 9 \qquad 12 - 4 = 8 \qquad 11 - 6 = 5 \qquad 11 - 2 = 9 \qquad 12 - 5 = 7 \qquad 12 - 7 = 5$$

3.
$$12 - 6 = 6 \qquad 11 - 7 = 4 \qquad 12 - 8 = 4 \qquad 11 - 8 = 3 \qquad 12 - 9 = 3 \qquad 12 - 4 = 8$$

Name _____

Facts to 10 (Use with Chapter 10)

4.
$$5 + 5 = 10 \qquad 3 + 6 = 9 \qquad 6 + 4 = 10 \qquad 9 + 1 = 10 \qquad 3 + 3 = 6 \qquad 7 + 1 = 8$$

5.
$$1 + 6 = 7 \qquad 0 + 9 = 9 \qquad 4 + 1 = 5 \qquad 5 + 3 = 8 \qquad 5 + 2 = 7 \qquad 0 + 9 = 9$$

6.
$$3 + 4 = 7 \qquad 3 + 1 = 4 \qquad 6 + 3 = 9 \qquad 7 + 0 = 7 \qquad 3 + 8 = 9 \qquad 0 + 7 = 7$$

Name _____

Subtract from 10 or Less (Use with Chapter 11)

4.
$$10 - 7 = 3 \qquad 8 - 4 = 4 \qquad 10 - 9 = 1 \qquad 10 - 7 = 3 \qquad 10 - 3 = 7$$

5.
$$10 - 8 = 2 \qquad 10 - 6 = 4 \qquad 10 - 4 = 6 \qquad 9 - 2 = 7 \qquad 10 - 8 = 2 \qquad 9 - 8 = 1$$

6.
$$10 - 2 = 8 \qquad 10 - 1 = 9 \qquad 10 - 6 = 4 \qquad 10 - 3 = 7 \qquad 9 - 6 = 3$$

Name _____

Facts to 14 (Use with Chapter 12)

1.
| 9
+4
13 | 5
+3
8 | 7
+2
9 | 6
+8
14 | 5
+8
13 | 4
+4
8 |

2.
| 1
+6
7 | 0
+6
6 | 6
+3
9 | 9
+0
9 | 7
+6
13 | 6
+2
8 |

3.
| 7
+7
14 | 4
+9
13 | 9
+5
14 | 1
+4
5 | 1
+8
9 | 8
+5
13 |

Name _____

Subtract from 14 or Less (Use with Chapter 12)

1.
| 14
−8
6 | 11
−5
6 | 14
−6
8 | 11
−2
9 | 14
−9
5 | 14
−7
7 |

2.
| 13
−9
4 | 14
−5
9 | 14
−8
6 | 12
−8
4 | 12
−7
5 | 12
−5
7 |

3.
| 13
−9
4 | 13
−8
5 | 14
−7
7 | 14
−6
8 | 13
−8
5 | 12
−9
3 |

Name _____

Facts to 12 (Use with Chapter 11)

4.
| 7
+5
12 | 4
+3
7 | 3
+6
9 | 8
+3
11 | 2
+4
6 | 5
+7
12 |

5.
| 2
+6
8 | 2
+2
4 | 1
+5
6 | 3
+6
9 | 6
+6
12 | 8
+2
10 |

6.
| 5
+3
8 | 6
+4
10 | 2
+7
9 | 1
+7
8 | 9
+2
11 | 3
+3
6 |

Name _____

Subtract from 12 or Less (Use with Chapter 12)

4.
| 12
−8
4 | 12
−9
3 | 10
−4
6 | 12
−3
9 | 12
−4
8 | 12
−5
7 |

5.
| 12
−5
7 | 12
−8
4 | 10
−7
5 | 12
−6
... | 12
−9
3 | ... |

6.
| 11
−4
7 | 11
−9
2 | 12
−3
9 | 12
−7
5 | 10
−6
... | 10
−9
1 |

Name _____

Facts to 16 (Use with Chapter 13)

1.
$\begin{array}{r} 8 \\ +8 \\ \hline 16 \end{array}$
$\begin{array}{r} 3 \\ +8 \\ \hline 11 \end{array}$
$\begin{array}{r} 5 \\ +2 \\ \hline 7 \end{array}$
$\begin{array}{r} 8 \\ +4 \\ \hline 12 \end{array}$
$\begin{array}{r} 3 \\ +9 \\ \hline 12 \end{array}$
$\begin{array}{r} 2 \\ +5 \\ \hline 7 \end{array}$

2.
$\begin{array}{r} 7 \\ +5 \\ \hline 12 \end{array}$
$\begin{array}{r} 9 \\ +7 \\ \hline 16 \end{array}$
$\begin{array}{r} 8 \\ +6 \\ \hline 14 \end{array}$
$\begin{array}{r} 6 \\ +6 \\ \hline 12 \end{array}$
$\begin{array}{r} 8 \\ +7 \\ \hline 15 \end{array}$
$\begin{array}{r} 9 \\ +6 \\ \hline 15 \end{array}$

3.
$\begin{array}{r} 9 \\ +4 \\ \hline 13 \end{array}$
$\begin{array}{r} 6 \\ +4 \\ \hline 10 \end{array}$
$\begin{array}{r} 5 \\ +8 \\ \hline 13 \end{array}$
$\begin{array}{r} 2 \\ +9 \\ \hline 11 \end{array}$
$\begin{array}{r} 5 \\ +9 \\ \hline 14 \end{array}$
$\begin{array}{r} 7 \\ +8 \\ \hline 15 \end{array}$

Name _____

Subtract from 16 or Less (Use with Chapter 13)

1.
$\begin{array}{r} 15 \\ -9 \\ \hline 6 \end{array}$
$\begin{array}{r} 13 \\ -8 \\ \hline 5 \end{array}$
$\begin{array}{r} 14 \\ -9 \\ \hline 5 \end{array}$
$\begin{array}{r} 14 \\ -6 \\ \hline 8 \end{array}$
$\begin{array}{r} 15 \\ -6 \\ \hline 9 \end{array}$
$\begin{array}{r} 16 \\ -9 \\ \hline 7 \end{array}$

2.
$\begin{array}{r} 14 \\ -7 \\ \hline 7 \end{array}$
$\begin{array}{r} 16 \\ -7 \\ \hline 9 \end{array}$
$\begin{array}{r} 16 \\ -8 \\ \hline 8 \end{array}$
$\begin{array}{r} 14 \\ -8 \\ \hline 6 \end{array}$
$\begin{array}{r} 13 \\ -9 \\ \hline 4 \end{array}$
$\begin{array}{r} 14 \\ -5 \\ \hline 9 \end{array}$

3.
$\begin{array}{r} 16 \\ -9 \\ \hline 7 \end{array}$
$\begin{array}{r} 15 \\ -7 \\ \hline 8 \end{array}$
$\begin{array}{r} 16 \\ -8 \\ \hline 8 \end{array}$
$\begin{array}{r} 16 \\ -7 \\ \hline 9 \end{array}$
$\begin{array}{r} 15 \\ -8 \\ \hline 7 \end{array}$
$\begin{array}{r} 16 \\ -8 \\ \hline 8 \end{array}$

Facts Practice

Name _____

Facts to 14 (Use with Chapter 12)

4.
$\begin{array}{r} 6 \\ +4 \\ \hline 10 \end{array}$
$\begin{array}{r} 2 \\ +9 \\ \hline 11 \end{array}$
$\begin{array}{r} 0 \\ +4 \\ \hline 4 \end{array}$
$\begin{array}{r} 5 \\ +9 \\ \hline 14 \end{array}$
$\begin{array}{r} 9 \\ +3 \\ \hline 12 \end{array}$
$\begin{array}{r} 0 \\ +9 \\ \hline 9 \end{array}$

5.
$\begin{array}{r} 0 \\ +7 \\ \hline 7 \end{array}$
$\begin{array}{r} 3 \\ +8 \\ \hline 11 \end{array}$
$\begin{array}{r} 2 \\ +3 \\ \hline 5 \end{array}$
$\begin{array}{r} 6 \\ +7 \\ \hline 13 \end{array}$
$\begin{array}{r} 3 \\ +7 \\ \hline 10 \end{array}$
$\begin{array}{r} 7 \\ +0 \\ \hline 7 \end{array}$

6.
$\begin{array}{r} 4 \\ +3 \\ \hline 7 \end{array}$
$\begin{array}{r} 8 \\ +0 \\ \hline 8 \end{array}$
$\begin{array}{r} 3 \\ +2 \\ \hline 5 \end{array}$
$\begin{array}{r} 8 \\ +6 \\ \hline 14 \end{array}$
$\begin{array}{r} 4 \\ +6 \\ \hline 10 \end{array}$
$\begin{array}{r} 5 \\ +1 \\ \hline 6 \end{array}$

Name _____

Subtract from 14 or Less (Use with Chapter 12)

4.
$\begin{array}{r} 14 \\ -9 \\ \hline 5 \end{array}$
$\begin{array}{r} 13 \\ -4 \\ \hline 9 \end{array}$
$\begin{array}{r} 14 \\ -8 \\ \hline 6 \end{array}$
$\begin{array}{r} 12 \\ -8 \\ \hline 4 \end{array}$
$\begin{array}{r} 13 \\ -5 \\ \hline 8 \end{array}$
$\begin{array}{r} 14 \\ -5 \\ \hline 9 \end{array}$

5.
$\begin{array}{r} 11 \\ -5 \\ \hline 6 \end{array}$
$\begin{array}{r} 11 \\ -9 \\ \hline 2 \end{array}$
$\begin{array}{r} 13 \\ -7 \\ \hline 6 \end{array}$
$\begin{array}{r} 14 \\ -6 \\ \hline 8 \end{array}$
$\begin{array}{r} 11 \\ -3 \\ \hline 8 \end{array}$
$\begin{array}{r} 14 \\ -7 \\ \hline 7 \end{array}$

6.
$\begin{array}{r} 12 \\ -8 \\ \hline 4 \end{array}$
$\begin{array}{r} 14 \\ -7 \\ \hline 7 \end{array}$
$\begin{array}{r} 14 \\ -6 \\ \hline 8 \end{array}$
$\begin{array}{r} 11 \\ -7 \\ \hline 4 \end{array}$
$\begin{array}{r} 14 \\ -9 \\ \hline 5 \end{array}$
$\begin{array}{r} 12 \\ -4 \\ \hline 8 \end{array}$

Facts Practice

Facts Practice

Name _____

Facts to 18 (Use with Chapter 15)

1.

$$\begin{array}{r}8\\+9\\\hline17\end{array}\qquad\begin{array}{r}8\\+7\\\hline15\end{array}\qquad\begin{array}{r}9\\+8\\\hline17\end{array}\qquad\begin{array}{r}8\\+6\\\hline \end{array}\qquad\begin{array}{r}9\\+7\\\hline16\end{array}$$

2.

$$\begin{array}{r}0\\+8\\\hline8\end{array}\qquad\begin{array}{r}9\\+6\\\hline15\end{array}\qquad\begin{array}{r}6\\+3\\\hline9\end{array}\qquad\begin{array}{r}1\\+8\\\hline9\end{array}\qquad\begin{array}{r}1\\+3\\\hline \end{array}$$

3.

$$\begin{array}{r}3\\+9\\\hline12\end{array}\qquad\begin{array}{r}8\\+5\\\hline13\end{array}\qquad\begin{array}{r}2\\+7\\\hline9\end{array}\qquad\begin{array}{r}8\\+2\\\hline10\end{array}\qquad\begin{array}{r}9\\+9\\\hline18\end{array}$$

✂ - - - - - - - - - - - - - - - - - - -

Name _____

Subtract from 18 or Less (Use with Chapter 14)

1.

$$\begin{array}{r}18\\-9\\\hline9\end{array}\qquad\begin{array}{r}13\\-8\\\hline5\end{array}\qquad\begin{array}{r}15\\-9\\\hline6\end{array}\qquad\begin{array}{r}14\\-5\\\hline9\end{array}\qquad\begin{array}{r}14\\-9\\\hline5\end{array}$$

2.

$$\begin{array}{r}16\\-7\\\hline9\end{array}\qquad\begin{array}{r}17\\-9\\\hline8\end{array}\qquad\begin{array}{r}14\\-8\\\hline6\end{array}\qquad\begin{array}{r}16\\-9\\\hline7\end{array}\qquad\begin{array}{r}16\\-8\\\hline8\end{array}$$

3.

$$\begin{array}{r}17\\-8\\\hline9\end{array}\qquad\begin{array}{r}14\\-7\\\hline7\end{array}\qquad\begin{array}{r}14\\-6\\\hline8\end{array}\qquad\begin{array}{r}15\\-6\\\hline9\end{array}\qquad\begin{array}{r}13\\-7\\\hline6\end{array}$$

Name _____

Facts to 16 (Use with Chapter 13)

4.

$$\begin{array}{r}1\\+8\\\hline9\end{array}\qquad\begin{array}{r}3\\+8\\\hline11\end{array}\qquad\begin{array}{r}5\\+7\\\hline12\end{array}\qquad\begin{array}{r}8\\+5\\\hline13\end{array}\qquad\begin{array}{r}7\\+4\\\hline11\end{array}\qquad\begin{array}{r}3\\+5\\\hline8\end{array}$$

5.

$$\begin{array}{r}7\\+9\\\hline16\end{array}\qquad\begin{array}{r}7\\+7\\\hline14\end{array}\qquad\begin{array}{r}7\\+6\\\hline13\end{array}\qquad\begin{array}{r}6\\+7\\\hline13\end{array}\qquad\begin{array}{r}5\\+9\\\hline14\end{array}\qquad\begin{array}{r}9\\+7\\\hline16\end{array}$$

6.

$$\begin{array}{r}6\\+5\\\hline11\end{array}\qquad\begin{array}{r}8\\+4\\\hline12\end{array}\qquad\begin{array}{r}4\\+8\\\hline12\end{array}\qquad\begin{array}{r}6\\+8\\\hline14\end{array}\qquad\begin{array}{r}7\\+8\\\hline15\end{array}\qquad\begin{array}{r}4\\+4\\\hline8\end{array}$$

- - - - - - - - - - - - - - - - - - -

Name _____

Subtract from 16 or Less (Use with Chapter 13)

4.

$$\begin{array}{r}16\\-9\\\hline7\end{array}\qquad\begin{array}{r}15\\-9\\\hline6\end{array}\qquad\begin{array}{r}14\\-7\\\hline7\end{array}\qquad\begin{array}{r}13\\-5\\\hline8\end{array}\qquad\begin{array}{r}13\\-7\\\hline6\end{array}\qquad\begin{array}{r}16\\-9\\\hline7\end{array}$$

5.

$$\begin{array}{r}15\\-7\\\hline8\end{array}\qquad\begin{array}{r}12\\-9\\\hline3\end{array}\qquad\begin{array}{r}13\\-9\\\hline4\end{array}\qquad\begin{array}{r}16\\-8\\\hline8\end{array}\qquad\begin{array}{r}13\\-8\\\hline5\end{array}\qquad\begin{array}{r}15\\-6\\\hline7\end{array}$$

6.

$$\begin{array}{r}14\\-9\\\hline5\end{array}\qquad\begin{array}{r}16\\-7\\\hline9\end{array}\qquad\begin{array}{r}13\\-4\\\hline9\end{array}\qquad\begin{array}{r}15\\-6\\\hline9\end{array}\qquad\begin{array}{r}14\\-6\\\hline8\end{array}\qquad\begin{array}{r}15\\-8\\\hline7\end{array}$$

WorkMat 1

Name _____

Facts to 18 (Use with Chapter 15)

4.
$$9 + 8 = 17 \quad 1 + 6 = 7 \quad 2 + 9 = 11 \quad 4 + 9 = 13 \quad 7 + 6 = 13 \quad 4 + 2 = 6$$

5.
$$3 + 4 = 7 \quad 8 + 9 = 17 \quad 4 + 5 = 9 \quad 6 + 4 = 10 \quad 5 + 8 = 13$$

6.
$$9 + 2 = 11 \quad 9 + 9 = 18 \quad 5 + 7 = 12 \quad 6 + 8 = 14 \quad 7 + 9 = 16 \quad 5 + 9 = 14$$

Name _____

Subtract from 18 or Less (Use with Chapter 15)

4.
$$13 - 6 = 7 \quad 12 - 4 = 8 \quad 12 - 9 = 3 \quad 18 - 9 = 9 \quad 13 - 4 = 9 \quad 12 - 7 = 5$$

5.
$$13 - 5 = 8 \quad 16 - 9 = 7 \quad 16 - 8 = 8 \quad 15 - 8 = 7 \quad 16 - 7 = 9 \quad 17 - 8 = 9$$

6.
$$12 - 8 = 4 \quad 12 - 5 = 7 \quad 18 - 9 = 9 \quad 12 - 9 = 3 \quad 15 - 9 = 6 \quad 12 - 6 = 6$$

Facts Practice

WorkMat 3: Part-Part-Whole

Whole

Part

Part

WorkMat 3

WorkMat 2

WorkMat 2: Ten-Frames

WorkMats

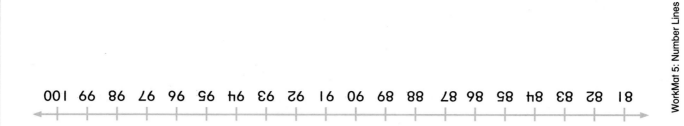

81 82 83 84 85 86 87 88 89 90 91 92 93 94 95 96 97 98 99 100

61 62 63 64 65 66 67 68 69 70 71 72 73 74 75 76 77 78 79 80

WorkMat 5

WorkMat 4

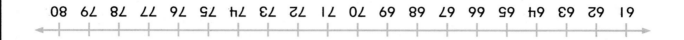

0 1 2 3 4 5 6 7 8 9 10 11 12 13 14 15 16 17 18 19 20

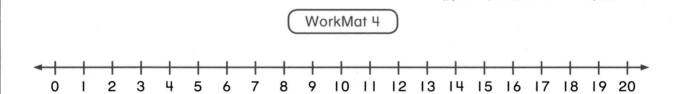

21 22 23 24 25 26 27 28 29 30 31 32 33 34 35 36 37 38 39 40

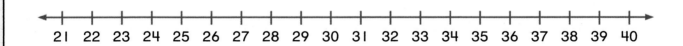

41 42 43 44 45 46 47 48 49 50 51 52 53 54 55 56 57 58 59 60

WorkMat 6

WorkMat 6: Grid

WorkMat 7

Tens	Ones

Copyright © Macmillan/McGraw-Hill, a division of The McGraw-Hill Companies, Inc.

WorkMat 7: Tens and Ones Chart

WorkMat 8

Hundreds	Tens	Ones

WorkMat 8: Hundreds, Tens, and Ones Chart

WorkMats

Index

A

Above-Level Suggestions. *See also* Early
Finishers.
 diagnostic assessment options, 14, 48,
   84, 120, 152, 182, 210, 240, 274, 314, 348,
   382, 416, 454, 482
 Game Time, 38, 58, 94, 136, 160, 202, 230,
   266, 284, 322, 374, 394, 426, 466, 494
 leveled assignments, 18, 20, 25, 28, 30,
   36, 38, 40, 52, 54, 56, 58, 60, 66, 68, 71,
   76, 88, 90, 92, 94, 96, 102, 104, 109, 112,
   124, 126, 130, 134, 136, 138, 144, 156,
   158, 160, 164, 166, 170, 172, 186, 190,
   196, 198, 200, 202, 214, 216, 218, 225,
   228, 230, 244, 246, 251, 256, 260, 262,
   264, 266, 278, 280, 282, 284, 287, 293,
   297, 302, 306, 318, 320, 322, 324, 330,
   332, 336, 340, 352, 354, 356, 358, 364,
   366, 372, 374, 386, 388, 392, 394, 396,
   403, 406, 408, 421, 424, 426, 431, 434,
   440, 444, 446, 458, 462, 464, 466, 470,
   472, 486, 488, 492, 494, 496, 500, 502,
   506
 leveled tests, 44, 80, 116, 148, 179, 206,
   236, 270, 310, 344, 378, 412, 450, 478,
   510

Addends, 151B, 155

Addition, 47A–82, 151A–180, 313A–346,
481A–512
 of 1, 2, or 3, 163–164
 in any order, 155–156
 count on 1, 2, or 3, 157–158
 doubles, 169–170, 317–318
 doubles plus 1, 171–172, 319–320
 estimate sums, 495–496
 making ten, 323–324
 modeling, 53–54
 number line for, 165–166
 subtraction related to, 197–198, 331–332
 of tens, 485–486
 two-digit, 487–488, 491–492
 vertical, 75–76
 of zero, 59–60

Addition sentences, 47B, 55–56

Addition stories, 51–52, 51A, 73

Addressing Individual Needs. *See*
Differentiated Instruction

After, 13B, 39, 209B, 213, 415B, 445

Afternoon, 209B, 213

Algebra Concepts of algebra develop
informally with the awareness of patterns,
sorting/classifying, use of symbols and
variables in expressions and equations, and
initial exposure to functions.

Algebra Readiness
 commutative property of addition, 313A
 comparing coins, 347A
 comparing data, 119A
 equation concepts, 47A, 151A, 239A
 estimating sums and differences, 481A
 extending and creating patterns, 13A
 guess and check strategy, 415A
 objects on a coordinate plane, 381A
 operation symbols, 181A
 ordering events, 209A
 ordering objects, 273A
 using number sentences, 83A

Analog clocks, 209B, 223

Area
 comparing, 301–304
 ordering, 305–306

Are You Ready for Chapter, 14, 48, 84,
120, 152, 182, 210, 240, 274, 314, 348, 382,
416, 454, 482

Art. *See* Learning Stations; Problem-
Solving

Assessment, *See also* Data-Driven Decision
Making; Mid-Chapter Check.
 Chapter Projects, 15, 43, 49, 79, 85, 115,
   121, 147, 153, 177, 183, 205, 211, 235,
   241, 269, 275, 309, 315, 343, 349, 377,
   383, 411, 417, 449, 455, 477, 483, 509
 Chapter Review/Test, 43–44, 79–80,
   115–116, 147–148, 177–179, 205–206,
   235–236, 269–270, 309–310, 343–344,
   377–378, 411–412, 449–450, 477–478,
   509–510
 Diagnostic Assessment, 13C, 13F, 14,
   47C, 47F, 48, 83C, 83F, 84, 119C, 119F,
   120, 151C, 151F, 152, 181C, 181E, 182,
   209C, 209E, 210, 239C, 239F, 240, 273C,
   273F, 274, 313C, 313F, 314, 347C, 347F,
   348, 381C, 381F, 382, 415C, 415F, 416,
   453C, 453E, 454, 481C, 481F, 482
 Formative Assessment, 13F, 18, 20, 22,
   26, 28, 30, 31, 32, 33, 36, 40, 45, 47F, 52,
   54, 56, 60, 62, 63, 64, 66, 68, 72, 74, 76,
   81, 83F, 88, 90, 92, 96, 98, 99, 100, 102,
   104, 106, 110, 112, 117, 119F, 124, 126,
   128, 130, 131, 132, 134, 138, 142, 144,
   148, 151F, 156, 158, 162, 164, 166, 167,
   168, 170, 172, 174, 179, 181E, 186, 188,
   190, 191, 192, 194, 196, 198, 200, 207,
   209E, 214, 216, 218, 220, 221, 222, 226,
   228, 232, 237, 239F, 244, 246, 248, 252,
   253, 254, 256, 260, 262, 264, 271, 273F,
   278, 280, 282, 288, 289, 290, 294, 298,
   300, 306, 311, 313F, 318, 320, 324, 326,
   327, 328, 330, 332, 334, 336, 340, 345,
   347F, 352, 354, 356, 358, 360, 361, 362,
   364, 366, 370, 372, 379, 378, 381F, 386,
   388, 390, 392, 396, 397, 398, 400, 404,
   406, 408, 413, 415F, 422, 424, 428, 432,
   434, 437, 438, 440, 442, 444, 446, 451,
   453E, 458, 460, 462, 464, 467, 468, 470,
   472, 474, 479, 481F, 486, 488, 490, 492,
   496, 497, 498, 500, 502, 504, 506, 511
 Spiral Review, 32, 64, 100, 132, 168, 192,
   222, 254, 290, 328, 362, 398, 438, 468,
   498
 Summative Assessment, 13F, 43, 45, 47F,
   79, 81, 83F, 115, 117, 119F, 148, 149,
   151F, 177, 179, 181E, 205, 207, 209E,
   235, 237, 239F, 269, 271, 273F, 309, 311,
   313F, 343, 345, 347F, 377, 379, 381F, 411,
   413, 415F, 449, 451, 453E, 477, 479, 481F,
   509, 511
 Test Practice, 45–46, 81–82, 117–118, 149–
   150, 180–181, 207–208, 237–238, 271–
   272, 311–312, 345–346, 379–380, 413–
   414, 451–452, 479–480, 511–512
 Vocabulary Review and Test, 43, 79, 115,
   147, 177, 205, 235, 269, 309, 343, 377,
   411, 449, 477, 509

Auditory Learners. *See* Learning Styles

B

Balance scale, 285B, 287

Bar graphs
 making, 137–140
 reading, 133–134

Before, 13B, 39, 209B, 213, 415B, 445

Below-Level Suggestions
 Game Time, 38, 58, 94, 136, 160, 202, 230,
   266, 284, 322, 374, 394, 426, 466, 494
 leveled assignments, 18, 20, 25, 28, 30,
   36, 38, 40, 52, 54, 56, 58, 60, 66, 68, 71,
   76, 88, 90, 92, 94, 96, 102, 104, 109, 112,
   124, 126, 130, 134, 136, 138, 144, 156,
   158, 160, 164, 166, 170, 172, 186, 190,
   196, 198, 200, 202, 214, 216, 218, 225,
   228, 230, 244, 246, 251, 256, 260, 262,
   264, 266, 278, 280, 282, 284, 287, 293,
   297, 302, 306, 318, 320, 322, 324, 330,
   332, 336, 340, 352, 354, 356, 358, 364,
   366, 372, 374, 386, 388, 392, 394, 396,
   403, 406, 408, 421, 424, 426, 431, 434,
   440, 444, 446, 458, 462, 464, 466, 470,
   472, 486, 488, 492, 494, 496, 500, 502,
   506
 leveled tests, 44, 80, 116, 148, 179, 206,
   234, 270, 310, 344, 378, 412, 450, 478,
   510
 Small Group Options, 17B, 27B, 29B,
   33B, 39B, 59B, 65B, 69B, 73B, 75B, 89B,
   95B, 97B, 107B, 129B, 133B, 137B, 163B,
   169B, 171B, 173B, 187B, 189B, 193B,
   215B, 223B, 227B, 231B, 249B, 255B,
   261B, 263B, 277B, 279B, 301B, 305B,
   317B, 319B, 331B, 333B, 335B, 339B,
   355B, 363B, 365B, 385B, 387B, 389A,
   391B, 399B, 401B, 405B, 407B, 419B,
   429B, 439B, 441B, 443B, 445B, 463B,
   469B, 473B, 495B, 499B, 503B, 505B
 Strategic Intervention, 14, 48, 84, 120,
   152, 182, 210, 240, 274, 314, 348, 382,
   416, 454, 482

Benchmark Students. *See* On-Level
Suggestions

Between, 13B, 39, 415B, 445

Big Idea
   addition and subtraction problems,
     313A
   addition concepts, 47A
   addition strategies, 151A
   coins, 347A
   data, organizing and using, 119A
   describing and comparing numbers, 13A
   fractions, 453A
   geometric figures, 381A
   measurement, 273A
   number patterns, 239A
   place value, 415A
   subtraction concepts, 83A
   subtraction strategies, 181A
   time, 209A
   two-digit addition and subtraction, 481A

C

Calendar Time, 13H, 47H, 83H, 119H, 151H, 181H, 209H, 239H, 273H, 313H, 347H, 381H, 415H, 453H, 481H

Capacity, 291–294

Cents, 347B, 351

Certain, 119B, 143

Chapter Projects, 15, 43, 49, 79, 85, 115, 121, 147, 153, 177, 183, 205, 211, 235, 241, 269, 275, 309, 315, 343, 349, 377, 383, 411, 417, 449, 455, 477, 483, 509

Chapter Review/Test, 43–44, 79–80, 115–116, 147–148, 177–179, 205–206, 235–236, 269–270, 309–310, 343–344, 377–378, 411–412, 449–450, 477–478, 509–510

Charts
   tally charts, 129–130

Circles, 381B, 395

Clocks, 209B, 223

Coins, 347A–380
   counting, 357–358, 371–372
   equal amounts, 363–364
   pennies and dimes, 353–354
   pennies and nickels, 351–352
   pennies, nickels, and dimes, 355–356
   quarters, 365–368

Communication Opportunities to develop mathematical fluency and vocabulary are provided in the *Talk About It* and the *Writing In Math* features. Students talk, listen, and write mathematically.

Communication, *See* Talk about it, Writing in math

Comparing
   area, 301–304
   capacity, 291–294
   lengths, 277–278
   measurement, 273A–312
   numbers to 100, 443–444
   temperature, 295–298
   weight, 285–288

Concepts and Skills Bank
   Half Dollars and Dollars, CS3–CS4
   Perimeter, CS7–CS8
   Symmetry and Congruence, CS5–CS6
   Temperature, CS9–CS10
   True and False Statements, CS1–CS2

Concepts in Motion, 17A, 39A, 53A, 69A, 89A, 107A, 123A, 137A, 165A, 171A, 185A, 189A, 227A, 233A, 245A, 255A, 279A, 323A, 329A, 331A, 339A, 357A, 363A, 391A, 407A, 423A, 433A, 463A, 469A, 471A, 491A, 501A

Cones, 381B, 385

Cooperative Groups. *See* Above-Level Suggestions; Below-Level Suggestions; English Language Learners (ELL); Gifted and Talented; On-Level Suggestions

Corners, of shapes, 387–388

Counting, 357–358
   on 1, 2, or 3 to add, 157–158
   to 20, 243–244
   back 1, 2, or 3, 185–186
   coins, 357–358, 371–372
   hundred chart, 249–252
   money, 357–358, 371–372
   skip, by 2's, 5's and 10's, 259–260
   skip on a hundred chart, 261–262
   by tens, 245–246

Critical thinking. *See* Problem-Solving

Cross-Curricular Links. *See* Learning Stations

Cubes, 381B, 385

Cylinders, 381B, 385

D

Daily Routine, 17A, 19A, 21A, 23A, 27A, 29A, 33A, 35A, 39A, 51A, 53A, 55A, 59A, 61A, 65A, 67A, 69A, 73A, 75A, 87A, 89A, 91A, 95A, 97A, 101A, 103A, 105A, 107A, 111A, 123A, 125A, 127A, 129A, 133A, 137A, 141A, 143A, 155A, 157A, 161A, 163A, 165A, 169A, 171A, 173A, 185A, 187A, 189A, 193A, 195A, 197A, 199A, 213A, 215A, 217A, 219A, 223A, 227A, 231A, 243A, 245A, 247A, 249A, 255A, 257A, 259A, 261A, 263A, 277A, 279A, 281A, 285A, 291A, 295A, 299A, 301A, 305A, 317A, 319A, 323A, 325A, 329A, 331A, 333A, 335A, 339A, 351A, 353A, 355A, 357A, 359A, 363A, 365A, 369A, 371A, 385A, 387A, 389A, 391A, 395A, 399A, 401A, 405A, 407A, 419A, 423A, 427A, 429A, 433A, 439A, 441A, 443A, 445A, 457A, 459A, 461A, 463A, 469A, 471A, 473A, 485A, 487A, 489A, 491A, 495A, 499A, 501A, 503A, 505A

Data Collection Real-world situations encourage students to gather, organize, and analyze data.

Data, 119A–150. *See also* Graphs.
   bar graphs, 133–134, 137–140
   certain or impossible, 143–144
   picture graphs, 125–126
   sort and classify, 123–124
   tally charts, 129–130

Data-Driven Decision Making, 31, 44, 63, 80, 99, 116, 131, 148, 167, 178, 191, 206, 221, 236, 253, 270, 289, 310, 327, 344, 361, 378, 397, 412, 437, 450, 467, 478, 497, 510

Data File, 26, 72, 110, 134, 164, 190, 228, 262, 288, 340, 368, 408, 432, 472, 486

Diagnostic Check A quick assessment of prerequisite skills required for each chapter is provided.

Diagnostic Assessment, 13C, 13F, 14, 47C, 47F, 48, 83C, 83F, 84, 119C, 119F, 120, 151C, 151F, 152, 181C, 181E, 182, 209C, 209E, 210, 239C, 239F, 240, 273C, 273F, 274, 313C, 313F, 314, 347C, 347F, 348, 381C, 381F, 382, 415C, 415F, 416, 453C, 453E, 454, 481C, 481F, 482

Differences, 83B, 91, 481B, 485
   estimating, 505–506

Differentiated Instruction
   adding zero, 59B
   addition, 53B, 155B, 163B
   addition of two-digit numbers, 487B, 491B
   addition related to subtraction, 197B, 331B
   addition sentences, 55B
   addition stories, 51B
   area, 301B, 305B
   bar graphs, 133B, 137B
   capacity, 291B
   certain or impossible, 143B
   coins, 351B, 353B, 355B, 365B
   comparing numbers, 35B, 443B
   counting back, 185B
   counting by tens, 245B
   counting money, 357B, 371B
   counting on, 157B
   counting to 20, 243B
   directions, 407B
   doubles, 169B, 195B, 317B, 329B
   doubles plus 1, 171B, 319B
   equal amounts, 363B
   equal parts, 457B
   estimating, 255B
   estimating differences, 505B
   estimating numbers, 439B
   estimating sums, 495B
   even and odd, 263B
   faces and corners, 387B
   fact families, 199B, 335B
   fractions of a set, 471B
   hundred chart, 249B, 261B
   length, 273B, 279B
   leveled assignments, 18, 20, 25, 28, 30, 36, 38, 40, 52, 54, 56, 58, 60, 66, 68, 71, 76, 88, 90, 92, 94, 96, 102, 104, 109, 112, 124, 126, 130, 134, 136, 138, 144, 156, 158, 160, 164, 166, 170, 172, 186, 190, 196, 198, 200, 202, 214, 216, 218, 225, 228, 230, 244, 246, 251, 256, 260, 262, 264, 266, 278, 280, 282, 284, 287, 293, 297, 302, 306, 318, 320, 322, 324, 330, 332, 336, 340, 352, 354, 356, 358, 364, 366, 372, 374, 386, 388, 392, 394, 396, 403, 406, 408, 421, 424, 426, 431, 434, 440, 444, 446, 458, 462, 464, 466, 470,

472, 486, 488, 492, 494, 496, 500, 502, 506
   making new figures, 405B
   making ten, 323B
   modeling numbers, 339B
   non-unit fractions, 469B
   number line, 165B, 189B
   numbers 11 to 15, 27B
   numbers 16 to 20, 29B
   numbers to 10, 23B
   numbers to 100, 433B
   numbers to 50, 429B
   one half, 461B
   ones, 423B
   one third and one fourth, 463B
   ordering events, 213B
   ordering numbers, 39B, 445B
   patterns, 17B, 19B
   picture graphs, 125B
   position, 401B
   problem-solving investigations, 33B, 73B, 105B, 141B, 173B, 193B, 231B, 257B, 299B, 333B, 369B, 399B, 441B, 473B, 503B
   problem-solving strategies, 21B, 61B, 97B, 127B, 161B, 187B, 219B, 247B, 281B, 325B, 359B, 389B, 427B, 459B, 489B
   skip counting, 259B, 261B
   sort and classify, 123B
   subtraction, 89B, 101B, 103B, 107B
   subtraction of two-digit numbers, 499B, 501B
   subtraction related to addition, 197B, 331B
   subtraction sentences, 91B
   subtraction stories, 87B
   subtract zero, 95B
   tally charts, 129B
   temperature, 295B
   tens, 419B, 423B
   tens, addition and subtraction of, 485B
   tens, counting by, 245B
   three-dimensional figures, 385B, 391B
   time, 215B, 217B, 223B, 227B
   two-dimensional figures, 385B, 391B
   vertical addition, 75B
   vertical subtraction, 111B
   ways to make numbers, 65B, 67B, 69B
   weight, 285B

Digital clocks, 209B, 223

Dimes, 353–354, 355–356

Directions, giving and following, 407–408

Doubles, 169–170, 195–196, 317–318, 329–330
   plus 1, 171–172, 319–320

Early Finishers, 17B, 19B, 21B, 23B, 27B, 29B, 33B, 35B, 39B, 51B, 53B, 55B, 59B, 61B, 65B, 67B, 69B, 73B, 75B, 87B, 89B, 91B, 95B, 97B, 101B, 103B, 105B, 107B, 111B, 123B, 125B, 127B, 129B, 133B, 137B, 141B, 143B, 155B, 157B, 161B, 163B, 165B, 169B, 171B,

173B, 185B, 187B, 189B, 193B, 195B, 197B, 199B, 213B, 215B, 217B, 219B, 223B, 227B, 231B, 243B, 245B, 247B, 249B, 255B, 257B, 259B, 261B, 263B, 277B, 279B, 281B, 285B, 291B, 295B, 299B, 301B, 305B, 317B, 319B, 323B, 325B, 329B, 331B, 333B, 335B, 339B, 351B, 353B, 355B, 357B, 359B, 363B, 365B, 369B, 371B, 385B, 387B, 389B, 391B, 395B, 399B, 401B, 405B, 407B, 419B, 423B, 427B, 429B, 433B, 439B, 441B, 443B, 445B, 457B, 459B, 461B, 463B, 469B, 471B, 473B, 485B, 487B, 489B, 491B, 495B, 499B, 501B, 503B, 505B

English Language Learners Concepts are presented visually to aid in reading comprehension. Opportunities are provided throughout the program to build math concepts as well as language skills. The ELL teaching suggestions assist in teaching not only the vocabulary but the concepts needed to *understand* the mathematics.

English Language Learners (ELL). *See also* English Learner Guide under separate cover. 17B, 19B, 21B, 23B, 27B, 29B, 33B, 35B, 39B, 51B, 53B, 55B, 59B, 61B, 65B, 67B, 69B, 73B, 75B, 87B, 89B, 91B, 95B, 97B, 101B, 103B, 105B, 107B, 111B, 123B, 125B, 127B, 129B, 133B, 137B, 141B, 143B, 155B, 157B, 161B, 163B, 165B, 169B, 171B, 173B, 185B, 187B, 189B, 193B, 195B, 197B, 199B, 213B, 215B, 217B, 219B, 223B, 227B, 231B, 243B, 245B, 247B, 249B, 255B, 257B, 259B, 261B, 263B, 277B, 279B, 281B, 285B, 291B, 295B, 299B, 301B, 305B, 317B, 319B, 323B, 325B, 329B, 331B, 333B, 335B, 339B, 351B, 353B, 355B, 357B, 359B, 363B, 365B, 369B, 371B, 385B, 387B, 389B, 391B, 395B, 399B, 401B, 405B, 407B, 419B, 423B, 427B, 429B, 433B, 439B, 441B, 443B, 445B, 457B, 459B, 461B, 463B, 469B, 471B, 473B, 485B, 487B, 489B, 491B, 495B, 499B, 501B, 503B, 505B

Equal amounts, 363–364, 363A, 365, 365A, 371, 457

Equal parts, 457–458

Equal to (=), 13B, 35, 47B, 55, 415B, 443

Estimating
   differences, 505–506
   groups of ten, 255–256
   numbers, 439–440
   sums, 495–496
   Evaluation.–*See* Assessment

Evening, 209B, 213

Even numbers, 263–264

Faces, of shapes, 387–388

Fact Strategies A strong foundation in basic skills is required for all students. Basic facts are presented in a sequential manner. Students receive extra practice throughout the program to increase

mastery, improve retention, and build confidence.

Fact Strategies, *See* addition, fact families, subtraction

Fact families, 199–200, 335–338

Figures
   faces and corners, 387–388
   making new, 405–406
   position, 401–404
   three-dimensional, 385–386
   two- and three- dimensional, 391–392
   two-dimensional, 395–396

Focal Points, iii, iv–v, T1, T14–T15

Focus on Math Background
   addition, 53A, 75A
   addition and subtraction connected, 197A, 331A
   addition of zero, 59A
   addition sentences, 55A, 165A
   addition stories, 51A
   analog clock, 215A, 217A, 223A
   bar graphs, 133A, 137A
   capacity, 291A
   commutative property of addition, 155A
   comparing coins, 371A
   comparing numbers, 35A, 443A
   comparing time, 227A
   counting, 23A
   counting back, 185A
   counting by tens, 245A
   counting coins, 355A, 357A
   counting on, 157A, 163A
   counting to 20, 243A
   directions, 407A
   doubles, 169A, 195A, 317A, 329A
   doubles plus 1, 171A, 319A
   equal amounts, 363A, 365A
   estimating, 255A, 439A
   estimating differences, 505A
   estimating sums, 495A
   faces and corners, 387A
   fact families, 199A, 335A
   fractions, 457A, 463A
   geometric vocabulary, 385A
   geometry, 385A, 391A, 395A
   hundred chart, 249A
   length, 277A, 279A
   making ten, 323A
   number line, 189A
   number sense, 27A
   one half, 461A
   ordering events, 213A
   ordering numbers, 39A
   patterns, 17A, 19A, 29A, 261A
   picture graphs, 125A
   place value, 419A, 429A, 433A, 445A
   place value notation, 487A, 501A
   position, 401A
   regrouping, 491A, 499A
   skip counting, 243A, 259A, 353A, 357A
   sorting and classifying, 123A
   subtraction, 89A, 101A, 103A, 107A, 111A
   subtraction of zero, 95A
   subtraction sentences, 91A
   subtraction stories, 87A

Index

tally charts, 129A
tens and ones, 423A
two-digit addition and subtraction, 485A
ways to make numbers, 65A, 67A, 69A
ways to name numbers, 339A
weight, 285A

Foldables study organizer
for addition, 47, 63, 79, 151, 167, 177,
313, 327, 343, 481, 497, 509
for data, 119, 131, 147
for fractions, 453, 467, 477
for geometry, 381, 397, 411
for measurements, 273, 289, 309
for money, 347, 361, 377
for number patterns, 239, 253, 269
for number sense, 13, 31, 43
for place value, 415, 437, 449
for subtraction, 83, 99, 115, 181, 191, 205,
313, 327, 343, 481, 497, 509
for time, 209, 221, 235

Formative Assessment, 13F, 18, 20, 22, 26,
28, 30, 31, 32, 33, 36, 40, 45, 47F, 52, 54, 56,
60, 62, 63, 64, 66, 68, 72, 74, 76, 81, 83F, 88,
90, 92, 96, 98, 99, 100, 102, 104, 106, 110, 112,
117, 119F, 124, 126, 128, 130, 131, 132, 134,
138, 142, 144, 148, 151F, 156, 158, 162, 164,
166, 167, 168, 170, 172, 174, 179, 181E, 186,
188, 190, 191, 192, 194, 196, 198, 200, 207,
209E, 214, 216, 218, 220, 221, 222, 226, 228,
232, 237, 239F, 244, 246, 248, 252, 253, 254,
256, 260, 262, 264, 271, 273F, 278, 280, 282,
288, 289, 290, 294, 298, 300, 306, 311, 313F,
318, 320, 324, 326, 327, 328, 330, 332, 334,
336, 340, 345, 347F, 352, 354, 356, 358, 360,
361, 362, 364, 366, 370, 372, 379, 378, 381F,
386, 388, 390, 392, 396, 397, 398, 400, 404,
406, 408, 413, 415F, 422, 424, 428, 432, 434,
437, 438, 440, 442, 444, 446, 451, 453E, 458,
460, 462, 464, 467, 468, 470, 472, 474, 479,
481F, 486, 488, 490, 492, 496, 497, 498, 500,
502, 504, 506, 511

Fractions, 453A–480
equal parts, 457–458
non-unit, 469–470
one half, 461–462
one third and one fourth, 463–464
of a set, 471–472

Game Time
Adding Colors-two digit addition, 494
All Mixed Up-addition math facts, 160
Animal Race-using data, 136
Bigger the Better, The-number sense, 38
Buy Beavers-length, 284
Circle Up-adding doubles, 322
Corners- three-dimensional figures, 394
The Equalizer-fractions, 466
Lizzie the Lizard-making ten, 426
Related or Not?-fact families, 202
Slide Through the Digits-comparing
numbers, 266
Snack Time-addition, 58
Subtracting to Swim-subtraction, 94

Switch It!-time, 230
Who Has More?-money, 374

Geometry, 381, 385, 385A, 387, 391, 391A,
395, 395A, 397, 405, 411

Gifted and Talented
diagnostic assessment options, 14, 48,
84, 120, 152, 182, 210, 240, 274, 314, 348,
382, 416, 454, 482
Game Time, 38, 58, 94, 136, 160, 202, 230,
266, 284, 322, 374, 394, 426, 466, 494
Small Group Options, 19B, 21B, 23B,
35B, 51B, 53B, 55B, 61B, 67B, 87B, 91B,
101B, 103B, 105B, 111B, 123B, 125B,
127B, 141B, 143B, 155B, 157B, 161B,
165B, 185B, 195B, 197B, 199B, 213B,
217B, 219B, 243B, 245B, 247B, 255B,
259B, 281B, 285B, 291B, 295B, 299B,
323B, 325B, 329B, 351B, 353B, 357B,
359B, 369B, 371B, 395B, 423B, 427B,
433B, 457B, 459B, 461B, 471B, 485B,
487B, 489B, 491B, 501B

Graphs. *See also* Data.
bar graphs, 133–134, 137–140
picture graphs, 125–126

Greater than (>), 13B, 35, 415B, 443

Half hour, 217–218, 223–226

Half past, 217

Hands-On Lab
addition, 53, 55, 75, 335, 487
addition and subtraction connected, 197,
199, 331
addition sentences, 59, 65, 155, 323, 329,
485
addition stories, 73
analog clock, 215, 217, 223
area, 301, 305
bar graphs, 133, 137
capacity, 291
certain or impossible, 143
coins, 351, 501
comparing numbers, 35B
comparing time, 227
counting, 27, 51
counting back, 185
counting by tens, 245
counting coins, 355, 357
counting on, 157, 163, 165
directions, 407
doubles, 195, 317
doubles plus 1, 319
equal amounts, 363, 365, 371, 457
equal parts, 463
estimating, 255, 439
estimating differences, 505
estimating sums, 495
fact families, 339
fractions, 469, 471
geometry, 385, 387, 391, 395, 405
hundred chart, 249
measurement, 277, 279
number lines, 39

number sentences, 111, 169, 171
numbers to 20, 29
number stories, 33
one half, 461
ordering events, 213
ordering numbers, 23, 443, 445
patterns, 17, 19, 21, 61, 263
picture graphs, 125
place value, 433
position, 401
regrouping, 491
skip counting, 259, 261, 353
subtraction, 87, 89, 335, 499
subtraction of zero, 95
subtraction sentences, 91, 101, 103, 107,
189, 329
tally charts, 129
temperature, 295
tens, 419, 423, 429
tens and ones, 243
Venn diagrams, 123
ways to make numbers, 67, 69
weight, 285
Health. *See* Learning Stations; Problem-
Solving

Heavy/heavier/heaviest, 273B, 285

Holds less/least, 273B, 291

Holds more/most, 273B, 291

H.O.T. Problems Higher Order Thinking
skills are developed and utilized in these
problems found throughout the Student
Edition.

H.O.T. Problems
algebra, 54, 170, 320
critical thinking, 92, 104
explaining math, 396
make it right, 60, 66, 76, 102, 260, 324,
406, 422, 464, 488
thinking math, 36, 140, 144, 156, 200,
226, 244, 304, 354

Hour hand, 215

Hour hand, on clocks, 209B

Hours, 215–216, 223–226

Hundred chart, 249–252
skip counting, 261–262

Impossible, 119B, 143

Independent Work Options, 17B, 19B,
21B, 23B, 27B, 29B, 33B, 35B, 39B, 51B, 53B,
55B, 59B, 61B, 65B, 67B, 69B, 73B, 75B, 87B,
89B, 91B, 95B, 97B, 101B, 103B, 105B, 107B,
111B, 123B, 125B, 127B, 129B, 133B, 137B,
141B, 143B, 155B, 157B, 161B, 163B, 165B,
169B, 171B, 173B, 185B, 187B, 189B, 193B,
195B, 197B, 199B, 213B, 215B, 217B, 219B,
223B, 227B, 231B, 243B, 245B, 247B, 249B,
255B, 257B, 259B, 261B, 263B, 277B, 279B,
281B, 285B, 291B, 295B, 299B, 301B, 305B,
317B, 319B, 323B, 325B, 329B, 331B, 333B,
335B, 339B, 351B, 353B, 355B, 357B, 359B,
363B, 365B, 369B, 371B, 385B, 387B, 389B,

Index

391B, 395B, 399B, 401B, 405B, 407B, 419B, 423B, 427B, 429B, 433B, 439B, 441B, 443B, 445B, 457B, 459B, 461B, 463B, 469B, 471B, 473B, 485B, 487B, 489B, 491B, 495B, 499B, 501B, 503B, 505B

Individual needs. *See* Differentiated Instruction

Instructional Planning and Support. *See also* Pacing; Technology.

Intensive Intervention. *See* Intervention Options

Interpersonal Learners. *See* Learning Styles

Intervention Options
Intensive Intervention, 14, 48, 84, 120, 152, 182, 210, 240, 274, 314, 348, 382, 416, 454, 482
Strategic Intervention, 14, 48, 84, 120, 152, 182, 210, 240, 274, 314, 348, 382, 416, 454, 482

Intrapersonal Learners. *See* Learning Styles

Kinesthetic Learners. *See* Learning Styles

Language Arts. *See* Learning Stations

Learning Stations
Art, 13H, 47G, 83G, 151G, 181G, 209G, 239G, 273G, 313G, 347G, 381G, 415G, 453G, 481G
Health, 83G, 119G, 151H, 181H, 209G, 239H, 453H, 481H
Language Arts, 13H, 47G, 83H, 119G, 151G, 181G, 209H, 239G, 273G, 313H, 347H, 381G, 415G, 453G, 481G
Music, 13G, 83G
Reading, 13G, 47G, 119G, 151G, 181G, 209G, 273G, 313G, 347G, 381G, 415G, 453G, 481G
Science, 13G, 47H, 83H, 119H, 151H, 181H, 209H, 239H, 273H, 313H, 347H, 381H, 415H, 453H, 481H
Social Studies, 47H, 119H, 239G, 273H, 313G, 347G, 381H, 415H

Learning Styles
Auditory, 13G, 17B, 19B, 23B, 65B, 69B, 73B, 83G, 95B, 97B, 103B, 125B, 129B, 133B, 163B, 165B, 185B, 189B, 193B, 197B, 213B, 217B, 219B, 223B, 227B, 245B, 249B, 259B, 371B, 385B, 387B, 423B, 453H, 481H
Interpersonal, 33B, 83H, 105B, 133B, 137B, 187B, 209G, 257B, 419B, 457B, 485B
Intrapersonal, 173B, 273H, 291B, 299B, 313G, 325B, 369B, 381H, 389A, 395B, 399B, 427B, 429B, 433B

Kinesthetic, 17B, 19B, 21B, 23B, 27B, 29B, 35B, 39B, 47H, 51B, 53B, 55B, 59B, 61B, 65B, 67B, 69B, 73B, 75B, 89B, 91B, 95B, 101B, 103B, 107B, 119G, 119H, 123B, 129B, 133B, 137B, 141B, 143B, 151H, 155B, 157B, 165B, 169B, 171B, 181G, 189B, 193B, 197B, 217B, 223B, 227B, 239G, 239H, 243B, 247B, 255B, 259B, 261B, 263B, 273G, 279B, 285B, 291B, 295B, 299B, 301B, 305B, 313G, 317B, 319B, 331B, 347H, 351B, 353B, 355B, 357B, 359B, 363B, 365B, 369B, 371B, 385B, 389A, 391B, 395B, 399B, 401B, 405B, 415G, 419B, 423B, 429B, 433B, 439B, 441B, 443B, 445B, 457B, 461B, 463B, 469B, 471B, 489B, 491B
Linguistic, 39B, 51B, 61B, 73B, 83H, 95B, 101B, 103B, 111B, 119G, 133B, 137B, 143B, 151G, 163B, 165B, 171B, 173B, 181H, 185B, 197B, 223B, 243B, 245B, 249B, 255B, 273G, 281B, 285B, 295B, 299B, 313H, 317B, 333B, 347G, 347H, 353B, 357B, 359B, 381G, 389A, 391B, 395B, 399B, 401B, 407B, 415G, 415H, 419B, 423B, 429B, 433B, 441B, 443B, 445B, 453G, 457B, 469B, 471B, 473B, 481G, 485B, 489B, 503B
Logical, 13G, 13H, 21B, 23B, 27B, 29B, 33B, 35B, 39B, 47G, 47H, 51B, 53B, 55B, 59B, 61B, 65B, 67B, 69B, 73B, 83G, 87B, 89B, 91B, 97B, 101B, 103B, 105B, 111B, 119G, 119H, 123B, 125B, 127B, 129B, 137B, 141B, 143B, 157B, 161B, 169B, 171B, 173B, 181G, 181H, 185B, 187B, 189B, 193B, 195B, 197B, 199B, 209G, 209H, 219B, 223B, 231B, 239G, 243B, 245B, 247B, 249B, 255B, 261B, 263B, 273G, 273H, 277B, 279B, 281B, 285B, 291B, 295B, 299B, 301B, 305B, 313G, 319B, 323B, 325B, 329B, 331B, 335B, 339B, 347G, 351B, 355B, 357B, 359B, 363B, 365B, 369B, 371B, 385B, 387B, 389A, 399B, 401B, 407B, 415H, 423B, 427B, 429B, 433B, 439B, 441B, 443B, 453H, 457B, 459B, 461B, 463B, 469B, 471B, 473B, 481H, 487B, 489B, 495B, 499B, 501B, 503B, 505B
Social, 23B, 33B, 51B, 55B, 59B, 61B, 65B, 67B, 69B, 75B, 83H, 91B, 97B, 111B, 143B, 155B, 157B, 163B, 165B, 171B, 181H, 185B, 187B, 189B, 195B, 199B, 209H, 213B, 217B, 223B, 227B, 243B, 255B, 261B, 263B, 273G, 277B, 285B, 313H, 317B, 325B, 335B, 347G, 351B, 353B, 355B, 357B, 359B, 363B, 365B, 371B, 381G, 457B, 461B, 463B, 471B, 473B, 487B, 489B, 499B, 501B, 503B, 505B
Verbal, 51B, 53B
Visual/Spatial, 13G, 13H, 17B, 19B, 27B, 29B, 35B, 39B, 47G, 51B, 53B, 55B, 59B, 61B, 65B, 67B, 73B, 75B, 83G, 87B, 89B, 91B, 95B, 97B, 101B, 105B, 107B, 111B, 119G, 119H, 123B, 125B, 127B, 129B, 133B, 137B, 143B, 151G, 151H, 155B, 157B, 163B, 165B, 169B, 171B, 173B, 181G, 185B, 193B, 195B, 197B, 199B,

209G, 213B, 215B, 217B, 219B, 223B, 227B, 231B, 239G, 239H, 243B, 245B, 247B, 249B, 255B, 259B, 261B, 263B, 273G, 277B, 279B, 285B, 295B, 301B, 305B, 313G, 317B, 319B, 323B, 325B, 329B, 331B, 333B, 335B, 339B, 347G, 347H, 351B, 353B, 355B, 357B, 359B, 363B, 365B, 369B, 371B, 381G, 381H, 387B, 389A, 391B, 395B, 401B, 405B, 407B, 415G, 419B, 423B, 429B, 433B, 439B, 443B, 445B, 453G, 457B, 459B, 461B, 463B, 469B, 471B, 481G, 485B, 487B, 489B, 491B, 495B, 499B, 501B, 505B

Length
comparing, 277–278
nonstandard units of, 279–280

Less than (<), 13B, 35, 415B, 443

Leveled assignments. *See* Differentiated Instruction

Light/lighter/lightest, 273B, 285

Linguistic Learners. *See* Learning Styles

Literature Support, *See also* Teacher Reference Handbook *under separate cover*
Chapter Literature List, 16, 50, 86, 122, 154, 184, 212, 242, 276, 316, 350, 384, 418, 456, 484
Read-Aloud Anthology, 15, 49, 85, 121, 153, 183, 211, 241, 275, 315, 349, 383, 417, 455, 483

Logical Learners. *See* Learning Styles

Logical Reasoning. *See* Problem-Solving

Long/longer/longest, 273B, 277

Looking Ahead,
Count On Tens and Ones, LA5
Hundreds, Tens, Ones, LA7
Place Value to 1,000, LA9
Measure to the Nearest Centimeter, LA13
Measure to the Nearest Inch, LA11
Missing Addends, LA3

Manipulatives
attribute blocks, 19A, 395A
base-ten blocks, 245A, 427A, 429A, 433A, 443A, 485A, 487A, 489A, 491A, 499A, 501A
coins, 351A, 353A, 355A, 357A, 359A, 363A, 365A, 369A, 371A, 501A
color tiles, 143A
connecting cubes, 33A, 39A, 55A, 69A, 87A, 89A, 101A, 103A, 105A, 107A, 111A, 137A, 143A, 155A, 157A, 161A, 163A, 169A, 171A, 173A, 185A, 197A, 199A, 219A, 243A, 245A, 255A, 257A, 259A, 279A, 281A, 301A, 319A, 323A, 331A, 389A, 419A, 423A, 427A, 429A, 433A, 441A, 443A, 459A, 471A, 489A
demonstration clocks, 215A, 217A, 223A, 227A
fraction circles, 457A

geometric solids, 385A, 387A, 399A

number cubes, 91A, 137A, 163A, 189A, 197A, 217A

number sense, 199A

pan balance, 285A

pattern blocks, 17A, 19A, 21A, 143A, 279A, 301A, 305A, 391A, 399A, 457A, 461A, 463A

spinners, 423A

student clocks, 215A, 217A, 219A, 223A, 227A, 231A

two-colored counters, 21A, 29A, 51A, 53A, 65A, 67A, 69A, 75A, 87A, 89A, 95A, 101A, 103A, 105A, 107A, 111A, 155A, 163A, 165A, 171A, 187A, 195A, 243A, 255A, 257A, 259A, 263A, 317A, 323A, 329A, 339A, 363A, 423A, 427A, 441A, 445A, 489A, 495A

Math at Home, 15–16, 18, 20, 22, 26, 28, 30, 34, 36, 49–50, 52, 54, 56, 60, 62, 66, 68, 72, 74, 76, 85–86, 88, 90, 92, 96, 98, 102, 104, 106, 110, 112, 121–122, 124, 126, 128, 130, 134, 138, 140, 142, 144, 153–154, 156, 158, 162, 164, 166, 170, 172, 183–184, 186, 188, 190, 194, 196, 198, 200, 211–212, 214, 216, 218, 226, 228, 241–242, 244, 246, 248, 252, 256, 258, 260, 262, 264, 275–276, 278, 280, 282, 288, 294, 298, 300, 304, 306, 315–316, 318, 320, 324, 326, 330, 332, 334, 336, 338, 340, 349–350, 352, 354, 356, 358, 360, 364, 368, 370, 372, 383–384, 386, 388, 390, 392, 396, 400, 404, 406, 408, 417–418, 422, 424, 428, 432, 436, 440, 442, 444, 446, 455–456, 460, 472, 474, 483–484, 486, 488, 490, 492, 496, 500, 502, 504, 506

Math Background. *See* Focus on Math Background

Math Online, 14, 31, 48, 63, 79, 84, 99, 115, 116, 120, 131, 135, 148, 152, 167, 178, 182, 191, 206, 210, 221, 229, 235, 236, 237, 240, 253, 265, 269, 270, 271, 274, 289, 310, 311, 314, 321, 327, 343, 344, 345, 348, 361, 377, 378, 382, 397, 411, 412, 413, 416, 437, 449, 450, 451, 454, 465, 467, 477, 478, 479, 482, 497, 509, 510, 511

Measurement
area, 301–304, 305–306
capacity, 291–294
comparing, 273A–312
lengths, 277–278
nonstandard units, 279–280
temperature, 295–298
time, 209A–238
weight, 285–288

Mid-Chapter Check, 31, 63, 99, 131, 167, 191, 221, 253, 289, 327, 361, 397, 437, 467, 497

Minus (−), 83B, 91

Minute hand, on clocks, 209B, 215

Modeling
addition, 53–54
numbers, 339–340
subtraction, 89–90

Money. *See also* entries for various money denominations.
counting, 357–358, 371–372

Morning, 209B, 213

Music. *See* Learning Stations; Problem-Solving

Nickels, 351–352, 355–356

Nonstandard units
of length, 279–280

Number lines, 13B, 39
for addition, 165–166
for subtraction, 189–190

Numbers, 13B, 23. *See also* Addition; Subtraction; Ways to make various numbers.
to 10, 23–26
to 100, 433–436
to 100, comparing, 443–444
to 100, ordering, 445–446
11 to 15, 27–28
16 to 20, 29–30
to 50, 429–432
comparing, 35–36
estimating, 439–440
even, 263–264
modeling, 339–340
odd, 263–264
ordering, 39–40
recognizing patterns, 239A–272

Number sentences, 61–62, 83A, 187–188. *See also* Problem-Solving Strategies.

O'clock, 209B, 215

Odd numbers, 263–264

One-fourth, 463–464

One-half, 461–462

Ones, 239B, 243
tens and, 423–424

One-third, 463–464

On-Level Suggestions. *See also* Early Finishers.
diagnostic assessment options, 14, 48, 84, 120, 152, 182, 210, 240, 274, 314, 348, 382, 416, 454, 482
Game Time, 38, 58, 94, 136, 160, 202, 230, 266, 284, 322, 374, 394, 426, 466, 494
leveled assignments, 18, 20, 25, 28, 30, 36, 38, 40, 52, 54, 56, 58, 60, 66, 68, 71, 76, 88, 90, 92, 94, 96, 102, 104, 109, 112, 124, 126, 130, 134, 136, 138, 144, 156, 158, 160, 164, 166, 170, 172, 186, 190, 196, 198, 200, 202, 214, 216, 218, 225, 228, 230, 244, 246, 251, 256, 260, 262, 264, 266, 278, 280, 282, 284, 287, 293, 297, 302, 306, 318, 320, 322, 324, 330, 332, 336, 340, 352, 354, 356, 358, 364, 366, 372, 374, 386, 388, 392, 394, 396, 403, 406, 408, 421, 424, 426, 431, 434, 440, 444, 446, 458, 462, 464, 466, 470, 472, 486, 488, 492, 494, 496, 500, 502, 506
leveled tests, 44, 80, 116, 148, 178, 206, 236, 270, 310, 344, 378, 412, 450, 478, 510

Ordering, 13B, 39
area, 305–306
capacity, 291–294
events, 213–214
lengths, 277–278
numbers to 100, 445–446
temperature, 295–298
weight, 285–288

Pacing, 13C–13E, 47C–47F, 83C–83F, 119C–119E, 151C–151E, 181C–181E, 209C–209E, 239C–239E, 273C–273E, 313C–313E, 347C–347E, 381C–381E, 415C–415E, 453C–453E, 481C–481E

Patterns Patterns are sometimes called the foundation of mathematics and are certainly required for future success in algebra.

Patterns, 13B, 17
creating, 19–20
extending, 17–18
in fact families, 335–338
problem-solving strategy with, 21–22, 247–248, 389–390
recognize number, 239A–272

Pattern unit, 13B, 17

Pennies, 351–352, 353–354, 355–356

Picture graphs, 125–126

Place value, 415A–452

Planning Guide. *See* Pacing

Plus (+), 47B, 55

Position, 401–404

Preparing for Standardized Tests,
Multiple-Choice Questions, TP2–TP4
Short-Response Questions, TP5–TP6

Problem of the Day, 17A, 19A, 21A, 23A, 27A, 29A, 33A, 35A, 39A, 51A, 53A, 55A, 59A, 61A, 65A, 67A, 69A, 73A, 75A, 87A, 89A, 91A, 95A, 97A, 101A, 103A, 105A, 107A, 111A, 123A, 125A, 127A, 129A, 133A, 137A, 141A, 143A, 155A, 157A, 161A, 163A, 165A, 169A, 171A, 173A, 185A, 187A, 189A, 193A, 195A, 197A, 199A, 213A, 215A, 217A, 219A, 223A, 227A, 231A, 243A, 245A, 247A, 249A, 255A, 257A, 259A, 261A, 263A, 277A, 279A, 281A, 285A, 291A, 295A, 299A, 301A, 305A, 317A, 319A, 323A, 325A, 329A, 331A, 333A, 335A, 339A, 351A, 353A, 355A, 357A, 359A, 363A, 365A, 369A, 371A, 385A, 387A, 389A, 391A, 395A, 399A, 401A, 405A, 407A, 419A, 423A, 427A, 429A, 433A, 439A, 441A, 443A, 445A, 457A, 459A, 461A, 463A, 469A,

471A, 473A, 485A, 487A, 489A, 491A, 495A, 499A, 501A, 503A, 505A

Problem Solving A three-pronged approach helps students apply skills to problem situations. Problem-Solving Strategy lessons teach strategies; Problem-Solving Investigations afford students diverse opportunities to select these strategies; Real-World Problem Solving exercises strengthen students' abilities to apply and solve problems outside the

Problem-Solving. *See also* Problem-Solving Investigations; Problem-Solving Strategies; Real-World Problem Solving.
    application, 124
    in art, 409–410
    critical thinking, 112, 318, 352, 392, 444, 462
    estimating, 496
    in health, 77–78
    logical reasoning, 18, 126, 246, 256, 356, 358, 372
    in music, 233–234
    number sense, 28, 30, 68, 96, 166, 172, 186, 198, 330, 332, 436, 440, 446, 500, 502
    reasoning, 214, 298, 492
    in science, 41–42, 145–146, 203–204, 307–308, 447–448, 475–476, 482
    in social studies, 113–114, 175–176, 203–204, 267–268, 341–342, 375–376, 507–508
    visual thinking, 52, 216, 264, 280, 294, 306, 388, 404, 458

Problem-Solving Investigations, 33–34, 73–74, 105–106, 141–142, 173–174, 193–194, 231–232, 257–258, 299–300, 333–334, 369–370, 399–400, 441–442, 473–474, 503–504. *See also* Problem-Solving; Problem-Solving Strategies; Real-World Problem Solving.

Problem-Solving Projects,
    Fruit Kabob Factory, P7
    I Spy Patterns. P3
    Let's Go to the Zoo!, P11
    Toys from the Past and Present, P15

Problem-Solving Strategies. *See also* Problem-Solving; Problem-Solving Investigations; Real-World Problem Solving.
    act it out, 161–162, 359–360
    draw a picture, 97–98, 325–326, 459–460
    find a pattern, 21–22, 247–248, 389–390
    guess and check, 281–282, 427–428, 489–490
    make a table, 127–128, 219–220
    write a number sentence, 61–62, 187–188
    Professional Development, 13F, 47F, 83F, 119F, 151F, 181E, 209E, 239F, 273F, 313F, 347F, 381F, 415F, 453E, 481F. *See also* Focus on Math Background.

Pyramids, 381B, 385

Quarters, 365–368

Reaching All Learners. *See* Differentiated Instruction; Learning Styles; Small Group Options; Universal Access

Read-Aloud Anthology. *See* Literature Support

Reading and Writing Mathematics. *See* Learning Stations; Literature Support; Real-World Problem Solving; Writing in Math

Real-World Math, 40, 77, 113, 145, 175, 203, 233, 267, 307, 341, 375, 409, 447, 475, 507

Real-World Problem Solving. *See also* Problem-Solving; Problem-Solving Investigations; Problem-Solving Strategies.
    in math, 21A, 33A, 61A, 73A, 97A, 105A, 127A, 141A, 161A, 173A, 187A, 193A, 219A, 231A, 247A, 257A, 281A, 299A, 325A, 333A, 359A, 369A, 389A, 399A, 427A, 441A, 459A, 473A, 489A, 503A
    in science, 61A, 73A, 97A, 105A, 187A, 193A, 247A, 255A, 281A, 299A, 325A, 333A, 389A, 399A, 427A, 441A
    in social studies, 21A, 33A, 127A, 141A, 161A, 173A, 219A, 231A, 359A, 369A, 459A, 473A, 489A, 503A

Reasoning. *See* Problem-Solving

Rectangles, 381B, 395

Rectangular prisms, 381B, 385

Regrouping, 415B, 423–424

Research on Program, 119F, 309F, 313F, 347F

Rounding, 481B, 495

Science. *See* Learning Stations; Problem-Solving; Real-World Problem Solving

Shapes. *See* Geometry

Short/shorter/shortest, 277

Sides, of shapes, 381B, 395

Skills Trace. *See* Vertical Alignment

Skip counting
    by 2's, 5's and 10's, 259–260
    on a hundred chart, 261–262
    Small Group Options. *See* Below-Level Suggestions; English Language Learners (ELL); Gifted and Talented

Social Learners. *See* Learning Styles

Social Sciences. *See* Learning Stations; Problem-Solving; Real-World Problem Solving

Sorting and classifying, 119B, 123

Special Needs Students. *See* Differentiated Instruction; Learning Styles; Universal Access

Spheres, 381B, 385

Spiral Review These systematic and continuous reviews help maintain previously acquired skills and improve retention.

Spiral Review, 32, 64, 100, 132, 168, 192, 222, 254, 290, 328, 362, 398, 438, 468, 498

Squares, 381B, 395

Staff Development. *See* Professional Development

Standards Alignment. *See* Vertical Alignment

Strategic Intervention. *See* Intervention Options

Struggling Students. *See* Below-Level Suggestions

Subtraction, 83A–118, 181A–208, 313A–346, 481A–512
    from 10, 11, and 12, 107–110
    from 4, 5, and 6, 101–102
    from 7, 8, and 9, 103–104
    addition related to, 197–198, 331–332
    of all, 95–96
    counting back 1, 2, or 3, 185–186
    doubles, 195–196, 329–330
    estimating differences, 505–506
    fact families, 199–200
    modeling, 89–90
    number line for, 189–190
    of tens, 485–486
    two-digit, 499–500, 501–502
    vertical, 111–112
    of zero, 95–96

Subtraction sentences, 83B, 91–92

Subtraction stories, 87–88

Summative Assessment, 13F, 43, 45, 47F, 79, 81, 83F, 115, 117, 119F, 147, 149, 151F, 177, 179, 181E, 205, 207, 209E, 235, 237, 239F, 269, 271, 273F, 309, 311, 313F, 343, 345, 347F, 377, 379, 381F, 411, 413, 415F, 449, 451, 453E, 477, 479, 481F, 509, 511

Sums, 47B, 55, 481B, 485
    estimating, 495–496

Surveys, 119B, 129

Tables, 127–128, 219–220

Talk About It, 17, 19, 24, 27, 29, 35, 39, 51, 53, 55, 59, 65, 67, 70, 75, 87, 89, 91, 95, 101, 103, 108, 111, 123, 125, 129, 133, 137, 143, 155, 157, 163, 165, 169, 171, 185, 189, 195, 197, 199, 213, 215, 217, 224, 227, 243, 245, 250, 255, 259, 261, 263, 277, 279, 286, 292, 296, 302, 305, 317, 323, 329, 331, 335, 339, 351, 353, 355, 357, 363, 365, 371, 385, 387, 391, 395, 402, 405, 407, 420, 423, 430, 433, 439, 443, 445, 457, 461, 463, 469, 471, 485, 487, 491, 495, 499, 501, 505

Tally charts, 129–130

Technology
practice with, 37, 57, 93, 135, 139–140, 159, 201, 229, 265, 283, 321, 337–338, 367–368, 373, 393, 425, 435, 465, 493
student, 17B, 19B, 21B, 23B, 27B, 29B, 33B, 35B, 39B, 51B, 53B, 55B, 59B, 61B, 65B, 67B, 69B, 73B, 75B, 87B, 89B, 91B, 95B, 97B, 101B, 103B, 105B, 107B, 111B, 123B, 125B, 127B, 129B, 133B, 137B, 141B, 143B, 155B, 157B, 161B, 163B, 165B, 169B, 171B, 173B, 185B, 187B, 189B, 193B, 195B, 197B, 199B, 213B, 215B, 217B, 219B, 223B, 227B, 231B, 243B, 245B, 247B, 249B, 255B, 257B, 259B, 261B, 263B, 277B, 279B, 281B, 285B, 291B, 295B, 299B, 301B, 305B, 317B, 319B, 323B, 325B, 329B, 331B, 333B, 335B, 339B, 351B, 353B, 355B, 357B, 359B, 363B, 365B, 369B, 371B, 385B, 387B, 389B, 391B, 395B, 399B, 401B, 405B, 407B, 419B, 423B, 427B, 429B, 433B, 439B, 441B, 443B, 445B, 457B, 459B, 461B, 463B, 469B, 471B, 473B, 485B, 487B, 489B, 491B, 495B, 499B, 501B, 503B, 505B
TeacherWorks Plus, 17A, 19A, 21A, 23A, 27A, 29A, 33A, 35A, 39A, 51A, 53A, 55A, 59A, 61A, 65A, 67A, 69A, 73A, 75A, 87A, 89A, 91A, 95A, 97A, 101A, 103A, 105A, 107A, 111A, 123A, 125A, 127A, 129A, 133A, 137A, 141A, 143A, 155A, 157A, 161A, 163A, 165A, 169A, 171A, 173A, 185A, 187A, 189A, 193A, 195A, 197A, 199A, 213A, 215A, 217A, 219A, 223A, 227A, 231A, 243A, 245A, 247A, 249A, 255A, 257A, 259A, 261A, 263A, 277A, 279A, 281A, 285A, 291A, 295A, 299A, 301A, 305A, 317A, 319A, 323A, 325A, 329A, 331A, 333A, 335A, 339A, 351A, 353A, 355A, 357A, 359A, 363A, 365A, 369A, 371A, 385A, 387A, 389A, 391A, 395A, 399A, 401A, 405A, 407A, 419A, 423A, 427A, 429A, 433A, 439A, 441A, 443A, 445A, 457A, 459A, 461A, 463A, 469A, 471A, 473A, 485A, 487A, 489A, 491A, 495A, 499A, 501A, 503A, 505A
Tech Link, 139–140, 337–338, 367–368, 435–436

Temperature, 295–298

Tens, 419–422
addition and subtraction of, 485–486
counting by, 245–246
estimating with groups of, 255–256
making to add, 323–324
ones and, 423–424
skip counting by, 259–260

Test Practice, 45–46, 81–82, 117–118, 149–150, 180–181, 207–208, 237–238, 271–272, 311–312, 345–346, 379–380, 413–414, 451–452, 479–480, 511–512

Thermometer, 295–298

Time, 209A–238
events related to, 227–228
to the half hour, 217–218, 223–226
to the hour, 215–216, 223–226
ordering events, 213–214

Triangles, 381B, 395

Twenty, counting to, 243–244

Units, 273B, 279

Universal Access. See also Above-Level Suggestions; Below-Level Suggestions; Differentiated Instruction; Learning Styles; On-Level Suggestions.

Venn diagrams, 123

Verbal Learners. See Learning Styles

Vertical addition, 75–76

Vertical Alignment, 13B, 47B, 83B, 119B, 151B, 181B, 209B, 239B, 273B, 313B, 347B, 381B, 415B, 453B, 481B

Vertical subtraction, 111–112

Visual/Spatial Learners. See Learning Styles

Visual Thinking. See Problem-Solving

Visual Vocabulary Cards, 13B, 17A, 19A, 35A, 39A, 47B, 53A, 55A, 65A, 67A, 69A, 75A, 83B, 87A, 89A, 91A, 103A, 107A, 111A, 119B, 125A, 129A, 133A, 137A, 151B, 155A, 163A, 165A, 181B, 189A, 199A, 209B, 215A, 217A, 223A, 227A, 239B, 243A, 255A, 273B, 313B, 323A, 331A, 335A, 347B, 351A, 353A, 357A, 365A, 371A, 381B, 385A, 387A, 395A, 405A, 415B, 429A, 433A, 453B, 481B, 485A, 487A, 491A, 495A, 499A, 501A, 505A

Vocabulary
add, 47B, 53, 481B, 485
addend, 151B, 155
addition sentence, 47B, 55
after, 13B, 39, 209B, 213, 415B, 445
afternoon, 209B, 213
analog, 209B, 223
bar graph, 119B, 133
before, 13B, 39, 209B, 213, 415B, 445
between, 13B, 39, 415B, 445
cent, 347B, 351
certain, 119B, 143
circles, 381B, 395
compare, 415B, 443
cones, 381B, 385
count back, 181B, 185
count on, 151B, 157
cubes, 381B, 385
cylinders, 381B, 385
data, 119B, 125
difference, 83B, 91, 481B, 485
digital, 209B, 223
dime, 347B, 353
doubles, 151B, 169, 313B, 317
doubles plus 1, 151B, 171, 313B, 319

equal parts, 453B, 457
equal to (=), 13B, 35, 47B, 55, 415B, 443
estimate, 239B, 255, 415B, 439, 481B, 495
even, 239B, 263
evening, 209B, 213
fact family, 181B, 199, 313B, 315
fraction, 453B, 461
graph, 119B, 125
greater than (>), 13B, 35, 415B, 443
half hour, 209B, 217
half past, 209B, 217
heavy/heavier/heaviest, 273B, 285
holds less/least, 273B, 291
holds more/most, 273B, 291
hour, 209B, 215
hour hand, 209B, 215
hundred chart, 239B, 261
impossible, 119B, 143
length, 273B, 277
less than (<), 13B, 35, 415B, 443
light/lighter/lightest, 273B, 285
long/longer/longest, 273B, 277
measure, 273B, 279
minus (−), 83B, 91
minute hand, 209B, 215
morning, 209B, 213
nickel, 347B, 351
number, 13B, 23
number line, 13B, 39
o'clock, 209B, 215
odd, 239B, 263
one fourth, 453B, 463
one half, 453B, 461
ones, 239B, 243, 415B, 423
one third, 453B, 463
order, 13B, 39
pattern, 13B, 17
pattern unit, 13B, 17
penny, 347B, 351
picture graph, 119B, 125
plus (+), 47B, 55
pyramids, 381B, 385
quarter, 347B, 365
rectangles, 381B, 395
rectangular prisms, 381B, 385
regroup, 415B, 423
round, 481B, 495
short/shorter/shortest, 273B, 277
sides, 381B, 395
skip count, 239B, 259
sort, 119B, 123
spheres, 381B, 385
squares, 381B, 395
subtract, 83B, 89, 481B, 485
subtraction sentence, 83B, 91
sum, 47B, 55, 481B, 485
survey, 119B, 129
tally chart, 119B, 129
tens, 415B, 419
triangles, 381B, 395
unit, 273B, 279
weight, 273B, 285
zero, 47B, 59

Vocabulary Review and Test, 43, 79, 115, 147, 177, 205, 235, 269, 309, 343, 377, 411, 449, 477, 509

W

Ways to make
 10, 11, and 12, 69–72
 4, 5, and 6, 65–66
 7, 8, and 9, 67–68

Weight, 285–288

Writing in Math, 15, 18, 20, 26, 28, 30, 36,
40, 42, 49, 54, 56, 60, 66, 68, 72, 76, 78, 85,
88, 90, 92, 96, 102, 104, 110, 112, 114, 121,
124, 126, 130, 134, 138, 144, 146, 153, 156,
158, 164, 166, 170, 172, 176, 183, 186, 190,
196, 198, 200, 204, 211, 214, 216, 218, 226,
228, 234, 241, 244, 246, 252, 256, 260, 262,
264, 275, 278, 280, 282, 288, 294, 298, 300,
303, 306, 308, 315, 318, 320, 324, 326, 330,
332, 334, 336, 338, 340, 342, 349, 352, 354,
356, 358, 364, 366, 372, 376, 383, 386, 390,
392, 396, 400, 404, 408, 410, 417, 422, 424,
432, 440, 444, 446, 448, 455, 458, 460, 462,
464, 470, 472, 474, 476, 483, 486, 488, 490,
492, 496, 500, 502, 504, 506, 508

Z

Zero, 47B
 addition of, 59–60
 subtraction of, 95–96

Index

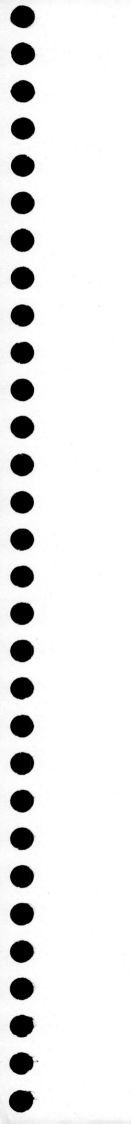